C Ca

Christel
+
Timothy Evan Harrell

~~Timmy~~
Timmy 2

$(3\cdot X^2)\cdot 4^2 \cdot X^3 Y Z A \cdot 424 \cdot (6X\ 9.7)$

$= 15X + Y + Z + A + 48$

20,874 GAL

pool

16

20 ft

2 ft

4 ft

6 ft

12 ft

10

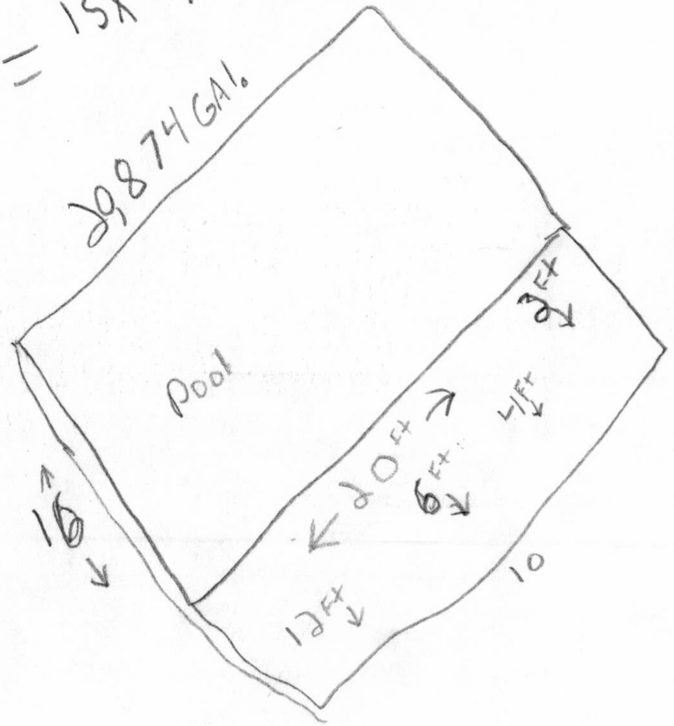

Mathematics Today

Curriculum and Instruction

Janet S. Abbott
Coordinator of Mathematics
Chula Vista City School District
Chula Vista, California

David W. Wells
Formerly Director of Instruction
and Mathematics Education
Oakland Schools
Pontiac, Michigan

Consulting Educators

Dr. Barbara Branch
Principal
White Station Junior High School
Memphis, Tennessee

Mary S. Driggers
Formerly Educational Consultant
and Mathematics Coordinator
Florence School District #3
Lake City, South Carolina

Dr. Phillip E. Duren
Mathematics Consultant, K-12
Stark County Department of
Education
Louisville, Ohio

Dr. E. Alma Flagg
Educational Consultant
Newark, New Jersey

Betty Jean Gould
Learning Development Specialist
Sachem Central School District
Holbrook, New York

William Ezra Hansen
Supervisor of Math and Science
Kindergarten through 12
Davis County School District
Farmington, Utah

Terri Katsulis
Administrator
Chicago Public Schools
Chicago, Illinois

Dr. Marsha Lilly
Mathematics Coordinator
Alief Independent School District
Alief, Texas

Alice D. Lombardi
Formerly Mathematics Specialist
Division of Curriculum & Instruction
New York City Board of Education
New York, New York

Otherie Winfield Love
Mathematics Consultant
Detroit Public Schools
Detroit, Michigan

Wallace Manning
Director of Federal Programs,
District 91
Idaho Falls, Idaho

Robert D. Postman
Mercy College
Westchester County, New York

Yvonne Tomlinson
Classroom Teacher
Riverdale High School
Jefferson, Louisiana

Mathematics Today

HBJ Harcourt Brace Jovanovich, Publishers

Orlando New York Chicago San Diego Atlanta Dallas

PHOTO CREDITS

Ken Karp: Cover
18 (top), Museum of Modern Art Film Still Archives, (bottom), © Phil Stern/Globe Photos. 72, The Bettmann Archive. 73, © George Dodge/DPI. 105, PHANTASIA quilt, © 1981, Michael James, courtesy American Craft Council. 109, © Aura, Inc. 111, © Sanford/DPI. 112, © Aura, Inc. 113, © Gary Ladd, 1972. 114, © Hans Pfletschinger/Peter Arnold. 115 (left), © De Wys; (right), © S. Lissau/H. Armstrong Roberts. 120 (bottom), © Fred D. Bodin/Stock, Boston. 129, © H. Armstrong Roberts. 139, © Alec Duncan. 143, © Cary Wolinsky/Stock, Boston. 161, © W. Ostgathe/De Wys. 181, © Werner Muller/ Peter Arnold. 187, © Ken Karp. 193, © Philip Harrington/Peter Arnold. 215 (top), © H. Armstrong Roberts; (bottom), © J. & D. Bartlett/Bruce Coleman. 244 (top), © J. Alex Langley/DPI; (bottom), © H. Armstrong Roberts. 266 (left), © Elaine Wicks/Taurus. 284, © H. Armstrong Roberts. 297, © E. Bordis/De Wys. 303, © Manfred Kage/Peter Arnold. 316, © THE RECORD, Hackensack, N.J. 320, © Wolf Von Dem Bussche/Photo Researchers. 322, © H. Armstrong Roberts. 341, © Paul Stephanus/DPI. 359, © H. Armstrong Roberts. 396, © Mick Roessler/H. Armstrong Roberts. 398, © Richard Choy/Peter Arnold. 407, © Jackie Foryst/Bruce Coleman. 431, © Chris Sorensen/DPI.

All other photography by Blaise Zito Associates Inc.

ART CREDITS

All illustrations by Tom Powers
All technical art, charts, graphs and maps by Blaise Zito Associates Inc.

Printed in the United States of America

ISBN: 0-15-350709-8

CONTENTS

chapter 1 Whole Numbers: Addition and Subtraction

Numbers and Place Value 2
Comparing and Ordering Numbers 4
Skills Maintenance 5
Rounding Numbers 6
Powers and Exponents 8
Midchapter Review 9
Problem Solving • Strategies: *Using a Table* 10
Addition and Subtraction 12
Estimating and Adding 14
Estimating and Subtracting 16
Skills Maintenance 17
Problem Solving • Strategies: *Using Inverse Operations* 18
Review 20
Project: *Ancient Systems of Writing Numbers* 21
Test 22
Enrichment: *The Binary System* 23
Calculator: *Calculator Review* 24
Skills Maintenance 26

chapter 2 Whole Numbers: Multiplication and Division

Multiplication and Division 28
Multiplying by One-Digit Numbers 30
Multiplying by Tens, Hundreds, and Thousands 32
Multiplying by Two-Digit Numbers 34
Multiplying by Three-Digit Numbers 36
Midchapter Review 37
Problem Solving • Strategies: *Choosing the Operation* 38
Dividing by One-Digit Numbers 40
Estimating and Correcting Estimates 42
Skills Maintenance 43
Two-Digit Divisors, Quotients to Four Digits 44
Divisors Greater Than 100 46
Skills Maintenance 47
Problem Solving • Strategies: *Too Much or Not Enough Information* 48
Order of Operations 50
Review 52
Project: *Patterns* 53
Test 54
Enrichment: *Choices* 55
Calculator: *Estimating Division* 56
Skills Maintenance 58

chapter 3 Equations

Addition and Subtraction Expressions 60
Addition and Subtraction Equations 62
Skills Maintenance 63

Multiplication and Division Expressions 64
Multiplication and Division Equations 66
Midchapter Review 67
Problem Solving • Strategies: *Choosing Equations* 68
Equations and Properties 70
Distance Formula 72
Skills Maintenance 73
Problem Solving • Strategies: *Using Equations* 74
Solving Inequalities 76
Review 78
Project: *Functions* 79
Test 80
Enrichment: *Experimenting with Equations* 81
Computer: *Computer Basics* 82
Skills Maintenance 84

chapter 4 Decimals: Addition and Subtraction

Tenths and Hundredths 86
The Decimal System 88
Comparing and Ordering Decimals 90
Skills Maintenance 91
Rounding Decimals 92
Midchapter Review 93
Estimating and Adding 94
Problem Solving • Strategies: *Reading a Map* 96
Estimating and Subtracting 98
Skills Maintenance 99
Problem Solving • Strategies: *Using Estimates* 100
Review 102
Project: *Writing Checks* 103
Test 104
Enrichment: *Sequences* 105
Calculator: *Lining Up Decimals* 106
Skills Maintenance 107

chapter 5 Decimals: Multiplication and Division

Estimating Products 110
Multiplying Decimals 112
Zeros in the Product 114
Skills Maintenance 115
Patterns in Multiplication 116
Midchapter Review 117
Problem Solving • Strategies: *Reasonable Answers* 118
Dividing by a Whole Number 120
Dividing by a Decimal 122
Writing Zeros in the Dividend 124
Rounding Quotients 126
Scientific Notation 128
Skills Maintenance 129
Problem Solving • Strategies: *Multistep Problems* 130
Review 132
Project: *Keeping a Checkbook Record* 133
Test 134
Enrichment: *Using Exponents* 135
Computer: *Computer Software* 136
Skills Maintenance 138

chapter 6 Number Theory

Divisibility 140
Divisibility by 3 and 9 142
Factors, Primes, and Composites 144
Midchapter Review 145
Prime Factorization 146
Skills Maintenance 147

Greatest Common Factor 148
Skills Maintenance 149
Multiples and Least Common Multiple 150
Problem Solving • Strategies: *Making an Organized List* 152
Review 154
Project: *Venn Diagrams* 155
Test 156
Enrichment: *Clock Arithmetic* 157
Computer: *Computer Operation* 159
Skills Maintenance 160

chapter 7 Fractions: Addition and Subtraction

Fractions and Whole Numbers 162
Equivalent Fractions 164
Lowest Terms 166
Comparing Fractions 168
Skills Maintenance 169
Fractions and Mixed Numbers 170
Midchapter Review 171
Adding Fractions 172
Adding Mixed Numbers 174
Problem Solving • Strategies: *Sensible Answers* 176
Subtracting Fractions 178
Subtracting Mixed Numbers and Whole Numbers 180
Practicing Subtraction with Mixed Numbers 182
Skills Maintenance 183
Problem Solving • Strategies: *Multistep Problems* 184
Review 186
Project: *Stock Market* 187
Test 188
Enrichment: *Flow Charts* 189
Calculator: *Deciding to Use the Calculator* 190
Skills Maintenance 191

chapter 8 Fractions: Multiplication and Division

Multiplying Fractions 194
Understanding a Shortcut 196
Multiplying Whole Numbers and Mixed Numbers 198
Skills Maintenance 199
Problem Solving • Strategies: *Using Graphs* 200
Reciprocals 202
Midchapter Review 203
Dividing by Fractions 204
Dividing by Whole Numbers 206
Using Mixed Numbers in Division 208
Fractions and Decimals 210
Skills Maintenance 211
Repeating Decimals 212
Problem Solving • Strategies: *Using Estimates* 214
Review 216
Project: *Using Recipes* 217
Test 218
Enrichment: *Operation Properties and Density* 219
Computer: *Machine Language* 221
Skills Maintenance 222

chapter 9 Ratio and Proportion

Ratio 224
Ratio and Proportion 226
Skills Maintenance 227
Solving Proportions 228
Midchapter Review 229
Rates 230
Skills Maintenance 231
Scale Drawing 232

Problem Solving • Strategies: *Unit Prices: Choosing a Method* 234
Review 236
Project: *Investigating Ratios and Rates* 237
Test 238
Enrichment: *Ratios and Functions* 239
Computer: *Computer Switches* 240
Skills Maintenance 242

chapter 10 Percent

Percent and Ratio 244
Percent and Proportion 246
Skills Maintenance 247
Percents and Decimals 248
Percents and Fractions 250
Midchapter Review 251
Finding the Percent of a Number 252
Finding the Percent One Number Is of Another 254
Finding a Number When a Percent of It Is Known 256
Skills Maintenance 257
Problem Solving • Strategies: *Using a Percent Formula* 258
Discount and Sales Tax 260
Simple Interest 262
Circle Graph and Percent 264
Problem Solving • Strategies: *Choosing a Method* 266
Review 268
Project: *Compound Interest* 269
Test 270
Enrichment: *Finding the Percent of Increase* or *Decrease* 271
Calculator: *Sales Tax and Discount* 272
Skills Maintenance 274

chapter 11 Measurement

Metric Units of Length 276
Changing Metric Units 278
Metric Units of Liquid Capacity 280
Skills Maintenance 281
Metric Units of Mass 282
Midchapter Review 283
Problem Solving • Strategies: *Write Your Own Question* 284
Customary Units of Length 286
Customary Units of Liquid Capacity 288
Customary Units of Weight 290
Skills Maintenance 291
Time 292
Problem Solving • Strategies: *Using a Table* 294
Review 296
Project: *Latitude and Longitude* 297
Test 298
Enrichment: *Precision in Measurement* 299
Computer: *Computer Instructions* 300
Skills Maintenance 301

chapter 12 Geometry

The Vocabulary of Geometry 304
Angles 306
Circles 308
Skills Maintenance 309
Constructing Congruent Segments and Angles 310
Bisecting Segments and Angles 312
Angle Relationships 314
Midchapter Review 315
Perpendicular and Parallel Lines 316
Polygons 318
Triangles 320

Quadrilaterals 322
Congruent Polygons 324
Skills Maintenance 325
Symmetry and Reflections 326
Similar Polygons 328
Solid Figures 330
Problem Solving • Strategies: *Using Logic* 332
Review 334
Project: *Exploring Constructions* 335
Test 336
Enrichment: *Angles and Polygons* 337
Computer: *Operation of an Assembler* 338
Skills Maintenance 340

chapter 13 Perimeter, Area, and Volume

Perimeter 342
Circumference 344
Area of Rectangles 346
Areas of Parallelograms and Triangles 348
Area of Trapezoids 350
Skills Maintenance 351
Area of Circles 352
Midchapter Review 353
Surface Area 354
Volume of Prisms 356
Volume of Cylinders 358
Skills Maintenance 359
Problem Solving • Strategies: *Using a Diagram* 360
Using Customary Units 362
Reviewing and Using Formulas 364
Problem Solving • Strategies: *Analyzing Conclusions* 366
Review 368
Project: *Direct Volume Measurement* 369
Test 370
Enrichment: *Square Roots* 371
Computer: *Computer Errors* 372
Skills Maintenance 374

chapter 14 Probability and Statistics

Probability 376
Using *and* and *or* in Probability 378
Skills Maintenance 379
Sample Spaces and Tree Diagrams 380
Problem Solving • Strategies: *Using Probability* 382
Probability of Independent Events 384
Midchapter Review 385
Organizing Data 386
Mean and Range 388
Median and Mode 390
Skills Maintenance 391
Pictographs 392
Bar Graphs 394
Broken-Line Graphs 396
Problem Solving • Strategies: *Sampling* 398
Review 400
Project: *Constructing a Circle Graph* 401
Test 402
Enrichment: *Finding the Mean from a Frequency Table* 403
Computer: *Careers: Systems Analyst* 404
Skills Maintenance 406

chapter 15 Integers

Integers 408
Integers and Temperature 410
Adding Integers with Like Signs 412

Skills Maintenance 413
Adding with Unlike Signs 414
Subtracting Integers 416
Midchapter Review 417
Multiplying Integers 418
Dividing Integers 420
Solving Equations with Integers 422
Rational Numbers 424
Points in a Coordinate Plane 426
Graphing Equations 428
Skills Maintenance 429
Problem Solving • Strategies: *Using Tables and Graphs* 430
Review 432
Project: *Translations and Rotations* 433
Test 434
Enrichment: *Extending Exponents and Scientific Notation* 435
Computer: *Computer Control* 437
Skills Maintenance 439

Extra Practice 441
Table of Measures 456
Table of Symbols 457
Glossary 458
Index 465

Whole Numbers: Addition and Subtraction

CHAPTER 1

Place Value • Comparing and Ordering • Rounding • Powers and Exponents • Problem Solving: Using a Table • Addition and Subtraction • Estimating • Problem Solving: Using Inverse Operations • Ancient Number Systems • Binary System

Numbers and Place Value

A sportscaster announced the paid attendance at two baseball games.
thirty-three thousand, three hundred thirty-three → 33,333
forty-one thousand, seven hundred eight → 41,708

Our system of naming numbers is based on ten. We use the ten **digits** 0, 1, 2, 3, 4, 5, 6, 7, 8, and 9 and **place value** to write numbers. Each place has a value ten times the value of the place at its right.

Trillions Period			Billions Period			Millions Period			Thousands Period			Ones Period		
Hundred Trillions	Ten Trillions	Trillions	Hundred Billions	Ten Billions	Billions	Hundred Millions	Ten Millions	Millions	Hundred Thousands	Ten Thousands	Thousands	Hundreds	Tens	Ones
										3	3	3	3	3
										4	1	7	0	8
					1	2	5	6	3	9	4	0	0	0

Sometimes the meaning of a number is shown in **expanded form.**

33,333 = 30,000 + 3,000 + 300 + 30 + 3
41,708 = 40,000 + 1,000 + 700 + 8
expanded form

To make the reading of large numbers easier, we use commas to separate the digits into groups of three (starting at the right). These groups of three digits are called **periods.**

1,256,394,000
Read: 1 billion, 256 million, 394 thousand.

In 1,256,394,000, the digit 6 is in the millions place. In which place is the digit 1?

Practice • Write the numbers.

1. two thousand, six hundred

2. four hundred thousand

3. 4 million, 718 thousand, 235

4. 109 million, 40 thousand

Read each number. In which place is the blue digit?

5. 19,331 **6.** 495,837 **7.** 2,673,426 **8.** 68,472,815

Write in expanded form.

9. 2,106

10. 84,345

Mixed Practice • Write the numbers.

11. twelve thousand, four hundred

12. six hundred fifty thousand

13. nine million

14. two hundred million

15. 4 thousand, 65

16. 180 thousand, 50

17. 534 thousand, 902

18. 2 million, 70 thousand

19. 26 million, 714 thousand

20. 2 billion, 350 million

21. 15 billion

★**22.** 1 trillion, 14 billion, 900 million

Read each number. In which place is the blue digit?

23. 8,647 **24.** 12,508 **25.** 136,435 **26.** 876,115

27. 3,500,000 **28.** 107,685 ★**29.** 65,000,000 ★**30.** 2,119,256,000

Write in expanded form.

31. 7,918 **32.** 23,802 **33.** 139,426 **34.** 960,125

35. 1,593,687 **36.** 47,423,192 ★**37.** 4,265,000,000 ★**38.** 578,020,000,000

Write the numbers.

39. 6,000 + 800 + 50

40. 200,000 + 90,000 + 800 + 6

Write in words.

41. 4,700,000

42. 9,802,053

PROBLEM SOLVING • APPLICATIONS

43. At one World Series game, the paid attendance was 92,706. How much more than 90,000 was this?

★**44.** During one season, the paid attendance at Los Angeles Dodgers' games was 3,347,776. How much less than 3,500,000 was this?

Comparing and Ordering Numbers

The Houston Astrodome has a seating capacity of 45,000. Wrigley Field has a seating capacity of 38,000. Which stadium seats a greater number of people? It is easy to see that 45,000 is greater than 38,000. 4 ten thousands is greater than 3 ten thousands.

$45{,}000 > 38{,}000$ — $>$ is greater than

$38{,}000 < 45{,}000$ — $<$ is less than

Sometimes you need to examine the digits carefully in comparing numbers.

Write $<$ or $>$ to compare these numbers.

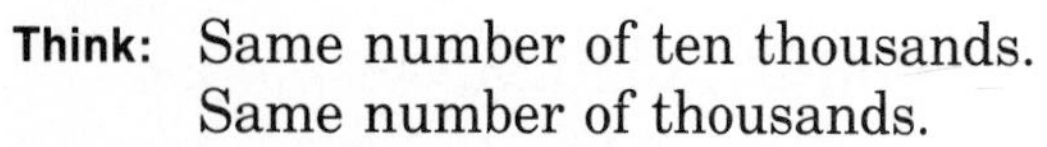

Think: Same number of ten thousands. 64,526 ● 64,531
Same number of thousands. 64,526 ● 64,531
Same number of hundreds. 64,526 ● 64,531
Compare the tens. $2 < 3$ So $64{,}526 < 64{,}531$.

The numbers we have been naming and comparing are **whole numbers.** The whole numbers can be shown this way:

0,1,2,3,4, . . . ← ***The three dots mean "and so on" in the same pattern.***

In some situations, you may need to list several numbers in order. Write in order from least to greatest: 2,053; 2,035; 2,503.

Think: $2{,}035 < 2{,}053$
$2{,}053 < 2{,}503$

So, from least to greatest, the numbers are: 2,035; 2,053; 2,503.

Practice • Write $<$ or $>$.

1. 365 ● 355 **2.** 7296 ● 7080 **3.** 15,917 ● 16,123

4. 23,516 ● 23,436 **5.** 97,890 ● 217,890 **6.** 314,543 ● 341,345

Write in order from least to greatest.

7. 601; 610; 602 **8.** 7,025; 7,205; 7,052

9. 75,291; 72,915; 72,519 **10.** 44,331; 44,134; 44,461

Mixed Practice • Write < or >.

11. 226 ● 286
12. 354 ● 345
13. 817 ● 819
14. 562 ● 608
15. 1,054 ● 1,004
16. 2,683 ● 2,383
17. 987 ● 8,771
18. 4,506 ● 4,508
19. 5,004 ● 5,024
20. 8,737 ● 8,373
21. 6,443 ● 6,473
22. 1,153 ● 1,115
23. 5,480 ● 4,480
24. 6,438 ● 6,346
25. 13,150 ● 13,156
26. 73,241 ● 76,842
27. 15,508 ● 9,978
28. 72,183 ● 72,182
29. 85,040 ● 85,400
30. 90,941 ● 99,941
31. 96,304 ● 96,640

★32. 726,400 ● 724,000
★33. 746,732 ● 746,632
★34. 85,118 ● 135,138
★35. 414,356 ● 414,566
★36. 371,624 ● 371,621
★37. 3,119,468 ● 3,111,978

Write in order from least to greatest.

38. 757; 577; 775
39. 4,683; 4,863; 4,386
40. 1,037; 857; 1,157; 907
41. 34,430; 34,046; 34,603; 34,063

★42. 101,458; 93,146; 111,329; 98,087; 110,126
★43. 4,303,750; 4,330,756; 4,300,756; 4,333,076; 4,353,567

PROBLEM SOLVING • APPLICATIONS

44. Keith said, "I used these number cards to make four-digit numbers." What is the greatest number he could make?

45. What is the least number he could make?

★46. How many different numbers could he make? List them.

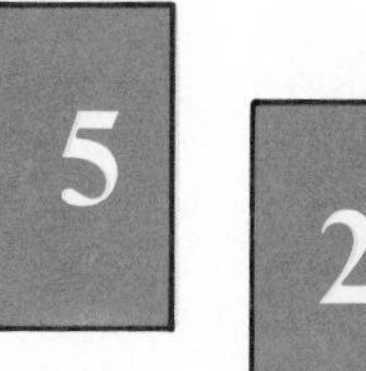

1. 5 × 5
2. 4 × 7
3. 9 × 3
4. 5 × 7
5. 6 × 6
6. 7 × 8
7. 6 × 7
8. 9 × 5
9. 7 × 7
10. 9 × 7
11. 8 × 8
12. 8 × 9

Rounding Numbers

Is the price of this automobile about 7,000 dollars or is it about 8,000 dollars? Often, in daily life, you **round** numbers to use them for estimates. This number line shows that 7,850 is between 7,000 and 8,000. It is closer to 8,000 than to 7,000. 7,850 rounded to the nearest thousand is 8,000.

You can round numbers without using a number line.

> ***To round a number, look at the first digit to the right of the place to which you are rounding. If the digit is less than 5, round down. If the digit is 5 or greater, round up.***

Round 364,972 to the nearest ten thousand.

Think: The digit in the ten-thousands place is 6. The digit to the right is less than 5. Round down. Keep the digit in the ten-thousands place the same.

↓
364,972
↑

364,972 rounded to the nearest ten thousand is 360,000.

Round 364,972 to the nearest hundred thousand.

Think: The digit in the hundred-thousands place is 3. The digit to the right is 5 or greater. Round up. Increase the digit in the hundred-thousands place by 1.

↓
364,972
↑

364,972 rounded to the nearest hundred thousand is 400,000.

More Examples

12,500,000 rounded to the nearest million is 13,000,000.
$217.49 rounded to the nearest dollar is $217.

Practice • Round the numbers as indicated.

Nearest ten:

1. 46 **2.** 73

Nearest hundred:

3. 542 **4.** 758

Nearest thousand:

5. 3,500
6. 34,280

Nearest ten thousand:

7. 25,435
8. 51,047

Mixed Practice • Round to the nearest ten.

9. 85
10. 52
11. 384
12. 4,828

Round to the nearest hundred.

13. 766
14. 1,734
15. 8,157
16. 73,444

Round to the nearest ten thousand.

17. 61,025
18. 75,734
19. 447,606
20. 1,723,217

Round to the nearest hundred thousand.

21. 216,510
22. 384,564
23. 725,440
24. 558,344

★25. 1,256,111
★26. 5,439,001
★27. 3,781,129
★28. 24,651,199

Round to the nearest million.

29. 1,685,444
30. 3,234,780
31. 7,199,835
32. 5,630,780

★33. 75,498,812
★34. 16,991,312
★35. 125,863,212
★36. 494,501,437

Round to the nearest dollar.

37. $811.47
38. $1,137.73
★39. $45,953.16
★40. $111,933.49

PROBLEM SOLVING • APPLICATIONS

41. Round each number in the table to the nearest ten thousand.

★42. Study the numbers you wrote for Problem 41. Rewrite them in order from greatest to least.

★43. To the nearest hundred dollars, a certain car cost $8,700. Could its actual cost have been $8,650? What is the greatest number of dollars the car could have cost?

State	Number of Automobiles
Alaska	156,000
California	12,852,000
Florida	6,429,000
New York	7,162,000
Texas	7,389,000

Powers and Exponents

A number sentence with an equal sign is an **equation.**

Look at this equation. The factor 10 is used 4 times. 10,000 is the product. 10,000 is a **power** of 10.

$$10 \times 10 \times 10 \times 10 = 10{,}000$$

factors product

You can use an **exponent** to show how many times 10 is used as a factor. The number 10 is called the **base.**

exponent

base→ $10^4 = 10{,}000$

Read: ten to the fourth power.

You can use exponents with other numbers.

$5^2 = 5 \times 5$
$= 25$
In 5^2 the base is 5.

$2^5 = 2 \times 2 \times 2 \times 2 \times 2$
$= 32$
In 2^5 the base is 2.

Look for a pattern in this chart. Compare the exponents to the numbers of zeros shown in the products in the third column.

Exponent Form	Read	Product
10^4	ten to the fourth power	10,000
10^3	ten to the third power	1,000
10^2	ten to second power or ten squared	100
10^1	ten to the first power	?
10^0	ten to the zero power	?

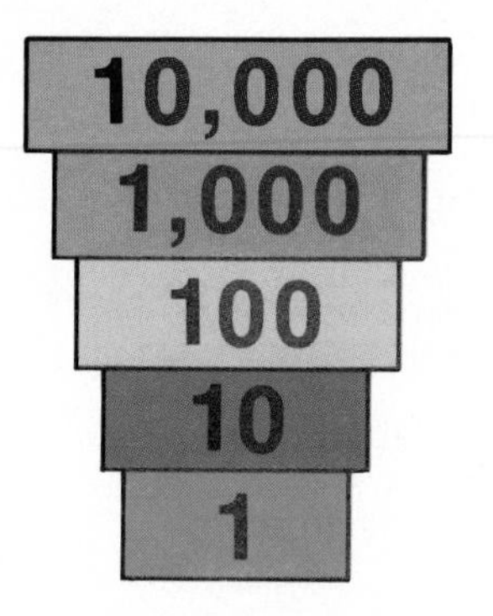

Suppose the pattern in the third column continues. Then 10^1 would be 10, and 10^0 would be 1.

Any number to the first power is that number.
Any number, except zero, to the zero power is 1.

$10^1 = 10 \quad 2^1 = 2$
$10^0 = 1 \quad 2^0 = 1$

You can use powers of ten and exponents to show numbers in expanded form. Parentheses are used to show the grouping of numbers.

$$\begin{aligned}32{,}647 &= 30{,}000 + 2{,}000 + 600 + 40 + 7\\ &= (3 \times 10{,}000) + (2 \times 1{,}000) + (6 \times 100) + (4 \times 10) + (7 \times 1)\\ &= (3 \times 10^4) + (2 \times 10^3) + (6 \times 10^2) + (4 \times 10^1) + (7 \times 10^0)\end{aligned}$$

Practice • Write in exponent form.

1. 3×3
2. $3 \times 3 \times 3$
3. 10×10
4. $6 \times 6 \times 6 \times 6$

Write the products.

5. 4^2
6. 2^6
7. 10^5
8. 5^1

Write in expanded form using powers of ten and exponents.

9. 7,582
10. 23,469

Mixed Practice • Write in exponent form.

11. $4 \times 4 \times 4$
12. $7 \times 7 \times 7 \times 7$
13. 9×9
14. $10 \times 10 \times 10$

Write the products.

15. 10^4
16. 2^3
17. 3^5
18. 9^1
19. 5^4
20. 6^3
21. 10^6
22. 2^8
23. 8^3
24. 10^0
25. 8^2
26. 7^4
27. 4^4
28. 10^7

★29. 5^6

★30. 9^4

Write in expanded form using powers of ten and exponents.

31. 3,281
32. 8,574
33. 37,945
34. 24,860
35. 127,558
36. 506,125

★37. 1,473,259

★38. 9,846,148

★39. 12,120,000

★40. 58,000,912

★41. 2,000,000,000

★42. 3,109,000,000

Midchapter Review

Write the numbers.

1. thirty-four thousand
2. 3 million, 18 thousand, 7

Write $<$ or $>$.

3. 4,756 ● 4,754
4. 682,833 ● 692,833

Round to the nearest hundred.

5. 738
6. 2,382

Round to the nearest ten thousand.

7. 78,301
8. 264,997

Write in exponent form.

9. $2 \times 2 \times 2$
10. 8×8

Write the products.

11. 3^4
12. 10^6

PROBLEM SOLVING • STRATEGIES

Using a Table

This table shows the populations of the fifteen American cities that have the largest populations. How many cities had a population greater than 1,000,000 in 1960?

CITIES WITH LARGEST POPULATIONS

Rank	City	1980	1970	1960
1	New York, NY	7,071,030	7,895,563	7,781,954
2	Chicago, IL	3,005,072	3,369,357	3,550,404
3	Los Angeles, CA	2,966,763	2,811,801	2,479,015
4	Philadelphia, PA	1,688,210	1,949,996	2,002,512
5	Houston, TX	1,594,086	1,233,535	938,219
6	Detroit, MI	1,203,339	1,514,063	1,670,144
7	Dallas, TX	904,078	844,401	679,684
8	San Diego, CA	875,504	697,471	573,224
9	Baltimore, MD	786,775	905,787	939,024
10	San Antonio, TX	785,410	654,153	587,718
11	Phoenix, AZ	764,911	584,303	439,170
12	Honolulu, HI	762,874	630,528	294,194
13	Indianapolis, IN	700,807	736,856	476,258
14	San Francisco, CA	678,974	715,674	740,316
15	Memphis, TN	646,356	623,988	497,524

These four steps can help you to solve problems.

Step 1 Read the problem.
What does it ask?

How many cities had a population greater than 1,000,000 in 1960?

Step 2 Make a plan.

Use the column labeled 1960. Count the number of entries that are greater than 1,000,000.

Step 3 Find the answer.

Five cities had a population greater than 1,000,000. (New York, Chicago, Los Angeles, Philadelphia, and Detroit)

Step 4 Check the answer.

Check to be sure that you looked in the correct column and counted each entry greater than 1,000,000.

Solve. Use the four steps to help you.

1. How many cities had a population greater than 1,000,000 in 1970?
2. How many cities had a population greater than 1,000,000 in 1980?
3. Did the population of New York City increase from 1960 to 1970?

Sometimes you need to obtain information from more than one column in a table.

4. Did the population of New York City increase from 1970 to 1980?
5. Did the population of Los Angeles increase from 1960 to 1970?
6. Did the population of Los Angeles increase from 1970 to 1980?
7. Which cities increased in population from 1970 to 1980?
8. Which cities decreased in population from 1970 to 1980?
9. In 1980, how much greater than 900,000 was the population of Dallas?
10. In 1980, what was the combined population of Dallas and Houston?

Be sure to read the correct rows in the table.

11. In 1980, what was the combined population of Los Angeles and San Francisco?
12. In 1980, the population of Philadelphia was how much less than 2,000,000?

★ 13. Which city had the greatest increase in population from 1960 to 1980?

★ 14. Which city had the smallest change in population from 1960 to 1980?

★ 15. In 1980, the combined population of Chicago, Los Angeles, Philadelphia, and Houston was how much greater than the population of New York City?

★ 16. Ali made a table showing the changes in population in Nova City during five consecutive ten-year periods. Then part of the table was torn off. Make a table that shows all the columns with the correct numbers.

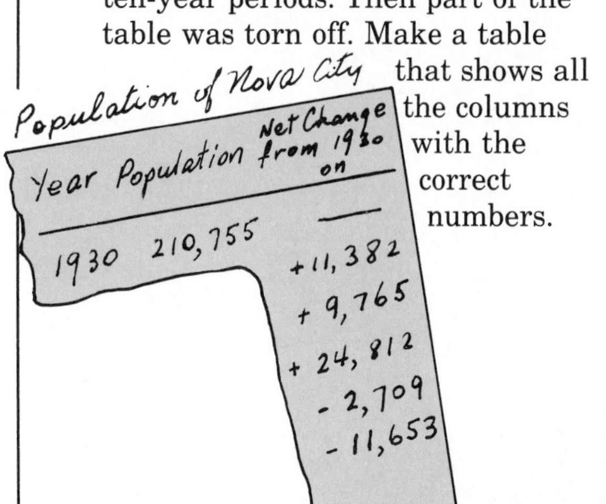

Addition and Subtraction

Addition has some important properties.

Addends	**Sum**
$14 + 12$	$= 26$
$12 + 14$	$= 26$

$14 + 12 = 12 + 14$

Commutative Property
You can change the order of two addends.
The sum is always the same.

Parentheses show which operation to do first.

$(8 + 1) + 6 = 15$
$8 + (1 + 6) = 15$
$(8 + 1) + 6 = 8 + (1 + 6)$

Associative Property
You can change the grouping of addends.
The sum is always the same.

$28 + 0 = 28$
$0 + 99 = 99$

Property of Zero
When one addend is 0, the sum is the same as the other addend.

You can use addition properties to check addition.

$$\begin{array}{r} 614 \\ +180 \\ \hline 794 \end{array} \downarrow \text{ Add down.}$$

$$\begin{array}{r} 614 \\ +180 \\ \hline 794 \end{array} \uparrow \text{ Add up to check.}$$

$$\begin{array}{r} 55 \\ 30 \\ +14 \\ \hline 99 \end{array} \downarrow \text{ Add down.}$$

$$\begin{array}{r} 55 \\ 30 \\ +14 \\ \hline 99 \end{array} \uparrow \text{ Add up to check.}$$

Addition and subtraction are **inverse operations.**

$8 + 6 = 14 \qquad 14 - 6 = 8 \leftarrow$ difference

In each of these equations, n stands for a missing number. Does the same number, 10, make both equations true?

$n + 15 = 25 \qquad 25 - 15 = n$

You can use addition to check subtraction.

$$\begin{array}{r} 758 \\ -126 \\ \hline 632 \end{array} \qquad \textbf{Check} \quad \begin{array}{r} 632 \\ +126 \\ \hline 758 \end{array}$$

Practice • Add or subtract.

1. $7 + 5 = n$
2. $8 + 6 = n$
3. $9 + 8 = n$
4. $7 + 9 = n$
5. $11 - 3 = n$
6. $13 - 7 = n$
7. $15 - 8 = n$
8. $18 - 9 = n$

Name the properties that are illustrated.

9. $5 + 6 = 6 + 5$
10. $3 + 0 = 3$

Mixed Practice • Add or subtract.

11. $4 + 7 = n$
12. $9 + 6 = n$
13. $8 + 2 = n$
14. $9 + 4 = n$
15. $7 + 8 = n$
16. $8 + 4 = n$
17. $9 + 5 = n$
18. $8 + 7 = n$
19. $6 + 4 = n$
20. $5 + 9 = n$
21. $3 + 8 = n$
22. $8 + 5 = n$
23. $9 + 7 = n$
24. $9 + 3 = n$
25. $8 + 8 = n$
26. $9 + 9 = n$
27. $12 - 3 = n$
28. $13 - 6 = n$
29. $15 - 9 = n$
30. $17 - 8 = n$
31. $14 - 6 = n$
32. $12 - 5 = n$
33. $13 - 8 = n$
34. $15 - 7 = n$
35. $16 - 8 = n$
36. $13 - 4 = n$
37. $16 - 7 = n$
38. $14 - 8 = n$
39. $12 - 9 = n$
40. $14 - 7 = n$
41. $15 - 6 = n$
42. $16 - 9 = n$

Name the properties that are illustrated.

43. $(8 + 3) + 2 = 8 + (3 + 2)$
44. $0 + 26 = 26$
45. $17 + 21 = 21 + 17$
46. $(272 + 3) + 10 = 272 + (3 + 10)$

Find the number that makes each equation true.

47. $n + 4 = 11$
48. $n + 5 = 13$
49. $n + 7 = 15$
★ 50. $n + 127 = 258$
★ 51. $n + 263 = 592$
★ 52. $425 + n = 542$

PROBLEM SOLVING • APPLICATIONS

53. The Sears Tower in Chicago is 443 meters high. The Empire State Building is 381 meters high. How much greater is the height of the Sears Tower?

★ 54. The Terminal Tower is the tallest building in Cleveland. It is 227 meters shorter than the Sears Tower. How many meters tall is the Terminal Tower?

Estimating and Adding

One day 3,795 tickets were sold for a computer exposition. The next day 6,352 tickets were sold. How many tickets were sold in all?

$3{,}795 + 6{,}352 = n$

Estimate the sum first.

Think: Round each addend to the nearest thousand. Add.

$$\begin{array}{rcr} 3{,}795 & \rightarrow & 4{,}000 \\ +\ 6{,}352 & \rightarrow & +\ 6{,}000 \\ \hline & & 10{,}000 \end{array}$$

About 10,000 tickets were sold in all.

Add to find the actual answer. As you add, you may need to regroup 10 ones as 1 ten, 10 tens as 1 hundred, and so on.

When you have finished adding, use your estimate to see if the answer is reasonable.

Step 1 Add the ones.

$$\begin{array}{r} 3{,}795 \\ +6{,}352 \\ \hline 7 \end{array}$$

Step 2 Add the tens. Regroup.

$$\begin{array}{r} 1 \\ 3{,}795 \\ +6{,}352 \\ \hline 47 \end{array}$$

Step 3 Add the hundreds. Regroup.

$$\begin{array}{r} 1\,1 \\ 3{,}795 \\ +\ 6{,}352 \\ \hline 147 \end{array}$$

Step 4 Add the thousands. Compare the answer with your estimate.

$$\begin{array}{r} 1 \\ 3{,}795 \\ +\ 6{,}352 \\ \hline 10{,}147 \end{array}$$

10,147 tickets were sold in all.

More Examples

$$\begin{array}{r} 1\ \ 11 \\ 68{,}463 \\ +18{,}079 \\ \hline 86{,}542 \end{array} \qquad \begin{array}{r} 112 \\ 46 \\ 709 \\ +4{,}585 \\ \hline 5{,}340 \end{array} \qquad \begin{array}{r} 12\ 23 \\ 14{,}587 \\ 326 \\ 1{,}878 \\ +237{,}519 \\ \hline 254{,}310 \end{array} \qquad \begin{array}{r} 1\ \ 1\ 1 \\ \$235.45 \\ +672.96 \\ \hline \$908.41 \end{array}$$

Practice • Estimate each sum. Then find the actual answer.

1. $696 + 512$
2. $547 + 163$
3. $4,329 + 1,877$
4. $38,865 + 13,902$
5. $22,132 + 51,398$

Add.

6. $729 + 457$
7. $3,781 + 2,064$
8. $21,684 + 3,572$
9. $76,175 + 12,599$
10. $731,658 + 203,076$

Mixed Practice • Estimate each sum. Then find the actual answer.

11. $925 + 182$
12. $716 + 829$
13. $8,943 + 4,876$
14. $33,815 + 27,289$
15. $68,575 + 24,149$

Add.

16. $4,806 + 3,693$
17. $7,645 + 4,768$
18. $15,432 + 2,697$
19. $639,742 + 56,398$
20. $554,136 + 284,967$
21. $381 + 76 + 412$
22. $4,753 + 38 + 1,267$
23. $3,468 + 1,870 + 2,568 + 4,773$
24. $50,118 + 35,656 + 2,813 + 82,736$
25. $298,416 + 374,382 + 129,345 + 6,327$
26. $\$86.25 + 41.03$
27. $\$96.77 + 29.36$
28. $\$89.65 + 7.35$
29. $\$125.60 + 108.70$
30. $\$347.62 + 507.89$

Solve the equations.

31. $3,962 + 846 = n$
32. $52,186 + 3,876 = n$

★ 33. $n + 7,825 = 9,975$

★ 34. $n + 5,245 + 3,655 = 9,999$

PROBLEM SOLVING • APPLICATIONS

35. This table shows the number of tickets sold during another computer exposition. What was the total number of tickets sold?

★ 36. Were more tickets sold during the first two days than during the last two days?

	Number of Tickets
Day 1	4,674
Day 2	7,932
Day 3	8,853
Day 4	3,508

Estimating and Subtracting

Jenny Rechner is an engineer. During a four-year period, she worked 6,840 hours at her job. During the same period, her son Ted worked 2,595 hours in a part-time job. How many fewer hours did Ted work than his mother?

$6{,}840 - 2{,}595 = n$

Estimate the difference first.

Think: Round each number to the nearest thousand. Subtract.

$$\begin{array}{rcr} 6{,}840 & \rightarrow & 7{,}000 \\ -2{,}595 & \rightarrow & -3{,}000 \\ \hline & & 4{,}000 \end{array}$$

Ted worked about 4,000 fewer hours than his mother. Was your estimate reasonable?

Subtract to find the actual answer. As you subtract, you may need to regroup 1 ten as 10 ones, 1 hundred as 10 tens, and so on.

Step 1 Regroup. Subtract the ones.

$$\begin{array}{r} \scriptstyle 3\ 10 \\ 6{,}8\,\not{4}\,\not{0} \\ -2{,}5\,9\,5 \\ \hline 5 \end{array}$$

Step 2 Regroup. Subtract the tens.

$$\begin{array}{r} \scriptstyle 13 \\ \scriptstyle 7\ \not{3}\ 10 \\ 6{,}\not{8}\,\not{4}\,\not{0} \\ -2{,}5\,9\,5 \\ \hline 4\,5 \end{array}$$

Step 3 Subtract the hundreds.

$$\begin{array}{r} \scriptstyle 13 \\ \scriptstyle 7\ \not{3}\ 10 \\ 6{,}\not{8}\,\not{4}\,\not{0} \\ -2{,}5\,9\,5 \\ \hline 2\,4\,5 \end{array}$$

Step 4 Subtract the thousands. Compare the answer with your estimate.

$$\begin{array}{r} \scriptstyle 13 \\ \scriptstyle 7\ \not{3}\ 10 \\ 6{,}\not{8}\,\not{4}\,\not{0} \\ -2{,}5\,9\,5 \\ \hline 4{,}2\,4\,5 \end{array}$$

Ted worked 4,245 fewer hours than his mother.

More Examples

$$\begin{array}{r} \scriptstyle 14\ 11 \\ \scriptstyle 7\ 4\ 1\ 10 \\ \not{8}{,}\,\not{5}\,\not{2}\,\not{0} \\ -7{,}5\,3\,7 \\ \hline 9\,8\,3 \end{array} \qquad \begin{array}{r} \scriptstyle 8\ 9\ 9\ 10 \\ \not{9}{,}\,\not{0}\,\not{0}\,\not{0} \\ -5{,}3\,4\,8 \\ \hline 3{,}6\,5\,2 \end{array} \qquad \begin{array}{r} \scriptstyle 2\ 9\ 9\ 15 \\ 1\,\not{3}{,}\,\not{0}\,\not{0}\,\not{5} \\ -\quad 2\,9\,6 \\ \hline 1\,2{,}7\,0\,9 \end{array} \qquad \begin{array}{r} \scriptstyle 14 \\ \scriptstyle 0\ 4\ \ 9\ 10 \\ \$4\,\not{1}\,\not{5}.\not{0}\,\not{0} \\ -1\,0\,5.6\,3 \\ \hline 3\,0\,9.3\,7 \end{array}$$

Practice • Estimate each difference. Then find the actual answer.

1. $\begin{array}{r} 796 \\ -685 \\ \hline \end{array}$ **2.** $\begin{array}{r} 638 \\ -219 \\ \hline \end{array}$ **3.** $\begin{array}{r} 5{,}847 \\ -2{,}052 \\ \hline \end{array}$ **4.** $\begin{array}{r} 24{,}216 \\ -13{,}897 \\ \hline \end{array}$ **5.** $\begin{array}{r} 76{,}325 \\ -45{,}108 \\ \hline \end{array}$

Subtract.

6. $\begin{array}{r} 847 \\ -139 \\ \hline \end{array}$ 7. $\begin{array}{r} 5{,}967 \\ -3{,}082 \\ \hline \end{array}$ 8. $\begin{array}{r} 9{,}000 \\ -2{,}858 \\ \hline \end{array}$ 9. $\begin{array}{r} 27{,}005 \\ -\ 4{,}634 \\ \hline \end{array}$ 10. $\begin{array}{r} 347{,}016 \\ -167{,}352 \\ \hline \end{array}$

Mixed Practice • Subtract.

11. $\begin{array}{r} 822 \\ -507 \\ \hline \end{array}$ 12. $\begin{array}{r} 700 \\ -542 \\ \hline \end{array}$ 13. $\begin{array}{r} 1{,}206 \\ -\ 173 \\ \hline \end{array}$ 14. $\begin{array}{r} 1{,}467 \\ -\ 984 \\ \hline \end{array}$ 15. $\begin{array}{r} 9{,}000 \\ -2{,}874 \\ \hline \end{array}$

16. $\begin{array}{r} 2{,}600 \\ -1{,}883 \\ \hline \end{array}$ 17. $\begin{array}{r} 53{,}265 \\ -\ 2{,}189 \\ \hline \end{array}$ 18. $\begin{array}{r} 17{,}624 \\ -11{,}385 \\ \hline \end{array}$ 19. $\begin{array}{r} 44{,}960 \\ -31{,}874 \\ \hline \end{array}$ 20. $\begin{array}{r} 189{,}203 \\ -\ 8{,}579 \\ \hline \end{array}$

21. $\begin{array}{r} 564{,}000 \\ -\ 28{,}936 \\ \hline \end{array}$ 22. $\begin{array}{r} 622{,}176 \\ -318{,}408 \\ \hline \end{array}$ 23. $\begin{array}{r} \$73.15 \\ -\ 8.89 \\ \hline \end{array}$ 24. $\begin{array}{r} \$110.60 \\ -\ 93.75 \\ \hline \end{array}$ 25. $\begin{array}{r} \$273.00 \\ -\ 76.94 \\ \hline \end{array}$

Solve the equations.

26. $631 - 495 = n$ 27. $8{,}053 - 657 = n$

28. $3{,}752 - 89 = n$ 29. $40{,}001 - 12{,}364 = n$

★30. $9{,}286 - n = 1{,}435$ ★31. $n - 2{,}372 = 1{,}528$

Solve. Do the operations in parentheses first.

★32. $(567 + 373) - 462 = n$

★33. $(1{,}283 - 906) + 4{,}572 = n$

PROBLEM SOLVING • APPLICATIONS

34. Jenny Rechner runs for exercise. One day she ran 2,875 meters. The next day she ran 3,400 meters. How much farther did she run the second day?

★35. How much less than 10,000 meters did Jenny Rechner run during the two days?

Skills Maintenance

1. $24 \div 4$ 2. $30 \div 6$ 3. $32 \div 8$ 4. $35 \div 5$

5. $49 \div 7$ 6. $45 \div 9$ 7. $54 \div 6$ 8. $56 \div 8$

9. $63 \div 9$ 10. $64 \div 8$ 11. $72 \div 8$ 12. $81 \div 9$

PROBLEM SOLVING • STRATEGIES

Using Inverse Operations

Paradise Motion Pictures is planning a movie. There are 96 parts for actors in the movie. 79 of the actors have been chosen. How many have not been chosen yet?

$$96 - 79 = n$$

total number ↗ 96; number chosen ↑ 79; number not chosen yet ↖ n

$$\begin{array}{r} 96 \\ -79 \\ \hline 17 \end{array}$$

17 actors have not been chosen yet.

It is important to check your answer. Often you can use inverse operations to check each other. Check subtraction by addition.

$$\begin{array}{r} 17 \\ +79 \\ \hline 96 \end{array}$$

Solve and check.

1. A western movie requires 1,025 actors. So far 659 actors have been chosen. How many actors have not been chosen yet?

2. In the western movie, 18 outdoor sets will be used. 46 indoor sets will be used. What is the total number of sets that will be used?

3. The cost of the western movie is budgeted at $1,859,000. How much less than $2,000,000 is this?

4. In 1983 Paradise Motion Pictures budgeted a space movie at $3,425,000. When the picture was finished, the actual cost was $4,217,000. How much over the budget was this?

COST OF 5 MOVIES	
Space Games	$5,143,000
Prairie Nights	$1,946,000
Trouble in the City	$1,235,000
U.F.O.	$6,789,000
Stony Point	$2,238,000

5. What was the combined cost of *Space Games* and *Stony Point*?

Check addition of two addends by subtraction. For three or more addends, do the addition again.

6. What was the combined cost of *Prairie Nights* and *Trouble in the City*?

7. What was the combined cost of the five movies?

8. What was the difference in cost between *Space Games* and *Prairie Nights*?

9. How much more did *U.F.O.* cost than *Trouble in the City*?

10. How much less than $10,000,000 did *U.F.O.* cost?

Be sure you understand the question in the problem.

★ 11. How much more than $10,000,000 was the combined cost of *U.F.O.* and *Space Games*?

★ 12. How much less than $20,000,000 was the combined cost of the five movies?

★ 13. Chizuko was the star of *Trouble in the City* and *Stony Point*. In *Trouble in the City* she earned $78,000. In *Stony Point* she earned $17,000 more than that. What was the total amount that she earned in these two movies?

★ 14. Paradise Motion Pictures is planning *U.F.O. II*, a sequel to *U.F.O.* *U.F.O. II* is budgeted at $12,919,000. This amount is how much less than twice the cost of the original *U.F.O.*?

CHAPTER 1

REVIEW

Write the numbers. (pp. 2–3)

1. fifteen thousand **2.** 68 thousand, 740 **3.** 73 million, 42 thousand

In which place is the blue digit? (pp. 2–3)

4. 80,624 **5.** 563,282 **6.** 2,741,596 **7.** 385,003,050

Write $<$ or $>$. (pp. 4–5)

8. 7,454 ● 7,445 **9.** 5,931,563 ● 5,934,563 **10.** 203,602 ● 87,958

11. Round to the nearest thousand: 7,485. (pp. 6–7)

12. Round to the nearest million: 13,500,912. (pp. 6–7)

13. Write in exponent form: $5 \times 5 \times 5$. (pp. 8–9)

14. Write the product: 8^1 (pp. 8–9)

Write in expanded form using powers of ten and exponents. (pp. 8–9)

15. 7,345 **16.** 35,970

Name the properties of addition that are illustrated. (pp. 12–13)

17. $(35 + 7) + 12 = 35 + (7 + 12)$ **18.** $19 + 0 = 19$ **19.** $16 + 21 = 21 + 16$

Add or subtract. (pp. 14–17)

20. $\begin{array}{r} 71{,}724 \\ +31{,}899 \\ \hline \end{array}$ **21.** $\begin{array}{r} 427{,}314 \\ 385{,}006 \\ +208{,}630 \\ \hline \end{array}$ **22.** $\begin{array}{r} \$264.08 \\ +\ 78.92 \\ \hline \end{array}$ **23.** $\begin{array}{r} 295{,}030 \\ -\ 87{,}072 \\ \hline \end{array}$ **24.** $\begin{array}{r} \$300.00 \\ -172.46 \\ \hline \end{array}$

Solve the equations. (pp. 14–17)

25. $2{,}852 + 673 = n$ **26.** $34{,}000 - 15{,}392 = n$

27. The George Washington Bridge is 1,067 meters long. The Golden Gate Bridge is 1,230 meters long. What is the difference between their lengths? (pp. 18–19)

28. One year Ms. Chan earned \$19,489. The next year she earned \$21,650. What were her total earnings for the two years? (pp. 18–19)

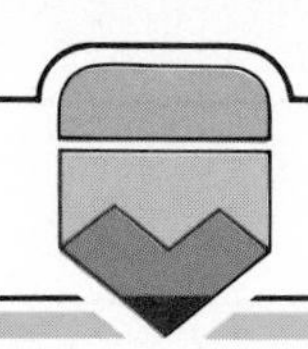

PROJECT

Ancient Systems of Writing Numbers

Ancient Egyptians used pictures to represent numbers.

Picture	Number
𓏺	1
𓎆	10
𓍢	100
𓆼	1,000
𓂭	10,000

The Romans used letters to represent numbers.

Symbol	Number
I	1
V	5
X	10
L	50
C	100
D	500
M	1,000

In the Egyptian system, the position of the pictures did not matter.

𓎆 𓏺𓏺𓏺 = 10 + 1 + 1 + 1 = 13

𓏺𓎆𓏺𓏺 = 10 + 1 + 1 + 1 = 13

The values of the pictures are added.

In the Roman system, the positions of the letters mattered.

VI = 5 + 1 = 6

The lesser symbol is at the right; add.

IV = 5 − 1 = 4

The lesser symbol is at the left; subtract.

Write the numbers in our system.

1. 𓎆𓎆𓏺𓏺𓏺 **2.** 𓍢𓍢𓎆𓎆𓎆𓎆 **3.** 𓏺𓏺𓏺𓏺 𓎆

4. 𓍢𓏺 **5.** 𓆼𓍢𓎆 **6.** 𓂭𓆼

7. XI **8.** IX **9.** CX **10.** XC **11.** LX

12. XL **13.** XVI **14.** XIV **15.** LXXIX **16.** CXIV

17. XCI **18.** DCCL **19.** CXCI **20.** DLX **21.** MCIX

Write the numbers in the Roman system.

22. 30 **23.** 204 **24.** 600 **25.** 1,049

26. Does the Egyptian system have a picture that represents zero?

27. Does the Roman system have a letter that represents zero?

CHAPTER 1 TEST

Write the numbers.

1. five thousand, seven hundred 2. 204 thousand, 81 3. 641 million, 113 thousand

In which place is the blue digit?

4. 14,931 5. 249,805 6. 9,600,147 7. 315,820,227

Write < or >.

8. 3,070 ● 3,700 9. 9,643,095 ● 9,643,059 10. 101,010 ● 101,100

11. Round to the nearest ten thousand: 285,651.

12. Round to the nearest dollar: $34,675.62.

13. Write in exponent form: $3 \times 3 \times 3 \times 3$.

14. Write the product: 4^6.

Write the expanded form using powers of ten and exponents.

15. 6,542 16. 48,739

Name the properties of addition that are illustrated.

17. $15 + 37 = 37 + 15$ 18. $(24 + 6) + 11 = 24 + (6 + 11)$ 19. $0 + 26 = 26$

Add or subtract.

20.	21.	22.	23.	24.
2,451	163,045	$347.16	516,070	$701.01
+2,629	254,786	+ 82.86	− 68,183	− 524.32
	+437,325			

Solve the equations.

25. $3{,}743 + 852 = n$ 26. $63{,}001 - 21{,}458 = n$

27. Eric needs to have his car repaired. The repair work costs $398.06. He has $417.80. How much money will be have left after he pays for the car repairs?

28. Lauren worked 142 hours in January, 117 hours in February, and 152 hours in March. What is the total number of hours that she worked in the three months?

ENRICHMENT

The Binary System

Some computers use the **binary system** of numbers. The binary system has the number two as its grouping number, or base. Each place has a value twice as great as the place to its right.

Sixteens	Eights	Fours	Twos	Ones	Meaning of Binary Number		Number in Our System
				1	1 one	→	1
			1	0	1 two + 0 ones	→	2
			1	1	1 two + 1 one	→	3
		1	0	0	1 four + 0 twos + 0 ones	→	4

When you write numbers in the binary system, use only the digits 0 and 1. You can write a small "two" to show that you are writing numbers in the binary system. The binary number 101_{two} is read "one zero one, base two."

$101_{\text{two}} = 5$ $110_{\text{two}} = 6$ $111_{\text{two}} = 7$

Write the numbers in our system.

1. $1000_{\text{two}} = n$
2. $1111_{\text{two}} = n$
3. $1001_{\text{two}} = n$
4. $1010_{\text{two}} = n$
5. $1011_{\text{two}} = n$
6. $1100_{\text{two}} = n$
7. $10000_{\text{two}} = n$
8. $10001_{\text{two}} = n$
9. $11111_{\text{two}} = n$
10. Copy the place-value chart above and extend it three more places to the left. Label each place.

Write the numbers in the binary system.

11. $32 = n_{\text{two}}$
12. $33 = n_{\text{two}}$
13. $34 = n_{\text{two}}$
14. $64 = n_{\text{two}}$
15. $65 = n_{\text{two}}$
16. $66 = n_{\text{two}}$
17. $128 = n_{\text{two}}$
18. $129 = n_{\text{two}}$
19. $130 = n_{\text{two}}$
20. $48 = n_{\text{two}}$
21. $96 = n_{\text{two}}$
22. $127 = n_{\text{two}}$
23. Find out how numbers can be represented by punched tape from a computer. Write a report on the method used.

CALCULATOR

Calculator Review

A calculator has number buttons and command buttons.

7 8 9 ÷ DIVIDE
4 5 6 × TIMES
1 2 3 – MINUS
0 + PLUS
= EQUALS

First turn the calculator on.

To subtract 27 from 65, push 6 5 – 2 7 =.

Look at the screen: 38. The answer is 38.

Addition and Subtraction Facts Drill

1. $28 + 13 =$?
2. $77 + 0 =$?
3. $46 - 21 =$?
4. $87 - 45 =$?
5. $14 + 66 =$?
6. $89 - 64 =$?

To divide 172 by 4, push 1 7 2 ÷ 4 =.

Look at the screen: 43. The answer is 43.

Multiplication and Division Facts Drill

7. $168 \div 8 =$?
8. $18 \times 9 =$?
9. $21 \times 37 =$?
10. $64 \times 62 =$?
11. $40 \div 8 =$?
12. $150 \div 3 =$?

Push CE if you make a mistake in your last entry.

Push C if you make a mistake and want to redo the problem.

The calculator has no commas and no dollar signs.

$$
\begin{array}{r}
\$8{,}459 \\
-\$6{,}273 \\
\hline
\end{array}
$$

Push   .

The screen shows 2186. . Write in the dollar sign and the comma. The correct answer is $2,186.

Calculate. Remember to write the dollar signs and commas.

13. $\begin{array}{r} \$8{,}034 \\ +\$2{,}045 \\ \hline \end{array}$

14. $\begin{array}{r} \$7{,}469 \\ -\$5{,}985 \\ \hline \end{array}$

15. $\begin{array}{r} \$6{,}032 \\ \times \quad 81 \\ \hline \end{array}$

Repeated operations can be done using only the equals button.

$7 \times 7 \times 7 \times 7 = \underline{\ ?\ }$ Push    .

The answer is 2,401. Note that you use *the same number* of equal signs as there are multiplication signs.

16. $5 \times 5 \times 5 \times 5 \times 5 = \underline{\ ?\ }$

17. $12 \times 12 \times 12 = \underline{\ ?\ }$

You must use *one more* equal sign than plus signs for repeated addition.
$8 + 8 + 8 + 8 = ?$

Push [8] [+] [=] [=] [=] [=] . The answer is 32.

18. $3 + 3 + 3 + 3 + 3 = \underline{\ ?\ }$

19. $9 + 9 + 9 = \underline{\ ?\ }$

You use *the same number* of equal signs as minus signs for repeated subtraction.
$81 - 3 - 3 - 3 - 3 = ?$

Push [8] [1] [−] [3] [=] [=] [=] [=]. The answer is 69.

20. $74 - 8 - 8 - 8 - 8 = \underline{\ ?\ }$

21. $57 - 2 - 2 - 2 - 2 - 2 = \underline{\ ?\ }$

You use *the same number* of equal signs as division signs for repeated division.
$1{,}000 \div 10 \div 10 = ?$

Push [1] [0] [0] [0] [÷] [1] [0] [=] [=] . The answer is 10.

22. $72 \div 2 \div 2 \div 2 = \underline{\ ?\ }$

23. $324 \div 3 \div 3 \div 3 \div 3 \div 3 = \underline{\ ?\ }$

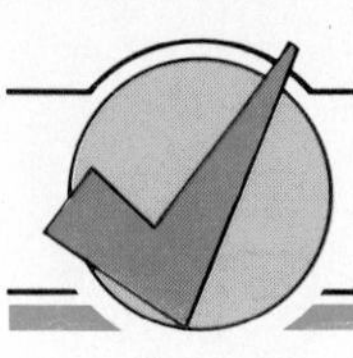

SKILLS MAINTENANCE

Chapter 1

Choose the correct answers.

1. In which place is the blue digit?

25,673,094

A. hundreds
B. thousands
C. millions
D. not here

2. Write <, =, or >.
4,638 ● 4,386

A. >
B. <
C. =
D. not here

3. Round 466,051 to the nearest ten thousand.

A. 460,000
B. 470,000
C. 466,000
D. not here

4. Write the product.
4^5

A. 256
B. 1,240
C. 20
D. not here

5. What property of addition is illustrated?
$23 + 46 = 46 + 23$

A. Commutative
B. Property of Zero
C. Associative
D. not here

6. Add.

$$\begin{array}{r} 35,623 \\ +44,708 \\ \hline \end{array}$$

A. 79,321
B. 80,331
C. 70,331
D. not here

7. Add.

$$\begin{array}{r} 4,365 \\ 276 \\ +2,801 \\ \hline \end{array}$$

A. 6,332
B. 7,342
C. 7,442
D. not here

8. Subtract.

$$\begin{array}{r} 70,516 \\ -52,807 \\ \hline \end{array}$$

A. 17,709
B. 17,719
C. 18,709
D. not here

9. Solve.
$46,007 - 37,678 = n$

A. $n = 8,329$
B. $n = 8,439$
C. $n = 83,685$
D. not here

10. At the beginning of the week, Carl's gas station had 15,856 liters of gasoline. During the week Carl's station sold 8,649 liters of gasoline. How many liters of gasoline were left?

A. 7,207 liters **B.** 24,505 liters
C. 7,208 liters **D.** not here

11. Watson bought a new car for $7,288 and a new motorcycle for $4,678. How much did he spend in all?

A. $11,856 **B.** $11,966
C. $11,956 **D.** not here

Whole Numbers: Multiplication and Division

CHAPTER 2

Multiplication and Division • Multiplying by One-, Two-, and Three-Digit Numbers • Problem Solving: Choosing the Operation • Dividing by One-Digit, Two-Digit, and Three-Digit Divisors • Estimating and Correcting Estimates • Problem Solving: Too Much or Not Enough Information • Order of Operations • Patterns • Choices

Multiplication and Division

Multiplication has some important properties.

$6 \times 7 = 42$
$7 \times 6 = 42$
$6 \times 7 = 7 \times 6$

Commutative Property
You can change the order of two factors. The product is always the same.

$(2 \times 3) \times 4 = 24$
$2 \times (3 \times 4) = 24$
$(2 \times 3) \times 4 = 2 \times (3 \times 4)$

Associative Property
You can group factors differently. The product is always the same.

$1 \times 35 = 35$
$76 \times 1 = 76$

Property of One
The product of any number and 1 is that number.

$0 \times 8 = 0$
$15 \times 0 = 0$

Property of Zero
The product of any number and 0 is 0.

Multiplication also has a **distributive property** over addition.

$3 \times (8 + 2) = (3 \times 8) + (3 \times 2)$
$3 \times 10 = 24 + 6$
$30 = 30$

To find the product of a number and the sum of two numbers, you can
- add first and then multiply.
- multiply each addend and then add.

Multiplication and division are **inverse operations.**

$5 \times 8 = 40 \qquad 40 \div 8 = 5 \leftarrow$ quotient

In each of these equations, n stands for a missing number. Does the same number, 20, make both equations true?

$n \times 3 = 60 \qquad 60 \div 3 = n$

Practice • Multiply or divide.

1. $6 \times 4 = n$ **2.** $7 \times 5 = n$ **3.** $6 \times 9 = n$ **4.** $8 \times 7 = n$

5. $12 \div 2 = n$ **6.** $20 \div 5 = n$ **7.** $30 \div 6 = n$ **8.** $54 \div 9 = n$

Name the properties that are illustrated.

9. $(2 \times 5) \times 3 = 2 \times (5 \times 3)$ **10.** $7 \times 9 = 9 \times 7$

Mixed Practice • Multiply or divide.

11. $3 \times 3 = n$ **12.** $4 \times 6 = n$ **13.** $5 \times 7 = n$ **14.** $6 \times 8 = n$

15. $4 \times 5 = n$ **16.** $5 \times 8 = n$ **17.** $6 \times 6 = n$ **18.** $7 \times 9 = n$

19. $5 \times 9 = n$ **20.** $6 \times 3 = n$ **21.** $7 \times 7 = n$ **22.** $8 \times 5 = n$

23. $6 \times 5 = n$ **24.** $7 \times 8 = n$ **25.** $8 \times 6 = n$ **26.** $9 \times 5 = n$

27. $2 \times 9 = n$ **28.** $9 \times 6 = n$ **29.** $5 \times 6 = n$ **30.** $9 \times 9 = n$

31. $8 \div 2 = n$ **32.** $6 \div 3 = n$ **33.** $20 \div 4 = n$ **34.** $30 \div 5 = n$

35. $21 \div 3 = n$ **36.** $45 \div 5 = n$ **37.** $42 \div 7 = n$ **38.** $36 \div 9 = n$

39. $48 \div 8 = n$ **40.** $54 \div 6 = n$ **41.** $45 \div 9 = n$ **42.** $56 \div 7 = n$

43. $63 \div 9 = n$ **44.** $48 \div 6 = n$ **45.** $64 \div 8 = n$ **46.** $54 \div 9 = n$

47. $36 \div 4 = n$ **48.** $49 \div 7 = n$ **49.** $72 \div 9 = n$ **50.** $63 \div 7 = n$

Name the properties that are illustrated.

51. $1 \times 63 = 63$ **52.** $12 \times 0 = 0$

53. $9 \times 12 = 12 \times 9$ **54.** $6 \times (10 + 2) = (6 \times 10) + (6 \times 2)$

Find the number that makes each equation true.

55. $n \times 4 = 32$ **56.** $n \times 7 = 35$ **57.** $n \times 3 = 27$ **58.** $n \times 8 = 56$

★ **59.** $n \times 5 = 185$ ★ **60.** $9 \times n = 198$ ★ **61.** $n \times 6 = 252$ ★ **62.** $4 \times n = 332$

PROBLEM SOLVING • APPLICATIONS

63. There are 96 people waiting to buy tickets. The same number of people are in each of 6 ticket lines. How many people are in each line?

★ **64.** During one week a ticket agent worked from 9:00 A.M. to 6:00 P.M. Monday through Friday. He had 1 hour per day for lunch. How many hours did he actually work that week?

Multiplying by One-Digit Numbers

A jet airliner can carry 375 passengers. How many passengers can be carried by 5 of these jets?

$5 \times 375 = n$

You can think of 375 as 300 + 70 + 5 and multiply as shown below. This is an application of the distributive property.

$$\begin{aligned} 5 \times (300 + 70 + 5) &= (5 \times 300) + (5 \times 70) + (5 \times 5) \\ &= 1{,}500 + 350 + 25 \\ &= 1{,}875 \end{aligned}$$

A multiplication example shows the work in a shorter form. You begin by multiplying the ones.

Step 1 Multiply the ones by 5.
$5 \times 5 = 25$

$$\begin{array}{r} {}^{2} \\ 375 \\ \times \quad 5 \\ \hline 5 \end{array}$$

Step 2 Multiply the tens by 5.
$5 \times 7 = 35$
$35 + 2 = 37$

$$\begin{array}{r} {}^{32} \\ 375 \\ \times \quad 5 \\ \hline 75 \end{array}$$

Step 3 Multiply the hundreds by 5.
$5 \times 3 = 15$
$15 + 3 = 18$

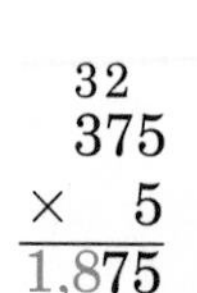

$$\begin{array}{r} {}^{32} \\ 375 \\ \times \quad 5 \\ \hline 1{,}875 \end{array}$$

1,875 passengers can be carried.

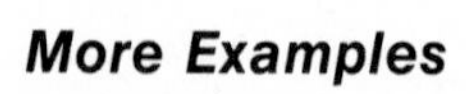

More Examples

$$\begin{array}{r} {}^{3} \\ 28 \\ \times\ 4 \\ \hline 112 \end{array} \qquad \begin{array}{r} {}^{4} \\ 560 \\ \times \quad 7 \\ \hline 3{,}920 \end{array} \qquad \begin{array}{r} {}^{2\ 64} \\ 4{,}276 \\ \times \quad 8 \\ \hline 34{,}208 \end{array} \qquad \begin{array}{r} {}^{2\quad 3} \\ 23{,}104 \\ \times \quad 9 \\ \hline 207{,}936 \end{array} \qquad \begin{array}{r} {}^{12} \\ \$125.82 \\ \times \quad 3 \\ \hline \$377.46 \end{array}$$

Practice • Multiply.

1. 32×4
2. 73×7
3. 108×9
4. 827×8
5. $3{,}702 \times 5$
6. $8{,}068 \times 6$
7. $6{,}977 \times 4$
8. $15{,}300 \times 9$
9. $36{,}189 \times 5$
10. $\$109.71 \times 3$

Mixed Practice • Multiply.

11. 43×2
12. 24×6
13. 35×8
14. 92×5
15. 48×6

16. 872×4
17. 307×9
18. 246×3
19. 885×2
20. 692×7

21. $5{,}648 \times 5$
22. $9{,}765 \times 9$
23. $3{,}172 \times 3$
24. $2{,}304 \times 4$
25. $8{,}152 \times 3$

26. $17{,}272 \times 5$
27. $26{,}343 \times 7$
28. $48{,}093 \times 9$
29. $135{,}219 \times 8$
30. $276{,}008 \times 7$

31. $\$3.98 \times 7$
32. $\$14.70 \times 8$
33. $\$17.95 \times 4$
34. $\$132.87 \times 6$
35. $\$1{,}125.50 \times 9$

Solve.

36. $4 \times 39 = n$
37. $6 \times 257 = n$
38. $843 \times 2 = n$
39. $1{,}607 \times 9 = n$
40. $3 \times 1{,}549 = n$
41. $5 \times 3{,}267 = n$
42. $2 \times 13{,}759 = n$
43. $42{,}680 \times 4 = n$
44. $7 \times 320{,}075 = n$
★ 45. $2 \times 3{,}275 \times 3 = n$
★ 46. $5 \times 9{,}999 \times 4 = n$
★ 47. $6^5 = n$

PROBLEM SOLVING • APPLICATIONS

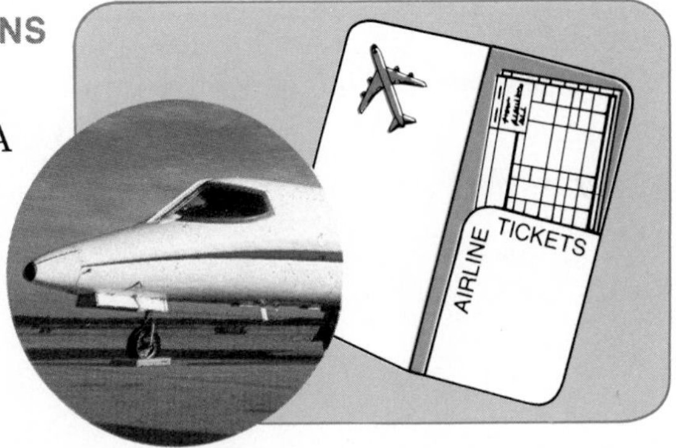

48. There are 9 jet airliners in the hangars for overnight servicing. A crew of 12 mechanics is assigned to each jet. How many mechanics are needed to service all of the jets at the same time?

49. A jet airliner flies at a speed of 965 kilometers per hour. At this rate, how far can the jet fly in 3 hours?

★ 50. The Cuomo family buys 4 airline tickets at $67.80 each. How much less than $300.00 is the total cost of the tickets?

★ 51. On a certain airline, a day flight to Miami costs $118.40. A "special" night flight costs $72.85. How much more do 6 tickets cost on a day flight than on the night flight?

Multiplying by Tens, Hundreds, and Thousands

Look for a pattern.

$$\begin{array}{r}36\\ \times 10\\ \hline 360\end{array}\qquad\begin{array}{r}36\\ \times 20\\ \hline 720\end{array}\qquad\begin{array}{r}36\\ \times 30\\ \hline 1{,}080\end{array}\qquad\begin{array}{r}36\\ \times 40\\ \hline 1{,}440\end{array}\qquad\begin{array}{r}36\\ \times 50\\ \hline 1{,}800\end{array}$$

When multiplying by tens, you can write a 0 in the ones place. Then you can multiply by the number of tens.

Look for a pattern.

$$\begin{array}{r}36\\ \times 100\\ \hline 3{,}600\end{array}\qquad\begin{array}{r}36\\ \times 200\\ \hline 7{,}200\end{array}\qquad\begin{array}{r}36\\ \times 300\\ \hline 10{,}800\end{array}\qquad\begin{array}{r}36\\ \times 400\\ \hline 14{,}400\end{array}\qquad\begin{array}{r}36\\ \times 500\\ \hline 18{,}000\end{array}$$

When multiplying by hundreds, you can write 0s in the ones place and the tens place. Then you can multiply by the number of hundreds.

Look for a pattern.

$$\begin{array}{r}36\\ \times 1{,}000\\ \hline 36{,}000\end{array}\qquad\begin{array}{r}36\\ \times 2{,}000\\ \hline 72{,}000\end{array}\qquad\begin{array}{r}36\\ \times 3{,}000\\ \hline 108{,}000\end{array}\qquad\begin{array}{r}36\\ \times 4{,}000\\ \hline 144{,}000\end{array}\qquad\begin{array}{r}36\\ \times 5{,}000\\ \hline 180{,}000\end{array}$$

When multiplying by thousands, you can write 0s in the ones place, the tens place, and the hundreds place. Then you can multiply by the number of thousands.

What number will make this equation true? $400 \times 516 = n$

Practice • Multiply.

1. $\begin{array}{r}77\\ \times 10\\ \hline\end{array}$
2. $\begin{array}{r}185\\ \times 10\\ \hline\end{array}$
3. $\begin{array}{r}32\\ \times 20\\ \hline\end{array}$
4. $\begin{array}{r}165\\ \times 40\\ \hline\end{array}$
5. $\begin{array}{r}176\\ \times 100\\ \hline\end{array}$
6. $\begin{array}{r}498\\ \times 100\\ \hline\end{array}$
7. $\begin{array}{r}324\\ \times 300\\ \hline\end{array}$
8. $\begin{array}{r}435\\ \times 1{,}000\\ \hline\end{array}$
9. $\begin{array}{r}709\\ \times 1{,}000\\ \hline\end{array}$
10. $\begin{array}{r}3{,}259\\ \times 5{,}000\\ \hline\end{array}$

Mixed Practice • Multiply.

11. 85×10
12. 92×30
13. 46×90
14. 85×30
15. 297×50
16. 192×70
17. 475×40
18. 802×50
19. $2,631 \times 60$
20. $1,797 \times 20$
21. 29×600
22. 83×100
23. 57×900
24. 92×300
25. 371×400
26. 392×500
27. 846×700
28. $7,915 \times 200$
29. $5,724 \times 800$
30. $4,612 \times 100$
31. $24 \times 4,000$
32. $846 \times 3,000$
33. $65 \times 8,000$
34. $306 \times 2,000$
35. $587 \times 7,000$
36. $342 \times 5,000$
37. $897 \times 1,000$
38. $446 \times 6,000$
★39. $14,921 \times 3,000$
★40. $48,637 \times 2,000$

Solve the equations.

41. $40 \times 46 = n$
42. $90 \times 315 = n$
43. $70 \times 914 = n$
44. $500 \times 75 = n$
45. $400 \times 825 = n$
46. $300 \times 4,104 = n$
47. $9,000 \times 82 = n$
48. $7,000 \times 193 = n$
★49. $11,000 \times 13,195 = n$

Solve. Do the operations in parentheses first.

50. $(20 \times 9) + 3 = n$
51. $(100 \times 7) + 99 = n$
★52. $(30^2) + 8 = n$
★53. $(400^2) + 75 = n$

PROBLEM SOLVING • APPLICATIONS

54. It takes 1 minute to fill 340 bottles at a bottling plant. At this rate, how many bottles are filled in 10 minutes?

★55. It takes 1 minute for a food company to make 120 packages of pasta. At this rate, how many packages can be made in 5 hours?

★56. Solve these equations and look for a pattern in the answers. Then write the next five equations in the pattern.

$(1 \times 8) + 1 = n$
$(12 \times 8) + 2 = n$
$(123 \times 8) + 3 = n$
$(1,234 \times 8) + 4 = n$

★57. Will the pattern continue for $(12,345,678,910 \times 8) + 10 = n$?

Multiplying by Two-Digit Numbers

During the summer the Land of Laughs Amusement Park is visited by an average of 1,825 people per day. At this rate, how many people will visit the amusement park during the 31 days of August?

$31 \times 1,825 = n$

Estimate the answer first.

Think: Round 1,825 to 2,000. Round 31 to 30. Multiply.

$$\begin{array}{r} 1,825 \\ \times \quad 31 \\ \hline \end{array} \begin{array}{c} \rightarrow \\ \rightarrow \\ \end{array} \begin{array}{r} 2,000 \\ \times \quad 30 \\ \hline 60,000 \end{array}$$

About 60,000 will visit the amusement park during August. Use your estimate to see if the computed answer is reasonable.

Step 1 Multiply by 1.

$$\begin{array}{r} 1,825 \\ \times \quad 31 \\ \hline 1,825 \end{array}$$

Step 2 Multiply by 3 tens.

$$\begin{array}{r} 1,825 \\ \times \quad 31 \\ \hline 1\,825 \\ 54\,75\uparrow \end{array}$$

The 0 in the ones place can be omitted.

Step 3 Add. Compare the answer with your estimate.

$$\begin{array}{r} 1,825 \\ \times \quad 31 \\ \hline 1\,825 \\ 54\,75 \\ \hline 56,575 \end{array}$$

56,575 people will visit the amusement park during August.

More Examples

$$\begin{array}{r} 47 \\ \times 35 \\ \hline 235 \\ 1\,41 \\ \hline 1,645 \end{array} \qquad \begin{array}{r} 894 \\ \times \quad 28 \\ \hline 7\,152 \\ 17\,88 \\ \hline 25,032 \end{array} \qquad \begin{array}{r} \$350.90 \\ \times \qquad 47 \\ \hline 2\,456\,30 \\ 14\,036\,0 \\ \hline \$16,492.30 \end{array} \qquad \begin{array}{r} 198,408 \\ \times \qquad 57 \\ \hline 1\,388\,856 \\ 9\,920\,40 \\ \hline 11,309,256 \end{array}$$

Practice • Estimate the product. Then find the actual product.

1. $\begin{array}{r} 26 \\ \times 12 \\ \hline \end{array}$ **2.** $\begin{array}{r} 78 \\ \times 32 \\ \hline \end{array}$ **3.** $\begin{array}{r} 436 \\ \times \ 54 \\ \hline \end{array}$ **4.** $\begin{array}{r} 504 \\ \times \ 72 \\ \hline \end{array}$ **5.** $\begin{array}{r} 715 \\ \times \ 37 \\ \hline \end{array}$

Multiply.

6. $\begin{array}{r} 23 \\ \times 14 \\ \hline \end{array}$ **7.** $\begin{array}{r} 437 \\ \times \ 55 \\ \hline \end{array}$ **8.** $\begin{array}{r} 3,893 \\ \times \quad 76 \\ \hline \end{array}$ **9.** $\begin{array}{r} \$690.74 \\ \times \qquad 23 \\ \hline \end{array}$ **10.** $\begin{array}{r} 135,610 \\ \times \qquad 49 \\ \hline \end{array}$

Mixed Practice • Estimate the product. Then find the actual product.

11. 23×18
12. 59×42
13. 514×67
14. 698×84
15. 805×41

Multiply.

16. 64×12
17. 73×94
18. 52×46
19. 36×55
20. 97×32
21. 463×25
22. 906×68
23. 247×92
24. 705×73
25. 596×36
26. $1,765 \times 41$
27. $8,017 \times 27$
28. $5,921 \times 15$
29. $7,030 \times 84$
30. $2,748 \times 22$
31. $31,498 \times 93$
32. $27,194 \times 48$
33. $45,906 \times 78$
34. $162,947 \times 57$
35. $274,871 \times 19$
36. $\$.75 \times 13$
37. $\$2.39 \times 42$
38. $\$14.49 \times 96$
39. $\$187.22 \times 37$

★ 40. $\$12,580.25 \times 29$

Solve the equations.

41. $19 \times 35 = n$
42. $49 \times 670 = n$
43. $86 \times 2,192 = n$
44. $9,005 \times 55 = n$
45. $17 \times 14,976 = n$

★ 46. $143,714 \times 300 = n$

Find the products. Then write $<$, $=$, or $>$.

★ 47. 12^3 ● 3^{12}

★ 48. 4^{11} ● 11^4

★ 49. 12^4 ● 11^5

PROBLEM SOLVING • APPLICATIONS

50. If 18 people can ride the roller coaster at one time, how many people can ride the roller coaster in 28 trips?

51. The Ferris wheel seats 42 people. How many people can ride if the Ferris wheel operates 36 times?

★ 52. How many more than 3,000 people can ride if the Ferris wheel operates 75 times?

★ 53. On Wednesday 1,876 people visited the amusement park. On Thursday the number of people was 118 fewer than on Wednesday. How many people visited the amusement park during the two days?

Multiplying by Three-Digit Numbers

Multiplying by three-digit numbers is like multiplying by two-digit numbers. In each step, begin writing each product directly below the digit by which you are multiplying.

```
  519
 ×324
 ↓↓↓
```

Multiply: 324 × 519.

Step 1 Multiply by 4.

```
  519
 ×324
 2076
```

Step 2 Multiply by 2 tens.

```
  519
 ×324
 2076
1038↑
```

A 0 is omitted.

Step 3 Multiply by 3 hundreds.

```
   519
  ×324
  2076
 1038
1557←
```

Two 0s are omitted.

Step 4 Add.

```
    519
   ×324
  2 076
 10 38
155 7
168,156
```

> ***You can check a multiplication example by changing the order of the factors and multiplying again.***

Sometimes, in multiplying, you can shorten your work.

Multiply: 470 × 368.

Think: Multiply by 0. Write a 0 in the ones place. On the same line, show the multiplication by 7 tens.

Multiply by 4 hundreds.

Add.

```
    368
   ×470
 25 760
147 2
172,960
```

Multiply: 309 × 1,625.

Think: Multiply by 9.

Multiply by 0 tens. Write 0 in the tens place. On the same line, show the multiplication by 3 hundreds.

Add.

```
  1,625
 ×  309
 14 625
487 50
502,125
```

Practice • Multiply.

1. 572 × 123
2. 612 × 240
3. 736 × 309
4. 2,508 × 452
5. 23,014 × 507

Mixed Practice • Multiply.

6. 216×198
7. 365×524
8. 598×498
9. 856×293
10. 807×414
11. 409×306
12. 692×480
13. 847×523
14. 180×430
15. 225×165
16. 860×426
17. 170×410
18. 362×149
19. 346×628
20. 119×178
21. $3,214 \times 500$
22. $4,493 \times 302$
23. $6,029 \times 285$
24. $3,726 \times 634$
25. $6,547 \times 712$
26. $14,364 \times 505$
27. $36,250 \times 602$
28. $43,146 \times 253$
29. $244,507 \times 343$
30. $124,684 \times 123$
31. $\$1.97 \times 200$
32. $\$9.62 \times 148$
33. $\$2.46 \times 602$
34. $\$68.41 \times 547$
35. $\$198.67 \times 250$

Solve the equations.

36. $103 \times 470 = n$
37. $280 \times 463 = n$
38. $300 \times 549 = n$
39. $615 \times 4,000 = n$
★40. $200^4 = n$
★41. $520^3 = n$

PROBLEM SOLVING • APPLICATIONS

42. Sound travels through air about 335 meters per second. How far does sound travel through air in 720 seconds?

★43. Sound travels through water about 1,432 meters per second. How far does sound travel through water in 3 minutes 25 seconds?

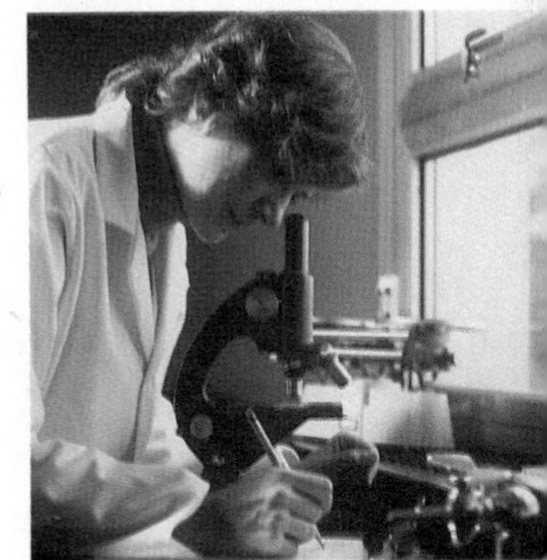

Midchapter Review

1. 764×9
2. $56,325 \times 8$
3. 236×20
4. 153×700
5. 36×29
6. 379×56
7. $16,509 \times 47$
8. 864×231
9. 753×408
10. 906×750

PROBLEM SOLVING • STRATEGIES

Choosing the Operation

Before you can solve a problem, you need to decide which operation or operations to use.

Juan is a cashier at the Cinema I theater.
Tickets for adults cost $3.75 each.
A customer buys 3 adult tickets.
What should Juan charge?

Think: 1 ticket costs $3.75.
You want to find the cost of 3 tickets.
The operation to use is multiplication.
3 tickets cost 3 × $1.75.

```
  $3.75
×     3
 $11.25
```

The total cost of 3 tickets is $11.25.

You know it is important to check your answer.

For a "rough" check to see if the answer is sensible, you can estimate.

Think: $3.75 is about $4.
3 × $4 = $12
$11.25 seems to be a sensible answer.

To check the accuracy of your computations, you can multiply again or you can use addition.

3 × $3.75 → $3.75 + $3.75 + $3.75

```
  $3.75
   3.75
 + 3.75
 $11.25
```
The answer checks.

Read each problem carefully. Decide which operation to use; write *addition, subtraction,* or *multiplication.* Then solve the problem.

1. Cinema I seats 750 people. 580 tickets were sold for the first show. How many empty seats were there?

2. Tickets for adults cost $3.75. Tickets for children cost $1.25. How much does it cost to buy one of each?

3. What is the total cost of 7 child's tickets?

4. What is the total cost of 15 adult tickets?

5. For one show, 726 tickets are sold. For the next show, 688 tickets are sold. How many fewer tickets are sold for the second show?

6. There are five shows on Saturday. One Saturday, there were these numbers of people for the five shows: 356, 477, 600, 748, 358. What was the total number of tickets sold that day?

Check each answer.

7. Cinema I sells an average of $15,450 worth of tickets per week. What amount does it sell in a year?

8. During a holiday season, Cinema I will be showing a very popular movie for 6 weeks. The manager's goal is to sell an average of $18,500 worth of tickets per week. If this goal is met, what will be the total amount sold for that movie?

Read the problem and think about which operation to use.

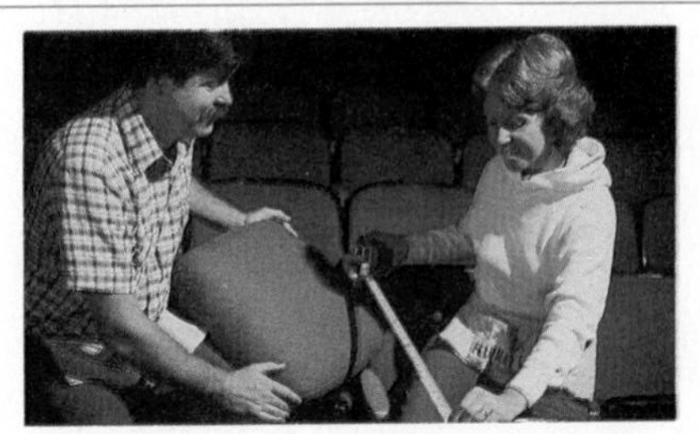

9. The manager of Cinema I is planning to have new seats installed in the theater. There will be 4 sections in the theater. Each section will have 18 rows with 15 seats in each row. How many seats will there be in the theater?

★ 10. How many additional seats will the theater gain by the remodeling?

★ 11. Which costs more, 4 adult tickets or 10 child's tickets? How much more?

★ 12. How much less than $20.00 do 5 adult tickets cost?

★ 13. For one show, Cinema I sells 286 adult tickets and 149 child's tickets. How much more than $1,000 did the theater collect?

★ 14. Mr. Selwyn buys 6 tickets. He gives the cashier $20.00 and receives $7.50 in change. How many adult tickets does Mr. Selwyn buy? How many child's tickets does he buy?

Dividing by One-Digit Numbers

A lamp manufacturer has 138 lamps.
The lamps are packaged 4 in each box.
How many boxes are filled?
How many lamps are left over?

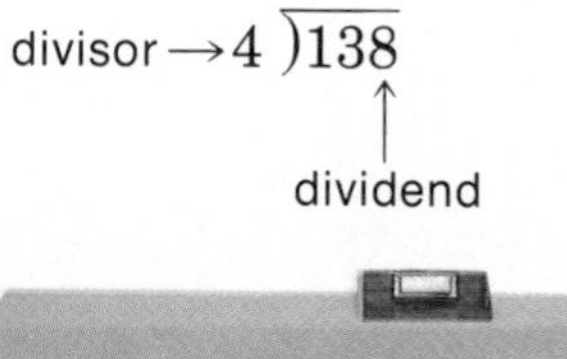

Divide: $138 \div 4$.

$4\overline{)1\ 3\ 8}$ There are not enough hundreds to divide.

$4\overline{)1\ 3\ 8}$ There are enough tens to divide. The first digit of the quotient is in the tens place.

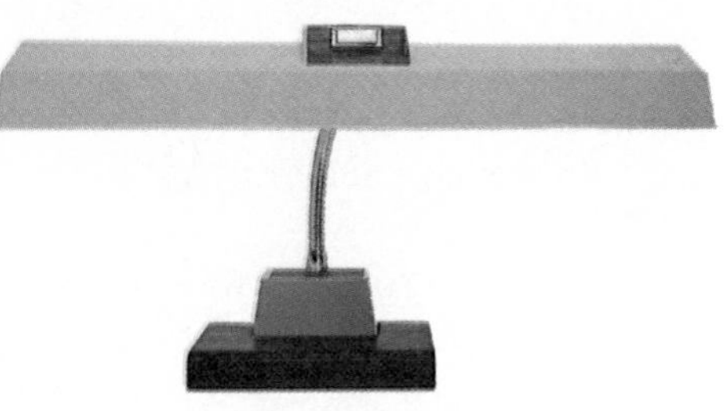

Step 1 Find the tens. Think: $4\overline{)13}$. Write 3 in the tens place. Multiply. Subtract.

$$\begin{array}{r} 3 \\ 4\overline{)138} \\ -12 \\ \hline 1 \end{array}$$

Is 1 less than the divisor?

Step 2 Bring down the 8. Find the ones. Think: $4\overline{)18}$. Write 4 in the ones place. Multiply. Subtract. Show the remainder in the answer.

$$\begin{array}{r} 34 \text{ r2} \\ 4\overline{)138} \\ -12\downarrow \\ \hline 18 \\ -16 \\ \hline 2 \end{array}$$

Is 2 less than 4?

34 boxes are filled. 2 lamps are left over.

You can check the answer for a division example by using this relationship:

$$(\text{quotient} \times \text{divisor}) + \text{remainder} = \text{dividend}$$

$$(34 \times 4) + 2 = 138$$

More Examples

$$\begin{array}{r} 9 \text{ r7} \\ 8\overline{)79} \\ -72 \\ \hline 7 \end{array}
\qquad
\begin{array}{r} 106 \text{ r3} \\ 7\overline{)745} \\ -7 \\ \hline 4 \\ -0 \\ \hline 45 \\ -42 \\ \hline 3 \end{array}
\qquad
\begin{array}{r} 470 \text{ r2} \\ 5\overline{)2{,}352} \\ -2\ 0 \\ \hline 35 \\ -35 \\ \hline 2 \\ -0 \\ \hline 2 \end{array}
\qquad
\begin{array}{r} \$2.43 \\ 6\overline{)\$14.58} \\ -12 \\ \hline 2\ 5 \\ -2\ 4 \\ \hline 18 \\ -18 \\ \hline 0 \end{array}$$

Practice • Divide.

1. $5\overline{)33}$
2. $4\overline{)70}$
3. $9\overline{)328}$
4. $5\overline{)650}$
5. $4\overline{)7{,}612}$
6. $8\overline{)6{,}251}$
7. $2\overline{)\$12.54}$
8. $9\overline{)6{,}251}$
9. $3\overline{)15{,}639}$
10. $7\overline{)64{,}438}$

Mixed Practice • Divide.

11. $4\overline{)39}$
12. $7\overline{)83}$
13. $6\overline{)300}$
14. $5\overline{)164}$
15. $7\overline{)203}$
16. $9\overline{)347}$
17. $5\overline{)470}$
18. $9\overline{)536}$
19. $3\overline{)457}$
20. $8\overline{)899}$
21. $9\overline{)4{,}668}$
22. $5\overline{)1{,}743}$
23. $8\overline{)3{,}163}$
24. $6\overline{)4{,}260}$
25. $8\overline{)3{,}264}$
26. $7\overline{)3{,}616}$
27. $4\overline{)3{,}467}$
28. $6\overline{)3{,}728}$
29. $2\overline{)1{,}892}$
30. $6\overline{)9{,}848}$
31. $6\overline{)18{,}042}$
32. $8\overline{)58{,}108}$
33. $9\overline{)27{,}094}$
34. $4\overline{)178{,}023}$
35. $5\overline{)436{,}152}$
36. $3\overline{)\$7.23}$
37. $4\overline{)\$4.68}$
38. $6\overline{)\$13.80}$
39. $7\overline{)\$7.14}$
40. $9\overline{)\$28.98}$

Solve the equations.

41. $490 \div 7 = n$
42. $6{,}864 \div 4 = n$
43. $14{,}802 \div 6 = n$

★44. $7{,}000{,}000 \div 4 = n$
★45. $8{,}004{,}300 \div 6 = n$
★46. $6{,}018{,}003 \div 9 = n$

★47. $n \times 8 = 17{,}600$
★48. $n \times 5 = 26{,}350$
★49. $n \times 7 = 43{,}498$

When the divisor is less than 10, there is a shorter way to divide. Divide: $4\overline{)138}$.

Step 1 Think: $4\overline{)13}$. Write 3.
$3 \times 4 = 12 \quad 13 - 12 = 1$
Write the 1 next to the 8.

$$\begin{array}{r} 3\phantom{{}^{1}8} \\ 4\overline{)13\,{}^{1}8} \end{array}$$

Step 2 Think: $4\overline{)18}$. Write 4.
$4 \times 4 = 16 \quad 18 - 16 = 2$
Write the remainder.

$$\begin{array}{r} 34 \text{ r2} \\ 4\overline{)13\ 8} \end{array}$$

Divide the shorter way.

50. $2\overline{)74}$
51. $3\overline{)87}$
52. $5\overline{)125}$
53. $7\overline{)140}$
54. $4\overline{)8{,}248}$

PROBLEM SOLVING • APPLICATIONS

55. The lamp company packages 6 lampshades in each box for shipment. How many boxes are needed for 216 lampshades?

56. The lamp company packages 2 desk lamps in each box. How many boxes are needed for 1,074 desk lamps?

Estimating and Correcting Estimates

Divide: 430 ÷ 78.

$78\overline{)430}$ There are not enough hundreds to divide.

$78\overline{)430}$ There are not enough tens to divide.

$78\overline{)430}$ There are enough ones to divide.
The first digit of the quotient is in the ones place.

Step 1 To estimate the quotient, round 78 to 80. Think: $8\overline{)43}$. Try 5.

$$\begin{array}{r} 5 \\ 78\overline{)430} \end{array}$$

Step 2 Multiply: 5 × 78 = 390.

$$\begin{array}{r} 5 \\ 78\overline{)430} \\ 390 \end{array}$$

Step 3 Subtract. Show the remainder.

$$\begin{array}{r} 5 \text{ r40} \\ 78\overline{)430} \\ -390 \\ \hline 40 \end{array}$$

Sometimes your estimates of the quotient may be too large or too small.

Divide: $24\overline{)196}$.

Think: To estimate, round 24 to 20.
Since $2\overline{)19}$ is about 9, try 9.

$$\begin{array}{r} 9 \\ 24\overline{)196} \\ -216 \\ \hline \end{array} \leftarrow \text{too much}$$

Since 216 is greater than 196, the estimated quotient 9 is too large. Try 8.

Divide: $66\overline{)398}$.

Think: To estimate, round 66 to 70.
Since $7\overline{)39}$ is about 5, try 5.

$$\begin{array}{r} 5 \\ 66\overline{)398} \\ -330 \\ \hline 68 \end{array} \leftarrow \text{68 is not less than 66.}$$

Since 68 is greater than the divisor, the estimated quotient 5 is too small. Try 6.

Study the completed examples below.

$$\begin{array}{r} 8 \text{ r4} \\ 24\overline{)196} \\ -192 \\ \hline 4 \end{array}$$

$$\begin{array}{r} 6 \text{ r2} \\ 66\overline{)398} \\ -396 \\ \hline 2 \end{array}$$

Practice • Divide.

1. $28\overline{)68}$ 2. $42\overline{)97}$ 3. $21\overline{)82}$ 4. $27\overline{)164}$ 5. $46\overline{)370}$

6. $93\overline{)174}$ 7. $32\overline{)127}$ 8. $48\overline{)429}$ 9. $56\overline{)348}$ 10. $75\overline{)680}$

Mixed Practice • Divide.

11. $17\overline{)67}$ 12. $23\overline{)97}$ 13. $14\overline{)32}$ 14. $46\overline{)189}$ 15. $59\overline{)318}$

16. $23\overline{)118}$ 17. $45\overline{)190}$ 18. $64\overline{)125}$ 19. $57\overline{)503}$ 20. $72\overline{)376}$

21. $74\overline{)643}$ 22. $66\overline{)615}$ 23. $38\overline{)108}$ 24. $32\overline{)267}$ 25. $76\overline{)648}$

26. $60\overline{)372}$ 27. $86\overline{)852}$ 28. $94\overline{)306}$ 29. $43\overline{)331}$ 30. $67\overline{)409}$

31. $37\overline{)251}$ 32. $71\overline{)504}$ 33. $34\overline{)200}$ 34. $47\overline{)371}$ 35. $56\overline{)328}$

36. $87\overline{)709}$ 37. $94\overline{)847}$ 38. $82\overline{)735}$ 39. $93\overline{)900}$ 40. $55\overline{)502}$

Solve.

41. $672 \div 84 = n$ 42. $108 \div 27 = n$ 43. $444 \div 74 = n$

44. $295 \div 59 = n$ 45. $680 \div 85 = n$ 46. $376 \div 94 = n$

★ 47. $n \times 13 = 91$ ★ 48. $63 \times n = 567$ ★ 49. $n \times 89 = 801$

PROBLEM SOLVING • APPLICATIONS

50. Today 156 students are going on a class trip. Each bus can seat 52 students. How many buses are needed to carry the students?

★ 51. Next week 240 students are going on a trip. Each bus can seat 52 students. How many buses are needed to carry all the students?

Skills Maintenance

1. $899 + 1{,}236$ 2. $7{,}246 + 159$ 3. $12{,}842 + 9{,}680$

4. $84{,}399 + 703$ 5. $672 + 54{,}328$ 6. $18{,}701 + 1{,}989$

Two-Digit Divisors, Quotients to Four Digits

Mario Medina is a building contractor. He pays $1,920 for 64 doorknobs with locks. How much does each doorknob cost?

$\$1,920 \div 64 = n$

$64\overline{)\$1,920}$ There are not enough thousands to divide.

$64\overline{)\$1,920}$ There are not enough hundreds to divide.

$64\overline{)\$1,920}$ There are enough tens to divide.
The first digit of the quotient is in the tens place.

Step 1 Find the tens.
To estimate the tens digit, round 64 to 60.
Think: $6\overline{)19}$. Try 3.
Multiply. Subtract.

$$\begin{array}{r} \$\quad 3 \\ 64\overline{)\$1,920} \\ -1\,92 \\ \hline 0 \end{array}$$

Step 2 Continue the division.
Find the ones.
Write 0 in the ones place.

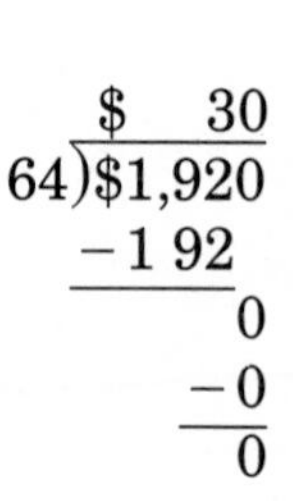

$$\begin{array}{r} \$\quad 30 \\ 64\overline{)\$1,920} \\ -1\,92 \\ \hline 0 \\ -0 \\ \hline 0 \end{array}$$

The cost of each doorknob is $30.
Check by multiplying. Do you need to add the remainder in this example?

More Examples

$$\begin{array}{r} 86 \text{ r3} \\ 79\overline{)6,797} \\ -6\,32 \\ \hline 477 \\ -474 \\ \hline 3 \end{array} \qquad \begin{array}{r} 105 \text{ r8} \\ 24\overline{)2,528} \\ -2\,4 \\ \hline 12 \\ -\ 0 \\ \hline 128 \\ -120 \\ \hline 8 \end{array} \qquad \begin{array}{r} 743 \text{ r8} \\ 58\overline{)43,102} \\ -40\,6 \\ \hline 2\,50 \\ -2\,32 \\ \hline 182 \\ -174 \\ \hline 8 \end{array} \qquad \begin{array}{r} 1,046 \text{ r13} \\ 73\overline{)76,371} \\ -73 \\ \hline 3\,3 \\ -\ 0 \\ \hline 3\,37 \\ -2\,92 \\ \hline 451 \\ -438 \\ \hline 13 \end{array}$$

Practice • Divide.

1. $63\overline{)4,662}$ **2.** $78\overline{)4,605}$ **3.** $47\overline{)2,820}$ **4.** $32\overline{)7,534}$ **5.** $28\overline{)8,748}$

6. $43\overline{)8,908}$ **7.** $58\overline{)53,380}$ **8.** $24\overline{)12,732}$ **9.** $58\overline{)72,098}$ **10.** $38\overline{)40,856}$

Mixed Practice • Divide.

11. $54\overline{)2,624}$ **12.** $65\overline{)2,512}$ **13.** $40\overline{)3,459}$ **14.** $59\overline{)5,075}$

15. $73\overline{)1,448}$ **16.** $89\overline{)8,099}$ **17.** $60\overline{)3,000}$ **18.** $37\overline{)2,900}$

19. $40\overline{)3,459}$ **20.** $28\overline{)1,460}$ **21.** $32\overline{)6,528}$ **22.** $18\overline{)2,556}$

23. $41\overline{)5,852}$ **24.** $25\overline{)5,075}$ **25.** $36\overline{)4,937}$ **26.** $48\overline{)10,032}$

27. $80\overline{)24,021}$ **28.** $35\overline{)21,028}$ **29.** $50\overline{)41,500}$ **30.** $92\overline{)74,880}$

31. $64\overline{)41,391}$ **32.** $48\overline{)10,656}$ **33.** $39\overline{)48,609}$ **34.** $30\overline{)56,168}$

35. $41\overline{)87,412}$ **36.** $32\overline{)32,456}$ **37.** $72\overline{)93,816}$ ★ **38.** $52\overline{)114,534}$

★ **39.** $26\overline{)182,001}$ ★ **40.** $87\overline{)557,061}$

Solve the equations.

41. $1,892 \div 22 = n$ **42.** $8,460 \div 90 = n$

43. $50,008 \div 76 = n$ **44.** $36,856 \div 68 = n$

45. $69,030 \div 45 = n$ **46.** $52,950 \div 50 = n$

Solve. Do the operations in parentheses first.

★ **47.** $(3,000 + 400) \div 25 = n$

★ **48.** $(7,000 + 600 + 50) \div 90 = n$

★ **49.** $(8,000 - 196) + 249 = n$

★ **50.** $(6,499 + 502) - 803 = n$

PROBLEM SOLVING • APPLICATIONS

51. Mario pays $2,451 for 43 doors. How much does each door cost?

52. He pays $3,060 for 85 light fixtures. How much does each fixture cost?

★ **53.** Mario pays $900 for 20 interior door frames. How much would 125 interior door frames cost?

★ **54.** Mario pays $1,200 for 40 exterior door frames. How much more would 125 interior door frames cost than 125 exterior door frames?

Divisors Greater Than 100

For a school project, 324 students collected 40,500 aluminum cans for recycling. What is the average number of aluminum cans collected per student?

$40{,}500 \div 324 = n$

$324\overline{)40{,}500}$ There are not enough ten thousands to divide.

$324\overline{)40{,}500}$ There are not enough thousands to divide.

$324\overline{)40{,}500}$ There are enough hundreds to divide.
The first digit of the quotient is in the hundreds place.

Step 1 Find the hundreds. Think: $3\overline{)4}$. Multiply. Subtract.

$$\begin{array}{r} 1 \\ 324\overline{)40{,}500} \\ -32\ 4 \\ \hline 8\ 1 \end{array}$$

Step 2 Continue the division. Find the tens.

$$\begin{array}{r} 12 \\ 324\overline{)40{,}500} \\ -32\ 4 \\ \hline 8\ 10 \\ -6\ 48 \\ \hline 1\ 62 \end{array}$$

Step 3 Continue the division. Find the ones.

$$\begin{array}{r} 125 \\ 324\overline{)40{,}500} \\ -32\ 4 \\ \hline 8\ 10 \\ -6\ 48 \\ \hline 1\ 620 \\ -1\ 620 \\ \hline 0 \end{array}$$

The average number of aluminum cans collected is 125 per student.

More Examples

$$\begin{array}{r} 63 \text{ r}42 \\ 117\overline{)7{,}413} \\ -7\ 02 \\ \hline 393 \\ -351 \\ \hline 42 \end{array}$$

$$\begin{array}{r} 704 \text{ r}52 \\ 692\overline{)487{,}220} \\ -484\ 4 \\ \hline 2\ 82 \\ -\quad 0 \\ \hline 2\ 820 \\ -2\ 768 \\ \hline 52 \end{array}$$

$$\begin{array}{r} 2{,}360 \\ 231\overline{)545{,}160} \\ -462 \\ \hline 83\ 1 \\ -69\ 3 \\ \hline 13\ 86 \\ -13\ 86 \\ \hline 00 \\ -\quad 0 \\ \hline 0 \end{array}$$

$$\begin{array}{r} 2 \text{ r}1{,}130 \\ 5{,}280\overline{)11{,}690} \\ -10\ 560 \\ \hline 1\ 130 \end{array}$$

Practice • Divide.

1. $435\overline{)896}$ **2.** $701\overline{)4{,}265}$ **3.** $200\overline{)7{,}728}$ **4.** $165\overline{)4{,}995}$

5. $275\overline{)37{,}468}$ **6.** $602\overline{)78{,}282}$ **7.** $573\overline{)118{,}651}$ **8.** $384\overline{)508{,}800}$

Mixed Practice • Divide.

9. $238\overline{)727}$ **10.** $355\overline{)799}$ **11.** $600\overline{)5,466}$ **12.** $178\overline{)1,463}$

13. $387\overline{)4,756}$ **14.** $428\overline{)8,660}$ **15.** $276\overline{)5,872}$ **16.** $520\overline{)7,295}$

17. $475\overline{)20,165}$ **18.** $700\overline{)49,340}$ **19.** $868\overline{)26,140}$ **20.** $842\overline{)44,384}$

21. $666\overline{)78,641}$ **22.** $435\overline{)69,625}$ **23.** $108\overline{)23,402}$ **24.** $547\overline{)63,142}$

25. $884\overline{)494,832}$ **26.** $725\overline{)221,200}$ **27.** $652\overline{)202,344}$ **28.** $185\overline{)384,160}$

★**29.** $2,100\overline{)16,000}$ ★**30.** $8,700\overline{)25,750}$ ★**31.** $5,280\overline{)38,000}$ ★**32.** $1,760\overline{)20,500}$

Solve the equations.

33. $3,252 \div 542 = n$ **34.** $7,800 \div 300 = n$ **35.** $51,048 \div 709 = n$

36. $66,040 \div 635 = n$ **37.** $55,520 \div 160 = n$ **38.** $182,350 \div 175 = n$

PROBLEM SOLVING • APPLICATIONS

39. The average household in the United States throws away about 1,460 cans each year. About how many cans does the average household throw away per day? (Hint: Use 365 days = 1 year.)

40. The average household also discards about 13,140 items of paper or cardboard each year. About how many items are discarded per day?

★**41.** There are approximately 46,000 aluminum cans in a ton. How many cans are in a pound?

★**42.** One student used a pedometer and found he walked 24,640 feet while collecting aluminum cans. Express this distance in miles and feet.

Skills Maintenance

1. $7,145 - 808$ **2.** $2,503 - 1,199$ **3.** $14,000 - 6,250$

4. $25,000 - 14,602$ **5.** $42,920 - 1,019$ **6.** $50,000 - 48,767$

PROBLEM SOLVING • STRATEGIES

Too Much or Not Enough Information

In life you will need to solve many problems.

Sometimes you will not be given enough information. You will need to decide what is missing and then try to get the additional information.

Other times you will have more information than is necessary. You will have to decide which facts are needed and then use only those facts.

Problem 1

Carol and Don pay $675 per month to rent space for their jewelry store. They have been in business for 3 years. How much rent do they pay each year?

Identify the question.
How much rent do they pay each year?

Find the information you need.
One month's rent is $675.

Solve.
12 × $675 = $8,100
They pay $8,100 each year.

Problem 2

Carol works 45 hours each week. How many more hours does she work than Don?

There is not enough information to solve the problem. You need to know how many hours Don works each week.

Solve each problem if you have enough information. If there is not enough information, identify what you need to know to solve the problem.

1. Carol sells a gold bracelet for $320 and a turquoise necklace for $146. Don sells an opal ring for $175. How much money does Carol receive for her sales?

2. Carol hires George to work on Friday evenings and on Saturdays. Carol pays George $4.25 an hour. How much does Carol pay George each week?

3. Don sells a new ring to a customer. It is a birthday gift for a boy who will be 14 years old. The price of the ring is $49.95. A sales tax is added to the price. What is the total cost of the ring?

Don't be confused if a problem gives too much information. Use only the facts you need.

4. Carol is showing some tableware to a customer. The customer wants to buy enough place settings for 8 people. Each place setting contains 6 pieces of stainless tableware. Each place setting costs $32. How many pieces of tableware does the customer want to buy?

5. Don repairs watches. He had 14 watches to repair today. He repaired 17 yesterday. It took him 90 minutes to repair one. It took only 5 minutes to repair another. If he has repaired 8 watches so far today, how many more must he repair?

6. Carol and Don are having an anniversary sale. They offer $10 off the price of luminous clocks. What is the sale price?

7. The store is open 6 days a week. On Mondays through Thursdays, it is open from 9:00 A.M. to 5:00 P.M. On Fridays it is open from 9:00 A.M. to 9:00 P.M. On Saturdays it is open from 9:00 A.M. to 6:00 P.M. How many hours is the store open each week?

8. Carol buys 84 rings. The total cost is $7,644. What is the average cost per ring?

Before you compute, make a plan for solving the problem.

★9. Carol works 45 hours per week. She takes 3 weeks vacation per year. How many hours does she work per year?

★10. Don works 50 weeks per year. He works about 1,780 hours per year. About how many hours does he work per week? Give your answer to the nearest whole number.

★11. Carol buys 125 pearl necklaces at an average cost of $127 each. She sells them at an average price of $255 per necklace. How much money will she receive from the sale of all the pearl necklaces?

★12. Jim works 15 hours per week during 40 weeks of the year and 35 hours per week during 12 weeks of the summer. How many hours does Jim work in a year?

Order of Operations

You have been working with the four basic operations of addition, subtraction, multiplication, and division.
Parentheses have been used to show the grouping of numbers.
Parentheses are also used to show multiplication.

4×6 can be written as $4(6)$.

$4 \times (8 - 1)$ can be written as $4(8 - 1)$.

There are also different ways to show division.

$12 \div 3$ can be written as $\frac{12}{3}$. ⟵ division bar

$(16 + 4) \div 2$ can be written as $\frac{16 + 4}{2}$.

Operations are done in a special order. Follow this order for doing operations.

First do the operations within parentheses or the computations above or below a division bar.

$$4(8 - 1) \quad 4(7) \quad 28$$

$$\frac{16 + 4}{2} \quad \frac{20}{2} \quad 10$$

Do any remaining multiplication and division from left to right. Multiply or divide before you add or subtract.

$$10 \times 4 \div 2 \quad 40 \div 2 \quad 20$$

$$32 + \frac{16}{8} \quad 32 + 2 \quad 34$$

Do addition and subtraction from left to right.

$$8 + 3 - 4 \quad 11 - 4 \quad 7$$

$$8 - 3 + 4 \quad 5 + 4 \quad 9$$

More Examples

$$9 - 1(5) = 9 - 5 = 4$$

$$\frac{18(6 \div 2)}{4} = \frac{18(3)}{4} = \frac{54}{4} = 13\frac{2}{4} = 13\frac{1}{2}$$

$$\frac{(9 - 3)6}{4} = \frac{(6)6}{4} = \frac{36}{4} = 9$$

Practice • Compute.

1. $(8 - 3) - 1$
2. $8 - (3 - 1)$
3. $8 - 3 + 1$
4. $8 + 3 - 1$
5. $2(9)$
6. $2(9) + 1$
7. $2(9 + 1)$
8. $2(9 - 1)$
9. $\frac{16}{8}$
10. $\frac{16 + 4}{5}$
11. $\frac{18}{2} - 6$
12. $\frac{18 - 6}{2}$

Mixed Practice • Compute.

13. $(10 - 4) - 2$
14. $10 - (4 - 2)$
15. $10 - 4 + 2$
16. $10 + 4 - 2$
17. $3(7)$
18. $3(7) + 2$
19. $3(7 + 2)$
20. $(7 + 2)3$
21. $6 \times 7 - 1$
22. $6 \times (7 - 1)$
23. $(7 - 1) \times 6$
24. $7 - 1(6)$
25. $\frac{8}{4}$
26. $\frac{8 + 12}{4}$
27. $\frac{8}{4} + 12$
28. $8 + \frac{12}{4}$
29. $7(9 - 3)$
30. $7(9) - 3$
31. $7(9 + 3)$
32. $7(9) + 3$
33. $3 \times 8 \div 2$
34. $3 \times (8 \div 2)$
35. $3\left(\frac{8}{2}\right)$
36. $\frac{3(8)}{2}$
37. $7(10 + 2)$
38. $7(10) + 2$
39. $\frac{7(10)}{2}$
40. $\frac{10(7)}{2}$
41. $\frac{40}{4} - 2$
42. $\frac{40}{2} - 4$
43. $\frac{40}{2(4)}$
44. $\frac{40}{4} - 2$

★45. $\frac{6 + 10}{2 + 2}$
★46. $\frac{6}{2} + \frac{10}{2}$
★47. $\frac{2(10 - 6)}{2}$
★48. $2(6) - \frac{10}{2}$

PROBLEM SOLVING • APPLICATIONS

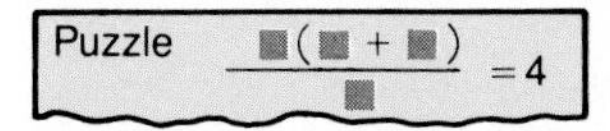

49. In this puzzle, ink blots are covering the numbers 2, 3, 4, and 5 at the left of the equal sign.

Puzzles are "problems" that need to be solved. You can experiment to solve this puzzle. Try different positions for 2, 3, 4, and 5. Check to see if the sentence is true.

Does $\frac{2(3 + 4)}{5} = 4$?

Does $\frac{2(3 + 5)}{4} = 4$?

Use 2, 3, 4, and 5. Solve each puzzle.

★50. ■(■ − ■) + ■ = 8

★51. $\frac{■(■) - ■}{■} = 1$

★52. $\frac{■ + ■}{■ - ■} = 3$

CHAPTER 2 REVIEW

Multiply or divide. (pp. 28–29)

1. $5 \times 8 = n$
2. $7 \times 8 = n$
3. $36 \div 4 = n$
4. $25 \div 5 = n$

Name the property of multiplication that is illustrated. (pp. 28–29)

5. $8 \times 6 = 6 \times 8$
6. $4 \times (3 \times 5) = (4 \times 3) \times 5$
7. $0 \times 11 = 0$

Multiply. (pp. 30–37)

8. $\begin{array}{r} 65 \\ \times\ 5 \\ \hline \end{array}$
9. $\begin{array}{r} 129 \\ \times\ \ 6 \\ \hline \end{array}$
10. $\begin{array}{r} 28{,}013 \\ \times\ \ \ \ 9 \\ \hline \end{array}$
11. $\begin{array}{r} 216 \\ \times\ 10 \\ \hline \end{array}$
12. $\begin{array}{r} 358 \\ \times 200 \\ \hline \end{array}$
13. $\begin{array}{r} 54 \\ \times 29 \\ \hline \end{array}$
14. $\begin{array}{r} 4{,}071 \\ \times\ \ 48 \\ \hline \end{array}$
15. $\begin{array}{r} 5{,}869 \\ \times\ 603 \\ \hline \end{array}$
16. $\begin{array}{r} 238{,}252 \\ \times\ \ \ 196 \\ \hline \end{array}$
17. $\begin{array}{r} \$206.29 \\ \times\ \ \ \ 473 \\ \hline \end{array}$

Solve the equations. (pp. 30–37)

18. $8 \times 278 = n$
19. $70 \times 2{,}656 = n$
20. $800 \times 87{,}329 = n$
21. $7{,}183 \times 67 = n$
22. $39 \times 31{,}406 = n$
23. $542 \times 4{,}736 = n$

Divide. (pp. 40–47)

24. $6\overline{)431}$
25. $8\overline{)2{,}453}$
26. $5\overline{)\$74.55}$
27. $63\overline{)589}$
28. $35\overline{)2{,}856}$
29. $27\overline{)35{,}002}$
30. $159\overline{)68{,}435}$
31. $432\overline{)967{,}942}$

Solve the equations. (pp. 40–47)

32. $7{,}032 \div 8 = n$
33. $1{,}404 \div 54 = n$
34. $75{,}576 \div 564 = n$

Compute. (pp. 50–51)

35. $13 - 1 + 3$
36. $6(5 + 7)$
37. $\left(\frac{9}{3} + 2\right) - 5$

38. The 9 students in the Camera Club have 25 rolls of film altogether. They can take 36 pictures with each roll. How many pictures can they take in all? (pp. 38–39)

39. Kane buys 25 zoom lenses for his camera store. He pays a total of \$2,975 for the lenses. What is the cost of each lens? (pp. 48–49)

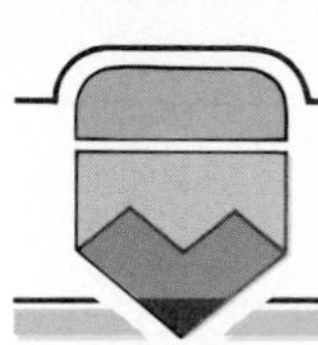

PROJECT

Patterns

Choose the correct response.

△ is to ▽ as ◠ is to ___?___.

a	b	c	d
◠	D	ᗡ	◡

Think: ▽ is the same as △, but it is upside down.

Look for the same figure as ◠ but upside down.

It is ◡. The correct response is **d.**

Now try this one.

○ ○ / ○ ○ is to ○ / ○ as □ □ / □ □ is to ___?___.

a	b	c	d
○ / ○	□ / □	○○ / ○○	□□ / □□

Did you choose **b**?

That is the correct response. Why?

Choose the correct response.

1. E is to Ǝ as P is to ___?___.
2. ○ is to ● as △ is to ___?___.
3. ○ is to ∘ as □ is to ___?___.
4. □ is to ▫▫▫ as ○ is to ___?___.
5. ○ is to [circle with notch] as ■ is to ___?___.
6. ○○ is to ○○○ as ▫▫ is to ___?___.
7. [triangle with line] is to [triangle with line] as [circle with line] is to ___?___.
8. [two stacked squares] is to ▫ as [two stacked circles] is to ___?___.

	a	b	c	d
1.	Ǝ	P	ꟼ	E
2.	△	▲	○	●
3.	▫	□	▫	■
4.	○○○	○	▫▫▫	□
5.	[square with notch]	[shaded circle with notch]	[shaded square with notch]	[circle with notch]
6.	○	▫▫▫	○○	▫▫▫
7.	[circle with line]	[triangle with line]	[triangle with line]	[circle with line]
8.	∘	[two stacked circles]	▫▫	▫

9. Write 5 exercises like the ones above and ask a classmate to solve them. Be sure that you know the solutions before you challenge your classmate.

CHAPTER 2 TEST

Multiply or divide.

1. $9 \times 5 = n$
2. $7 \times 4 = n$
3. $42 \div 7 = n$
4. $72 \div 8 = n$

Name the property of multiplication that is illustrated.

5. $1 \times 28 = 28$
6. $(3 \times 9) \times 2 = 3 \times (9 \times 2)$
7. $17 \times 0 = 0$

Multiply.

8. 47×6
9. 783×2
10. $10{,}961 \times 8$
11. 529×30
12. 634×100
13. 56×39
14. $3{,}162 \times 81$
15. $9{,}235 \times 470$
16. $153{,}162 \times 513$
17. $\$460.32 \times 547$

Solve the equations.

18. $9 \times 680 = n$
19. $40 \times 15{,}293 = n$
20. $600 \times 3{,}768 = n$
21. $4{,}381 \times 35 = n$
22. $24 \times 96{,}287 = n$
23. $809 \times 6{,}995 = n$

Divide.

24. $8\overline{)835}$
25. $6\overline{)3{,}764}$
26. $3\overline{)\$67.44}$
27. $47\overline{)636}$
28. $62\overline{)2{,}418}$
29. $48\overline{)54{,}389}$
30. $175\overline{)78{,}350}$
31. $316\overline{)829{,}757}$

Solve the equations.

32. $2{,}956 \div 4 = n$
33. $72{,}800 \div 364 = n$
34. $5{,}832 \div 72 = n$

Compute.

35. $8 - (2 + 2)$
36. $4 + 5(6)$
37. $\left(\frac{16}{4} + 5\right) - 5$

38. Earl works 7 hours a day as a supervisor in his plant. One of the machines in the plant fills 2,356 cans of oil in one hour. How many cans will it fill in 18 hours?

39. Cases of oil are carried to the warehouse twice a day. There are 24 cans of oil in each case. Each can contains 1 quart of oil. How many cases will 2,592 cans fills?

ENRICHMENT

Choices

Carla is buying a bike. She can buy a five-speed bike or a ten-speed bike. Each comes in four colors: red, blue, green, or white. How many choices are there?

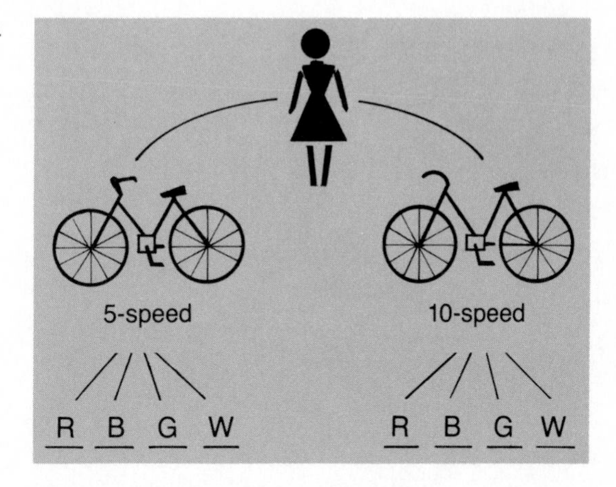

The diagram shows that there are 8 choices. First, Carla has two possibilities: five-speed or ten-speed. With each of these possibilities, there are four possible colors: red, blue, green, or white. In all, there are 2×4, or 8 choices.

You can use multiplication to solve such problems without a diagram.

For example, suppose Carla can also choose one of three types of odometers to have on the bicycle. Then the total number of choices is $2 \times 4 \times 3$, or 24.

Solve.

1. One automobile manufacturer makes 7 different models. Each model comes in 12 different colors. How many choices does this manufacturer offer?

2. These are buttons on a jukebox. You push a letter. Then you push a digit. How many choices do you have?

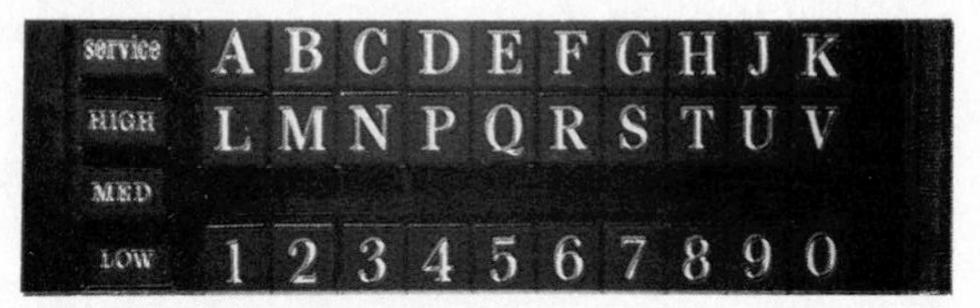

3. To get from Apple Creek to Carter City, you must go through Brownsville. You have a choice of 4 roads from Apple Creek to Brownsville. Then there are 3 roads from Brownsville to Carter City. How many different ways are there to get from Apple Creek to Carter City?

4. One style of shoe comes in 3 colors. It comes in 8 lengths. Each length comes in 5 widths. A store manager wants to have one pair of each in stock. How many different pairs must be ordered?

CALCULATOR

Estimating Division

Always estimate before using a calculator to divide.

Divide: $62\overline{)5{,}022}$. Estimate: 5,000 divided by 60 is a little more than 80.

Push [5] [0] [2] [2] [÷] [6] [2] [=] . The answer is 81.

The answer is close to your estimate. It is correct.

Divide. Be careful to write dollar signs where you need them.

1. $68\overline{)4{,}964}$	**2.** $24\overline{)\$8.88}$	**3.** $73\overline{)\$0.00}$	**4.** $39\overline{)975}$
5. $104\overline{)728}$	**6.** $58\overline{)11{,}774}$	**7.** $91\overline{)\$53.69}$	**8.** $33\overline{)\$13.20}$
9. $19\overline{)\$18.43}$	**10.** $7\overline{)48{,}545}$	**11.** $82\overline{)4{,}018}$	**12.** $202\overline{)\$4{,}040.00}$

You can find remainders with the calculator.

Divide: $24\overline{)4{,}717}$. Estimate: A little less than 4,800 divided by 24 is a little less than 200.

Push [4] [7] [1] [7] [÷] [2] [4] [=] . Copy the quotient: 196.

Note that the quotient agrees with your estimate.

Now multiply 196 by 24. Push [1] [9] [6] [×] [2] [4] [=] .

Copy the product: 4,704. Now subtract 4,704 from 4,717.

Push [4] [7] [1] [7] [−] [4] [7] [0] [4] [=] . The remainder is 13. The answer is 196 r13.

Use the same procedure to find remainders when you divide amounts of money.

Divide: $19\overline{)\$5{,}038.51}$. Estimate: A little more than \$5,000 divided by 19 is a little more than \$250.

Push [5] [0] [3] [8] [·] [5] [1] [÷] [1] [9] [=] .

Copy the quotient: 265.

Calculator, *continued*

Now multiply 265 by 19.

Push [2] [6] [5] [×] [1] [9] [=] .

Copy the product: 5,035. Now subtract 5,035 from 5,038.51.

Push [5] [0] [3] [8] [·] [5] [1] [−] [5] [0] [3] [5] [=] .

The remainder is 3.51.
Add commas and dollar signs where appropriate. The answer is $265 r$3.51.

Divide. Find the quotients and the remainders.

13. 16)787 **14.** 40)549 **15.** 31)1,991 **16.** 56)$864

17. 347)$8,439 **18.** 28)5,096 **19.** 170)$8.43 **20.** 59)87,234

21. 742 ÷ 36 = ? **22.** $5,004 ÷ 819 = ? **23.** 41,378 ÷ 4 = ?

24. 1,468 ÷ 73 = ? **25.** 96,031 ÷ 8 = ? **26.** $2,137 ÷ 32 = ?

27. 3,924 ÷ 704 = ? **28.** $44.05 ÷ 225 = ? **29.** $6,945 ÷ 46 = ?

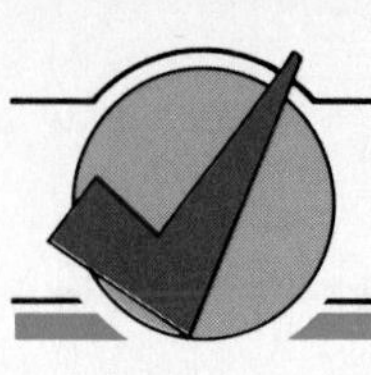

SKILLS MAINTENANCE

Chapters 1 Through 2

Choose the correct answers.

1. In which place is the blue digit?

1**4**5,304,962

A. millions
B. ten millions
C. ten thousands
D. not here

2. Write $<$, $=$, or $>$.

5,328 ● 5,382

A. $>$
B. $<$
C. $=$
D. not here

3. Round 47,543 to the nearest thousand.

A. 48,000
B. 47,000
C. 50,000
D. not here

4. Solve.

$36{,}708 + 40{,}180 = n$

A. $n = 76{,}788$
B. $n = 76{,}878$
C. $n = 76{,}888$
D. not here

5. Solve.

$47{,}071 - 39{,}582 = n$

A. $n = 7{,}489$
B. $n = 17{,}489$
C. $n = 7{,}589$
D. not here

6. Multiply.

$$\begin{array}{r} 462 \\ \times\ 87 \\ \hline \end{array}$$

A. 40,184
B. 40,194
C. 39,194
D. not here

7. Multiply.

$$\begin{array}{r} 7{,}154 \\ \times\ 406 \\ \hline \end{array}$$

A. 2,903,524
B. 2,904,624
C. 2,904,524
D. not here

8. Divide.

$251\overline{)236{,}907}$

A. 942 r249
B. 943 r24
C. 943 r214
D. not here

9. Solve.

$8{,}432 \div 68 = n$

A. $n = 125$
B. $n = 124$
C. $n = 123$
D. not here

10. Erik sells a jacket for \$59.85 and a hat for \$11.98. Brad sells a pair of gloves for \$14.75. How much money does Erik receive for his sales?

A. \$86.58 **B.** \$47.87
C. \$71.83 **D.** not here

11. A parking garage is expanding. There will be 5 levels in the garage. Each level will have 12 rows with 13 parking spaces in each row. How many parking spaces will there be in the garage?

A. 221 **B.** 780
C. 125 **D.** not here

CHAPTER 3

Equations

Addition and Subtraction: Expressions and Equations • Multiplication and Division: Expressions and Equations • Problem Solving: Choosing Equations • Equations and Properties • Distance Formula • Problem Solving: Using Equations • Solving Inequalities • Functions • Experimenting with Equations

Addition and Subtraction Expressions

Rebecca is three years older than Christopher.
You can write mathematical **expressions** to stand for their ages.

Let a letter stand for Christopher's age. Use x. → x
Then $x + 3$ stands for Rebecca's age. → $x + 3$

The letter x is a **variable.**
To **evaluate** an expression, you substitute a number for the variable.

How old is Rebecca if Christopher is 15 years old?
Evaluate the expression $x + 3$ when $x = 15$.

Step 1 Write the expression. → $x + 3$
Step 2 Substitute 15 for x. → $15 + 3$
Step 3 Add. → 18

If Christopher is 15 years old, then Rebecca is 18.

Jasmine is 2 years younger than Tony.
If Tony is n years old, does the expression $n - 2$ stand for Jasmine's age?

How old is Jasmine if Tony is 16?

Expressions can be used in solving problems. Compare each phrase and the mathematical expression.

Phrase	Expression
5 more than a number n	$n + 5$
A number n increased by 5	$n + 5$
The sum of a number n and 9	$n + 9$
7 less than a number y	$y - 7$
A number y decreased by 7	$y - 7$
7 decreased by a number y	$7 - y$
The difference between a number y and 12	$y - 12$
The difference between 12 and a number y	$12 - y$

Practice • Evaluate the given expressions for the values shown.

$x + 6$: **1.** $x = 2$ **2.** $x = 10$ **3.** $x = 18$ **4.** $x = 100$

$y - 5$: **5.** $y = 9$ **6.** $y = 12$ **7.** $y = 23$ **8.** $y = 102$

Write the expressions.

9. 8 less than a number x

10. the sum of a number n and 15

11. a number y increased by 4

12. 20 decreased by a number x

Mixed Practice • Evaluate the given expressions for the values shown.

$17 + n$: **13.** $n = 3$ **14.** $n = 11$ **15.** $n = 16$ **16.** $n = 90$

$y - 3$: **17.** $y = 9$ **18.** $y = 12$ **19.** $y = 20$ **20.** $y = 81$

$40 - x$: **21.** $x = 10$ **22.** $x = 25$ **23.** $x = 31$ **24.** $x = 40$

$n + 99$: **25.** $n = 1$ **26.** $n = 12$ **27.** $n = 101$ **28.** $n = 901$

$n + 5 - 5$: **29.** $n = 14$ ★ **30.** $n = 1{,}000{,}000$

$y - 8 + 8$: **31.** $y = 17$ ★ **32.** $y = 1{,}000{,}000{,}000$

Write the expressions.

33. 12 more than a number n

34. a number x decreased by 10

35. 15 less than a number y

36. the sum of 18 and a number b

37. 50 decreased by a number c

38. a number n increased by 18

★ **39.** the difference between a number a and $4\frac{3}{4}$

★ **40.** a number x increased by the difference between 8 and a number y

PROBLEM SOLVING • APPLICATIONS

41. Nina is 3 years younger than Jeff. Susan is 4 years older than Jeff. Write expressions for their ages. Use n as the variable. Let n stand for Jeff's age.

42. When Jeff is 21, how old will Nina be? How old will Susan be?

★ **43.** When Jeff is 30, what will be the sum of all their ages?

★ **44.** When the sum of their ages is 115, how old will Nina, Jeff, and Susan be?

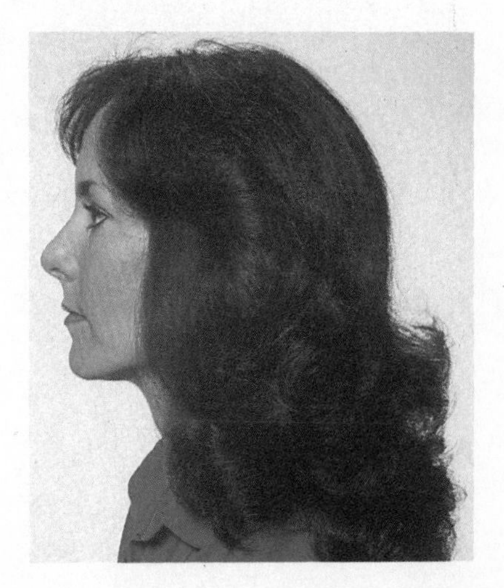

Addition and Subtraction Equations

Think of a number.	35	n
Add 28.	$35 + 28$	$n + 28$
Now subtract 28.	$35 + 28 - 28$	$n + 28 - 28$
You get back the original number.	35	n

Think of a number.	40	y
Subtract 12.	$40 - 12$	$y - 12$
Now add 12.	$40 - 12 + 12$	$y - 12 + 12$
You get back the original number.	40	y

Addition and subtraction are inverse operations.
Adding and subtracting the same number undo each other.

You can use this idea in your work with equations.

Solve: A certain number plus 17 equals 41. What is the number?

Step 1 Let n stand for the number.
Write the equation. → $n + 17 = 41$

Step 2 The equation shows addition.
Use subtraction to solve.
Subtract 17 from both sides. → $n + 17 - 17 = 41 - 17$

Step 3 Show the solution. → $n = 24$

Step 4 Check the solution. → $24 + 17 = 41$
$41 = 41$ ✓

Solve: A certain number minus 15 equals 8. What is the number?

Step 1 Let x stand for the number.
Write the equation. → $x - 15 = 8$

Step 2 The equation shows subtraction.
Use addition to solve.
Add 15 to both sides. → $x - 15 + 15 = 8 + 15$

Step 3 Show the solution. → $x = 23$

Step 4 Check the solution. → $23 - 15 = 8$
$8 = 8$ ✓

Practice • Use subtraction to solve the equations.

1. $n + 6 = 14$ **2.** $y + 12 = 28$ **3.** $x + 29 = 50$

Use addition to solve the equations.

4. $y - 3 = 8$ **5.** $x - 21 = 14$ **6.** $n - 16 = 48$

Solve the equations. Check your answers.

7. $c - 17 = 42$ **8.** $y + 39 = 60$ **9.** $b - 29 = 71$

Mixed Practice • Use addition or subtraction to solve the equations.

10. $x + 8 = 13$ **11.** $y + 23 = 37$ **12.** $n + 54 = 80$

13. $a + 12 = 71$ **14.** $n + 99 = 113$ **15.** $x + 19 = 106$

16. $n - 7 = 5$ **17.** $y - 13 = 41$ **18.** $x - 17 = 35$

19. $a - 46 = 29$ **20.** $x - 32 = 68$ **21.** $b - 99 = 29$

22. $n + 23 = 32$ **23.** $x - 15 = 4$ **24.** $y - 26 = 35$

25. $x + 59 = 94$ **26.** $a + 36 = 83$ **27.** $n - 82 = 19$

28. $d - 19 = 25$ **29.** $x + 49 = 121$ **30.** $n - 60 = 73$

31. $y + 103 = 120$ **32.** $n - 116 = 36$ **33.** $x + 98 = 201$

★**34.** $72 = n - 19$ ★**35.** $85 = y + 28$ ★**36.** $105 = x - 37$

★**37.** $n + 8 - 5 = 18$ ★**38.** $y + 25 - 17 = 26$ ★**39.** $x - 3 - 8 = 15$

PROBLEM SOLVING • APPLICATIONS

Write an equation for each problem. Then solve it and check.

40. A certain number plus 15 equals 51. What is the number?

41. A certain number minus 23 equals 40. What is the number?

42. The difference between a number and 16 is 65. What is the number?

★**43.** In 17 years, Beth will be 30 years old. How old is she now?

Skills Maintenance

Write < or >.

1. 526 ● 489 **2.** 3,749 ● 4,379 **3.** 12,642 ● 9,998

4. 47,200 ● 72,400 **5.** 132,507 ● 132,750 **6.** 296,810 ● 296,809

Multiplication and Division Expressions

The small gear turns around three times as often as the large gear.

You can write expressions to tell about the turning of the gears.

Let n stand for the number of turns the large gear makes. Then $3(n)$ stands for the number of turns the small gear makes.

$3(n)$ may be written as $3n$.

How many turns does the small gear make if the large gear turns around 12 times?

Evaluate the expression $3(n)$ when $n = 12$.

Step 1 Write the expression. → $3(n)$
Step 2 Substitute 12 for n. → $3(12)$
Step 3 Multiply. → 36

Evaluate the expression $\frac{x}{2}$ when $x = 160$.

Step 1 Write the expression. → $\frac{x}{2}$

Step 2 Substitute 160 for x. → $\frac{160}{2}$

Step 3 Divide. → 80

Compare each phrase and the mathematical expression.

Phrase	Expression
5 times a number y	$5y$
A number c multiplied by 10	$10c$
A number x divided by 6	$\frac{x}{6}$
The product of 8 and a number n	$8n$
The quotient when a number y is divided by 4	$\frac{y}{4}$
The quotient when $2n$ is divided by 2	$\frac{2n}{2}$
The product when $\frac{y}{3}$ is multiplied by 3	$3\left(\frac{y}{3}\right)$ or $\frac{3y}{3}$

Practice • Evaluate the given expressions for the values shown.

$2n$: **1.** $n = 3$ **2.** $n = 10$ **3.** $n = 16$ **4.** $n = 100$

$\frac{x}{4}$: **5.** $x = 8$ **6.** $x = 20$ **7.** $x = 48$ **8.** $x = 72$

Write the expressions.

9. 11 times a number b

10. a number y divided by 5

Mixed Practice • Evaluate the given expressions for the values shown.

$4y$: **11.** $y = 2$ **12.** $y = 7$ **13.** $y = 15$ **14.** $y = 120$

$\frac{n}{5}$: **15.** $n = 20$ **16.** $n = 45$ **17.** $n = 85$ **18.** $n = 140$

$n = 8$: **19.** $\frac{4 \times n}{4}$ **20.** $\frac{4n}{4}$ **21.** $4 \times \frac{n}{4}$ **22.** $4\left(\frac{n}{4}\right)$

$y = 90$: **23.** $\frac{3 \times y}{3}$ **24.** $\frac{3y}{3}$ **25.** $3 \times \frac{y}{3}$ **26.** $3\left(\frac{y}{3}\right)$

$n = 24$: **27.** $(n \times 2) \div 2$ **28.** $(n \div 2) \times 2$

$a = 75$: ★ **29.** $\frac{2a + 6}{2}$ ★ **30.** $\frac{2(a + 6)}{2}$

Write the expressions.

31. 7 times a number b

32. a number c divided by 9

33. the quotient when $8y$ is divided by 8

34. the product of 12 and a number d

PROBLEM SOLVING • APPLICATIONS

35. To get to school, Ken walks 4 times as great a distance as Ben. Write expressions for the distances that the boys walk. Use n to stand for the number of kilometers that Ben walks.

36. If Ben walks 675 meters to get to school, how many meters does Ken walk to get to school?

37. Each day Ken does twice as many push-ups as Ben. Write expressions to stand for the number of push-ups they do. Use y to stand for the number of push-ups Ben does.

38. If Ken does 58 push-ups one day, how many does Ben do?

★ **39.** Stan can do one more push-up than Ben. If Ben does 24 push-ups one day, how many push-ups do all three boys do that day?

Multiplication and Division Equations

Think of a number.	5	n
Multiply by 3.	3(5)	$3n$
Now divide by 3.	$\frac{3(5)}{3}$	$\frac{3n}{3}$
You get back the original number.	5	n

Think of a number.	10	n
Divide by 2.	$\frac{10}{2}$	$\frac{n}{2}$
Now multiply by 2.	$\frac{2(10)}{2}$	$\frac{2n}{2}$
You get back the original number.	10	n

Multiplication and division are inverse operations. Multiplying and dividing by the same number (not zero) undo each other.

You can use this idea in your work with equations.

Solve: 3 times a certain number equals 63. What is the number?

Step 1 Let y stand for the number.
Write the equation. $\rightarrow$ $3y = 63$

Step 2 The equation shows multiplication.
Use division to solve. $\rightarrow$ $\frac{3y}{3} = \frac{63}{3}$
Divide both sides by 3.

Step 3 Show the solution. $\rightarrow$ $y = 21$

Step 4 Check the solution. $\rightarrow$ $3(21) = 63$
$63 = 63$ ✓

Solve: A certain number divided by 6 is 15. What is the number?

Step 1 Let n stand for the number.
Write the equation. $\rightarrow$ $\frac{n}{6} = 15$

Step 2 The equation shows division.
Use multiplication to solve. $\rightarrow$ $\frac{6n}{6} = 6(15)$
Multiply both sides by 6.

Step 3 Show the solution. $\rightarrow$ $n = 90$

Step 4 Check the solution. $\rightarrow$ $\frac{90}{6} = 15$
$15 = 15$ ✓

Practice • Use division or multiplication to solve the equations.

1. $4n = 28$
2. $7x = 56$
3. $2y = 146$
4. $\frac{x}{3} = 8$
5. $\frac{a}{8} = 9$
6. $\frac{n}{5} = 21$
7. $\frac{y}{9} = 5$
8. $6n = 42$
9. $\frac{x}{2} = 43$

Mixed Practice • Solve the equations. Check your answers.

10. $5y = 45$
11. $3n = 96$
12. $9x = 225$
13. $\frac{n}{4} = 8$
14. $\frac{x}{6} = 11$
15. $\frac{b}{7} = 24$
16. $11n = 44$
17. $\frac{x}{15} = 3$
18. $13y = 78$
19. $\frac{a}{10} = 12$
20. $14y = 112$
21. $\frac{n}{12} = 7$
22. $4b = 276$
23. $\frac{x}{3} = 36$
24. $8y = 384$
25. $n - 36 = 24$
26. $5n = 65$
27. $\frac{x}{2} = 45$
28. $12n = 108$
29. $x + 57 = 100$
30. $\frac{y}{11} = 10$

★ 31. $105 = 7n$
★ 32. $16 = \frac{x}{3}$
★ 33. $192 = 6y$
★ 34. $2n + 3 = 29$
★ 35. $4x - 8 = 24$
★ 36. $5y + 11 = 76$

PROBLEM SOLVING • APPLICATIONS

37. If a certain number is divided by 4, the quotient is 17. What is the number?

★ 38. Mrs. Jones is twice as old as her daughter, Mrs. Mendoza. Mrs. Mendoza is 22 years older than her daughter, Ines. If Mrs. Jones is 72, how old is Mrs. Mendoza? How old is Ines?

Midchapter Review

Evaluate the expressions when $x = 18$.

1. $x + 9$
2. $x - 17$
3. $4x$
4. $\frac{x}{2}$

Solve and check.

5. $y - 12 = 17$
6. $x + 15 = 60$
7. $\frac{n}{8} = 12$
8. $4x = 92$

PROBLEM SOLVING • STRATEGIES

Choosing Equations

Writing an equation can be helpful in summarizing a problem situation. However, many equations can be written using the same numbers. You need to be able to recognize or write an equation that is appropriate for the problem.

Jim says, "My grandmother is 4 times as old as I am." If Jim's grandmother is 64 years old, how old is Jim?

Suppose n stands for Jim's age. Which equation would you use to summarize the problem?

A. $n + 4 = 64$
B. $4 \times 64 = n$
C. $4n = 64$

The problem tells us that 4 times Jim's age (n) is 64. So $4n = 64$ is the correct choice.

$$4n = 64$$
$$\frac{4n}{4} = \frac{64}{4}$$
$$n = 16$$

Jim is 16 years old.

Check: Does 4 times Jim's age equal 64?
$4(16) = 64$
$64 = 64$ ✓

Choose the equation that you would use to solve the problem. Then solve.

1. Tania has saved \$54. This is \$18 more than Sandy has saved. How much money has Sandy saved?

A. $54 + 18 = n$
B. $n + 18 = 54$
C. $18n = 54$

2. One year Ellen buys electronics stocks. The next year she sells her stock for \$654. This is twice the amount that she paid for it. How much did she pay for her stock?

A. $n + 2 = 654$
B. $2 \times 654 = n$
C. $2n = 654$

3. Mr. Forbes pays \$24 for gasoline. He has \$48 left. How much money did he have before he bought the gasoline?

A. $n + 24 = 48$
B. $n - 24 = 48$
C. $\frac{48}{24} = n$

4. Beth has \$28. She spends \$7 for books. How much money does she have left?

A. $28 - 7 = n$
B. $\frac{28}{7} = n$
C. $28 + 7 = n$

5. Dan worked 30 hours per week during July and August. This is 12 hours more per week than he worked from September through June. How many hours did he work per week in September?

A. $n - 12 = 30$
B. $n + 12 = 30$
C. $12(30) = n$

Read each problem more than once to be sure you understand it.

6. The Book Mark received a shipment of 132 books. Then it had 1,188 books in all. How many books did it have before the shipment came?

A. $1{,}188 + 132 = n$
B. $\frac{1{,}188}{132} = n$
C. $n + 132 = 1{,}188$

7. During July there were 21,828 visitors to Science Museum. This was 12 times the number of visitors in December. How many visitors were there in December?

A. $21{,} 828 - 12 = n$
B. $12n = 21{,}828$
C. $21{,}828 + 12 = n$

8. Bill jogs 2,400 meters in 20 minutes. What is his average speed per minute?

A. $20 \times 2{,}400 = n$
B. $\frac{2{,}400}{20} = n$
C. $2{,}400 - 20 = n$

9. During Saturday and Sunday, a total of 3,525 people visited the Art Museum. On Sunday 1,485 people visited. How many people visited it on Saturday?

A. $n + 1{,}485 = 3{,}525$
B. $1{,}485 + 3{,}525 = n$
C. $1{,}485 \times 3{,}525 = n$

10. Vinnie says, "My mother is half as old as my grandmother." If Vinnie's mother is 36, how old is Vinnie's grandmother?

A. $36 - \frac{1}{2} = n$
B. $\frac{n}{2} = 36$
C. $\frac{n}{2} + \frac{n}{2} = 36$

Decide which operation is involved in the problem. Then choose the equation.

★ 11. Eartha runs 4,270 meters in the morning and 3,880 meters in the afternoon. How many meters must she run in the evening if she wants to run 10,000 meters that day?

A. $4{,}270 - 3{,}880 = n$
B. $4{,}270 + 3{,}880 = n$
C. $4{,}270 + 3{,}880 + n = 10{,}000$

★ 12. Ken's father is 28 years older than Ken. The sum of their ages is 50. What are their ages?

A. $50 - 28 = n$
B. $50 + 28 = n$
C. $n + (n + 28) = 50$

Equations and Properties

Suppose you have a board that is a centimeters long and another board that is b centimeters long. If you connect the boards end to end, will the length equal $a + b$? Will it also equal $b + a$?

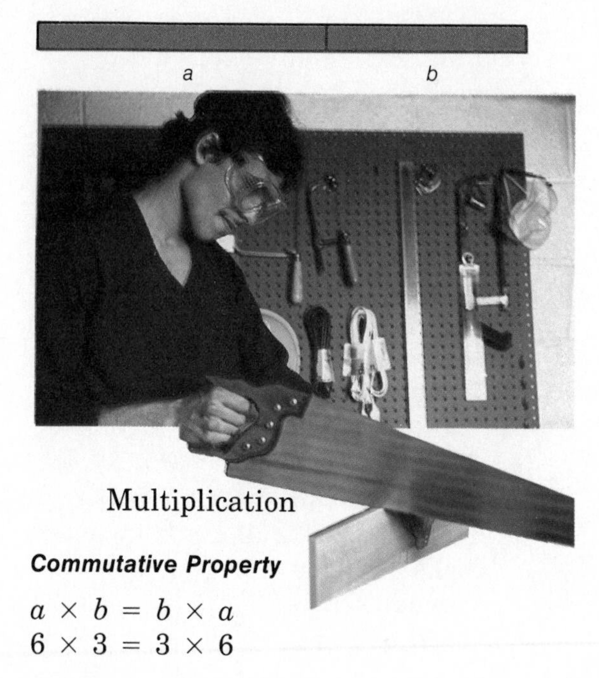

Which property of addition does this illustrate?

We can use equations with several variables to show properties of addition and multiplication. Check to see if each equation is true for all the numbers you use as replacements for the variables.

Addition

Commutative Property

$a + b = b + a$
$6 + 3 = 3 + 6$

Associative Property

$(a + b) + c = a + (b + c)$
$(8 + 4) + 2 = 8 + (4 + 2)$

Property of Zero

$a + 0 = a$ and $0 + a = a$
$9 + 0 = 9$ and $0 + 9 = 9$

Multiplication

Commutative Property

$a \times b = b \times a$
$6 \times 3 = 3 \times 6$

Associative Property

$(a \times b) \times c = a \times (b \times c)$
$(8 \times 4) \times 2 = 8 \times (4 \times 2)$

Property of One

$1 \times a = a$ and $a \times 1 = a$
$1 \times 9 = 9$ and $9 \times 1 = 9$

Distributive Property

$a \times (b + c) = (a \times b) + (a \times c)$
$4 \times (10 + 2) = (4 \times 10) + (4 \times 2)$

Now think of subtraction.

If you have a piece of wire 3 meters long, can you cut off a piece that is 1 meter long?

If you have a piece of wire 1 meter long, can you cut off a piece that is 3 meters long?

$3 - 1 \neq 1 - 3$

↑ is not equal to

Practice • Answer the questions.

1. If you have 5 dimes, can you give 2 dimes to a friend?
2. If you have 2 dimes, can you give 5 dimes to a friend?
3. Which of these sentences is true?
   $5 - 2 = 2 - 5$ $\quad$ $5 - 2 \neq 2 - 5$
4. Which of these sentences is true?
   $(8 - 6) - 2 = 8 - (6 - 2)$ $\quad$ $(8 - 6) - 2 \neq 8 - (6 - 2)$

Mixed Practice • Answer the questions.

5. If you have 12 dimes, can you put them in 3 equal stacks?
6. If you have 3 dimes, can you put them in 12 equal stacks?
7. Which of these sentences is true?
   $12 \div 3 = 3 \div 12$ $\quad$ $12 \div 3 \neq 3 \div 12$
8. Which of these sentences is true?
   $(18 \div 6) \div 3 = 18 \div (6 \div 3)$ $\quad$ $(18 \div 6) \div 3 \neq 18 \div (6 \div 3)$

Write *true* or *false*.

9. $8 - 0 = 8$
10. $0 - 8 = 8$
11. $8 - 0 = 0 - 8$
12. $7 \div 1 = 7$
13. $1 \div 7 = 7$
14. $7 \div 1 = 1 \div 7$
15. $0 - 9 = 9$
16. $9 - 0 = 9$
17. $0 - 9 = 9 - 0$
18. $1 \div 3 = 3$
19. $3 \div 1 = 3$
20. $1 \div 3 = 3 \div 1$
21. $8 \times 4 = 32$
22. $4 \times 8 = 32$
23. $8 \times 4 = 4 \times 8$
24. $(14 + 8) + 19 = 14 + (8 + 19)$
25. $(12 \times 6) \times 3 = 12 \times (6 \times 3)$
26. ★ $(17 - 9) - 5 = 17 - (9 - 5)$
27. ★ $(54 \div 9) \div 3 = 54 \div (9 \div 3)$

PROBLEM SOLVING • APPLICATIONS

28. Does subtraction have the commutative property? the associative property?
29. Does division have the commutative property? the associative property?
30. ★ List three numbers that make this sentence false. Find one number that makes this sentence true. Remember, even if you find a number that makes it true, this does not make subtraction associative.
    $(15 - 6) - n = 15 - (6 - n)$

Distance Formula

Sixty years ago, a plane flew at a rate of 125 kilometers per hour **(km/h).** How far did it fly in 3 hours?

You can use a **formula** to help you to solve the problem.

distance = rate × time

$d = rt$ ← rt means r × t.

Step 1 Write the formula. → $d = rt$

Step 2 You know the rate (125 km/h) and the time (3 hours).
Substitute the numbers for r and t. → $d = 3(125)$

Step 3 Solve. → $d = 375$

The plane flew 375 kilometers in 3 hours. Check to be sure the answer makes sense.

A jet plane flies at a rate of 980 kilometers per hour. How many hours will it take for the jet to travel 4,900 kilometers?

Step 1 Write the formula. → $d = rt$

Step 2 You know the distance (4,900 km) and the rate (980 km/h).
Substitute the numbers for d and r. → $4{,}900 = 980t$

Step 3 Solve. The equation shows multiplication.
Divide both sides by 980. → $\frac{4{,}900}{980} = \frac{980t}{980}$

$$5 = t$$

It will take the jet 5 hours to fly 4,900 kilometers.
Check to be sure the answer makes sense. You can also check by substituting 5 into the formula:

$$4{,}900 = (980)5$$
$$4{,}900 = 4{,}900 \checkmark$$

Practice • Use the distance formula. Solve.

1. $r = 72$ km/h
$t = 5$ hours
Find d.

2. $d = 570$ km
$r = 95$ km/h
Find t.

3. $d = 340$ km
$t = 4$ hours
Find r.

Mixed Practice • Use the distance formula.

4. $r = 86$ km/h
   $t = 5$ hours
   Find d.

5. $d = 3{,}800$ km
   $t = 4$ hours
   Find r.

6. $d = 12{,}600$ km
   $r = 900$ km/h
   Find t.

PROBLEM SOLVING • APPLICATIONS

7. A jet plane flies nonstop from San Francisco to Honolulu in 4 hours. The plane flies at a rate of 959 km/h. How far does it fly?

8. A supersonic jet flies 11,900 km in 5 hours. At what average rate of speed is the jet flying?

9. A hot-air balloon is flying at a rate of 38 km/h. How long does it take to fly 190 km?

10. A blimp is flying at a rate of 84 km/h. How far does it fly in 6 hours?

11. Eddie drives 768 km from his home to Columbus, Ohio. He drives at a rate of 96 km/h. How long does the trip take?

12. Bayard and Larry hiked from 9:00 A.M. to noon along the Timberline Trail. They hiked at a rate of 5 km/h. How far did Bayard and Larry hike?

13. The Metroliner train travels 620 kilometers in 4 hours. What is the train's average rate of speed?

14. Sara rides her bicycle 42 kilometers to her grandmother's house. Sara rides at a rate of 14 km/h. How long does the trip take?

15. Sean jogs from 11:00 A.M. to 1:00 P.M. along the trail in Hocking State Park. He jogs a distance of 16 kilometers. What is Sam's average rate of speed?

★16. Maria leaves the house at 9:00 A.M. and drives at a rate of 60 km/h. Her brother Luis leaves the house 1 hour later and drives the same route as Maria at 80 km/h. About what time will Luis pass Maria on the highway?

Skills Maintenance

Round to the nearest dollar.

1. $6.25
2. $7.80
3. $8.50
4. $12.49
5. $14.05
6. $36.75
7. $100.52
8. $250.31

PROBLEM SOLVING • STRATEGIES

Using Equations

Mr. Johnson orders 250 boxes of birthday cards for his stationery store. He receives a delivery of 195 boxes of birthday cards. How many more boxes of cards still have to be delivered to complete Mr. Johnson's order?

You can write an equation to help solve the problem. Decide what you must find and represent it with a variable.

Think: boxes delivered + boxes still to be delivered = Mr. Johnson's order
Let x = the number of boxes still to be delivered.

Since $195 + x$ is equal to $x + 195$, solve by subtracting 195 from both sides.

Write the equation. $195 + x = 250$

Solve. $195 + x - 195 = 250 - 195$
$x = 55$

There are 55 boxes of cards still to be delivered to complete Mr. Johnson's order.

Check the answer by using the original problem.

Does the number delivered (195) plus 55 equal 250?

$195 + 55 = 250$
$250 = 250$ ✓

Norma buys 3 boxes of note cards with the same number of cards in each box. She gets a total of 108 cards. How many cards are in each box?

Think: 3 boxes × same number in each box = total number of cards
Let n = the number of cards in each box.

Write the equation. $3n = 108$

Solve. $\frac{3n}{3} = \frac{108}{3}$
$n = 36$

Check the answer by using the original problem.

Does 3 boxes of 36 cards each give a total of 108 cards?

$3(36) = 108$
$108 = 108$ ✓

Write an equation for each problem. Then solve the problem.

1. Juanita and Ray work part-time. Last week Juanita worked 8 hours more than Ray. If Juanita worked 25 hours, how many hours did Ray work?

2. Mr. Johnson orders 3 times as many blue pens as red pens for his store. He orders a total of 135 blue pens. How many red pens does he order?

3. A customer buys wrapping paper and a bow. The total cost is $2.68. The bow costs $.75. How much does the wrapping paper cost?

4. During a sale day, 27 stuffed animals are sold. At the end of the day, there are 19 stuffed animals left. How many stuffed animals did the store have at the beginning of the sale day?

Decide what you must find and represent it using a variable.

5. During a two-week period, Mr. Johnson works a total of 76 hours. This is twice as many hours as Ray works during those same weeks. How many hours does Ray work?

6. Pierre buys 3 cards at $.75 each. How much does Pierre pay?

7. Mrs. Kim spends $12 on presents. Afterward she has $39 left in her purse. How much money did she have before she bought the presents?

8. Mrs. Aviles spends $10.20 for 12 colored markers. What is the price of each marker?

9. Mr. Johnson orders 4 cartons of address books with the same number of books in each carton. There are 192 books in all. How many books are in each carton?

10. Juanita has saved $87 to buy an electric typewriter. The price of the typewriter is $312. How much does she still need to save?

★ 11. Juanita is 3 years older than Ray. The sum of their ages is 31. What are their ages?

★ 12. Mr. Johnson is 4 times as old as his son. The sum of their ages is 60. What are their ages?

Solving Inequalities

A number sentence such as $n + 3 < 7$ or $n + 3 > 7$ is an **inequality.** The signs $<$ and $>$ are used to compare numbers and expressions that are not equal to each other.

The solutions for the inequalities $n + 3 < 7$ and $n + 3 > 7$ can be found by testing values for n. For all of this work, n stands for all whole numbers.

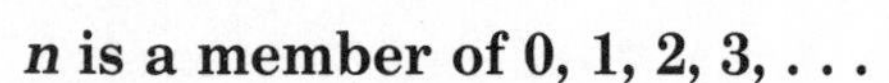

***n* is a member of 0, 1, 2, 3, . . .**

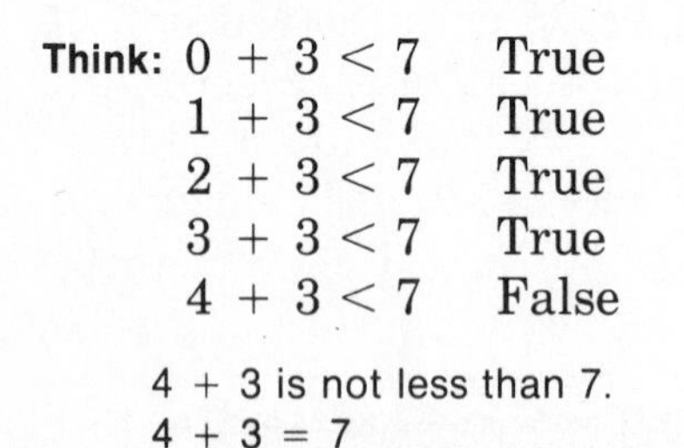

Think:

$0 + 3 < 7$	True
$1 + 3 < 7$	True
$2 + 3 < 7$	True
$3 + 3 < 7$	True
$4 + 3 < 7$	False

$4 + 3$ is not less than 7.
$4 + 3 = 7$

So the solutions of $n + 3 < 7$ are 0,1, 2, and 3.

Think:

$4 + 3 > 7$	False
$5 + 3 > 7$	True
$6 + 3 > 7$	True
$7 + 3 > 7$	True

So the solutions of $n + 3 > 7$ are all the whole numbers that are greater than 4. You can show the solutions as: 5, 6, 7, . . .

Another way to solve an inequality such as $n + 3 < 7$ or $n + 3 > 7$ is to use the related equation, $n + 3 = 7$.

$n + 3 = 7$
$n = 4$

Solution:
4

$n + 3 < 7$
$n < 4$

Solutions:
All whole numbers less than 4

$n + 3 > 7$
$n > 4$

Solutions:
All whole numbers greater than 4

The solutions of these sentences can be **graphed** on number lines.

Thick dots show the solutions.
Open circles show that the number is not included.

The thick arrow shows that the solutions go on and on.

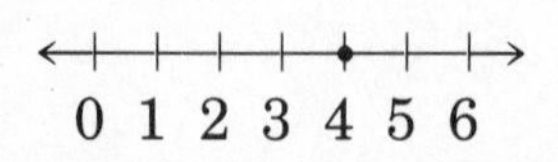

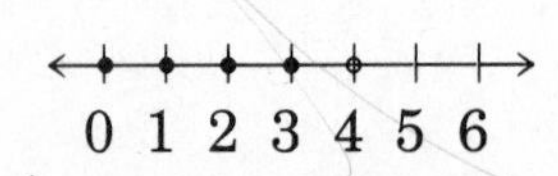

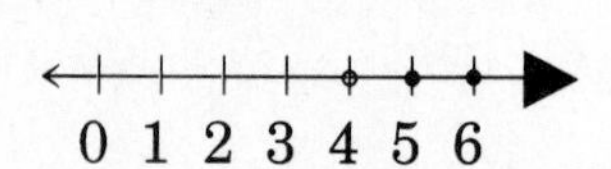

Practice • Write the solutions and graph them on number lines.

1. $n + 1 = 4$
2. $n + 1 < 4$
3. $n + 1 > 4$
4. $2x = 10$
5. $2x < 10$
6. $2x > 10$

Mixed Practice • Write the solutions and graph them on number lines.

7. $n + 1 = 3$
8. $n + 1 < 3$
9. $n + 1 > 3$
10. $y + 8 = 12$
11. $y + 8 < 12$
12. $y + 8 > 12$
13. $3x = 18$
14. $3x < 18$
15. $3x > 18$
16. $\frac{n}{2} = 5$
17. $\frac{n}{2} < 5$
18. $\frac{n}{2} > 5$
19. $x + 1 = 2$
20. $x + 1 < 2$
21. $x + 1 > 2$

Write the solutions for each inequality. You do not need to graph the solutions.

22. $4n < 40$
23. $4n > 40$
24. $\frac{x}{3} < 5$
25. $\frac{x}{3} > 5$
26. $y + 8 < 20$
27. $y + 8 > 20$
★28. $n + 15 < 30$
★29. $n + 15 > 30$
★30. $5y < 160$
★31. $5y > 160$

The signs ≤ and ≥ are also used in inequalities. The solutions of $n + 3 \leq 10$ are 0, 1, 2, 3, 4, 5, 6, 7. The 7 is included because 7 + 3 is 10, and 10 makes the sentence true. Similarly, $n + 3 \geq 7$ has 7, 8, 9, . . . as its solutions.

$\mathbf{n + 3 \leq 10}$
$n + 3$ is less than or equal to 10.

$\mathbf{n + 3 \geq 10}$
$n + 3$ is greater than or equal to 10.

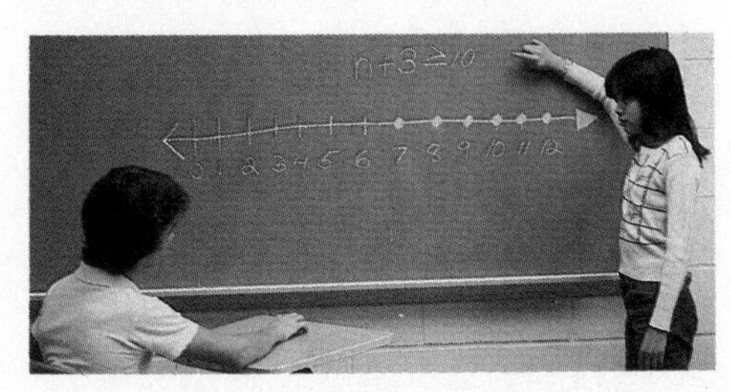

Write the solutions.

★32. $3y \leq 18$
★33. $n + 5 \geq 17$
★34. $\frac{n}{4} \leq 5$

PROBLEM SOLVING • APPLICATIONS

35. After 3 more birthdays, Donna will still be less than 18 years old. Write the ages she might be now.

★36. Mr. Carruthers is more than twice as old as Bob. Mr. Carruthers is 32 years old. What is the greatest age Bob might be?

★37. Nara deposits \$12 in her bank account. Afterward she has less than \$60 in the account. What is the greatest number of dollars she could have had before the deposit?

CHAPTER 3 REVIEW

Evaluate the given expressions for the values shown. (pp. 60–61)

$3 + x$: **1.** $x = 4$ **2.** $x = 12$ **3.** $x = 20$ **4.** $x = 75$

$27 - y$: **5.** $y = 7$ **6.** $y = 18$ **7.** $y = 23$ **8.** $y = 27$

Write the expressions. (pp. 60–61)

9. 8 less than a number y

10. 9 more than a number w

Solve the equations. Check your answers. (pp. 62–63)

11. $g - 2 = 6$ **12.** $s + 6 = 12$ **13.** $m - 12 = 42$

Evaluate the given expressions for the values shown. (pp. 64–65)

$7x$: **14.** $x = 4$ **15.** $x = 10$ **16.** $x = 18$ **17.** $x = 101$

$\frac{y}{8}$: **18.** $y = 8$ **19.** $y = 40$ **20.** $y = 88$ **21.** $y = 96$

$\frac{4x}{2}$: **22.** $x = 3$ **23.** $x = 15$ **24.** $x = 21$ **25.** $x = 40$

Write the expressions. (pp. 64–65)

26. 12 times a number b

27. a number t divided by 2

Solve the equations. Check your answers. (pp. 66–67)

28. $4n = 24$ **29.** $\frac{y}{2} = 6$ **30.** $81 = 9r$

Use the distance formula, $d = rt$. (pp. 72–73)

31. $r = 94$ km/h
$t = 3$ hours
Find d.

32. $d = 3{,}625$ km
$t = 5$ hours
Find r.

33. $d = 11{,}920$ km
$r = 745$ km/h
Find t.

n is a whole number. Write the solutions. Do not graph the solutions. (pp. 76–77)

34. $3n < 12$ **35.** $n + 2 > 6$ **36.** $4n > 8$

37. Mrs. Cato is 3 times as old as her grandson. If Mrs. Cato is 78, how old is her grandson? (pp. 74–75)

38. Mr. Jessup spends \$28 and has \$44 left. How much money did he have at first? (pp. 74–75)

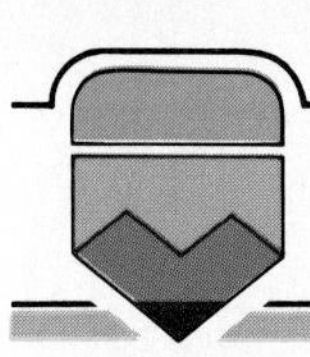

PROJECT

Functions

There are 6 children in the Smith family.
If none is a boy, how many are girls?
If 1 is a boy, how many are girls?
If 2 are boys, how many are girls?

Let x stand for the number of boys.
Let y stand for the number of girls.
The equation $x + y = 6$ tells about the boys and girls in the Smith family.

The solutions for $x + y = 6$ are pairs of numbers. The table shows all the possible solutions.

boys →	x	0	1	2	3	4	5	6
girls →	y	6	5	4	3	2	1	0

The table shows a **function.** If we choose a number for x, we obtain just one number for y.

The equation $x + y = 6$ is a **rule** for the function.

Jamyce can walk 4 kilometers in 1 hour.
How many kilometers can she walk in 2 hours? in 3 hours? in 4 hours?

Let x stand for the number of hours and y stand for the total distance she walks. Copy and complete this table.

hours →	x	1	2	3	4	5
distance →	y	4	?	?	?	?

Write a rule for this function.

Study the rule. Then copy and complete the table.

1. $x - y = 6$

x	10	9	8	7	6
y	?	?	?	?	?

2. $\frac{x}{3} = y$

x	3	6	9	12	15
y	1	?	?	?	?

3. $x + y = 15$

x	0	1	2	3	4
y	?	?	?	?	?

4. Many things in real life are examples of functions. Find five examples of functions. Describe each situation and write a rule for the function.

CHAPTER 3

TEST

Evaluate the given expressions for the values shown.

$5 + b$:	**1.** $b = 7$	**2.** $b = 14$	**3.** $b = 21$	**4.** $b = 65$
$41 - a$:	**5.** $a = 6$	**6.** $a = 10$	**7.** $a = 23$	**8.** $a = 41$

Write the expressions.

9. 16 less than a number q

10. 11 more than a number p

Solve the equations. Check your answers.

11. $3 + x = 10$

12. $t - 11 = 20$

13. $r + 4 = 53$

Evaluate the given expressions for the values shown.

$9t$:	**14.** $t = 6$	**15.** $t = 11$	**16.** $t = 17$	**17.** $t = 42$
$\frac{s}{7}$:	**18.** $s = 14$	**19.** $s = 49$	**20.** $s = 77$	**21.** $s = 112$
$\frac{8t}{2}$:	**22.** $t = 3$	**23.** $t = 11$	**24.** $t = 30$	**25.** $t = 41$

Write the expressions.

26. 13 times a number c

27. A number w is divided by 9

Solve the equations. Check your answers.

28. $3t = 18$

29. $\frac{x}{4} = 10$

30. $144 = 16q$

Use the distance formula, $d = rt$.

31. $r = 216$ km/h
$t = 4$ hours
Find d.

32. $d = 2{,}172$ km
$t = 6$ hours
Find r.

33. $d = 9{,}350$ km
$r = 850$ km/h
Find t.

n is a whole number. Write the solutions. Do not graph the solutions.

34. $4n < 8$

35. $n + 3 > 8$

36. $5n > 15$

37. Mr. Callahan is 4 times as old as his oldest grandson, Nathaniel. If Mr. Callahan is 68 years old, how old is Nathaniel?

38. Mrs. Briar pays $73 for groceri Afterwards she has $19 left in purse. How much money did s have originally?

ENRICHMENT

Experimenting with Equations

An inkblot is covering an expression on Marie's sheet of paper.

Marie
$\quad - 4 = 26$

If $\quad - 4$ equals 26, what must  equal?

Now study the equation on Jon's paper. Is it similar to Marie's equation? How is it different?

Jon
$3y - 4 = 26$

If $3y$ equals 30, what must y equal?

Here are three equations. If you start with $3y - 4 = 26$, what must you do to obtain the equation $3y = 30$? What must you do to $3y = 30$ to obtain the equation $y = 10$?

$$3y - 4 = 26$$
$$3y = 30$$
$$y = 10$$

Study these equations. What is the solution of each equation?

$$5n + n = 72$$
$$6n = 72$$

$5n + n$ means $5n + 1n$, or $6n$

Solve each of these equations. Check your solution by substituting the number in the original equation.

1. $\quad + 2 = 98$ **2.** $4x + 2 = 98$ **3.** $\quad - 8 = 37$ **4.** $5n - 8 = 37$

5. $n + n = 26$ **6.** $2y + y = 45$ **7.** $3x + 2x = 60$ **8.** $y + y + y = 48$

9. $7x - 2 = 110$ **10.** $8n + 3 = 99$ **11.** $5x - x = 20$ **12.** $10y - 3y = 126$

13. $\frac{y}{2} - 1 = 7$ **14.** $\frac{n}{3} + 2 = 6$ **15.** $\frac{x}{4} - 7 = 3$ **16.** $\frac{n}{9} + 6 = 9$

Study the equation that is given. Then write two equations that have the same solution.

17. $3n + 5 = 29$ **18.** $4y - 9 = 39$ **19.** $\frac{x}{5} + 2 = 9$ **20.** $\frac{n}{8} - 4 = 2$

21. Here is a more complicated equation. See if you can solve it.

$$7n + 5 + 2n = 4n + 80$$

COMPUTER

Computer Basics

A *computer* is a machine that works with numbers and letters. *Computer hardware* is the metal or plastic machinery of the computer itself. *Computer systems* have input, output, hardware, and software.

A *programmer* writes instructions to computers in programs. A *program* is a list of step-by-step input to a computer.

Computer software includes all the programs and data in the computer hardware. *Data* are the numbers, letters, and instructions with which the computer works.

A computer can get *input* from a keyboard, punched cards, tape, or disks. A *keyboard* is a typewriter that is attached to a computer. Punched cards, tape, and disks can hold much data. Data input to one program may have been data output from another program.

A computer can place *output* on any or all of these types of output devices:
Cathode-ray tubes (CRTs) display output on television screens.
Printers print output on paper to make permanent documents.
Punched cards can save output for years.
Magnetic tapes hold output data in a very condensed form.
Diskettes, sometimes called *floppy disks,* are very portable.
Hard disks can hold millions of letters or numbers.

Computers use *binary numbers*, which have only the numbers 0 and 1. Each 0 or 1 is called a *bit*. A group of *four bits* is called a *nibble*. A group of *eight bits* is called a *byte*. Each byte can have one of 256 different *decimal values*. Each value of a byte can be translated into a different character. A *character* can be a number, a letter, a command, or a special symbol such as a question mark or dollar sign.

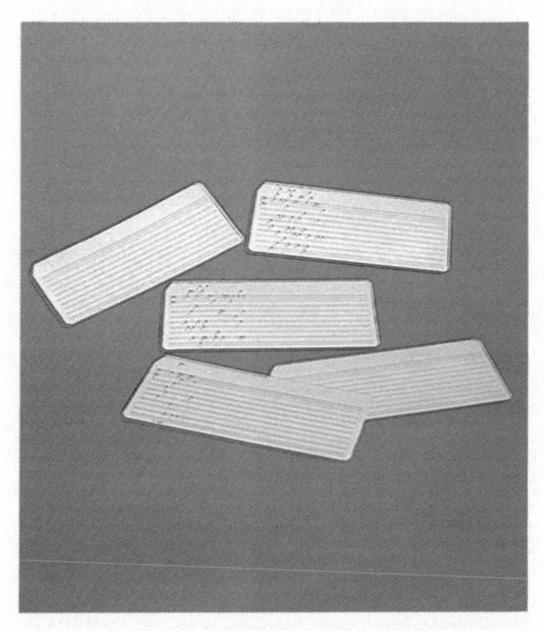

You have just read that a computer can use a cathode-ray tube (CRT) for display. The smallest square of light on a CRT is called a *pixel*. All digits and letters can be made from groups of pixels.

Computer *storage* is measured in K. *K* stands for a storage of 1,024 bytes. A 32K computer can hold about as much information as 16 pages such as this one. Hard disks contain *megabytes,* millions of bytes, of storage. A 12-megabyte hard disk can hold as much information as 6,000 pages such as this.

Match each letter with the correct phrase.

1. A group of eight bits is	**A.** a megabyte.
2. K stands for a storage of	**B.** a keyboard.
3. The machinery of a computer is	**C.** 1,024 bytes.
4. A typewriter attached to a computer is	**D.** a program.
5. A number, letter, command, or symbol is	**E.** a byte.
6. One million bytes is	**F.** a character.
7. Step-by-step input to a computer is	**G.** hardware.

SKILLS MAINTENANCE

Chapters 1 Through 3

Choose the correct answers.

1. In which place is the blue digit?

46,871,064

A. hundred thousands
B. ten thousands
C. thousands
D. not here

2. Add.

$$\begin{array}{r} 6{,}742 \\ 386 \\ +2{,}426 \\ \hline \end{array}$$

A. 8,424
B. 9,454
C. 9,554
D. not here

3. Multiply.

$$\begin{array}{r} 3{,}260 \\ \times \ 745 \\ \hline \end{array}$$

A. 2,528,700
B. 2,428,700
C. 2,428,800
D. not here

4. Divide.

$27\overline{)196{,}417}$

A. 7,274 r9
B. 7,273 r26
C. 7,274 r19
D. not here

5. Solve.

$x - 6 = 15$

A. $x = 21.$
B. $x = 9$
C. $x = 90$
D. not here

6. Solve.

$y + 27 = 36$

A. $y = 63$
B. $y = 10$
C. $y = 8$
D. not here

7. Solve.

$b - 15 = 28$

A. $b = 33$
B. $b = 13$
C. $b = 43$
D. not here

8. Solve.

$12n = 108$

A. $n = 8$
B. $n = 9$
C. $n = 96$
D. not here

9. Use the distance formula, $d = rt$.
$r = 88$ km/h
$t = 4$ hours
Find d.

A. $d = 352$ km
B. $d = 92$ km
C. $d = 22$ km
D. not here

10. Lew has some money in his wallet. He buys a book for $13. Then he has $28 left in his wallet. How much money did he have before he bought the book?

A. $41
B. $15
C. $364
D. not here

11. Mrs. Clare orders 4 more rolls of red ribbon than blue ribbon. She orders a total of 17 rolls of red ribbon. How many rolls of blue ribbon does she order?

A. 21 rolls
B. 13 rolls
C. 4 rolls
D. not here

Decimals: Addition and Subtraction

CHAPTER 4

Decimals Through Millionths • Comparing and Ordering • Rounding • Estimating and Adding • Problem Solving: Reading a Map • Estimating and Subtracting • Problem Solving: Using Estimates Using a Checking Account • Sequences

Tenths and Hundredths

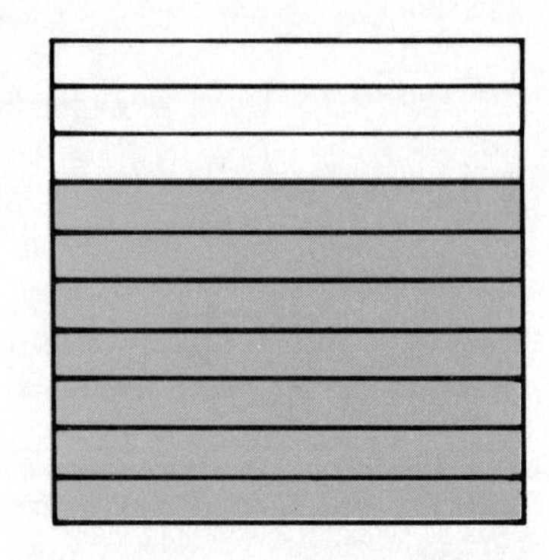

About seven-tenths of the earth's surface is water. We can write a **decimal** to show this.

0.7 Read: seven-tenths.

This square is divided into ten equal parts. Seven-tenths is blue.

Drawings can help us to understand decimals.

0.7 is blue.
↑
decimal point

The vertical lines divide this square into tenths. The horizontal lines divide each tenth into ten equal parts. The square is divided into 100 equal parts. Ten-hundredths is green.

0.10 Read: ten-hundredths.

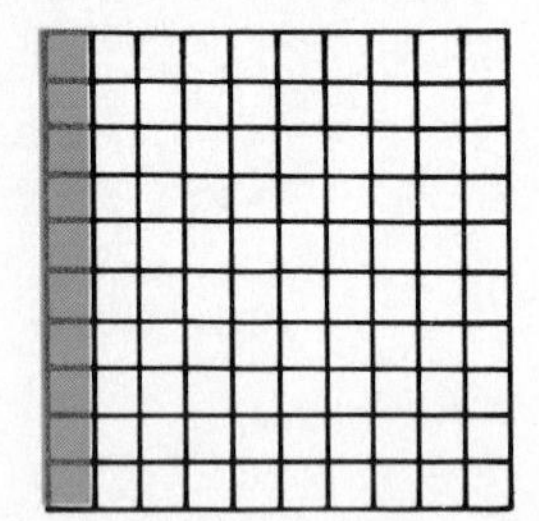

The drawing also shows:

1 tenth = 10 hundredths
0.1 = 0.10

In this square, fourteen-hundredths is blue.

0.14

Six-hundredths is yellow.

0.06

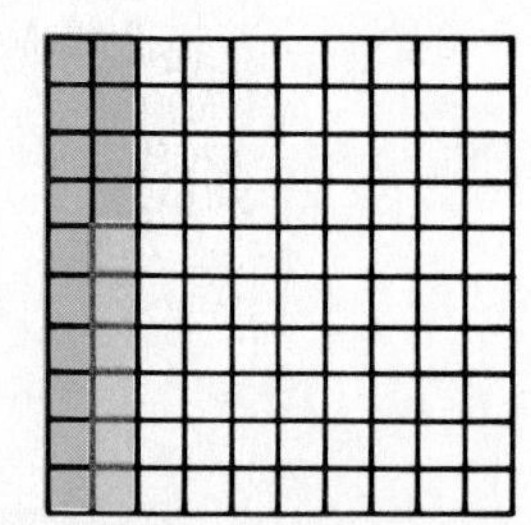

Look at the blue part again. The drawing shows:

14 hundredths = 1 tenth 4 hundredths

Practice • Write decimals for the shaded parts.

1. 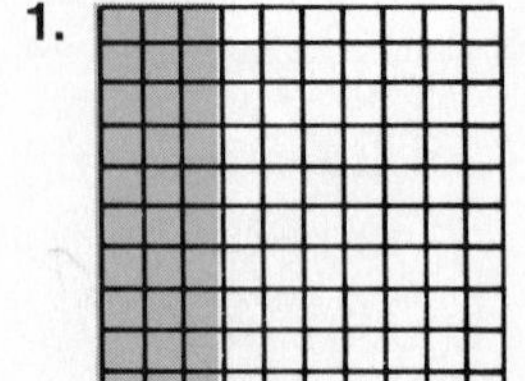

2. 

3. 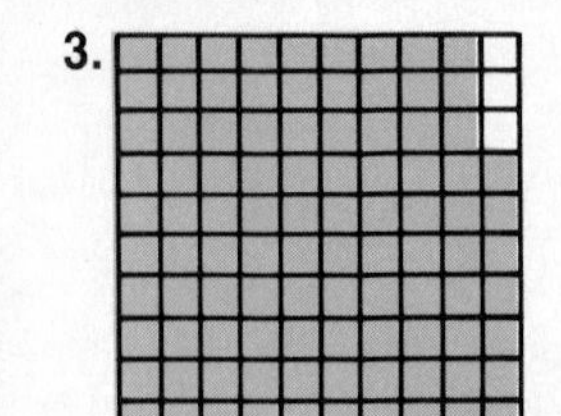

4. 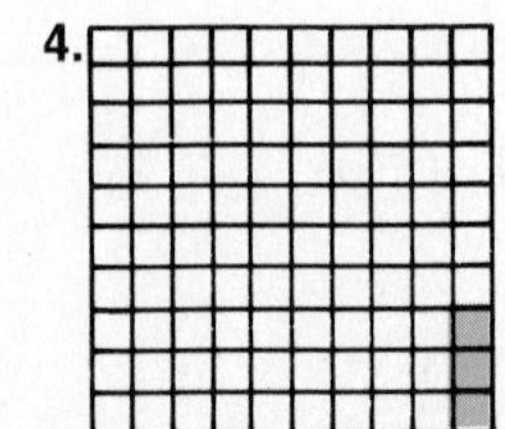

Write the decimals.

5. eight-tenths
6. eight-hundredths
7. twenty-one hundredths
8. two-tenths
9. one-hundredth
10. ninety-nine hundredths

Mixed Practice • Write decimals for the shaded parts.

11.
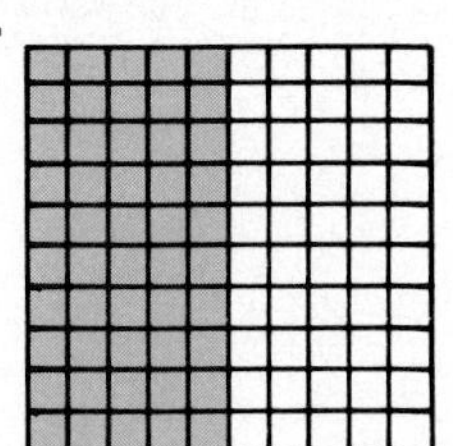

12.
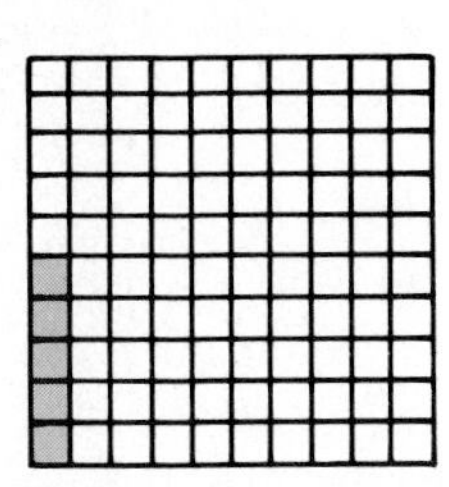

13.
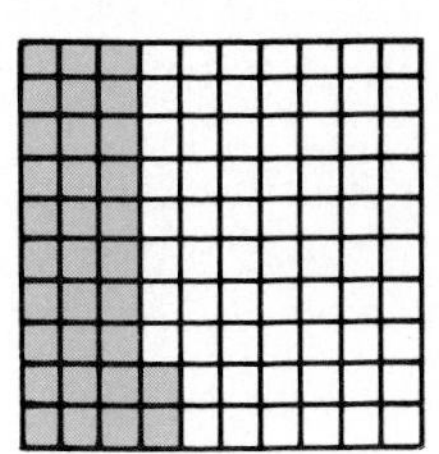

14.
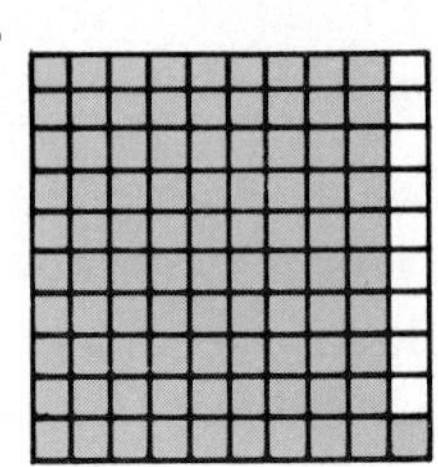

Write the decimals.

15. nine-tenths
16. nine-hundredths
17. twenty-four hundredths
18. two-hundredths
19. four-tenths
20. eighty-one hundredths
21. one-tenth
22. seventeen-hundredths
23. seven-hundredths
24. six-tenths
25. four-hundredths
26. eighty-three hundredths

Write in words.

27. 0.2
28. 0.57
29. 0.07
30. 0.5
31. 0.05
32. 0.62
33. 0.09
34. 0.9
35. 0.80
36. 0.01

★37. On graph paper draw a 10-by-10 square. Shade 0.4 of the square. Write a decimal in hundredths for the shaded part.

★38. What part of your drawing is *not* shaded?

PROBLEM SOLVING • APPLICATIONS

Write decimals for the underlined words.

39. About eighteen-hundredths of the earth's surface is the Atlantic Ocean.

40. About three-hundredths of the earth's surface is the Arctic Ocean.

★41. Which is larger, the Atlantic Ocean or the Arctic Ocean? About how many times as large is it?

The Decimal System

Oceanographers are scientists who study oceans. They have found that the Pacific Ocean at its deepest point is about eleven and thirty-three thousandths kilometers deep.

11.033 Read: eleven and thirty-three thousandths.
The decimal point is read as **and.**

Our system of naming numbers is called the **decimal system.** In the decimal system, we use digits and place value.
Each place in a decimal has a value

- 10 times the value of the place at its right.
- one-tenth of the value of the place at its left.

A place-value chart can help you read decimals.

In reading a decimal such as 0.075, you use the name of the place in which the last digit is located.

	Millions	Hundred-thousands	Ten-thousands	Thousands	Hundreds	Tens	Ones	Tenths	Hundredths	Thousandths	Ten-thousandths	Hundred-thousandths	Millionths
seventy-five **thousandths** →							0	0	7	5			
one hundred twenty-six **ten-thousandths** →							0	0	1	2	6		
two and eight-**millionths** →							2	0	0	0	0	0	8

Using place value, you can also identify the place in which a digit is located. For example, in 0.0126, the 2 is three places to the right of the decimal point. The 2 is in the thousandths place.

Practice • In which place is the blue digit?

1. 86.437 **2.** 0.732 **3.** 112.526 **4.** 6.935 **5.** 72.1504

6. Write the decimal: six and twenty-five thousandths.

7. Write in words: 0.0287.

Mixed Practice • In which place is the blue digit?

8. 42.873 9. 1.4217 10. 708.372 11. 0.906

12. 640.805 13. 94.839 14. 0.37627 15. 4.34

16. 7.64 17. 598.3025 18. 41.0006 ★19. 6.173208

Write the decimals.

20. sixteen and twenty-four hundredths
21. nine and seven hundred three thousandths
22. one hundred eighty-five and six-tenths
23. four hundred seventy-six and eighty-two hundredths
24. sixty-five and three-thousandths
25. fifty and seven ten-thousandths
26. three thousand, fifty-seven and nine-tenths
27. three hundred forty-five hundred-thousandths
28. fifty-six and two-hundredths
29. six hundred thirty-four hundred-thousandths

★30. fifteen millionths

Write in words.

31. 0.035 32. 906.24 33. 0.00001 34. 50.009 ★35. 6.000725

PROBLEM SOLVING • APPLICATIONS

36. The annual precipitation in Hilo, Hawaii, is 3.393 meters. How much more than 3 meters is this?

37. The annual precipitation in Phoenix, Arizona, is 0.179 meter. How much more than 0.17 meter is this?

★38. How much less than 0.18 meter is the annual precipitation in Phoenix?

Comparing and Ordering Decimals

Equivalent decimals are decimals that name the same number. The number lines show some equivalent decimals.

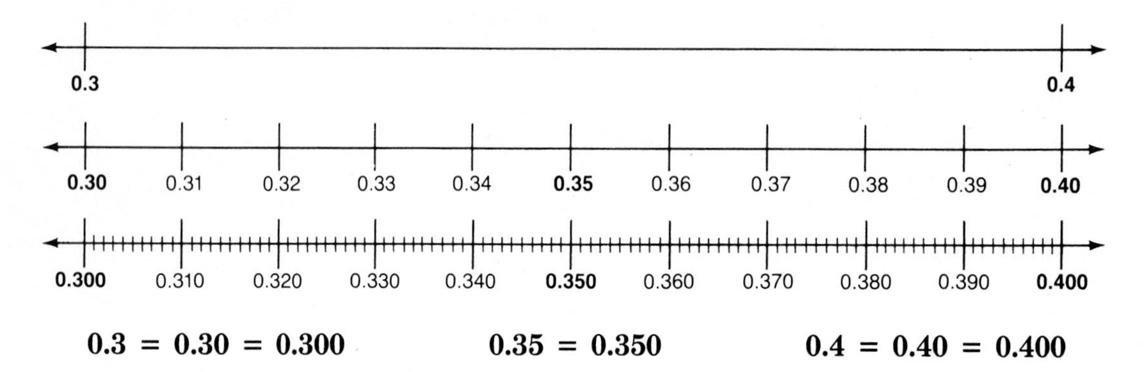

0.3 = 0.30 = 0.300 **0.35 = 0.350** **0.4 = 0.40 = 0.400**

A whole number such as 7 can also be named by using a decimal point and zeros following the decimal point.

7 = 7.0 = 7.00 = 7.000 = . . .

Sometimes you need to compare decimals. Comparing decimals is like comparing whole numbers. You use place value. First compare the digits to the left of the decimal point. Then compare the digits to the right of the decimal point.

Compare the decimals. Use $<$, $=$, or $>$ to make a true sentence.

3.7 ● 3.4

Think: Same number of ones.
Compare tenths. $7 > 4$

$3.7 > 3.4$

0.56 ● 0.58

Think: Same number of ones.
Same number of tenths.
Compare hundredths. $6 < 8$
$0.56 < 0.58$

2.49 ● 2.493

Think: $2.49 = 2.490$
Compare 2.490 and 2.493.
Same number of ones.
Same number of tenths.
Same number of hundredths.
Compare thousandths. $0 < 3$

$2.490 < 2.493$

$2.49 < 2.493$

8 ● 7.989

Think: Compare ones. $8 > 7$
No need to compare tenths, hundredths, or thousandths.

$8 > 7.989$

Practice • Write <, =, or >.

1. 5.63 ● 5.53
2. 0.764 ● 0.766
3. 63.4 ● 63.24
4. 18.4 ● 18.40
5. 3 ● 3.00
6. 33.8 ● 338.00

Mixed Practice • Write <, =, or >.

7. 4.2 ● 4.12
8. 0.05 ● 0.5
9. 6.031 ● 6.887
10. 6 ● 6.00
11. 85.346 ● 8.53
12. 9.213 ● 9.2
13. 0.06 ● 0.060
14. 7.771 ● 77.7
15. 18.53 ● 185.3
16. 1.237 ● 1.2237
17. 11.405 ● 7.999
18. ★ 234.620 ● 234.620001

Write in order from least to greatest.

19. 2.5; 2.6; 2.58
20. 3.8; 3.7; 3.75
21. 0.635; 0.629; 0.616
22. 11.145; 11.414; 11.362
23. 320.4; 320.35; 32.45
24. ★ 865.4; 8.654; 86.54; 8,654; 8,564
25. Any number that is greater than 1.5 and less than 1.6 is **between** 1.5 and 1.6. Which of these numbers are between 1.5 and 1.6?

    1.49 1.63 1.51 1.58 1.505 1.605 1.7 1.5342

26. ★ List 10 numbers that are between 2.3 and 2.4.
27. ★ Is it possible to list 20 numbers that are between 2.3 and 2.4? Is it possible to list *all* the numbers that are between 2.3 and 2.4?

PROBLEM SOLVING • APPLICATIONS

Write decimals for your answers.

28. Booneville has a population of 10,000. 5,378 are female. What part of the population is female?
29. ★ What part of Booneville's population is not female?

Skills Maintenance

1. 300 − 126
2. 5,000 − 2,412
3. 8,000 − 4,725
4. 21,605 − 9,206
5. 38,791 − 37,802
6. 50,000 − 1,643

Rounding Decimals

A falling object took 6.3 seconds to reach the ground. To the nearest second, how long did it take?

6.3 is between 6 and 7.
It is closer to 6 than to 7.
6.3 rounded to the nearest whole number is 6.

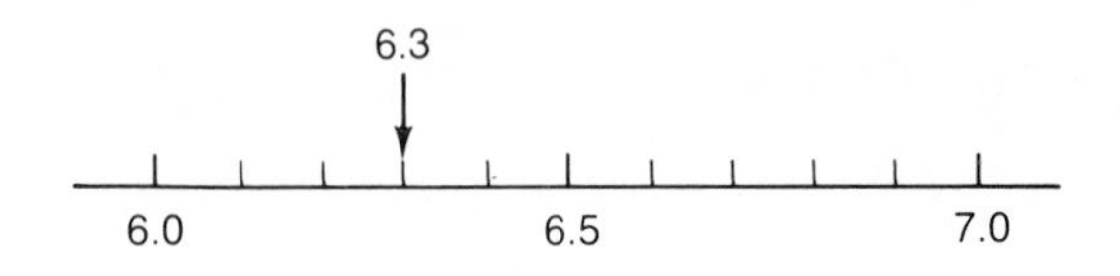

You can round decimals without using a number line. Use the same ideas you used in rounding whole numbers.

> ***To round a decimal, always look at the first digit to the right of the place to which you are rounding.***
> ***If the digit is less than 5, round down.***
> ***If the digit is 5 or greater, round up.***

Round 123.837 to the nearest whole number.

Think: The digit in the ones place is 3.
The digit to the right is 5 or greater.
Round up. Increase the digit in the ones place by 1.

↓
123.837
↑

123.837 rounded to the nearest whole number is 124.

Round 123.837 to the nearest tenth.

Think: The digit in the tenths place is 8.
The digit to the right is less than 5.
Round down. Keep the digit in the tenths place the same.

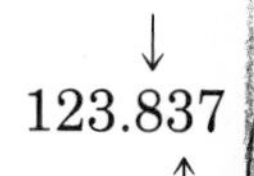

123.837 rounded to the nearest tenth is 123.8.

More Examples

↓
123.837 rounded to the nearest hundredth is 123.84.
↑

↓
0.4615 rounded to the nearest thousandth is 0.462.
↑

↓
1.9998 rounded to the nearest thousandth is 2.000.
↑

Practice • Round the numbers as indicated.

Nearest whole number:

1. 8.7 **2.** 3.51

Nearest tenth:

3. 0.43 **4.** 1.68

Nearest hundredth:

5. 6.032 **6.** 1.729

Nearest thousandth:

7. 0.3842 **8.** 5.6265

Mixed Practice • Round the numbers as indicated.

Nearest whole number:

9. 26.49 **10.** 29.5

11. 71.025 **12.** 26.385

Nearest tenth:

13. 15.47 **14.** 3.96

15. 17.42 **16.** 9.97

Nearest hundredth:

17. 0.937 **18.** 3.572

19. 0.295 ★**20.** 4.999

Nearest thousandth:

21. 0.7643 **22.** 2.0331

23. 3.4049 ★**24.** 10.0096

Round 6.0352497 to the nearest

★**25.** ten-thousandth. ★**26.** hundred-thousandth. ★**27.** millionth.

PROBLEM SOLVING • APPLICATIONS

28. Cynthia Woodhead set a swimming record. She swam 200 meters in 1 minute 58.23 seconds. Round this time to the nearest second.

29. Cynthia also set a record for swimming 800 meters. Her time was 8 minutes 18.77 seconds. Round this time to the nearest second.

★**30.** Express Cynthia's actual time for the 200-meter swim in seconds instead of minutes and seconds.

Midchapter Review

Write the decimals.

1. two and twelve-hundredths **2.** seventy-six thousandths

Write <, =, or >. **3.** 0.4 ● 0.40 **4.** 1.354 ● 1.355 **5.** 10.1 ● 9.997

Round to the nearest whole number.

6. 8.6 **7.** 3.47 **8.** 6.298 **9.** 9.513

Estimating and Adding

One week Julio worked 11.25 hours using the computer. The next week he worked 6.95 hours using the computer. Altogether, how many hours did he use the computer?

$$11.25 + 6.96 = n$$

Estimate the answer first.

Think: Round to the nearest whole numbers.
Add.

$$\begin{array}{r} 11.25 \\ +\ 6.96 \\ \hline \end{array} \rightarrow \begin{array}{r} 11 \\ +\ 7 \\ \hline 18 \end{array}$$

The sum is about 18.

Add to find the actual answer. Adding decimals is like adding whole numbers.

Step 1 Line up the decimal points. Add the hundredths.

$$\begin{array}{r} \scriptstyle 1 \quad \\ 11.25 \\ +\ 6.96 \\ \hline 1 \end{array}$$

Step 2 Add the tenths.

$$\begin{array}{r} \scriptstyle 1\,1 \quad \\ 11.25 \\ +\ 6.96 \\ \hline 21 \end{array}$$

Step 3 Add the ones. Add the tens. Write the decimal point in the answer.

$$\begin{array}{r} \scriptstyle 1\,1 \quad \\ 11.25 \\ +\ 6.96 \\ \hline 18.21 \end{array}$$

Each place to the right of the decimal point is called a **decimal place.**

Sometimes, in an example such as $4.87 + 3.2 + 6$, the addends do not have the same number of decimal places. You can write zeros at the ends of decimals. Remember, $3.2 = 3.20$. Also, $6 = 6.0 = 6.00$.

$$\begin{array}{r} 4.87 \\ 3.2 \\ +6 \\ \hline \end{array} \longrightarrow \begin{array}{r} 4.87 \\ 3.20 \\ +6.00 \\ \hline 14.07 \end{array}$$

In every addition example with decimals, be sure the decimal points are lined up.

Practice • Estimate each sum. Then find the actual answer.

1. $\begin{array}{r} 4.8 \\ +2.9 \\ \hline \end{array}$ **2.** $\begin{array}{r} 7.86 \\ +6.07 \\ \hline \end{array}$ **3.** $\begin{array}{r} 14.63 \\ +\ 2.2 \\ \hline \end{array}$ **4.** $\begin{array}{r} 76.081 \\ +\ 3.952 \\ \hline \end{array}$ **5.** $\begin{array}{r} 0.89 \\ +1.913 \\ \hline \end{array}$

Mixed Practice • Estimate each sum. Then find the actual answer.

6. $5.2 + 1.7$ **7.** $3.18 + 8.54$ **8.** $12.14 + 3.92$ **9.** $4.763 + 0.848$ **10.** $35.333 + 12.749$

Add.

11. $0.7 + 0.9$ **12.** $4.3 + 6.8$ **13.** $135.2 + 58.4$ **14.** $971.3 + 8.8$ **15.** $152.7 + 39.6$

16. $0.71 + 0.82$ **17.** $81.35 + 6.50$ **18.** $\$12.34 + 31.83$ **19.** $19.589 + 810.264$ **20.** $77.24 + 33.075$

21. $14.4 + 21.6 + 7.3$ **22.** $\$18.24 + 3.56 + 27.85$ **23.** $108.6 + 24.17 + 6.543$ **24.** $314.23 + 28.7654 + 143.612$ **25.** $0.9164 + 0.32 + 24.7$

Solve the equations.

26. $34.124 + 76.85 = n$

27. $1.53 + 6.25 + 12.64 = n$

28. $851.43 + 312.96 = n$

29. $76.9 + 5.36 + 105.8 = n$

30. $543 + 27.65 = n$

31. $106.5 + 11.834 + 89.63 = n$

★**32.** $0.3 + 1.28 + 36 + 4.037 = n$

★**33.** $8.65 + 20 + 27.5962 + 30.9 = n$

You know that 529 can be written in expanded form as 500 + 20 + 9. In a similar way, 529.368 can be written in expanded form.

$$529.368 = 500 + 20 + 9 + 0.3 + 0.06 + 0.008$$

Write in expanded form.

34. 32.76 **35.** 283.549 **36.** 0.7856 ★**37.** 61.49503

PROBLEM SOLVING • APPLICATIONS

38. Julio's school is located 2.8 kilometers from his home. What is the distance to school and back?

39. Julio bicycled 3.7 kilometers from his home to the park. In the afternoon he bicycled home. What was the total distance that he bicycled?

40. Julio has a part-time job on Friday afternoon and Saturday. He earns $6.75 on Friday and $11.55 on Saturday. How much money does he earn?

★**41.** Julio buys a book about computer programming for $4.25 and a marking pen for $1.89. He gives the clerk a ten-dollar bill. How much change does he receive?

Reading a Map

Sometimes you must use a map to solve a problem. It is important to read the map carefully and check to be sure you are using the correct data.

This section of a road map shows part of the state of Kansas.

KANSAS (detail)

Interstate Highway
U.S. Highway
State Highway

The numbers inside these symbols are the route numbers.

Many towns and the intersections of highways have blue stars near them. A small number along the highway shows the number of kilometers between stars.

Problem 1

What is the distance between Hays and Phillipsburg?

Solution

Find the blue star at Hays. Go north on route 183 until you find the dot at Phillipsburg. The distance between Hays and Phillipsburg is 98.2 kilometers.

Problem 2

How far is it from Oberlin to Phillipsburg driving east on route 36?

Solution

From Oberlin to Norton	→ 46.7 km
From Norton to Phillipsburg	64.4 km
Total distance	111.1 km

It is 111.1 kilometers from Oberlin to Phillipsburg.

Use the map to answer the questions.

1. You drive east from Oakley to Hays along route 70. How far do you drive?

2. You start at Phillipsburg and drive north on route 183. How far is it to the intersection of route 183 and route 383?

3. Which state highway would you take to get from Leoti to Scott City?

4. Mr. Jones starts at Hays and drives south on route 183. He turns east on route 156 to Larned. How far does Mr. Jones drive?

5. Which highways would you take to drive from Plainville to Hill City?

6. You start at Norton and drive east on route 36 to Phillipsburg. From there you drive south on route 183 to Hays. How far do you drive?

Be sure you read the distances correctly.

7. You drive east from Garden City to Great Bend along route 156. How far do you drive?

8. Mr. Reilly wants to drive from Hays to Garden City. His wife advises him to take route 183 south to route 156 and go west to Garden City. His son advises him to take route 70 west to route 83 and go south to Garden City. Which person's advice should Mr. Reilly follow if he wants to drive the shorter distance?

Always study a map to see what information it contains.

9. Which highways would you take to drive from Wakeeny to Garden City? Tell the direction you would be traveling on each.

10. You start at Norton and drive southwest on route 383 to route 83. Take route 83 to Garden City. How far do you drive?

★ 11. You want to drive from Larned to Oakley. You have to stop in Hays on the way. Which highways would you take? Tell the direction you would be traveling on each.

★ 12. Mr. Jarvis wants to drive from Oberlin to Osborne. He has to stop in Stockton on the way. Which highways should Mr. Jarvis take? Tell the direction he would be traveling on each.

Estimating and Subtracting

The Meara family hiked along the Appalachian Trail with backpacks. The first day they hiked 14.08 kilometers. The second day they hiked 10.63 kilometers. How much farther did they hike the first day?

$14.08 - 10.63 = n$

You can estimate the answer first.

Think: Round to the nearest whole number. Subtract.
The answer is about 3.

$$\begin{array}{r} 14.08 \\ -10.63 \\ \hline \end{array} \rightarrow \begin{array}{r} 14 \\ -11 \\ \hline 3 \end{array}$$

Subtract to find the actual answer. Subtracting decimals is like subtracting whole numbers.

Step 1 Line up the decimal points. Subtract the hundredths.

$$\begin{array}{r} 14.08 \\ -10.63 \\ \hline 5 \end{array}$$

Step 2 Subtract the tenths.

$$\begin{array}{r} \scriptstyle 3\;10 \\ 14.08 \\ -10.63 \\ \hline 45 \end{array}$$

Step 3 Subtract the ones. Subtract the tens. Write the decimal point in the answer.

$$\begin{array}{r} \scriptstyle 3\;10 \\ 14.08 \\ -10.63 \\ \hline 3.45 \end{array}$$

The actual answer is close to the estimate.
The Meara family hiked 3.45 kilometers farther the first day.

When subtracting decimals, it is often helpful to write zeros at the end of a decimal.

To find the difference for the example $76.2 - 52.13$, express 76.2 as 76.20. Then subtract.

$$\begin{array}{r} 76.2 \\ -52.13 \\ \hline \end{array} \rightarrow \begin{array}{r} \scriptstyle 1\;10 \\ 76.20 \\ -52.13 \\ \hline 24.07 \end{array}$$

Practice • Estimate each difference. Then find the actual answer.

1. $\begin{array}{r} 6.8 \\ -1.7 \\ \hline \end{array}$ **2.** $\begin{array}{r} 7.34 \\ -4.27 \\ \hline \end{array}$ **3.** $\begin{array}{r} 15.06 \\ -9.83 \\ \hline \end{array}$ **4.** $\begin{array}{r} 3.22 \\ -1.47 \\ \hline \end{array}$ **5.** $\begin{array}{r} 9. \\ -4.873 \\ \hline \end{array}$

Mixed Practice • Estimate each difference. Then find the actual difference.

6. $8.4 - 2.1$
7. $9.72 - 1.58$
8. $12.94 - 3.16$
9. $5.19 - 2.37$
10. $6.142 - 1.935$

Subtract.

11. $0.9 - 0.6$
12. $7.8 - 1.9$
13. $14.7 - 11.5$
14. $20.2 - 19.8$
15. $7.0 - 1.4$
16. $0.64 - 0.07$
17. $88.44 - 2.15$
18. $\$6.90 - 3.92$
19. $2.76 - 0.93$
20. $14.20 - 2.34$
21. $16.453 - 12.213$
22. $19.802 - 18.907$
23. $7.2 - 3.84$
24. $6 - 4.75$

★25. $29.004 - 4.12368$

Solve the equations.

26. $34.5 - 16.7 = n$
27. $46.27 - 3.14 = n$
28. $35.45 - 17.663 = n$
29. $28 - 11.5 = n$
30. $387.1 - 251.447 = n$
31. $364.87 - 53.4 = n$
32. $115.2 - 78.64 = n$
33. $451.3 - 271.4652 = n$
34. $(3.78 + 5.96) - 2.13 = n$
35. $(4.25 - 1.19) + 3.46 = n$

★36. $n + (2.5 + 3.9) = 10$

★37. $n + (1.76 + 8.95) = 12$

Write <, =, or >.

38. $2.46 + 3.85$ ● 5.31
39. $3.68 + 5.22$ ● 8.90
40. $8.34 - 6.75$ ● 1.71

PROBLEM SOLVING • APPLICATIONS

41. Bob Meara has $40.00. He spends $36.75 for a new sleeping bag. How much money does he have left?

★42. Nina Meara cuts a 4-meter piece of rope into three pieces. One is 1.76 meters long. Another is 1.15 meters long. How long is the third?

Skills Maintenance

1. 6×214
2. $8 \times 3{,}405$
3. $9 \times 6{,}037$
4. $7 \times 9{,}876$
5. 20×53
6. 34×74
7. 126×252
8. 309×678

PROBLEM SOLVING • STRATEGIES

Using Estimates

In daily life it is useful to estimate. An exact answer is often not needed.

Suppose your school has an International Food Day. Here is the menu.

Prices Including Tax

Meat

Chinese Roast Pork Strips	$1.45
Spaghetti and Meat Balls	1.08
Arroz Con Pollo (Chicken with Rice)	1.15
Tacos	.87
Lamb and Yam Stew	.95

Fish

Sashimi	1.35
Fish Imojo	1.04

Salads

Mixed Greens	.75
Vegetable	.85
Fruit	.90

Soups

Gazpacho	$.65
Sumashi Wan	.75
Minestrone	.42
Chicken Noodle Soup	.52
Egg Drop Soup	.52
African Bean Soup	.63

Drinks

Milk	.41
Juice (Apple, Orange, Grapefruit)	.45

You have $2.80. You want to buy sashimi, vegetable salad, minestrone, and apple juice. Do you have enough money?

You can estimate to find out. Round the numbers to the nearest ten cents.

Think:

sashimi	$1.40
vegetable salad	.90
minestrone	.40
apple juice	.50
	$3.20

$3.20 is more than $2.80. You do not have enough money for all four items.

Do you have enough money to buy the lunch? Write *yes* or *no*. Estimate to answer the question.

1. You have $2.25. You want tacos, egg drop soup, a mixed green salad, and milk.

2. You have $2.50. You want spaghetti and meat balls, chicken noodle soup, and apple juice.

If the digit at the right is 5 or greater, round *up*.

3. You have $1.50. You want fish imojo and milk.

4. You have $2.40. You want lamb and yam stew, gazpacho, and orange juice.

5. You have $2.30. You want Chinese roast pork strips, African bean soup, and grapefruit juice.

6. You have $2.60. You want arroz con pollo, minestrone, fruit salad, and milk.

Solve these problems. Give an exact answer for problems 7–11.

7. Jamie buys sashimi and orange juice. How much does she spend?

8. Bob buys tacos, sumashi wan, and milk. How much does he spend?

Estimating will help you to decide if your answer is sensible.

★ 9. Toni buys arroz con pollo, mixed green salad, and milk. Bena buys lamb and yam stew, vegetable salad, and egg drop soup. Who spends more? How much more?

★ 10. Mel buys spaghetti and meat balls, minestrone, and orange juice. He pays with a five-dollar bill. How much change does he receive?

★ 11. Vivette buys the meals for herself and her two friends. She buys 3 tacos, 2 apple juices, and 1 milk. How much change does she receive from a five-dollar bill?

★ 12. Stan has $1.50. He wants to buy a meat dish and one of the drinks. Which pairs of items can he buy? List as many different pairs as you can.

CHAPTER 4

REVIEW

Write the decimals. (pp. 86–87)

1. three-tenths
2. fifty-six hundredths
3. six-hundredths

In which place is the blue digit? (pp. 88–89)

4. 6.872
5. 0.0065
6. 1.523
7. 516.0097

Write the decimals. (pp. 88–89)

8. seventy-two and one hundred twelve thousandths
9. five and forty-one ten-thousandths
10. two hundred fifteen and fifty-nine hundred-thousandths

Write <, =, or >. (pp. 90–91)

11. 9.04 ● 9.040
12. 0.816 ● 0.0816
13. 52.73 ● 52.8
14. 71.564 ● 715.64
15. 101.011 ● 101.0110
16. 0.165 ● 0.156

Write in order from least to greatest. (pp. 90–91)

17. 3.022; 3.2; 3.002
18. 4.895; 4.985; 4.5
19. Round to the nearest tenth: 24.536. (pp. 92–93)
20. Round to the nearest thousandth: 75.4186. (pp. 92–93)

Add or subtract. (pp. 94–95, 98–99)

21. $\begin{array}{r} 46.3 \\ +17.5 \\ \hline \end{array}$
22. $\begin{array}{r} 40.506 \\ +51.8 \\ \hline \end{array}$
23. $\begin{array}{r} 89.569 \\ 0.8532 \\ +70.26 \\ \hline \end{array}$
24. $\begin{array}{r} 9.640 \\ -3.064 \\ \hline \end{array}$
25. $\begin{array}{r} 64 \\ -\ 3.953 \\ \hline \end{array}$

Solve the equations. (pp. 94–95, 98–99)

26. $0.81 - 0.4 = n$
27. $75.031 + 9.08 = n$
28. At a swimming meet, Karen scores 8.70, 9.35, and 9.65 points for her three dives. What is her total score for the three dives? (pp. 94–95)
29. Jennifer's best score at the swimming meet is 506.19. Karen's best score is 495.68. What is the difference between their scores? (pp. 98–99)

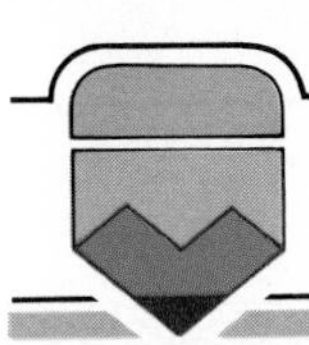

PROJECT

Writing Checks

Many people put their money into checking accounts. In order to use the money, they write checks. A check tells the bank how much money to give the company or person to whom the check is written.

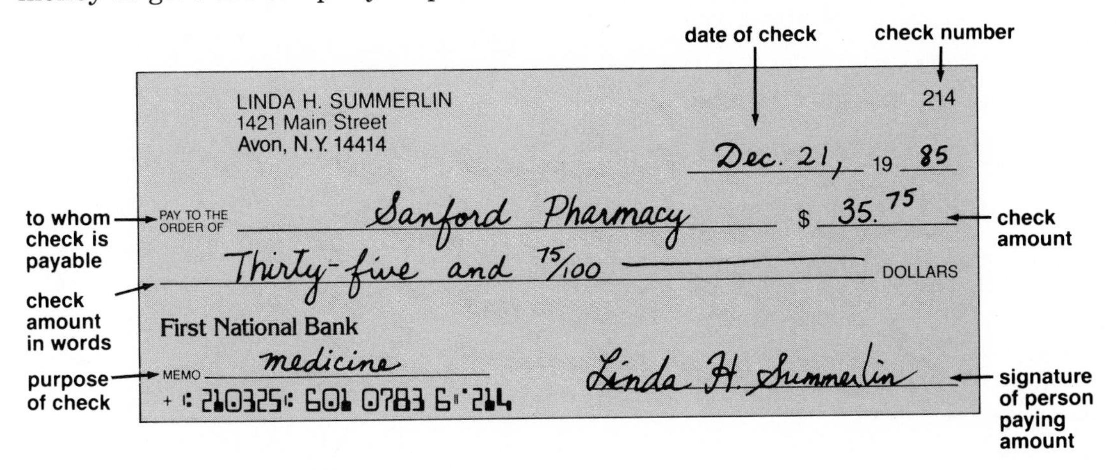

1. What is the number of the check?
2. What is the date on the check?
3. To whom is the check written?
4. What is the amount of the check?
5. Who signed the check?
6. On January 15, 1986, Maria Dapontes buys a television set. She writes check number 344 to Steinway Appliances for $337.25. Draw a picture of the completed check.
7. On May 5, 1986, Kathy Romano buys supplies for her pets. She writes check number 218 to Pet World in the amount of $16.45. Draw a picture of the completed check.

Imagine that you have a checking account. Draw pictures of completed checks to pay for the following.

8. groceries for everyone in your family for one week
9. the telephone bill for one month
10. a new winter coat for someone in your family
11. Show the checks to one of your parents or grandparents. Ask whether the amounts are realistic.

CHAPTER 4

TEST

Write the decimals.

1. four-tenths
2. two-hundredths
3. ninety-one hundredths

In which place is the blue digit?

4. 3.167
5. 35.829
6. 0.904
7. 1.4263

Write the decimals.

8. thirty-six and fifty-eight thousandths
9. four hundred six and seventeen hundred-thousandths
10. three and seventy-six ten-thousandths

Write <, =, or >.

11. 3.26 ● 3.206
12. 0.070 ● 0.07
13. 0.845 ● 0.85
14. 56.49 ● 5.649
15. 6.01 ● 6.010
16. 315.06 ● 315.60

Write in order from least to greatest.

17. 5.845; 5.96; 5.854
18. 3.011; 3.01; 3.1
19. Round to the nearest hundredth: 29.373.
20. Round to the nearest thousandth: 31.9258

Add or subtract.

21. $\begin{array}{r} 24.017 \\ +\ 9.67 \\ \hline \end{array}$

22. $\begin{array}{r} 126.104 \\ 8.89 \\ +\ 31.7862 \\ \hline \end{array}$

23. $\begin{array}{r} 8.71 \\ -3.5962 \\ \hline \end{array}$

24. $\begin{array}{r} 1.9554 \\ -0.386 \\ \hline \end{array}$

25. $\begin{array}{r} 49 \\ -\ 6.913 \\ \hline \end{array}$

Solve the equations.

26. $732.49 - 95.183 = n$
27. $44.69 + 0.296 = n$
28. In Saddle Junction the amounts of rainfall were 1.62 centimeters, 2.09 centimeters, and 1.23 centimeters. What was the total rainfall?
29. Easton received 5.63 centimeters of rain. Carterville received 2.86 centimeters of rain. How much more rain did Easton receive than Carterville?

ENRICHMENT

Sequences

A **sequence** is a set of numbers in a definite order. Each number (after the first) can be obtained from the preceding number by using a fixed rule. In the sequence 1, 3, 5, 7, . . . , each number (after the first) can be obtained by adding 2 to the preceding number.

The rule for this sequence can be given as "Start with 1 and then keep adding 2."

Sometimes a sequence has a complicated rule. Study these sequences.

	Rule
2, 3, 5, 8, 12, 17, . . .	Start with 2, add 1, then add 2, then add 3, and so on.
1, 2, 4, 8, 16, 32, . . .	Start with 1 and then keep multiplying by 2.
0.5, 1.3, 1.0, 1.8, 1.5, . . .	Start with 0.5, then add 0.8, then subtract 0.3, then add 0.8, and so on.

Sometimes you are given a sequence and you must find the rule for it. In such cases, look for a pattern. Check to see how the numbers are increasing or decreasing. Try to determine which operations are being used.

Look for a pattern and give the next three numbers in the sequence. Write a rule for the sequence.

1. 0, 2, 4, 6, _____, _____, _____, . . .
2. 0.4, 0.8, 1.2, 1.6, _____, _____, _____, . . .
3. 12.0, 10.5, 9.0, 7.5, _____, _____, _____, . . .
4. 1, 3, 9, 27, _____, _____, _____, . . .
5. 10^1, 10^2, 10^3, 10^4, _____, _____, _____, . . .
6. 0.9, 1.4, 1.3, 1.8, 1.7, 2.2, _____, _____, _____, . . .
7. 0.75, 1.5, 1.3, 2.05, 1.85, 2.6, _____, _____, _____, . . .
8. 0.1, 0.21, 0.321, 0.4321, _____, _____, _____, . . .

CALCULATOR

Lining Up Decimals

You do not have to line up decimals when using a calculator. Add 5.73 and 0.024. Push (5) (.) (7) (3) (+) (.) (0) (2) (4) (=) .

The answer is 5.754. The calculator lined up decimals for you. Note that you do not need to push the 0 before the decimal.

Calculate. It is always a good idea to estimate the sum or the difference first.

1. $4.86 + 0.054 + 2{,}308 =$ ___?___
2. $8.7 - 2.36 =$ ___?___
3. $2.306 + 0.23 + 79.01 =$ ___?___
4. $3{,}807 - 24 =$ ___?___
5. $0.04 + 0.06 + 0.004 =$ ___?___
6. $48.72 - 35 =$ ___?___

You must follow the proper order of operations with a calculator. If you perform operations in the wrong order, the calculator will give the wrong answer. Always estimate.

First do operations within parentheses. Then do multiplications and divisions from left to right. Then do additions and subtractions from left to right.

Calculate. The first example has been done for you. Check that you get the same answer.

7. $(4.8 - 3.6) \div 2 + 1.7 - 0.24 = 2.06$
8. $500.3 \times (4 + 4 + 4 + 4 + 4) - 7{,}355 + 604 - 22.3 =$ ___?___
9. $(277 - 2 - 2 - 2 - 2) \times 15 - 17.8 + 0.6 =$ ___?___
10. $(18.37 + 0.63) \times 22 - (98.35 - 42.08) =$ ___?___
11. $2.75 + ($8.33 - $.86) - ($.19 + $2.45) = ___?___
12. $(4{,}840 \div 55) - (6{,}688 \div 76) =$ ___?___
13. $6 + 4 - 4 + 8 - 8 + 55 - 55 + 248 - 248 =$ ___?___
14. $8.8 \div 4.4 \times 2 \div 4 \times 75{,}466 - 3 =$ ___?___
15. $16 \times 16 \div 16 + 16 - 16 - 16 =$ ___?___

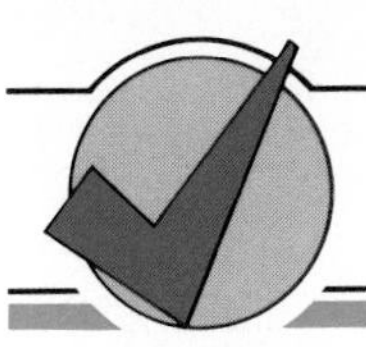

SKILLS MAINTENANCE

Chapters 1 Through 4

Choose the correct answers.

1. In which place is the blue digit?

284,375

A. tens
B. thousands
C. hundreds
D. not here

2. Write $<$, $=$, or $>$.

4.07 ● 4.070

A. $>$
B. $<$
C. $=$
D. not here

3. Write in order from least to greatest.

6.784; 6.874; 6.8

A. 6.784; 6.8; 6.874
B. 6.8; 6.874; 61,784
C. 6.874; 6.784; 6.8
D. not here

4. Round 31.054 to the nearest tenth.

A. 31.0
B. 31.1
C. 31.154
D. not here

5. Round 75.386 to the nearest hundredth.

A. 75.396
B. 75.38
C. 75.39
D. not here

6. Add.

$$\begin{array}{r} 69.408 \\ 0.8764 \\ +32.18 \\ \hline \end{array}$$

A. 102.4644
B. 92.3644
C. 101.4644
D. not here

7. Subtract.

$$\begin{array}{r} 8.35 \\ -6.408 \\ \hline \end{array}$$

A. 1.958
B. 1.942
C. 1.952
D. not here

8. Multiply.

$$\begin{array}{r} 485 \\ \times 274 \\ \hline \end{array}$$

A. 132,990
B. 132,890
C. 122,890
D. not here

9. Divide.

$32\overline{)485,312}$

A. 1,516
B. 15,236
C. 15,166
D. not here

10. Solve.

$0.74 - 0.5 = n$

A. $n = 0.24$
B. $n = 0.69$
C. $n = 1.24$
D. not here

11. Solve.

$21{,}042 + 8{,}096 = n$

A. $n = 27{,}138$
B. $n = 29{,}238$
C. $n = 29{,}138$
D. not here

12. Solve.

$3.407 + 12.006 = n$

A. $n = 15.413$
B. $n = 46.070$
C. $n = 15.403$
D. not here

Choose the correct answers.

13. battery $38.95
tire $46.75
shocks $25.70

Steven bought a new battery for his car. He also bought one new tire. How much did he spend all together?

A. $111.40 **B.** $85.70
C. $72.45 **D.** not here

14. The Wonder Tire Company made 12,804 tires. It sold 9,958 of the tires. How many tires did it have left?

A. 2,846 **B.** 2,746
C. 2,864 **D.** not here

15. In the first year, a sports car company built 3,563 cars. The next year it built 4,859 cars. How many cars did the company build in the two years?

A. 8,412 **B.** 8,322
C. 8,422 **D.** not here

16. Melba bought 3 cans of oil for her car. Each can of oil cost $1.47. She also bought a new battery for $39.50. How much did she spend on the oil?

A. $4.41 **B.** $.42
C. $1.50 **D.** not here

17. A motorcycle importer is expanding his parts department. There will be 15 sections. Each section will have 9 racks with 12 shelves in each rack. How many shelves will there be all together?

A. 315 **B.** 1,620
C. 1,520 **D.** not here

18. This week 58,632 visitors came to the Auto Show. This was 8 times the number of visitors that came last week. How many visitors came to the Auto Show last week?

A. 58,624 **B.** 58,640
C. 7,329 **D.** not here

19. Mr. Tannis buys a motor bike. The price of the bike is $2,086. A sales tax is added to the price. What is the total amount that Mr. Tannis pays?

A. $2,172 **B.** $2,100
C. $2,086 **D.** not here

20. Jeffrey bought a book for $5.95 and a pen for $4.50. Larry bought a book for $3.98, a birthday card for $.75, and a pad for $2.98. Who spent more? How much more?

A. Jeffrey; $2.74 **B.** Larry; $7.71
C. Jeffrey; $2.76 **D.** not here

Decimals: Multiplication and Division

CHAPTER 5

Estimating Products • Multiplying Decimals • Zeros in the Product • Patterns in Multiplication • Problem Solving: Reasonable Answers • Dividing by a Whole Number • Dividing by a Decimal • Writing Zeros in the Dividend • Rounding Quotients • Scientific Notation • Problem Solving: Multistep Problems • Keeping a Checkbook Record • Using Exponents

Estimating Products

The planets in our solar system travel in orbits around the sun. Earth travels in its orbit at a speed of 29.6 kilometers per second. How many kilometers does it travel in 4 seconds?

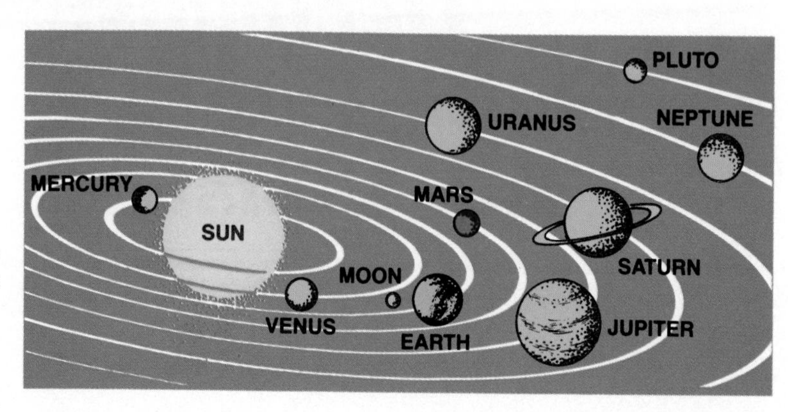

$4 \times 29.6 = n$

The multiplication has been done for you. You must place the decimal point in the answer.

$$\begin{array}{r} 29.6 \\ \times \quad 4 \\ \hline 1184 \end{array}$$

Think: Round 29.6 to 30.
$4 \times 30 = 120$
The answer is about 120.
The answer must be 118.4.

Earth travels 118.4 kilometers in 4 seconds.

Another multiplication example is shown below. Where do you think the decimal point should be placed in the answer?

$$\begin{array}{r} 14.72 \\ \times \quad 5.8 \\ \hline 85376 \end{array}$$

Think: Round 14.72 to 15.
Round 5.8 to 6.
$6 \times 15 = 90$

Since 85 is close to 90, the correct answer is 85.376.

Practice • Estimate to place the decimal point in the answer.

1. $\begin{array}{r} 6.9 \\ \times \ 3 \\ \hline 207 \end{array}$
2. $\begin{array}{r} 8.3 \\ \times \ 2 \\ \hline 166 \end{array}$
3. $\begin{array}{r} 4.8 \\ \times 1.3 \\ \hline 624 \end{array}$
4. $\begin{array}{r} 8.7 \\ \times 6.6 \\ \hline 5742 \end{array}$
5. $\begin{array}{r} 9.2 \\ \times 2.4 \\ \hline 2208 \end{array}$
6. $\begin{array}{r} 15.85 \\ \times \ 4.3 \\ \hline 68155 \end{array}$
7. $\begin{array}{r} 43 \\ \times 2.7 \\ \hline 1161 \end{array}$
8. $\begin{array}{r} 9.04 \\ \times \ 7.9 \\ \hline 71416 \end{array}$
9. $\begin{array}{r} 12.53 \\ \times \quad 5 \\ \hline 6265 \end{array}$
10. $\begin{array}{r} 51.2 \\ \times 3.04 \\ \hline 155648 \end{array}$

Mixed Practice • Estimate to place the decimal point in the answer.

11. $\begin{array}{r} 1.9 \\ \times\ 5 \\ \hline 95 \end{array}$	**12.** $\begin{array}{r} 7.3 \\ \times\ 8 \\ \hline 584 \end{array}$	**13.** $\begin{array}{r} 6.2 \\ \times\ 9 \\ \hline 558 \end{array}$	**14.** $\begin{array}{r} 10.62 \\ \times\ 7 \\ \hline 7434 \end{array}$	**15.** $\begin{array}{r} 1.18 \\ \times\ 6 \\ \hline 708 \end{array}$
16. $\begin{array}{r} 42 \\ \times 1.3 \\ \hline 546 \end{array}$	**17.** $\begin{array}{r} 16 \\ \times 4.8 \\ \hline 768 \end{array}$	**18.** $\begin{array}{r} 29 \\ \times 3.1 \\ \hline 899 \end{array}$	**19.** $\begin{array}{r} 86 \\ \times 2.4 \\ \hline 2064 \end{array}$	**20.** $\begin{array}{r} 78 \\ \times 4.3 \\ \hline 3354 \end{array}$
21. $\begin{array}{r} 38.4 \\ \times\ 2.1 \\ \hline 8064 \end{array}$	**22.** $\begin{array}{r} 3.7 \\ \times\ 16 \\ \hline 592 \end{array}$	**23.** $\begin{array}{r} 7.6 \\ \times 3.4 \\ \hline 2584 \end{array}$	**24.** $\begin{array}{r} 28.2 \\ \times\ 9.8 \\ \hline 27636 \end{array}$	**25.** $\begin{array}{r} 16.2 \\ \times\ 1.8 \\ \hline 2916 \end{array}$
26. $\begin{array}{r} 4.3 \\ \times\ 8 \\ \hline 344 \end{array}$	**27.** $\begin{array}{r} 2.7 \\ \times\ 16 \\ \hline 432 \end{array}$	**28.** $\begin{array}{r} 6.1 \\ \times\ 24 \\ \hline 1464 \end{array}$	**29.** $\begin{array}{r} 5.9 \\ \times\ 30 \\ \hline 1770 \end{array}$	**30.** $\begin{array}{r} 32.4 \\ \times\ 1.8 \\ \hline 5832 \end{array}$
31. $\begin{array}{r} 4.86 \\ \times\ 4.1 \\ \hline 19926 \end{array}$	**32.** $\begin{array}{r} 33.29 \\ \times\ 5.8 \\ \hline 193082 \end{array}$	**33.** $\begin{array}{r} 7.26 \\ \times\ 6.2 \\ \hline 45012 \end{array}$	**34.** $\begin{array}{r} 5.18 \\ \times 11.4 \\ \hline 59052 \end{array}$	**35.** $\begin{array}{r} 18.21 \\ \times\ 12.3 \\ \hline 223983 \end{array}$
36. $\begin{array}{r} 5.817 \\ \times\ 6 \\ \hline 34902 \end{array}$	**37.** $\begin{array}{r} 3.721 \\ \times\ 8 \\ \hline 29768 \end{array}$	**38.** $\begin{array}{r} 5.922 \\ \times\ 4 \\ \hline 23688 \end{array}$	**39.** $\begin{array}{r} 6.212 \\ \times\ 3.1 \\ \hline 192572 \end{array}$	**40.** $\begin{array}{r} 24.307 \\ \times\ 5.6 \\ \hline 1361192 \end{array}$

Estimate to place the decimal point in the underlined factor.

★ **41.** $7.5 \times \underline{23} = 17.25$ ★ **42.** $4.25 \times \underline{33} = 14.025$ ★ **43.** $10.2 \times \underline{24} = 24.48$

★ **44.** $15.6 \times \underline{204} = 31.824$ ★ **45.** $\underline{88} \times 6.3 = 55.44$ ★ **46.** $122 \times \underline{34} = 41.48$

Solve the equations.

47. $3.65 + 2.72 = n$ **48.** $8 - 1.16 = x$ **49.** $0.83 - 0.74 = y$

★ **50.** $y + 5.7 = 8.2$ ★ **51.** $0.74 + n = 1.03$ ★ **52.** $x - 3.68 = 1.32$

PROBLEM SOLVING • APPLICATIONS

53. The planet Saturn travels at an orbital speed of 9.6 kilometers per second. How many kilometers does it travel in 4 seconds?

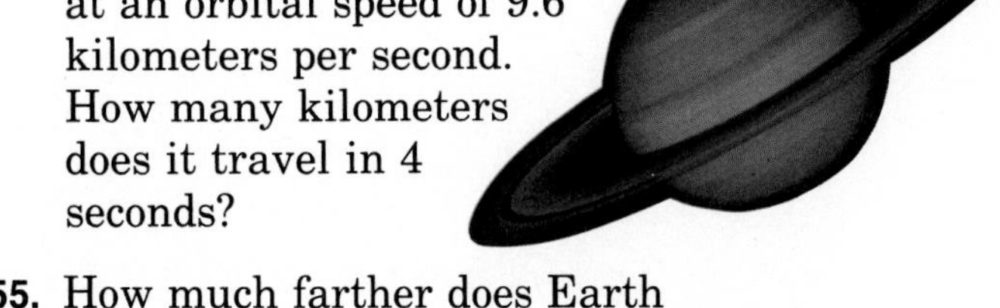

54. The planet Venus travels at an orbital speed of 34.8 kilometers per second. How many kilometers does it travel in 2.5 seconds?

★ **55.** How much farther does Earth travel in 2 minutes than Saturn?

Multiplying Decimals

The planet Mercury has a greater orbital speed than any other planet. It travels 47.6 kilometers per second. How many kilometers does it travel in 5.3 seconds?

$5.3 \times 47.6 = n$

Step 1 Multiply as if you were multiplying whole numbers.

$$\begin{array}{r} 47.6 \\ \times\ 5.3 \\ \hline 142\ 8 \\ 2380 \\ \hline 2522\ 8 \end{array}$$

Step 2 Place the decimal point.
Think: $5 \times 48 = 240$.
The answer is about 240.
The answer must be 252.28.

$$\begin{array}{r} 47.6 \\ \times\ 5.3 \\ \hline 14\ 28 \\ 238\ 0 \\ \hline 252.28 \end{array}$$

You know that each place to the right of the decimal point is a decimal place. Compare the number of decimal places in the product with the total number of decimal places in the factors.

$$\begin{array}{rl} 76.8 & \leftarrow \boxed{1} \\ \times\ \ 3 & \leftarrow \boxed{0} \\ \hline 230.4 & \leftarrow \boxed{1} \end{array} \qquad \begin{array}{rl} 4.93 & \leftarrow \boxed{2} \\ \times\ 2.7 & \leftarrow \boxed{1} \\ \hline 34\ 51 & \\ 98\ 6 & \\ \hline 13.311 & \leftarrow \boxed{3} \end{array} \qquad \begin{array}{rl} 1.875 & \leftarrow \boxed{3} \\ \times\ 0.65 & \leftarrow \boxed{2} \\ \hline 9\ 375 & \\ 112\ 50 & \\ \hline 1.21875 & \leftarrow \boxed{5} \end{array}$$

The number of decimal places in the product equals the sum of the numbers of decimal places in the factors.

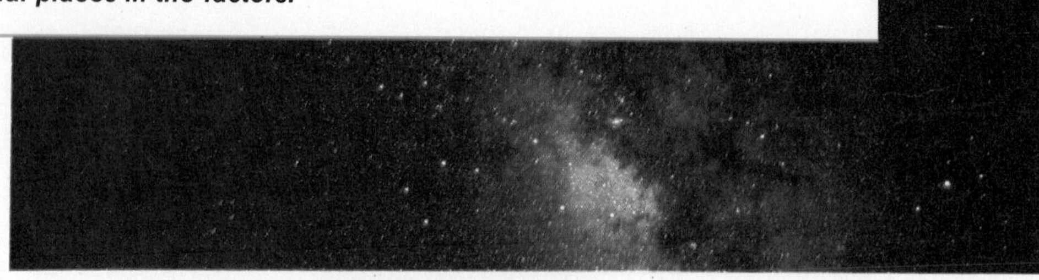

Practice • Multiply.

1. $\begin{array}{r} 3.7 \\ \times\ 4 \\ \hline \end{array}$ **2.** $\begin{array}{r} 1.34 \\ \times\ \ 6 \\ \hline \end{array}$ **3.** $\begin{array}{r} 9.8 \\ \times 1.4 \\ \hline \end{array}$ **4.** $\begin{array}{r} 2.97 \\ \times\ 0.6 \\ \hline \end{array}$ **5.** $\begin{array}{r} 7.5 \\ \times 0.85 \\ \hline \end{array}$

6. $\begin{array}{r} 0.68 \\ \times 0.43 \\ \hline \end{array}$ **7.** $\begin{array}{r} 59 \\ \times 1.8 \\ \hline \end{array}$ **8.** $\begin{array}{r} 1.92 \\ \times 0.16 \\ \hline \end{array}$ **9.** $\begin{array}{r} 0.813 \\ \times\ 2.23 \\ \hline \end{array}$ **10.** $\begin{array}{r} 0.918 \\ \times\ 4.26 \\ \hline \end{array}$

Mixed Practice • Multiply.

11. 4.7×8
12. 8.31×9
13. 3.761×1.7
14. 5.9×16
15. 2.73×42
16. 52×3.1
17. 96×0.8
18. 45×3.15
19. 147×5.2
20. 87×0.14
21. 4.6×8.4
22. 3.9×0.7
23. 5.7×1.9
24. 17.6×4.7
25. 42.3×7.5
26. 5.96×0.8
27. 0.47×1.9
28. $\$3.96 \times 64$
29. 1.472×5.2
30. 8.41×9.7
31. 1.47×0.25
32. 4.87×0.46
33. 3.91×1.53
34. 7.64×1.08
35. 9.67×4.92
36. 4.8×0.572
37. 4.62×0.138
38. 0.946×0.27
39. 0.477×1.46
40. 1.921×34.2

Solve the equations.

41. $3.4 \times 8.12 = n$
42. $0.31 \times 6.24 = n$
43. $9.4 \times 3.19 = n$
44. $0.14 \times 91 = n$
45. $0.75 \times 12.48 = n$
46. $36.4 \times 0.018 = n$
47. $32.15 \times 2.03 = n$
48. $176.9 \times 1.303 = n$
49. $238.97 \times 0.83 = n$

★50. $1.2 \times 1.3 \times 1.4 = x$

★51. $2.5 \times 3.5 \times 4.5 = y$

★52. $0.75 \times 0.85 \times 0.95 = n$

★53. $1.2 \times 1.31 \times 1.42 = x$

PROBLEM SOLVING • APPLICATIONS

54. The diameter of Mercury is about 4,990 kilometers. Earth's diameter is 2.55 times as great. What is Earth's diameter in kilometers?

55. The diameter of Venus is 12,390 kilometers. Neptune's diameter is 3.60 times as great. What is Neptune's diameter in kilometers?

★56. Which has a greater diameter—Venus or Earth? About how many kilometers greater is it?

Zeros in the Product

Sometimes you need to insert one or more zeros in the product in order to locate the decimal point.

Solve: $0.3 \times 0.16 = n$.

Step 1 Multiply as if you were multiplying whole numbers.

$$\begin{array}{r} 0.16 \\ \times\ 0.3 \\ \hline 48 \end{array}$$

Step 2 The product must have three decimal places. Insert a zero to locate the decimal point.

$$\begin{array}{rl} 0.16 & \leftarrow \boxed{2} \\ \times\ 0.3 & \leftarrow \boxed{1} \\ \hline 0.048 & \leftarrow \boxed{3} \end{array}$$

More Examples

$$\begin{array}{rl} 0.0003 & \leftarrow \boxed{4} \\ \times\ \ \ 5 & \leftarrow \boxed{0} \\ \hline 0.0015 & \leftarrow \boxed{4} \end{array}$$

$$\begin{array}{rl} 0.37 & \leftarrow \boxed{2} \\ \times 0.014 & \leftarrow \boxed{3} \\ \hline 148 & \\ 37\ & \\ \hline 0.00518 & \leftarrow \boxed{5} \end{array}$$

$$\begin{array}{rl} 0.012 & \leftarrow \boxed{3} \\ \times 0.011 & \leftarrow \boxed{3} \\ \hline 12 & \\ 12\ & \\ \hline 0.000132 & \leftarrow \boxed{6} \end{array}$$

Practice • Multiply.

1. 0.3×0.2
2. 0.7×0.1
3. 0.04×0.6
4. 0.002×2
5. 0.008×0.06
6. 0.17×0.03
7. 2.31×0.04
8. 1.38×0.06
9. 0.043×0.21
10. 0.024×0.016

Mixed Practice • Multiply.

11. 0.03×0.7
12. 0.003×6
13. 1.08×0.09
14. 0.62×0.08
15. 0.79×0.05
16. 0.032×0.31
17. 0.27×0.19
18. 0.051×0.24
19. 0.516×0.17
20. 0.427×0.22
21. 0.148×0.36
22. 0.064×0.18
23. 0.253×0.25
24. 0.834×0.73
25. 0.603×0.13

26. $\begin{array}{r} 1.06 \\ \times 0.052 \\ \hline \end{array}$

27. $\begin{array}{r} 1.432 \\ \times\ 0.28 \\ \hline \end{array}$

28. $\begin{array}{r} 0.018 \\ \times 0.034 \\ \hline \end{array}$

29. $\begin{array}{r} 0.742 \\ \times 0.037 \\ \hline \end{array}$

30. $\begin{array}{r} 0.0382 \\ \times\ 0.021 \\ \hline \end{array}$

31. $\begin{array}{r} 0.003 \\ \times\ \ 15 \\ \hline \end{array}$

32. $\begin{array}{r} 0.0012 \\ \times\ \ 27 \\ \hline \end{array}$

33. $\begin{array}{r} 1.006 \\ \times 0.004 \\ \hline \end{array}$

34. $\begin{array}{r} 0.0075 \\ \times\ \ 1.8 \\ \hline \end{array}$

35. $\begin{array}{r} 2.006 \\ \times 0.012 \\ \hline \end{array}$

Solve the equations.

36. $0.06 \times 1.2 = n$

37. $0.0004 \times 3.2 = n$

38. $0.008 \times 1.75 = n$

39. $0.36 \times 0.072 = n$

40. $0.17 \times 0.83 = n$

41. $0.048 \times 1.26 = n$

★ 42. $0.02 \times 0.03 \times 0.7 = n$

★ 43. $0.4 \times 0.07 \times 0.006 = n$

★ 44. $x - (3.7 \times 1.6) = 0.08$

★ 45. $y + (0.75 \times 0.6) = 1.5$

PROBLEM SOLVING • APPLICATIONS

46. It takes 0.005 second for a honeybee's wings to beat one stroke. How long does it take for a honeybee's wings to beat 15 strokes?

47. It takes 0.09 second for a butterfly's wings to beat one stroke. How long does it take for a butterfly's wings to beat 5 strokes?

★ 48. How much less than a second does it take for a butterfly's wings to beat 5 strokes?

★ 49. How much more than a minute does it take for a butterfly's wings to beat 1,000 strokes?

Skills Maintenance

1. $238 \div 7$

2. $5,139 \div 9$

3. $6,900 \div 5$

4. $6,432 \div 8$

5. $3,538 \div 61$

6. $72,127 \div 79$

7. $13,600 \div 340$

8. $43,462 \div 701$

Patterns in Multiplication

Look for patterns. Watch the decimal points.

10 × 46.83 (one zero)	46.83	468.3	The decimal point moves one place to the right.
100 × 46.83 (two zeros)	46.83	4683	The decimal point moves two places to the right.
1,000 × 46.83 (three zeros)	46.83	46,830	The decimal point moves three places to the right.

Note that sometimes zeros must be inserted in the product to locate the decimal point.

> ***Multiplying by 10, 100, 1,000, . . . , moves the decimal point to the right. The number of zeros in the power of ten shows the number of places to move the decimal point.***

Next consider multiplying by 0.1, 0.01, and 0.001.

0.1 × 46.83 (one decimal place)	46.83	4.683	The decimal point moves one place to the left.
0.01 × 46.83 (two decimal places)	46.83	0.4683	The decimal point moves two places to the left.
0.001 × 46.83 (three decimal places)	46.83	0.04683	The decimal point moves three places to the left.

Note that sometimes zeros must be inserted to show the correct number of decimal places in the product.

> ***Multiplying by 0.1, 0.01, 0.001, . . . , moves the decimal point to the left. The number of decimal places in 0.1, 0.01, and 0.001, . . . shows the number of places to move the decimal point.***

Practice • Multiply.

1. 10 × 16.7 **2.** 100 × 16.7 **3.** 1,000 × 16.7

4. 0.1 × 16.7 **5.** 1,000 × 4.6 **6.** 0.001 × 0.072

Mixed Practice • Multiply.

7. 10×197
8. 0.1×324.6
9. 100×46.3
10. 0.01×6.8
11. $1{,}000 \times \$5.76$
12. 0.001×9.126
13. 10×0.0172
14. 0.1×2.4
15. 100×578
16. 10×7.23
17. $0.1 \times 3{,}787$
18. 100×0.964
19. 0.01×24.26
20. $1{,}000 \times 725$
21. 0.001×0.43
22. 10×11.5
23. 0.1×514
24. 100×8.93
25. 0.01×3.97
26. $1{,}000 \times 34.6$
27. 0.001×764.2

★28. $10{,}000 \times 6.8$
★29. 0.0001×12.9
★30. 0.00001×53.1
★31. $100{,}000 \times 7.26$
★32. 0.00001×9.4
★33. $10{,}000 \times 19.45$
★34. 0.001×1000
★35. $0.0001 \times 10{,}000$
★36. $0.00001 \times 100{,}000$

You know that exponents can be used to show multiplication by the same factor. Just as 10^2 means 10×10, the expression $(0.1)^2$ means 0.1×0.1.

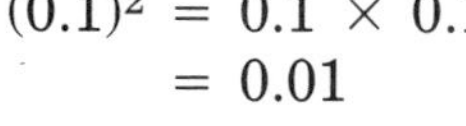

$(0.1)^2 = 0.1 \times 0.1$
$= 0.01$

$(0.1)^3 = 0.1 \times 0.1 \times 0.1$
$= 0.001$

Find the products.

37. $10^3 = n$
38. $(0.1)^4 = n$
39. $10^2 = n$
40. $10^5 = n$
41. $10^4 = n$

★42. $10^9 = n$
★43. $(0.1)^9 = n$
★44. $10^{15} = n$

PROBLEM SOLVING • APPLICATIONS

45. A magazine sells for \$1.75 a copy. What is the total cost of 10 of these magazines?

46. A newspaper sells for \$.35 a copy. What is the total cost of 100 of these newspapers?

Midchapter Review

1. 8.2×7
2. 4.9×3.4
3. 54×0.6
4. 7.26×3.8
5. 0.2×0.3
6. 0.15×0.5
7. 0.012×0.14
8. 1.002×0.072
9. $1{,}000 \times 234.2$
10. 0.01×2.94

PROBLEM SOLVING • STRATEGIES

Reasonable Answers

As you decide how to solve a problem, it is useful to think: About how large will the answer be? After you have found an "answer," look at it and ask yourself: "Is this answer reasonable? Does it make sense in the situation?"

Ms. Perez uses about 240 liters of gasoline in her car during a month. About how much gasoline does she use in a year?

Which is a reasonable answer?

About 20 liters — About 2,900 liters

Since Ms. Perez uses 240 liters in one month, 20 liters is not a reasonable answer for a year. (A year is 12 months.)

$12 \times 200 = 2{,}400$, and so the answer must be more than 2,400 liters. 2,900 liters is a reasonable answer.

Find the actual answer by multiplying.

$$12 \times 240 = n$$
$$2{,}880 = n$$

Ms. Perez uses about 2,880 liters of gasoline in a year.

Read the problem and choose the answer that seems reasonable to you. Then find the actual answer.

1. Mr. Kendall bought 18.9 liters of gasoline one week and 27.2 liters of gasoline the next week. How many more liters did he buy the second week than the first?

   About 8 liters
   About 46 liters

2. On a turnpike, Mrs. Golden can drive about 78 kilometers per hour. At this speed, how many kilometers can she drive in 3.2 hours?

   About 2,400 kilometers
   About 240 kilometers

3. Mr. Ramirez drove about 427 kilometers last week. What was the average number of kilometers that he drove per day?

   About 60 kilometers
   About 2,800 kilometers

4. Ms. Fuji spent $67.50 on car repairs in February and $42.26 on car repairs in March. How much less did she spend in March than in February?

   About $26
   About $110

Solve each problem. Make sure the answer is reasonable.

5. During a day trip, Mr. Kean bought box lunches for his wife, himself, and their three children. Each lunch cost $2.75. What was the total cost of the lunches?

6. In city driving, Ms. Turner can drive about 42 kilometers per hour. At this speed, how many kilometers can she drive in 2.1 hours?

Reread the problem. What does it ask you to find?

7. Bill drove 900 kilometers in 12 hours. What was his average speed per hour?

8. Tina's car averages about 36 kilometers per liter of gasoline. How many liters of gasoline are used on a 1,800-kilometer trip?

Estimate the answer first.

★ 9. Mr. Jessup spent $42.30 on car repairs in October, $35.13 in November, and $65.25 in December. How much money did he spend during the last two months of the year?

★ 10. What was the average amount per month that Mr. Jessup spent on car repairs during October, November, and December?

This table shows the amounts of money that Mrs. Torres spent on car repairs during the five years she owned her car.

Amounts Spent on Car Repairs	
Year 1	$ 185.75
Year 2	$ 450.58
Year 3	$ 960.64
Year 4	$1,200.77
Year 5	$1,700.62

★ 11. How much less than $1,000 did Mrs. Torres spend in years 1 and 2?

★ 12. How much more was the total amount Mrs. Torres spent in years 4 and 5 than the total amount she spent in years 1, 2, and 3?

Dividing by a Whole Number

Four students collected a total of 119.76 kilograms of glass bottles for recycling. What was the average amount collected per student?

$119.76 \div 4 = n$

You can estimate to place the decimal point in the quotient.

$$4\overline{)119.76} = 29\ 94$$

Think: 119.76 is about 120.

$4\overline{)120}$ is 30, and so the quotient is about 30. It is 29.94.

Here is a way to divide a decimal by a whole number.

Step 1 Place the decimal point in the quotient directly above the decimal point in the dividend.

$$4\overline{)119.76} \quad (\text{quotient: } .)$$

Step 2 Divide as if you were dividing whole numbers.

$$\begin{array}{r} 29.94 \\ 4\overline{)119.76} \\ -8 \\ \hline 39 \\ -36 \\ \hline 3\ 7 \\ -3\ 6 \\ \hline 16 \\ -16 \\ \hline 0 \end{array}$$

The average amount collected per student was 29.94 kilograms.

More Examples

$$\begin{array}{r} 0.3 \\ 25\overline{)7.5} \\ -7\ 5 \\ \hline 0 \end{array} \qquad \begin{array}{r} 0.03 \\ 25\overline{)0.75} \\ -75 \\ \hline 0 \end{array} \qquad \begin{array}{r} 0.003 \\ 25\overline{)0.075} \\ -75 \\ \hline 0 \end{array}$$

Practice • Estimate. Write the quotient with the decimal point placed correctly.

1. $3\overline{)14.7}$ quotient: 4 9
2. $4\overline{)20.48}$ quotient: 5 12
3. $2\overline{)124.36}$ quotient: 62 18
4. $3\overline{)149.46}$ quotient: 49 82

Divide.

5. $4\overline{)93.2}$
6. $8\overline{)17.84}$
7. $5\overline{)0.75}$
8. $24\overline{)11.088}$

Mixed Practice • Divide.

9. $8\overline{)33.6}$
10. $6\overline{)42.6}$
11. $3\overline{)32.4}$
12. $7\overline{)11.48}$
13. $6\overline{)2.64}$
14. $7\overline{)29.12}$
15. $9\overline{)\$8.82}$
16. $5\overline{)76.90}$
17. $9\overline{)62.766}$
18. $8\overline{)0.48}$
19. $6\overline{)0.0054}$
20. $8\overline{)675.032}$
21. $7\overline{)64.456}$
22. $8\overline{)13.808}$
23. $9\overline{)0.072}$
24. $12\overline{)104.4}$
25. $23\overline{)0.92}$
26. $42\overline{)122.22}$
27. $71\overline{)1.278}$
28. $22\overline{)0.154}$
29. $22\overline{)27.412}$
30. $34\overline{)26.826}$
31. $46\overline{)189.750}$
32. $52\overline{)525.408}$

★ 33. $293\overline{)73.25}$
★ 34 $507\overline{)131.82}$
★ 35. $725\overline{)1087.5}$
★ 36. $876\overline{)376.68}$

Solve the equations.

37. $0.201 \div 3 = n$
38. $15.6 \div 4 = n$
39. $5.508 \div 9 = n$
40. $0.049 \div 7 = n$
41. $58.95 \div 9 = n$
42. $74.16 \div 6 = n$

★ 43. $\frac{n}{7} = 36.2$
★ 44. $\frac{x}{3.2} = 5.8$
★ 45. $2.4 = \frac{y}{0.75}$

PROBLEM SOLVING • APPLICATIONS

46. Lisa, Akule, and Jodi collected a total of 95.73 kilograms of glass for recycling. What was the average amount collected by each person?

47. Ken bought 6 pads of paper, each of which cost the same amount. The total cost was $7.74. What did each pad cost?

48. Gina ran 4.25 kilometers on each of 5 days. What was the total amount of kilometers that she ran?

★ 49. Beth had a board 3.72 meters long. She sawed it into 4 equal parts. How much less than 1 meter long is each part?

Dividing by a Decimal

Study these division examples. Look for a pattern.

$$8\overline{)56} = 7 \qquad 80\overline{)560} = 7 \qquad 800\overline{)5600} = 7$$

$10 \times 8 \quad 10 \times 56 \qquad\qquad 100 \times 8 \quad 100 \times 56$

You can multiply the dividend and the divisor by the same number. The quotient does not change.

When dividing by decimals, you always want to divide by a whole number. So sometimes you must multiply the dividend and the divisor by a power of 10.

Divide: $3.2\overline{)17.28}$.

Step 1 There is one decimal place in the divisor. Multiply the dividend and the divisor by 10. The arrow in the dividend shows where to place the decimal point in the quotient.

$3.2\overline{)17.28}$

Step 2 Divide as if you were dividing whole numbers.

$$\begin{array}{r} 5.4 \\ 3.2\overline{)17.28} \\ -16\,0 \\ \hline 1\,28 \\ -1\,28 \\ \hline 0 \end{array}$$

Divide: $0.43\overline{)3.741}$.

Step 1 There are two decimal places in the divisor. Multiply the dividend and the divisor by 100. Place the decimal point in the quotient.

$0.43\overline{)3.741}$

Step 2 Divide as if you were dividing whole numbers.

$$\begin{array}{r} 8.7 \\ 0.43\overline{)3.741} \\ -3\,44 \\ \hline 301 \\ -301 \\ \hline 0 \end{array}$$

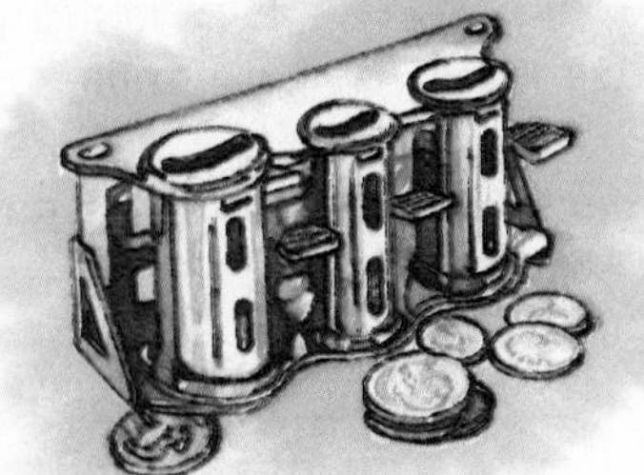

More Examples

$$\begin{array}{r} 0.2 \\ 0.07\overline{)0.014} \end{array} \qquad\qquad \begin{array}{r} 1.1 \\ 0.005\overline{)0.0055} \end{array}$$

Practice • Write the quotient with the decimal point placed correctly.

1. $0.8\overline{)3.28}$ — 41
2. $0.6\overline{)0.738}$ — 123
3. $0.41\overline{)9.43}$ — 23
4. $8.4\overline{)3.024}$ — 36

Divide.

5. $0.7\overline{)5.88}$
6. $0.54\overline{)3.294}$
7. $9.2\overline{)46.92}$
8. $0.008\overline{)0.0024}$

Mixed Practice • Divide.

9. $0.4\overline{)3.44}$
10. $0.03\overline{)2.22}$
11. $0.92\overline{)6.624}$
12. $0.83\overline{)18.26}$
13. $1.4\overline{)1.96}$
14. $3.4\overline{)2.924}$
15. $0.28\overline{)1.148}$
16. $0.33\overline{)15.18}$
17. $4.2\overline{)5.502}$
18. $8.7\overline{)21.402}$
19. $6\overline{)1.182}$
20. $4.2\overline{)2.604}$
21. $0.75\overline{)2.25}$
22. $1.2\overline{)0.732}$
23. $17\overline{)151.64}$
24. $0.65\overline{)0.0325}$
25. $0.09\overline{)1.548}$
26. $0.4\overline{)0.132}$
27. $0.031\overline{)0.2325}$
28. $0.071\overline{)0.639}$

★ 29. $2.15\overline{)9.030}$

★ 30. $2.75\overline{)8.4150}$

★ 31. $0.113\overline{)0.678}$

★ 32. $26.2\overline{)7.860}$

Solve the equations.

33. $4.16 \div 0.8 = n$
34. $4.41 \div 0.07 = n$
35. $10.396 \div 0.23 = n$
36. $5.472 \div 1.8 = n$
37. $0.0144 \div 0.012 = n$
38. $0.252 \div 0.21 = n$
39. $8y = 128$
40. $\frac{n}{12} = 17$

★ 41. $2.5y = 9.25$

PROBLEM SOLVING • APPLICATIONS

42. A penny is 0.15 centimeter thick. How many pennies are in a stack that is 3.45 centimeters high?

43. A quarter is 0.18 centimeter thick. How many quarters are in a stack that is 13.86 centimeters high?

★ 44. How high would a stack of 100 quarters be?

★ 45. How much higher would a stack of 100 quarters be than a stack of 100 pennies?

Writing Zeros in the Dividend

Sometimes you must write zeros in the dividend in order to locate the decimal point.

Divide: 4.5 ÷ 0.25.

Step 1 Multiply by 100. Since 100 × 4.5 = 450, you must write a zero in the dividend. Place the decimal point in the quotient.

$$0.25\overline{)4.50}$$

Step 2 Divide as if you were dividing whole numbers.

$$
\begin{array}{r}
18.\\
0.25\overline{)4.50}\\
2\,5\\
\hline
2\,00\\
2\,00\\
\hline
0
\end{array}
$$

When dividing decimals, you want to obtain a quotient without a remainder. So sometimes you must write more zeros in the dividend until there is a zero remainder.

Divide: $0.015\overline{)0.126}$.

Step 1 Multiply by 1,000. Place the decimal point in the quotient.

$$0.015\overline{)0.126}$$

Step 2 Divide. There is a remainder of 6.

$$
\begin{array}{r}
8.\\
0.015\overline{)0.126}\\
120\\
\hline
6
\end{array}
$$

Step 3 Write a zero in the dividend. Divide.

$$
\begin{array}{r}
8.4\\
0.015\overline{)0.126.0}\\
120\\
\hline
6\,0\\
6\,0\\
\hline
0
\end{array}
$$

Practice • Divide.

1. $0.05\overline{)1.2}$ **2.** $0.08\overline{)3.6}$ **3.** $0.004\overline{)0.12}$ **4.** $0.5\overline{)6.9}$

5. $0.12\overline{)7.2}$ **6.** $0.25\overline{)12.5}$ **7.** $0.34\overline{)78.2}$ **8.** $0.135\overline{)0.351}$

Mixed Practice • Divide.

9. $0.06\overline{)2.4}$	**10.** $0.09\overline{)4.5}$	**11.** $0.003\overline{)0.18}$	**12.** $0.4\overline{)0.2}$
13. $7.6\overline{)0.38}$	**14.** $0.35\overline{)10.5}$	**15.** $0.74\overline{)3.7}$	**16.** $0.12\overline{)0.3}$
17. $0.016\overline{)0.8}$	**18.** $0.024\overline{)0.12}$	**19.** $0.072\overline{)0.18}$	**20.** $0.75\overline{)0.3}$
★ **21.** $1.36\overline{)0.68}$	★ **22.** $1.14\overline{)5.7}$	★ **23.** $0.755\overline{)0.302}$	★ **24.** $1.95\overline{)7.8}$

Solve the equations.

25. $28.1 \div 0.5 = n$ **26.** $0.525 \div 0.075 = n$ ★ **27.** $n \div 2.4 = 0.05$

Evaluate each expression when $n = 15.2$.

28. $n + 3.8$ **29.** $n - 3.8$ **30.** $n \times 3.8$

Look for patterns. Watch the decimal points.

$2.96 \div 10 = 0.296$ — one zero — The decimal point moves one place to the left.

$2.96 \div 100 = 0.0296$ — two zeros — The decimal point moves two places to the left.

$2.96 \div 1{,}000 = 0.00296$ — three zeros — The decimal point moves three places to the left.

Dividing by 10, 100, 1,000, . . . moves the decimal point to the left. The number of zeros in the power of 10 shows the number of places to move the decimal point.

Divide.

31. $78.6 \div 10$ **32.** $78.6 \div 100$ **33.** $78.6 \div 1{,}000$

★ **34.** $8{,}765 \div 10^3$ ★ **35.** $8{,}765 \div 10^4$ ★ **36.** $8{,}765 \div 10^5$

PROBLEM SOLVING • APPLICATIONS

★ **37.** Chet calculated that he had worked 1,000 hours in 7 months. His earnings for that period of time were $5,670. What was his rate of pay per hour?

★ **38.** What was his average pay per month?

Rounding Quotients

You can round a quotient to give an approximate answer.

Bob cut a piece of wire that was 14 meters long into 12 equal parts. How long was each part? Give the answer to the nearest tenth.

$14 \div 12 = n$

$$\begin{array}{r} 1.16 \approx 1.2 \\ 12\overline{)14.00} \\ \underline{12} \\ 2\,0 \\ \underline{1\,2} \\ 80 \\ \underline{72} \\ 8 \end{array}$$

Divide to two decimal places so that you can round to the nearest tenth.

Each part was about 1.2 meters long.

Divide: $0.73 \div 0.3$. Give the answer to the nearest hundredth.

Divide to three decimal places so that you can round to the nearest hundredth.

$$\begin{array}{r} 2.433 \approx 2.43 \\ 0.3\overline{)0.7300} \end{array}$$

> ***When you want to round a quotient to a given number of decimal places, divide to one extra place. Then round.***

Practice • Divide. Round each quotient to the nearest tenth.

1. $6\overline{)8}$ **2.** $11\overline{)15}$ **3.** $0.9\overline{)2.8}$ **4.** $3\overline{)11.29}$

Divide. Round each quotient to the nearest hundredth.

5. $7\overline{)64.46}$ **6.** $4\overline{)6.93}$ **7.** $2.3\overline{)3.14}$ **8.** $0.83\overline{)0.762}$

Mixed Practice • Divide. Round each quotient to the nearest tenth.

9. $4\overline{)7}$ **10.** $0.9\overline{)1.1}$ **11.** $0.6\overline{)1.01}$ **12.** $7\overline{)13.23}$

13. $12\overline{)10.7}$ 14. $1.6\overline{)4.53}$ 15. $11\overline{)1.3}$ 16. $2.5\overline{)3.37}$

17. $0.76\overline{)2.85}$ 18. $15\overline{)2.6}$ 19. $8.2\overline{)19.9}$ 20. $0.77\overline{)2.93}$

Divide. Round each quotient to the nearest hundredth.

21. $6\overline{)2.889}$ 22. $3.5\overline{)7.2}$ 23. $21\overline{)27.4}$ 24. $46\overline{)189.7}$

25. $1.3\overline{)0.335}$ 26. $2.1\overline{)1.7}$ 27. $0.48\overline{)3.1}$ 28. $0.57\overline{)0.702}$

29. $2.2\overline{)1.4}$ 30. $70\overline{)8.638}$ 31. $13\overline{)3.762}$ 32. $15\overline{)16}$

Divide. Round each quotient to the nearest thousandth.

★ 33. $9\overline{)5.1}$ ★ 34. $7\overline{)10.3}$ ★ 35. $11\overline{)18}$ ★ 36. $13\overline{)18}$

★ 37. $2\overline{)0.0047}$ ★ 38. $23\overline{)6.3}$ ★ 39. $8\overline{)0.3}$ ★ 40. $13\overline{)7}$

Solve the equations.

41. $n + 86 = 200$ 42. $x - 73 = 168$ 43. $27y = 567$ 44. $\frac{n}{32} = 15$

45. $y - 9.4 = 17.7$ 46. $n + 3.5 = 12.0$ ★ 47. $\frac{x}{3.9} = 4.1$ ★ 48. $7.3n = 24.82$

PROBLEM SOLVING • APPLICATIONS

In baseball, batting averages are expressed in thousandths, using decimals such as .250 or .286. (The zero at the left of the decimal point is omitted.)

To find a batting average, you divide the number of hits by the number of times at bat. You round to the nearest thousandth when necessary.

1 hit in 4 times at bat → $4\overline{)1.000}$ = .250

2 hits in 7 times at bat → $7\overline{)2.0000}$ = .2857 ≈ .286

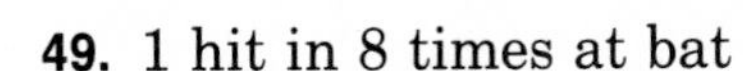

Find the batting averages.

49. 1 hit in 8 times at bat

50. 3 hits in 10 times at bat

★ 51. 15 hits in 43 times at bat

★ 52. 14 hits in 42 times at bat

★ 53. List the four batting averages in order from greatest to least.

Scientific Notation

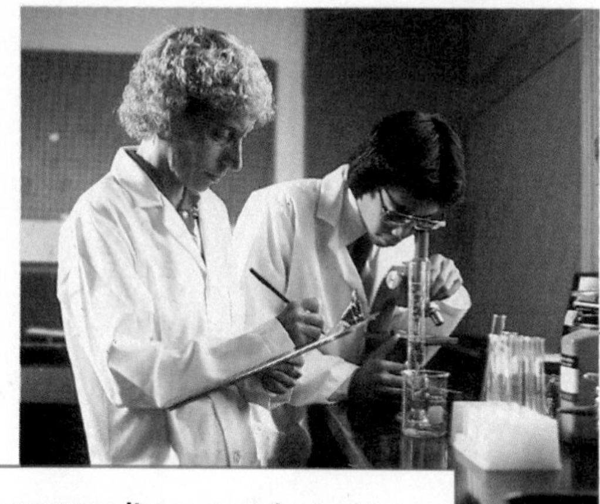

In a vacuum, light travels about 299,800 kilometers per second. Scientists often write numbers such as 299,800 or 156,000,000 in **scientific notation.**

$299{,}800 = 2.998 \times 10^5$

scientific notation

To write a number in scientific notation, you express it as a product of two factors. The first factor is a number less than 10 but not less than 1. The second factor is a power of 10 in exponent form.

The example below shows how to use scientific notation for the number 156,000,000.

Step 1

Find the first factor. Move the decimal point to the left to name a number that is less than 10 but not less than 1. That is like dividing by 100,000,000 or 10^8. The number of places you move the decimal point is the power of 10.

→ 1.56000000

8 places to the left

Step 2

To name the number you started with, you must use 10^8 as the second factor.

→ 1.56×10^8

1.56×10^8 is scientific notation for 156,000,000.

Here are more examples.

$2{,}850 = 2.85 \times 10^3$ $\quad$ $1{,}367{,}000 = 1.367 \times 10^6$

Sometimes you are given scientific notation for a number and you need to write the number. You can multiply.

$3.26 \times 10^5 = 3.26 \times 100{,}000$

$= 326{,}000$ 5 places to the right

Practice • Complete, using the correct exponents.

1. $9{,}200 = 9.2 \times 10^{■}$

2. $76{,}300 = 7.63 \times 10^{■}$

3. $102{,}000 = 1.02 \times 10^{■}$

4. $1{,}500{,}000 = 1.5 \times 10^{■}$

5. $90{,}900 = 9.09 \times 10^{■}$

6. $85{,}430{,}000 = 8.543 \times 10^{■}$

Use scientific notation to name the numbers.

7. 4,900
8. 36,700
9. 412,300
10. 2,300,000
11. 123,600
12. 15,400,000

Write the numbers.

13. 4.5×10^2
14. 2.18×10^5
15. 6.739×10^7

Mixed Practice • Complete, using the correct exponents.

16. $2,300 = 2.3 \times 10^{■}$
17. $7,200 = 7.2 \times 10^{■}$
18. $40,700 = 4.07 \times 10^{■}$
19. $512,000 = 5.12 \times 10^{■}$
20. $9,402,000 = 9.402 \times 10^{■}$
21. $68,000,000 = 6.8 \times 10^{■}$

Use scientific notation to name the numbers.

22. 7,600
23. 9,230
24. 34,000
25. 77,500
26. 640,000
27. 820,000
28. 982,000
29. 124,630
30. 6,500,000
31. 24,000,000
32. 85,600,000
33. 570,000,000
★34. 8,400,000,000
★35. 27,000,000,000
★36. 3,500,000,000

Write the numbers.

37. 2.3×10^4
38. 4.67×10^5
39. 7.3×10^7

PROBLEM SOLVING • APPLICATIONS

40. The nearest that Mercury comes to the sun is 45,755,000 kilometers. Use scientific notation to name the distance.

★41. The nearest that Pluto comes to the sun is 4.410283×10^9 kilometers. Write the distance without scientific notation. Is this distance more or less than 1 billion kilometers?

Skills Maintenance

1. $3.82 + $1.08
2. 3 × $1.25
3. $7.70 − $1.90
4. $6.60 ÷ 2
5. 3 × $4.73
6. $8.24 ÷ 4
7. $1.15 + $6.67
8. $7.34 − $1.48

PROBLEM SOLVING • STRATEGIES

Multistep Problems

Sometimes you need to use more than one operation to solve a problem.

The Flower Barn is having a sale. Gino buys 2 hanging baskets for \$6.75 each. How much change does he receive from a twenty-dollar bill?

Step 1 Find the cost of the 2 baskets.

$$\begin{array}{r} \$6.75 \\ \times \quad 2 \\ \hline \$13.50 \end{array}$$

Step 2 Find the change from \$20.00.

$$\begin{array}{r} \$20.00 \\ -\ 13.50 \\ \hline \$\ 6.50 \end{array}$$

Gino receives \$6.50 in change.

	Cost	+ change	= total amount
Check:	(2 × \$6.75)	+ \$6.50	= \$20.00
	\$13.50	+ \$6.50	= \$20.00
		\$20.00	= \$20.00 ✓

Solve.

1. Tana buys 3 potted philodendrons at \$6.95 each and 2 ceramic flowerpots at \$3.50 each. Find the total cost.

2. The Flower Barn is open 8 hours a day Monday through Thursday. The store is open 9 hours on Friday and Saturday. How many hours is the store open per week?

3. Erin works at the Flower Barn. She earns \$4.50 per hour for regular work time and \$6.75 per hour for overtime. How much does Erin earn for 35 hours plus 6 hours overtime?

4. Chandra buys 3 packets of marigold seeds at 99¢ each and 4 flowerpots at \$3.49 each. How much does Chandra spend?

5. Greenhouse Suppliers made a delivery to the Flower Barn of 24 geraniums and 30 daffodils. The geraniums cost $2.25 each and the daffodils cost $3.49 each. Find the total cost of this shipment of flowers.

6. Mr. Forbes owes $25 on his account at the Flower Barn. He buys a floral arrangement for $15.95 and makes a twenty-dollar payment on the total amount that he owes. How much does he still owe?

When a problem has more than one step, be sure to use the correct data in each step.

7. Ayita has a $10.00 gift certificate to use at the Flower Barn. She buys 3 hanging baskets for $12.50 each. How much money must she pay if she uses the gift certificate to help with the purchase?

8. Joanna earns $45 in one week while working part-time at the Flower Barn. She works 4 hours on Tuesday, 3 hours on Thursday, and 5 hours on Saturday. How much does she earn per hour?

9. Mrs. Barton manages the Flower Barn. She buys 8 plants from a supplier at $3.50 each. She sells the plants at $4.95 each. How much profit is made when the plants are sold?

Check the computation in each step.

10. Laura makes a $25 deposit on a bill at the Flower Barn. The bill is $53. If she makes a $7.00 payment each week, how many weeks will it take to pay the bill?

★ 11. Jill spends a total of $36.25 for 5 plants and a bag of potting soil. The bag of soil costs $3.75. What is the average cost of each plant?

★ 12. Mrs. Barton buys 4 new tires for her delivery truck and has the oil changed. Each tire costs $79.90. The oil change costs $15.95. How much less than $400.00 is the total bill?

CHAPTER 5

REVIEW

Multiply. (pp. 110–115)

1. $\begin{array}{r} 7.2 \\ \times\ 6 \\ \hline \end{array}$
2. $\begin{array}{r} 0.88 \\ \times\ 9.6 \\ \hline \end{array}$
3. $\begin{array}{r} 5.07 \\ \times 3.16 \\ \hline \end{array}$
4. $\begin{array}{r} 6.5 \\ \times 8.08 \\ \hline \end{array}$
5. $\begin{array}{r} 3.49 \\ \times\ 5.3 \\ \hline \end{array}$
6. $\begin{array}{r} 0.39 \\ \times 0.04 \\ \hline \end{array}$
7. $\begin{array}{r} 0.448 \\ \times\ 0.03 \\ \hline \end{array}$
8. $\begin{array}{r} 0.163 \\ \times\ 0.09 \\ \hline \end{array}$
9. $\begin{array}{r} 0.009 \\ \times 1.006 \\ \hline \end{array}$
10. $\begin{array}{r} 0.481 \\ \times\ 0.12 \\ \hline \end{array}$

Solve the equations. (pp. 112–117)

11. $55.9 \times 1.21 = n$
12. $5.6 \times 7.23 = n$
13. $7.2 \times 4.38 = n$
14. $10 \times 2.74 = n$
15. $100 \times 41.8 = n$
16. $1{,}000 \times 35.3 = n$
17. $0.01 \times 51.76 = n$
18. $0.001 \times 0.89 = n$
19. $0.01 \times 604 = n$

Divide. (pp. 120–125)

20. $6\overline{)29.4}$
21. $28\overline{)97.16}$
22. $463\overline{)398.18}$
23. $0.14\overline{)53.34}$
24. $3.9\overline{)20.514}$
25. $0.018\overline{)0.9}$

Solve the equations. (pp. 120–125)

26. $86.4 \div 12 = n$
27. $0.0108 \div 0.04 = n$
28. $36.2 \div 0.5 = n$

29. Divide: $0.7\overline{)3.4}$. Round the quotient to the nearest tenth. (pp. 126–127)

30. Divide: $8\overline{)52.9}$. Round the quotient to the nearest hundredth. (pp. 126–127)

Use scientific notation to name the numbers. (pp. 128–129)

31. 7,500
32. 42,400
33. 9,380,000

34. A strip of wood 34.4 centimeters long is cut into pieces that are each 8.6 centimeters long. How many pieces are there? (pp. 122–123)

35. Carl buys 3 books at \$8.95 each and 2 notebooks at \$.85 each. He gives the clerk \$30. How much change does he receive? (pp.130–131)

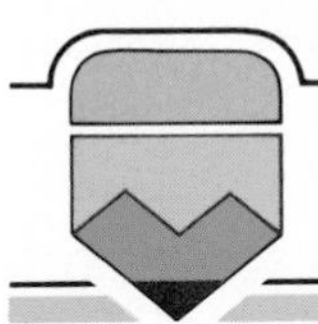

PROJECT

Keeping a Checkbook Record

When you have a checking account (see page 103), you need to keep a checkbook record of the **balance**—the money that is in the account.

Each time you write a check, that amount must be subtracted to show the new balance. Each time money is deposited in the account, that amount must be added to show the new balance.

Here is part of Shari Johnson's checkbook record. Her original balance was $302.50. On January 8, she paid a $45.24 telephone bill. On January 12, she paid a $38.50 supermarket bill. These amounts were subtracted, as you can see. Then, on January 15, she deposited $235.00. This amount was added to give the new balance.

Check Number	Date	Description	Payment		Deposit		Balance	
							302	50
1	1/8/84	To GTI Telephone For	45	24			257	26
2	1/12	To Ace Market For	38	50			218	76
	1/15	To Deposit For			235	00	453	76
		To For						
		To For						
		To For						

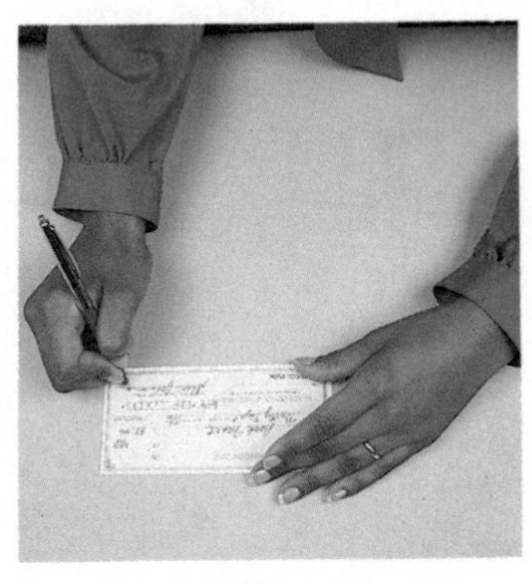

1. On January 20, Shari Johnson made out a check for $38.46 to the Book Mart. On January 29, she deposited $235.00. On February 2, she made out a check for $285.00 to the ABC Realty Company. Draw a picture of her checkbook record and show all these transactions. Begin with her balance on January 15.

2. From February 1 to February 28, Bob Alvarez makes out three checks for $37.90 each. During that same period, he makes two deposits for $56.95 each. Is his balance at the end of February greater or less than it was on February 1? How much greater or less?

3. Imagine that you have a $500.00 balance in a new checking account. Write five checks, each one for a different amount but none for more than $74.99. Make one deposit for no more than $99.50. Draw the complete record for these transactions.

CHAPTER 5

TEST

Multiply.

1. $\begin{array}{r} 3.5 \\ \times\ 9 \\ \hline \end{array}$

2. $\begin{array}{r} 0.76 \\ \times\ 4.3 \\ \hline \end{array}$

3. $\begin{array}{r} 1.62 \\ \times\ 2.7 \\ \hline \end{array}$

4. $\begin{array}{r} 0.509 \\ \times\ 6.11 \\ \hline \end{array}$

5. $\begin{array}{r} 8.39 \\ \times 0.725 \\ \hline \end{array}$

6. $\begin{array}{r} 0.68 \\ \times 0.03 \\ \hline \end{array}$

7. $\begin{array}{r} 1.86 \\ \times 0.02 \\ \hline \end{array}$

8. $\begin{array}{r} 0.46 \\ \times 0.006 \\ \hline \end{array}$

9. $\begin{array}{r} 2.083 \\ \times 0.008 \\ \hline \end{array}$

10. $\begin{array}{r} 0.007 \\ \times 2.004 \\ \hline \end{array}$

Solve the equations.

11. $8.65 \times 24.7 = n$
12. $4.7 \times 3.59 = n$
13. $0.38 \times 4.21 = n$
14. $100 \times 0.382 = n$
15. $10 \times 3.01 = n$
16. $1{,}000 \times 71.9 = n$
17. $0.01 \times 85.96 = n$
18. $0.001 \times 0.62 = n$
19. $0.1 \times 810 = n$

Divide.

20. $5\overline{)89.5}$
21. $265\overline{)177.55}$
22. $0.9\overline{)15.57}$
23. $6.1\overline{)50.02}$
24. $0.39\overline{)37.44}$
25. $0.072\overline{)0.18}$

Solve the equations.

26. $33.18 \div 14 = n$
27. $3.128 \div 4.6 = n$
28. $8.54 \div 0.4 = n$

29. Divide: $0.15\overline{)0.366}$. Round the quotient to the nearest tenth.

30. Divide: $3.8\overline{)9.26}$. Round the quotient to the nearest hundredth.

Use scientific notation to name the numbers.

31. 5,200
32. 72,600
33. 9,341,000

34. Sally buys 2 cans of paint at \$5.75 each and 3 brushes at \$2.20 each. How much less than \$20 is the total cost of these items?

35. Each lap of the track measures 0.56 kilometer. How many laps must Steve run if he wants to run 2.8 kilometers?

ENRICHMENT

Using Exponents

You are already familiar with these fractions and decimals.

$$0.1 = \frac{1}{10} \qquad 0.01 = \frac{1}{100} \qquad 0.001 = \frac{1}{1{,}000}$$

Since $10 = 10^1$, $100 = 10^2$, and $1{,}000 = 10^3$, you can write:

$$0.1 = \frac{1}{10^1} \qquad 0.01 = \frac{1}{10^2} \qquad 0.001 = \frac{1}{10^3}$$

Note that the exponent in each denominator is equal to the number of decimal places in the decimal.

Are these sentences true?

$$0.3 = 3 \times \frac{1}{10} \qquad 0.05 = 5 \times \frac{1}{100} \qquad 0.007 = 7 \times \frac{1}{1{,}000}$$

$$0.3 = 3 \times \frac{1}{10^1} \qquad 0.05 = 5 \times \frac{1}{10^2} \qquad 0.007 = 7 \times \frac{1}{10^3}$$

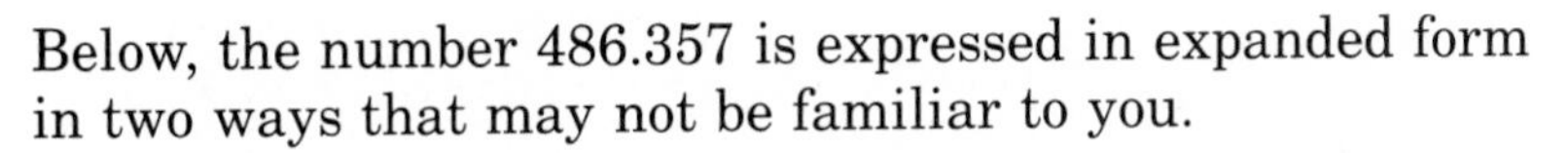

Below, the number 486.357 is expressed in expanded form in two ways that may not be familiar to you.

$$468.357 = (4 \times 100) + (6 \times 10) + (8 \times 1) + (3 \times \frac{1}{10}) + (5 \times \frac{1}{100}) + (7 \times \frac{1}{1{,}000})$$

$$468.357 = (4 \times 10^2) + (6 \times 10^1) + (8 \times 10^0) + (3 \times \frac{1}{10^1}) + (5 \times \frac{1}{10^2}) + (7 \times \frac{1}{10^3})$$

Remember, in the decimal system, the grouping number or base is 10. Each place value involves a power of 10.

Test your "ten" strength. Write in expanded form in the ways shown above.

1. 93.28 **2.** 71.645 **3.** 206.7359 **4.** 5.234987

Write <, =, or >.

5. $1 \times \frac{1}{10^2}$ ● $(9 \times \frac{1}{10^3}) + (8 \times \frac{1}{10^4})$

6. 3×10^0 ● 2×10^1

7. Write a place-value chart that uses exponents to show the place values from millions to millionths.

COMPUTER

Computer Software

The lesson in Chapter 3 was mostly about computer hardware. *Computer software* is any program that contains information or instructions for the computer. Many *levels* of computer software are described below. Remember that computers can use only the bits 0 and 1.

Computer
↑
SOFTWARE LEVEL 1
Interpreter
↑
SOFTWARE LEVEL 2
Machine language
↑
SOFTWARE LEVEL 3
Assembler
↑
SOFTWARE LEVEL 4
Instructions
↑
SOFTWARE LEVEL 5
Compiler
↑
SOFTWARE LEVEL 6
Programming language

Interpreters translate bytes into bits and bits into bytes for each computer. Interpreters are programs. Hardware designers use interpreters.

Machine language communicates directly with a computer's hardware. Machine language might say "*A* means add." Software designers use machine language.

Assemblers translate instructions into machine language. Assemblers are programs. Computer manufacturers write assemblers.

Instructions are written by programmers. Each computer has its own instruction set. Instructions are assembled into machine language.

Compilers translate programming-language statements into instructions. Compilers are programs written by computer experts. Each computer has a compiler for each programming language.

Programming languages use statements that are like the natural languages of English or mathematics. Every programming language has *grammar* that must be followed exactly. Programming languages are *computer-independent,* which means they can be used with any computer. Programmers and all computer users write programs in programming languages.

Each computer has its own *computer-dependent controlling program* to connect all these software levels in operation.

Here are the names of some programming languages.

BASIC means Beginner's All-purpose Symbolic Instruction Code. It is used mainly in education and in computers for beginning programmers.

PASCAL is named after the Frenchman Blaise Pascal, who built the first digital adding machine. PASCAL is used mainly in education and in computer-systems design.

FORTRAN means FORmula TRANslation and is used mainly in scientific work.

COBOL means COmmon Business-Oriented Language and is used mainly by businesses.

LISP means LISt Processor and is used in work on artificial intelligence.

PL/I means Programming Language I and is used in business and science.

Each programming language includes about one hundred kinds of statements. *Statements* are used to specify data, input/output use, and calculations.

- Data must be defined according to quantity and type. Data may be *alphabetic data* (letters) or *numeric data* (numbers).
- Input/output must be defined by quantity and by the type and speed of input and output devices used in the system.
- Calculations process input data to obtain output data.

Write whether these statements are *true* or *false*.

1. Computer software contains only instructions.
2. Machine language communicates directly with hardware.
3. Instructions are computer-independent.
4. Compiling programs are computer-independent.
5. Programming languages are used only by programmers.
6. BASIC means BASic Instructions for Compilers.
7. FORTRAN means FORmula TRANslation and is used in business.
8. COBOL means COmmercial Business-Oriented Language.
9. PL/I means Programming Language I and is used in business and science.

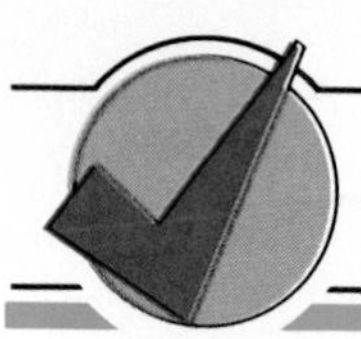

SKILLS MAINTENANCE

Chapters 1 Through 5

Choose the correct answers.

1. Solve.

   $n + 29 = 87$

   A. $n = 116$
   B. $n = 3$
   C. $n = 58$
   D. not here

2. Multiply.

   $$\begin{array}{r} 43.8 \\ \times 6.59 \\ \hline \end{array}$$

   A. 28.8642
   B. 2.88642
   C. 288.642
   D. not here

3. Solve.

   $\frac{x}{15} = 30$

   A. $x = 2$
   B. $x = 450$
   C. $x = 45$
   D. not here

4. Divide.

   $0.016\overline{)0.8}$

   A. 50
   B. 5.0
   C. 0.5
   D. not here

5. Divide. Round the quotient to the nearest hundredth.

   $4.8\overline{)7.3369}$

   A. 1.54
   B. 1.52
   C. 1.53
   D. not here

6. Use scientific notation to name this number.

   36,500

   A. 36.5×10^3
   B. 3.65×10^4
   C. 365×100
   D. not here

7. Write in order from least to greatest.

   7.631; 7.64; 7.463

   A. 7.631; 7.463; 7.64
   B. 7.64; 7.463; 7.631
   C. 7.463; 7.631; 7.64
   D. not here

8. Add.

   $$\begin{array}{r} 47{,}806 \\ 4{,}787 \\ +51{,}010 \\ \hline \end{array}$$

   A. 103,603
   B. 103,503
   C. 102,603
   D. not here

9. Subtract.

   $$\begin{array}{r} 700{,}492 \\ -589{,}687 \\ \hline \end{array}$$

   A. 110,805
   B. 110,815
   C. 111,805
   D. not here

10. In highway driving, Mrs. Lee can drive about 88 kilometers per hour. At this speed, how many kilometers can she drive in 2.6 hours?

    A. 34 km B. 228.8 km
    C. 228 km D. not here

11. Mr. Clarke buys 6 English ivy plants for $5.95 each and 4 flowerpots for $2.75 each. How much does Mr. Clarke spend in all?

    A. $35.70 B. $38.50
    C. $46.70 D. not here

Number Theory

CHAPTER 6

Divisibility • Divisibility by 3 and 9 • Factors, Primes, and Composites • Prime Factorization • Greatest Common Factor • Multiples and Least Common Multiple • Problem Solving: Making an Organized List • Venn Diagrams • Clock Arithmetic

Divisibility

Divide one whole number by another. If the remainder is 0, the first number is **divisible** by the second.

16 is divisible by 2.

$$\begin{array}{r} 8 \\ 2\overline{)16} \end{array}$$

17 is not divisible by 2.

$$\begin{array}{r} 8 \text{ r1} \\ 2\overline{)17} \end{array}$$

Here are rules for finding whether a number is divisible by 2, 5, or 10.

Even numbers are divisible by 2.
A whole number is even if the ones digit is 0, 2, 4, 6, or 8. → Divisible by 2: 30, 32, 34, 36, 38

Odd numbers are not divisible by 2.
A whole number is odd if the ones digit is 1, 3, 5, 7, or 9. → Not divisible by 2: 31, 33, 35, 37, 39

A whole number is divisible by 5 if the ones digit is 0 or 5. → Divisible by 5: 5, 10, 15, 20, 25

A whole number is divisible by 10 if the ones digit is 0. → Divisible by 10: 10, 20, 30, 40, 50

The rule for divisibility by 4 is different. You use the last two digits. If that part of the number is divisible by 4, then the number is divisible by 4.

128 28 is divisible by 4, and so 128 is divisible by 4.
129 29 is not divisible by 4, and so 129 is not divisible by 4.

Practice • Is the first number divisible by the second?

1. 12, 4 **2.** 19, 2 **3.** 75, 5 **4.** 56, 2

5. 79, 10 **6.** 118, 4 **7.** 930, 10 **8.** 556, 5

Mixed Practice • Is the first number divisible by the second?

9. 37, 4	**10.** 60, 5	**11.** 90, 10	**12.** 83, 2
13. 305, 10	**14.** 126, 4	**15.** 372, 2	**16.** 258, 5

Which numbers are divisible by 2?

17. 28	**18.** 76	**19.** 251	**20.** 420
21. 1,189	**22.** 2,314	**23.** 24,681	**24.** 32,486

Which numbers are divisible by 4?

25. 166	**26.** 384	**27.** 428	**28.** 518
29. 1,208	**30.** 3,212	**31.** 22,765	★**32.** 214,000

Which numbers are divisible by 5?

33. 57	**34.** 95	**35.** 340	**36.** 585
37. 1,370	**38.** 5,552	**39.** 21,825	★**40.** 189,770

Which numbers are divisible by 10?

41. 80	**42.** 201	**43.** 304	**44.** 550
45. 1,275	**46.** 1,040	**47.** 24,730	★**48.** 101,011

PROBLEM SOLVING • APPLICATIONS

49. In basketball, a field goal counts as 2 points. In one game, the score is 68 to 53. Can both scores have been made with field goals only?

50. There are 74 students who want to play basketball. Can an even number of teams with 5 players be formed using all of these students?

Suppose that a and b are even numbers and that c and d are odd numbers. What kind of number is

★**51.** $a + b$?	★**52.** $b + c$?	★**53.** $c + d$?
★**54.** $a \times b$?	★**55.** $b \times c$?	★**56.** $c \times d$?

Divisibility by 3 and 9

Can you tell whether a number is divisible by 3?
Add the digits of the number.
If the sum is divisible by 3, then the number is divisible by 3.

168 $1 + 6 + 8 = 15$

15 is divisible by 3, and so 168 is divisible by 3.

170 $1 + 7 + 0 = 8$

8 is not divisible by 3, and so 170 is not divisible by 3.

Can you tell whether a number is divisible by 9?
Add the digits. If the sum is divisible by 9, then the number is divisible by 9.

198 $1 + 9 + 8 = 18$

18 is divisible by 9, and so 198 is divisible by 9.

218 $2 + 1 + 8 = 11$

11 is not divisible by 9, and so 218 is not divisible by 9.

Practice • Which numbers are divisible by 3?

1. 36 **2.** 108 **3.** 163 **4.** 213 **5.** 506

Which numbers are divisible by 9?

6. 45 **7.** 216 **8.** 342 **9.** 818 **10.** 624

Mixed Practice • Which numbers are divisible by 3?

11. 33 **12.** 42 **13.** 82 **14.** 93 **15.** 231

16. 147 **17.** 333 **18.** 700 **19.** 474 **20.** 870

21. 525 **22.** 604 **23.** 647 **24.** 900 **25.** 15,999

Which numbers are divisible by 9?

26. 96 **27.** 180 **28.** 117 **29.** 184 **30.** 198

31. 252 **32.** 321 **33.** 567 **34.** 600 **35.** 650

36. 630 **37.** 742 **38.** 926 **39.** 900 **40.** 12,998

Copy and complete the table. Write *yes* or *no*.

Number	Divisible by					
	2	3	4	5	9	10
41. 3,708	Yes	Yes	Yes	No		
42. 6,392						
43. 5,344						
44. 42,760						
45. 36,081						
★ **46.** 115,020						
★ **47.** 488,304						
★ **48.** 2,310,000						

49. Write a four-digit number divisible by 2.

50. Write a five-digit number divisible by 5.

51. Write a four-digit number divisible by 3.

52. Write a four-digit number divisible by 9.

★ **53.** Write a five-digit number divisible by 3 but not by 9.

★ **54.** Write a six-digit number that is divisible by 2, 3, 4, 5, 9, and 10.

A number is divisible by 6 if it is divisible by 2 and by 3.

126

126 is even, and so 126 is divisible by 2.

$1 + 2 + 6 = 9$

9 is divisible by 3, and so 126 is divisible by 3.

126 is divisible by 2 and by 3, and so 126 is divisible by 6.

Which numbers are divisible by 6?

55. 72 **56.** 126 **57.** 3,123 **58.** 6,390 **59.** 6,008 **60.** 13,500

PROBLEM SOLVING • APPLICATIONS

61. Here is a number puzzle. List all the different numbers that n might be.

n is a whole number.

$50 < n$ and $n < 100$.

n is divisible by both 3 and 4.

★ **62.** Write a number puzzle similar to the one in problem 61.

Factors, Primes, and Composites

A number is divisible by its factors.

Find all the factors of 16.
List them in order.

Step 1 Write 16 as the product of pairs of whole numbers. → $16 = 1 \times 16$
$16 = 2 \times 8$
$16 = 4 \times 4$

Step 2 List the factors in order. Show each factor only once. 1, 2, 4, 8, and 16 are the only factors. → Factors of 16:
1, 2, 4, 8, 16

A number such as 5 has exactly two factors: itself and 1. $5 = 5 \times 1$

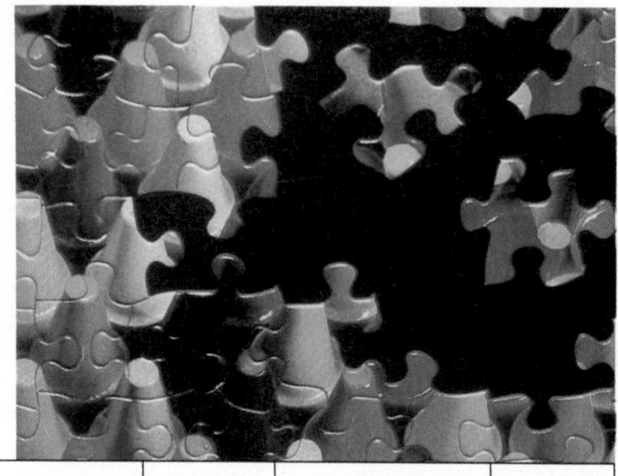

A **prime number** is a whole number that has exactly two factors: itself and 1. 5 is a prime number.

The number 1 is not a prime number. It has only itself as a factor.

If a whole number greater than 1 has more than two factors, it is a **composite number.**
16 is a composite number.

Number	2	3	10	13	15	29
Factors	1, 2	1, 3	1, 2, 5, 10	1, 13	1, 3, 5, 15	1, 29
Prime or Composite?	Prime	Prime	Composite	Prime	Composite	Prime

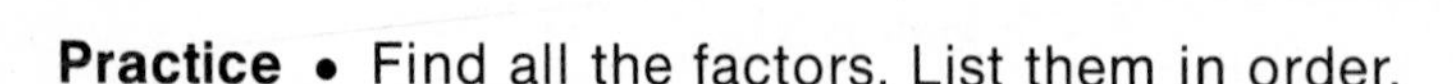

Practice • Find all the factors. List them in order.

1. 8 **2.** 12 **3.** 20 **4.** 24 **5.** 48 **6.** 64

Write *prime* or *composite.*

7. 11 **8.** 14 **9.** 37 **10.** 49 **11.** 59 **12.** 73

Mixed Practice • Find all the factors. List them in order.

13. 6 **14.** 9 **15.** 16 **16.** 22 **17.** 40 **18.** 45

19. 55 **20.** 66 **21.** 70 **22.** 72 **23.** 80 **24.** 27

25. 35 **26.** 36 **27.** 28 **28.** 50 **29.** 60 **30.** 65

31. 74 **32.** 75 **33.** 96 **34.** 100 **35.** 110 **36.** 120

Write *prime* or *composite*.

37. 7 **38.** 13 **39.** 17 **40.** 25 **41.** 29 **42.** 31

43. 24 **44.** 39 **45.** 56 **46.** 61 **47.** 63 **48.** 65

49. 76 **50.** 81 **51.** 83 **52.** 85 **53.** 90 **54.** 93

55. 97 **56.** 103 **57.** 105 **58.** 113 ★**59.** 116 ★**60.** 121

PROBLEM SOLVING • APPLICATIONS

★**61.** Make a table of whole numbers from 1 to 100.

1	2	3	4	5	6	7	8	9	10
11	12	13	14	15	16	17	18	19	20

Cross out 1, which is not a prime number. Cross out all the numbers greater than 2 that have 2 as a factor. Then cross out all the numbers greater than 3 that have 3 as a factor. Do the same for 5 and 7. When you finish, the numbers left are prime numbers. List all the prime numbers less than 100.

Write *always, sometimes,* or *never.*

62. If a and b are prime numbers, then $a \times b$ is _____ a prime number.

★**63.** If x is an even number, then $\frac{x}{2}$ is ________ a prime number.

Midchapter Review

Is the number divisible by 4? **1.** 336 **2.** 502

Is the number divisible by 9? **3.** 872 **4.** 765

Find all the factors. List them in order. **5.** 32 **6.** 54

Write *prime* or *composite*. **7.** 51 **8.** 47

Prime Factorization

A composite number can be shown as the product of prime factors. This product is called the **prime factorization** of the number.

Find the prime factorization of 24. Use a **factor tree.**

Choose any two factors of 24. →

12 is not prime. Express 12 as 2×6. →

6 is not prime. Express 6 as 2×3. →

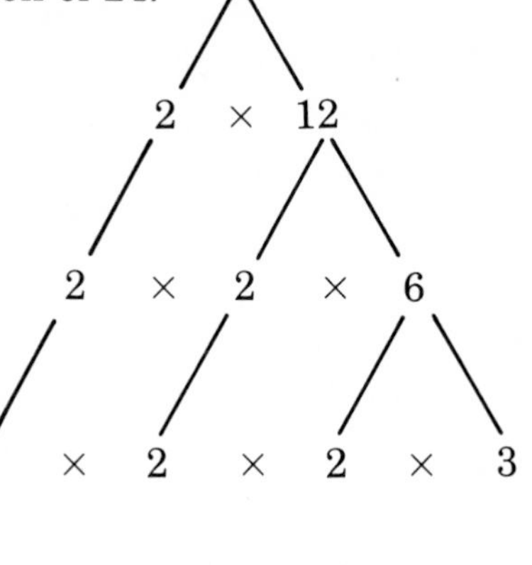

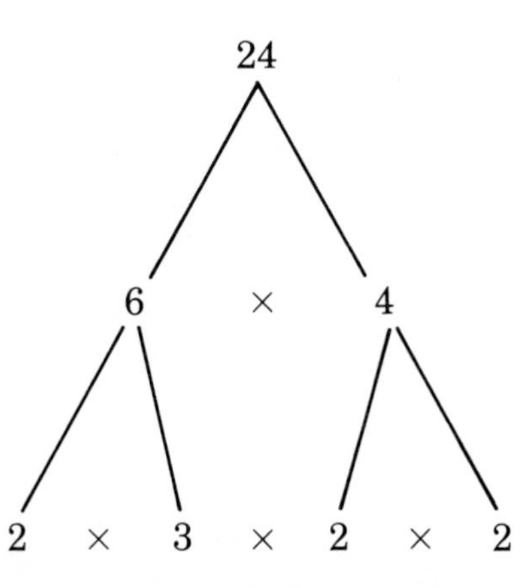

You can also try these factors.

$24 = 6 \times 4$

Neither 6 nor 4 is prime.

$6 = 2 \times 3 \quad 4 = 2 \times 2$

It makes no difference how you begin. Except for order, the result is the same.

$$24 = 2 \times 2 \times 2 \times 3$$

The prime factorization of 24 can also be written with exponents.

$$24 = 2^3 \times 3$$

More Examples

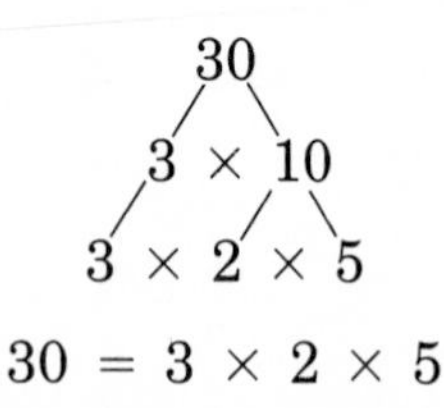

$30 = 3 \times 2 \times 5$

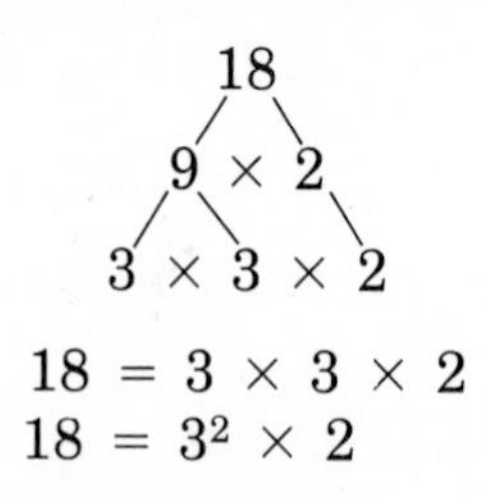

$18 = 3 \times 3 \times 2$

$18 = 3^2 \times 2$

Practice • Find the prime factorization. Use a factor tree.

1. 6 **2.** 10 **3.** 14 **4.** 16 **5.** 21

6. 25 **7.** 26 **8.** 32 **9.** 40 **10.** 45

Find the prime factorization. Use a factor tree. Write your answer using exponents.

11. 27 **12.** 48 **13.** 32 **14.** 8 **15.** 50

Mixed Practice • Find the prime factorization. Use a factor tree.

16. 12 **17.** 36 **18.** 20 **19.** 42 **20.** 28

21. 51 **22.** 58 **23.** 62 **24.** 76 **25.** 84

26. 99 **27.** 85 **28.** 54 **29.** 92 **30.** 78

Find the prime factorization. Use a factor tree. Write your answer using exponents.

31. 100 **32.** 120 **33.** 96 ★**34.** 144 ★**35.** 180

Write the number represented by the prime factorization.

36. $2^2 \times 3$ **37.** $2^3 \times 5$ **38.** $2^2 \times 3^2$

PROBLEM SOLVING • APPLICATIONS

You can use a "downward" division process to find the prime factorization of a number. Divide the number and then the quotients by primes until the final quotient is 1. The divisors are the prime factors of the number.

$$200 = 2 \times 2 \times 2 \times 5 \times 5$$
$$= 2^3 \times 5^2$$

First step
2⟌200
100
quotient

Second step
2⟌200
2⟌100

Completed process
2⟌200
2⟌100
2⟌50
5⟌25
5⟌5
1

Use division to find the prime factorization.

★**39.** 160 ★**40.** 300 ★**41.** 420

Skills Maintenance

Evaluate the expressions when $a = 76$ and $b = 19$.

1. $a + 28$ **2.** $a - 28$ **3.** $\frac{a}{4}$ **4.** $12a$

5. $a + b$ **6.** $b + a$ **7.** $a(b)$ **8.** $\frac{a}{b}$

Greatest Common Factor

The factors of 12 and 16 are listed below.

Factors of 12: 1, 2, 3, 4, 6, 12
Factors of 16: 1, 2, 4, 8, 16

The numbers 1, 2, and 4
are factors of both 12 and 16.

1, 2, and 4 are **common factors**
of 12 and 16.
4 is the **greatest common factor**
(GCF) of 12 and 16.

Find the GCF of 24 and 36.

Step 1 List the factors of each number. → Factors of 24: 1, 2, 3, 4, 6, 8, 12, 24
Factors of 36: 1, 2, 3, 4, 6, 9, 12, 18, 36

Step 2 List the common factors. → Common factors: 1, 2, 3, 4, 6, 12

Step 3 Select the greatest common factor. → GCF: 12

You can use prime factorizations to find the GCF of two numbers.

Find the GCF of 40 and 60.

Step 1 Write the prime factorization of each number. → 40: $2 \times 2 \times 2 \times 5$
60: $2 \times 2 \times 3 \times 5$

Step 2 List all their common prime factors. → $2 \times 2 \times 5$

Step 3 Find the product of these common factors. → GCF: 20

Practice • List the factors of each number. Then find the GCF.

1. 4, 6 **2.** 9, 12 **3.** 10, 12 **4.** 20, 30 **5.** 15, 30

Use the prime factorizations of each pair of numbers to find their GCF.

6. 12, 16 **7.** 9, 15 **8.** 30, 34 **9.** 42, 60 **10.** 9, 14

Mixed Practice • List the factors of each number. Then find the GCF.

11. 7, 28 **12.** 10, 25 **13.** 8, 12 **14.** 9, 45 **15.** 8, 14

16. 12, 36 **17.** 24, 36 **18.** 42, 70 **19.** 50, 60 **20.** 25, 75

21. 35, 49 **22.** 40, 48 **23.** 14, 26 **24.** 35, 40 **25.** 30, 42

Use the prime factorizations of each pair of numbers to find their GCF.

26. 18, 24 **27.** 24, 60 **28.** 15, 60 **29.** 8, 15 **30.** 14, 35

31. 28, 42 **32.** 60, 90 **33.** 45, 66 **34.** 9, 90 **35.** 55, 100

36. 12, 18 **37.** 24, 84 **38.** 25, 40 **39.** 30, 21 **40.** 160, 270

★**41.** 15, 45, 60 ★**42.** 24, 30, 90 ★**43.** 72, 104, 32

PROBLEM SOLVING • APPLICATIONS

Vince likes to experiment with numbers. He made this conjecture, or guess, about odd numbers and primes.

Every odd number greater than 7 can be shown as the sum of three prime numbers.

$9 = 3 + 3 + 3$

$13 = 3 + 5 + 5$

Check Vince's conjecture. Try to write an equation to show each number as the sum of three primes.

44. 15 ★**45.** 37 ★**46.** 93

47. Anton wrote this number puzzle. What number is n?

$n < 100$

n has 7 and 11 as its prime factors.

★**48.** Memdi wrote this number puzzle. List all the numbers that n might be.

$n < 100$

Its prime factorization includes 2 and 5 and no other numbers. Each factor may appear more than once.

Skills Maintenance

1. $x + 12 = 25$ **2.** $y - 35 = 14$ **3.** $5n = 80$ **4.** $\frac{x}{8} = 21$

5. $y + 17 = 56$ **6.** $32 = n + 19$ **7.** $25 = x - 18$ **8.** $324 = 12n$

Multiples and Least Common Multiple

Multiply a whole number such as 6 by 0, 1, 2, 3, and so on. Each product is a **multiple** of that number.

The multiples of a number are divisible by that number.

	0×6	1×6	2×6	3×6	4×6	5×6	6×6
Multiples of 6:	0	6	12	18	24	30	36
Multiples of 9:	0	9	18	27	36	45	54
	0×9	1×9	2×9	3×9	4×9	5×9	6×9

Any numbers that are multiples of both 6 and 9 are **common multiples** of 6 and 9. 0, 18, and 36 are common multiples of 6 and 9. Excluding 0, 18 is the least number that is a common multiple of 6 and 9. 18 is called the **least common multiple (LCM)** of 6 and 9.

Is 0 a multiple of every number?
Zero is not used as an LCM for any pair of numbers.

Find the least common multiple of 8 and 12.

Step 1 Begin by listing the nonzero multiples of the greater number in order. Check each time to see if the multiple of 12 is a multiple of 8.

1×12
12
↑
Not a multiple of 8

2×12
24
↑
Multiple of 8
$24 = 3 \times 8$

Step 2 Select the least nonzero multiple of both 8 and 12.

24 is the LCM of 8 and 12.

You can also use prime factorizations to find the LCM of two or more numbers.

Find the LCM of 15 and 18.

Step 1 Write the prime factorization of each number. Use exponents.

$15 = 3^1 \times 5^1$
$18 = 3^2 \times 2^1$

Step 2 Write each prime factor with its greatest exponent shown in the factorization.

LCM: $3^2 \times 5^1 \times 2^1 = 90$
$9 \times 5 \times 2$

90 is the LCM of 15 and 18.

Practice • List the first five nonzero multiples of each number.

1. 2 **2.** 3 **3.** 5 **4.** 8 **5.** 10

Find the least common multiple.

6. 2, 3 **7.** 2, 5 **8.** 2, 8 **9.** 3, 5 **10.** 8, 10

Mixed Practice • List the first five nonzero multiples of each number.

11. 4 **12.** 9 **13.** 12 **14.** 15 **15.** 18

16. 20 **17.** 25 **18.** 40 **19.** 50 **20.** 100

Find the least common multiple.

21. 4, 10 **22.** 4, 9 **23.** 5, 9 **24.** 6, 12 **25.** 6, 15

26. 12, 15 **27.** 12, 18 **28.** 12, 20 **29.** 9, 15 **30.** 4, 20

31. 20, 25 **32.** 20, 50 **33.** 25, 50 **34.** 15, 20 **35.** 15, 25

Use prime factorizations to find the LCM.

36. 10, 15 **37.** 40, 60 **38.** 40,100 ★**39.** 72, 60 ★**40.** 49, 50

To find the LCM of three numbers such as 4, 6, and 10, you can begin by naming the nonzero multiples of 10 in order. Each time, check to see if the multiple is also a multiple of 4 and 6.

10, 20, 30, 40, 50, 60, 70, . . .

60 is the least number that is also a multiple of 4 and 6.
60 is the LCM of 4, 6, and 10.

Find the LCM. (You can use prime factorizations if you like.)

41. 3, 6, 9 **42.** 2, 6, 10 ★**43.** 3, 4, 5 ★**44.** 2, 3, 7 ★**45.** 4, 8, 9

PROBLEM SOLVING • APPLICATIONS

46. If a and b are nonzero whole numbers, is $a \times b$ always a common multiple of a and b?

47. Is $a \times b$ always the LCM for a and b?

a	b
3	5
6	7
6	9
2	8

★**48.** Jessie has enough eggs to divide them into 2, 3, 4, 6, or 9 groups of the same number. What is the least number of eggs she can have?

PROBLEM SOLVING • STRATEGIES

Making an Organized List

Sometimes a problem has more than one possible solution.

In a baseball game, Sam had 3 hits. None of them was a home run. What combinations of hits might Sam have had?

The problem tells us that Sam did not hit any home runs, but it does not tell the number of triples, doubles, or singles he had.

Could all 3 of his hits have been triples? Could he have had 2 triples and 1 double?

You can make an organized list to show all the possibilities.

The list shows the ten possible combinations of hits Sam might have had.

Triples	Doubles	Singles
3	0	0
2	1	0
2	0	1
1	2	0
1	1	1
1	0	2
0	3	0
0	2	1
0	1	2
0	0	3

Solve.

1. Tina had 4 hits in a series of games. None of them was a home run or a single. Show all the possible combinations of hits Tina might have had.

2. Carla had 6 hits in a series of games. None of them was a home run or a triple. Show all the possible combinations of hits Carla might have had.

3. Jim had 7 hits in a series of games. All of his hits were doubles or singles. He had more doubles than singles. Show all the possible combinations of hits he might have had.

An organized list or a table is useful in solving various problems.

4. Arlene had 8 hits in a series of games. All of her hits were singles or home runs. She had fewer home runs than singles. Show all the possible combinations of hits she might have had.

5. Tony has 9 coins. All of them are dimes or pennies. Show all the possible combinations of coins he could have.

6. Angela has 8 coins. All of them are dimes or nickels. Show all the possible combinations of coins Angela could have.

7. Janos has 7 coins. All of them are quarters, dimes, or nickels. Show all the possible combinations of coins Janos could have.

8. What are the greatest and least amounts of money Janos could have?

Be sure your list shows *all* the possibilities.

9. Willa has 8 coins. All of them are half-dollars, nickels, or pennies. Show all the possible combinations of coins Willa could have.

10. What are the greatest and least amounts of money Willa could have?

★11. How many different ways can you give $.75 in change if you have only dimes and pennies? List the ways.

★12. How many different ways can you give $.62 in change if you have only quarters, dimes, and pennies? List the ways.

CHAPTER 6

REVIEW

Which numbers are divisible by 4? (pp. 140–141)

1. 28 **2.** 96 **3.** 108 **4.** 3,614 **5.** 14,128

Which numbers are divisible by 10? (pp. 140–141)

6. 325 **7.** 90 **8.** 505 **9.** 1,410 **10.** 58,740

Which numbers are divisible by 3? (pp. 142–143)

11. 66 **12.** 715 **13.** 609 **14.** 957 **15.** 600

Which numbers are divisible by 9? (pp. 142–143)

16. 225 **17.** 171 **18.** 638 **19.** 450 **20.** 601

Find all the factors. List them in order. (pp. 144–145)

21. 36 **22.** 54 **23.** 80 **24.** 92 **25.** 105

Write *prime* or *composite*. (pp. 144–145)

26. 29 **27.** 16 **28.** 99 **29.** 41 **30.** 81

31. Find the prime factorization of 30. (pp. 146–147)

32. Find the prime factorization of 56. Write your answer using exponents. (pp. 146–147)

Find the greatest common factor. (pp. 148–149)

33. 9, 24 **34.** 15, 40 **35.** 8, 36 **36.** 18, 27 **37.** 12, 36

Find the least common multiple. (pp. 150–151)

38. 2, 7 **39.** 8, 12 **40.** 6, 21 **41.** 9, 12 **42.** 12, 15

43. n is a whole number. $20 < n$ and $n < 50$. n is divisible by both 3 and 5. List all the different whole numbers that n might be. (pp. 142–143)

44. You have dimes and pennies. How many different ways can you make \$.65 in change? (pp. 152–153)

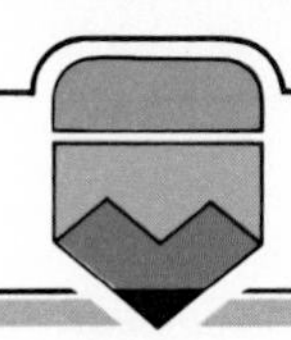

PROJECT

Venn Diagrams

A **Venn diagram** is a useful method for showing relationships.

This rectangle stands for all the whole numbers.

This **Venn diagram** shows that:

All multiples of 10 are even numbers.

The diagram also shows that:

Some even numbers are not multiples of 10.

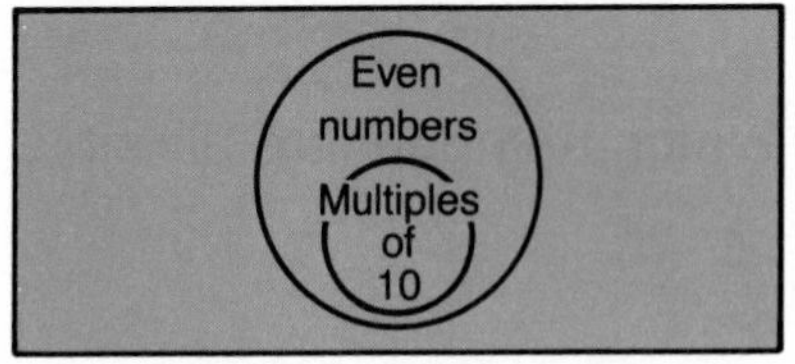

WHOLE NUMBERS

This diagram shows that:

Some even numbers are divisible by 5.
Some numbers that are divisible by 5 are even numbers.
Not all even numbers are divisible by 5.
Not all numbers divisible by 5 are even numbers.

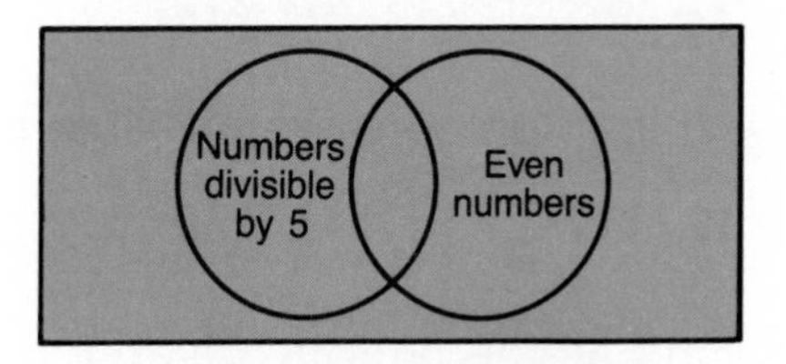

WHOLE NUMBERS

This diagram shows that:

No even numbers are odd numbers.
No odd numbers are even numbers.

We can also say:

None of the even numbers is an odd number.
None of the odd numbers is an even number.

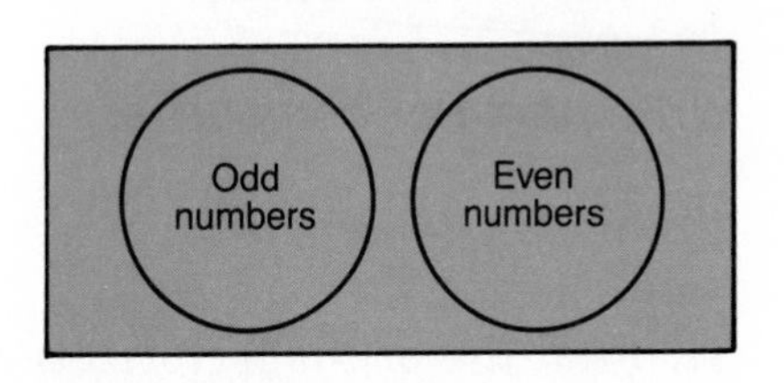

Look at the diagrams. Then write two true statements for each diagram. Use the words *all, some,* and *no* (or *none*).

1. WHOLE NUMBERS

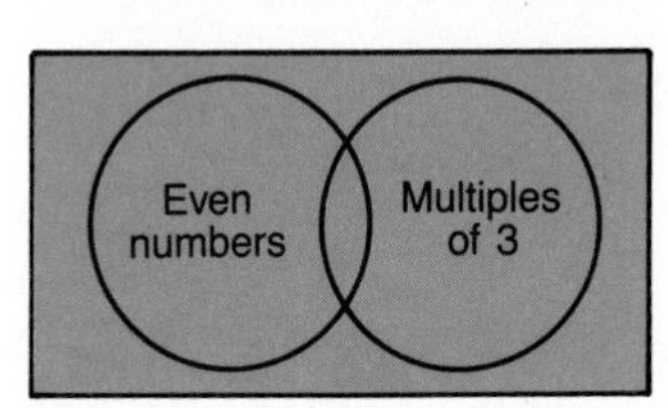

2. WHOLE NUMBERS

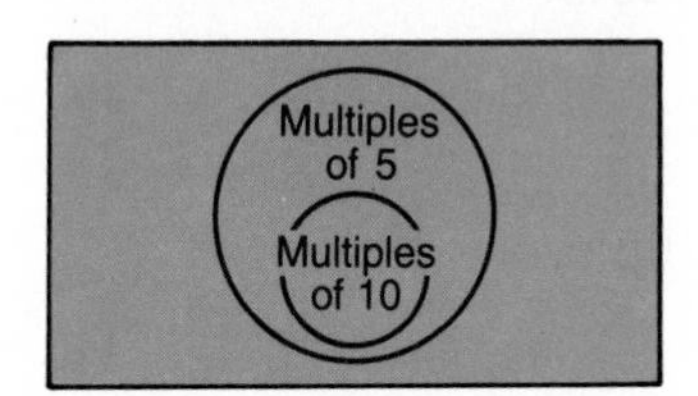

3. WHOLE NUMBERS

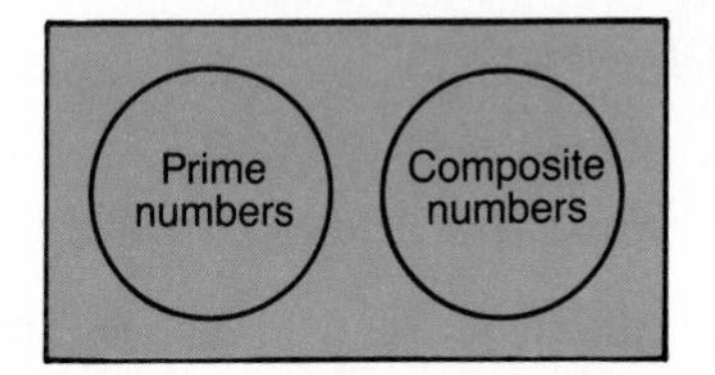

4. Try to draw a Venn diagram to show that: All even numbers are divisible by 2. All numbers divisible by 2 are even numbers.

5. Find the names of all the Presidents of the United States. Find the names of all the Vice Presidents of the United States. Draw a Venn diagram that shows how these groups are related.

CHAPTER 6 TEST

Which numbers are divisible by 2?

1. 20 **2.** 131 **3.** 460 **4.** 1,123 **5.** 17,814

Which numbers are divisible by 5?

6. 75 **7.** 130 **8.** 613 **9.** 6,505 **10.** 11,871

Which numbers are divisible by 3?

11. 42 **12.** 273 **13.** 907 **14.** 657 **15.** 400

Which numbers are divisible by 9?

16. 117 **17.** 159 **18.** 729 **19.** 630 **20.** 973

Find all the factors. List them in order.

21. 18 **22.** 20 **23.** 35 **24.** 42 **25.** 63

Write *prime* or *composite*.

26. 14 **27.** 26 **28.** 39 **29.** 53 **30.** 19

31. Find the prime factorization of 70.

32. Find the prime factorization of 54. Write your answer using exponents.

Find the greatest common factor.

33. 10, 35 **34.** 9, 30 **35.** 12, 66 **36.** 18, 45 **37.** 15, 30

Find the least common multiple.

38. 3, 8 **39.** 6, 10 **40.** 9, 24 **41.** 8, 20 **42.** 15, 45

43. n is a whole number. $40 < n$ and $n < 100$. n is divisible by both 5 and 9. List all the different numbers that n might be.

44. You have nickels and pennies. How many different ways can you make $.37 in change?

ENRICHMENT

Clock Arithmetic

Seth boards a bus at 7 o'clock and travels 3 hours. He arrives at 10 o'clock.

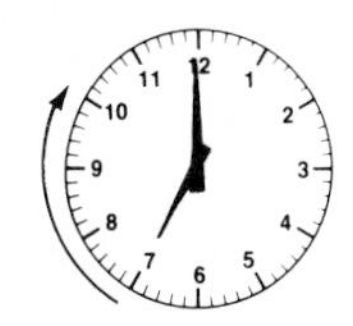

Maria boards a bus at 10 o'clock and travels 4 hours. She arrives at 2 o'clock.

We can work in a special number system that uses only the numbers on a clock face: 1, 2, 3, 4, 5, 6, 7, 8, 9, 10, 11, 12. This is a **finite** (limited) set of numbers. Here are the special "addition" equations that tell about the two bus trips.

$7 + 3 = 10$ $\qquad\qquad$ $10 + 4 = 2$

The second equation may look very strange to you. But remember that this is addition of clock numbers.

Copy and solve these equations using only the clock numbers.

1. $9 + 2 = n$ **2.** $9 + 3 = n$ **3.** $9 + 4 = n$

4. $11 + 3 = n$ **5.** $11 + 4 = n$ **6.** $11 + 5 = n$

7. $6 + 7 = n$ **8.** $6 + 9 = n$ **9.** $6 + 11 = n$

10. $2 + 12 = n$ **11.** $5 + 12 = n$ **12.** $8 + 12 = n$

13. Study your equations for exercises 10–12. If x is any clock number, what does $x + 12$ equal?

14. Copy and complete this table to show the basic facts for addition of clock numbers.

+	1	2	3	4	5	6	7	8	9	10	11	12
1	2	3	4	5	6	7	8	9	10	11	12	1
2	3	4	5								1	2
3												
11	12											
12	1	2	3	4	5	6	7	8	9			

15. Does addition of clock numbers have the commutative property?

16. In the clock number system, does $(5 + 4) + 7 = 5 + (4 + 7)$? Does addition of clock numbers have the associative property? Write 10 equations that support your answer.

You can multiply in the clock number system. For example, 3×6 means $6 + 6 + 6$.

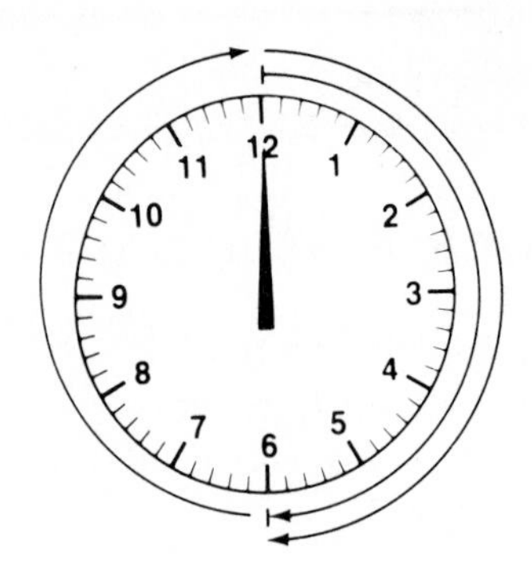

Begin at 12 on the clock face.
Make 3 moves, each one a move of 6 hours forward.
You end at 6.

So $3 \times 6 = 6$ in the clock number system.

Copy and solve these equations using only the clock numbers. Start at 12 on the clock face.

17. $3 \times 3 = n$ **18.** $4 \times 3 = n$ **19.** $5 \times 3 = n$

20. $1 \times 8 = n$ **21.** $2 \times 8 = n$ **22.** $3 \times 8 = n$

When the moves go past 12 or go around the clock face several times, you can use ordinary division to identify the product in the clock number system. For example, consider 5×7.

First multiply the ordinary way. ⟶ $5 \times 7 = 35$

Next divide by 12. If $r \neq 0$, then the remainder gives the answer in the clock number system. ⟶ $12\overline{)35}$ = 2 r11

2 complete revolutions + 11 more hours.

$5 \times 7 = 11$ in the clock number system.

Find the products in the clock number system.

23. $9 \times 3 = n$ **24.** $10 \times 3 = n$ **25.** $11 \times 3 = n$

26. $6 \times 9 = n$ **27.** $7 \times 9 = n$ **28.** $8 \times 9 = n$

29. Make a table for multiplication facts in the clock number system. Show all the facts, from 1×1 to 12×12.

30. In the clock number system, does multiplication have the commutative property? the associative property?

31. In the clock number system, for any number y, does $1 \times y = y$ and $y \times 1 = y$? Is this different from or similar to ordinary multiplication?

32. Use a library to find out what is meant by a **modular system** in mathematics. Write a short report on a modular system.

COMPUTER

Computer Operation

The speed of a computer is measured in relation to cycle time. *Cycle time* is the amount of time for one tick of the computer's internal clock. In the time of one clock tick, a bit can turn from on to off. In the fastest computer today, a bit can turn on or off eighty million times per second.

Storage density measures the amount of data stored in the computer. Microcomputers today store about 400,000 bits per square inch. Research will find methods to increase storage density greatly.

Computer hardware operates by certain rules called *rules of logic.* These rules never change.

The *NOT rule of logic* says: Make a bit what it is NOT.
If the input is 0, the output is 1.
If the input is 1, the output is 0.

The *AND rule of logic* says: Turn on the output bit if BOTH input bits are 1.
If the input is 1 and 1, the output is 1.
If the input is anything else, the output is 0.

The *OR rule of logic* says: Turn on the output bit if EITHER input bit is 1 or if BOTH input bits are 1.
If the input is 0 and 0, the output is 0.
If the input is anything else, the output is 1.

Copy and complete these tables of logic.

NOT rule	AND rule	OR rule
Input → Output	Input → Output	Input → Output
1. 0 → ?	**5.** 0 and 1 → ?	**9.** 1 and 1 → ?
2. 1 → ?	**6.** 1 and 0 → ?	**10.** 0 and 0 → ?
3. 1 → ?	**7.** 1 and 1 → ?	**11.** 1 and 0 → ?
4. 0 → ?	**8.** 0 and 0 → ?	**12.** 0 and 1 → ?

13. Suppose the output according to the AND rule is 1. What was the input?

14. Suppose the output according to the OR rule is 0. What was the input?

SKILLS MAINTENANCE

Chapters 1 Through 6

Choose the correct answers.

1. Add.

$$\begin{array}{r} 468{,}309 \\ +\ 59{,}876 \\ \hline \end{array}$$

A. 408,433
B. 428,185
C. 528,185
D. not here

2. Subtract.

$$\begin{array}{r} 9.07 \\ -7.4832 \\ \hline \end{array}$$

A. 16.5532
B. 1.5868
C. 1.6868
D. not here

3. Multiply.

$$\begin{array}{r} 0.652 \\ \times\ 4.79 \\ \hline \end{array}$$

A. 312.308
B. 31.2308
C. 3.12308
D. not here

4. Divide.

$0.37\overline{)57.831}$

A. 156.3
B. 15.63
C. 1,563
D. not here

5. Which list shows numbers that are all divisible by 3?

A. 99; 128; 306
B. 33; 903; 657
C. 300; 426; 716
D. not here

6. Multiply.

$$\begin{array}{r} 978 \\ \times 407 \\ \hline \end{array}$$

A. 45,966
B. 398,064
C. 398,406
D. not here

7. Solve.

$21n = 315$

A. $n = 294$
B. $n = 336$
C. $n = 15$
D. not here

8. Find the GCF of 16 and 72.

A. 8
B. 4
C. 9
D. not here

9. Find the LCM of 9 and 24.

A. 216
B. 72
C. 18
D. not here

10. Robert earned \$12.75 on Monday, \$14.20 on Tuesday, and \$13.05 on Wednesday. He worked about 4 hours each day. How much money did he earn in the three days?

A. \$10.00 **B.** \$40.00
C. \$160.00 **D.** not here

11. Laura has 5 coins. All of them are dimes or nickels. How many possible combinations of coins could Laura have?

A. 2 **B.** 4
C. 6 **D.** not here

Fractions: Addition and Subtraction

CHAPTER 7

Fractions and Whole Numbers • Equivalent Fractions • Lowest Terms • Comparing Fractions • Fractions and Mixed Numbers • Adding Fractions • Adding Mixed Numbers • Problem Solving: Sensible Answers • Subtracting Fractions • Subtracting Mixed Numbers and Whole Numbers • Problem Solving: Multistep Problems • Stocks • Flowcharts

Fractions and Whole Numbers

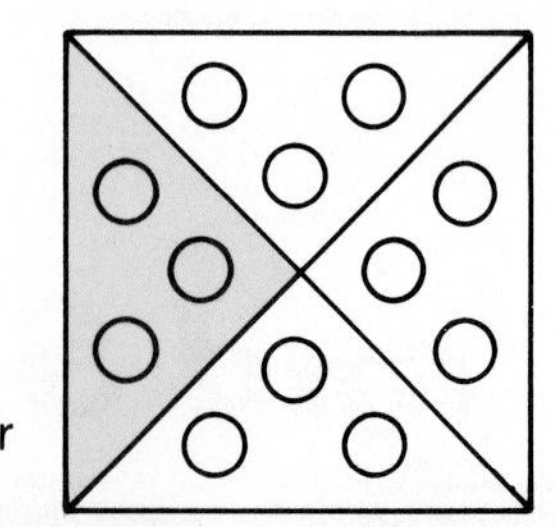

This gameboard is divided into 4 equal parts. 1 of the parts is yellow. One-fourth of the gameboard is yellow. The **fraction** $\frac{1}{4}$ tells what part of the game board is yellow.

terms of the fraction $\frac{1}{4}$ ← numerator, ← denominator

There are 3 boxes.
2 boxes have nails in them.
There are nails in $\frac{2}{3}$ of the boxes.

On this number line, the distance from 0 to 1 has been divided into 3 equal parts.

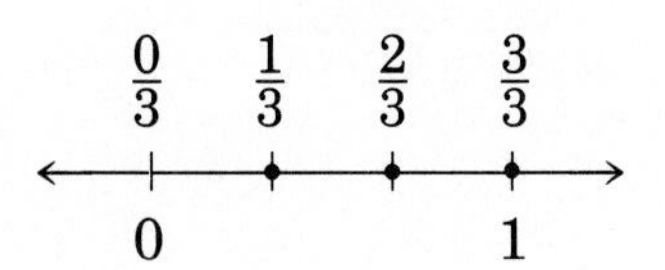

The point for $\frac{1}{3}$ is one-third of the distance from 0 to 1.

The point for $\frac{2}{3}$ is two-thirds of the distance from 0 to 1.

You can also see that $\frac{3}{3} = 1$. $\frac{3}{3}$ and 1 name the same number.

Fractions are often used to show quotients of whole numbers. Sometimes the quotient is a whole number.

$1 \div 4 = \frac{1}{4}$ $\qquad 4 \div 4 = \frac{4}{4} = 1$ $\qquad 8 \div 4 = \frac{8}{4} = 2$

> ***If a and b are whole numbers,* $a \div b = \frac{a}{b}$.**
> ***Remember, b cannot be 0. You cannot divide by 0.***

Practice • Write the fraction for the part that is blue.

1.

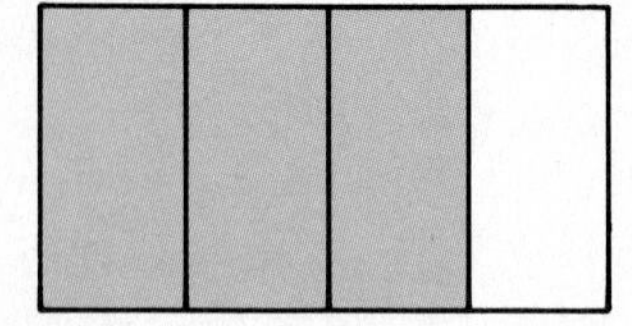

2.

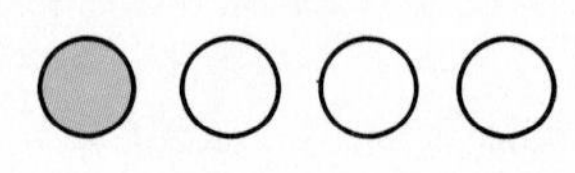

3.

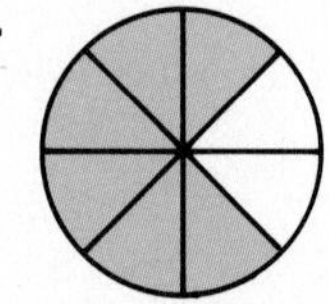

What fraction should replace the question mark?

4.

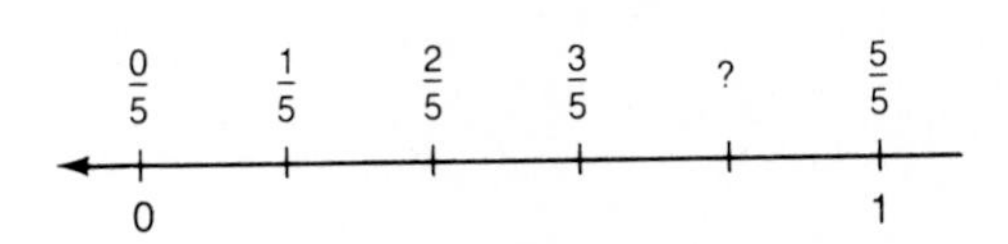

5.

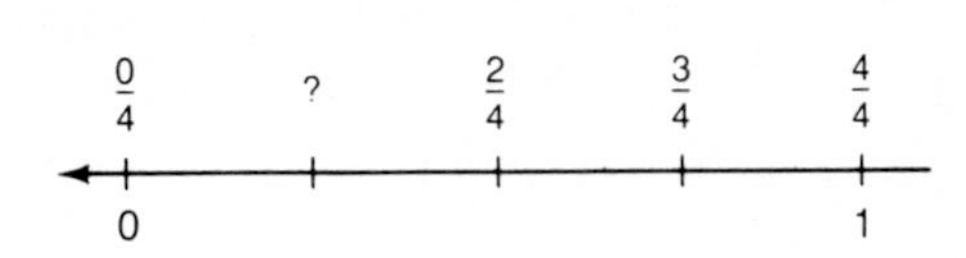

Write the fractions.

6. one-half **7.** two-ninths **8.** seven-eighths **9.** one-twelfth

Write the quotients as fractions.

10. $1 \div 8$ **11.** $5 \div 6$ **12.** $1 \div 10$ **13.** $3 \div 7$

Write as whole numbers.

14. $\frac{6}{6}$ **15.** $\frac{8}{8}$ **16.** $\frac{20}{10}$ **17.** $\frac{6}{2}$

18. $\frac{35}{7}$ **19.** $\frac{24}{6}$ **20.** $\frac{60}{3}$ **21.** $\frac{27}{9}$

Mixed Practice • Write the fractions.

22. five-ninths **23.** three-fifths **24.** one-tenth **25.** four-sevenths

Write the quotients as fractions.

26. $1 \div 2$ **27.** $1 \div 9$ **28.** $3 \div 5$ **29.** $5 \div 8$

Write as whole numbers.

30. $\frac{3}{3}$ **31.** $\frac{4}{2}$ ★**32.** $\frac{100}{10}$ ★**33.** $\frac{500}{100}$

PROBLEM SOLVING • APPLICATIONS

34. Leon was building a bird-feeding station for Environmental Awareness Day at his school. He began by cutting a board into 5 equal pieces. He used 3 pieces for his project. What fractional part of the board did he use?

★**35.** What fractional part of the board was not used by Leon?

★**36.** Susan spent $\frac{1}{3}$ of a day building a bookcase. How many hours did she work?

Equivalent Fractions

Equivalent fractions name the same number. $\frac{1}{2}$, $\frac{2}{4}$, and $\frac{4}{8}$ are equivalent fractions.

There are two ways to find equivalent fractions.

1. Multiply the numerator and denominator by the same number.

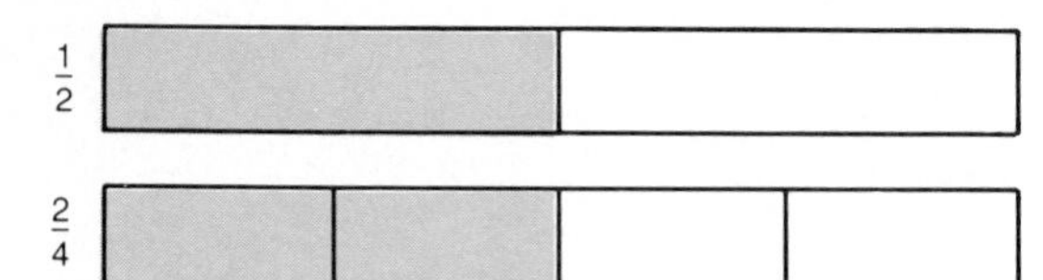

$$\frac{1}{2} = \frac{2 \times 1}{2 \times 2} = \frac{2}{4}$$

Make the fractions equivalent.

$$\frac{3}{4} = \frac{n}{20}$$

Think: What number times 4 is 20?
Multiply both terms by 5

$$\frac{3}{4} = \frac{5 \times 3}{5 \times 4} = \frac{15}{20}$$

2. Divide the numerator and the denominator by the same number.

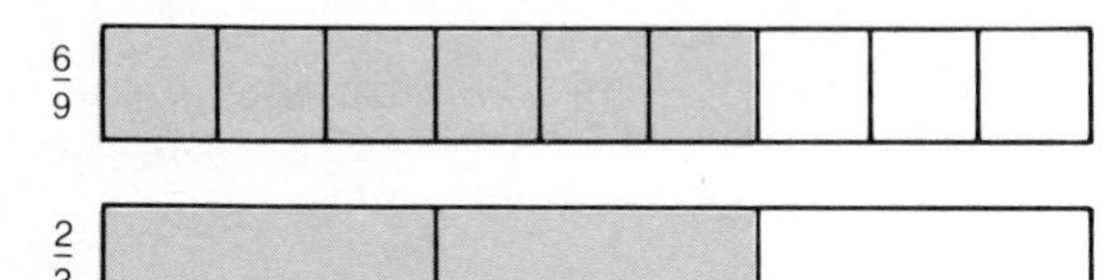

$$\frac{6}{9} = \frac{6 \div 3}{9 \div 3} = \frac{2}{3}$$

Make the fractions equivalent.

$$\frac{20}{24} = \frac{n}{6}$$

Think: 24 divided by what number is 6?
Divide both terms by 4.

$$\frac{20}{24} = \frac{20 \div 4}{24 \div 4} = \frac{5}{6}$$

Multiplying or dividing both terms of a fraction by the same number (not zero) results in an equivalent fraction.

Practice • Make the fractions equivalent.

1. $\frac{2}{3} = \frac{n}{6}$ **2.** $\frac{3}{4} = \frac{n}{20}$ **3.** $\frac{7}{20} = \frac{n}{40}$ **4.** $\frac{2}{9} = \frac{n}{45}$ **5.** $\frac{7}{8} = \frac{n}{32}$

6. $\frac{4}{8} = \frac{n}{2}$ **7.** $\frac{6}{10} = \frac{n}{5}$ **8.** $\frac{9}{12} = \frac{3}{n}$ **9.** $\frac{20}{32} = \frac{5}{n}$ **10.** $\frac{25}{100} = \frac{1}{n}$

Mixed Practice • Make the fractions equivalent.

11. $\frac{1}{2} = \frac{n}{10}$ 12. $\frac{2}{3} = \frac{n}{12}$ 13. $\frac{3}{4} = \frac{n}{24}$ 14. $\frac{1}{6} = \frac{n}{18}$ 15. $\frac{7}{10} = \frac{n}{20}$

16. $\frac{5}{6} = \frac{n}{30}$ 17. $\frac{1}{2} = \frac{n}{8}$ 18. $\frac{1}{3} = \frac{n}{21}$ 19. $\frac{3}{8} = \frac{n}{40}$ 20. $\frac{9}{10} = \frac{n}{50}$

21. $\frac{5}{20} = \frac{n}{4}$ 22. $\frac{12}{18} = \frac{n}{3}$ 23. $\frac{6}{12} = \frac{1}{n}$ 24. $\frac{15}{20} = \frac{3}{n}$ 25. $\frac{8}{10} = \frac{4}{n}$

26. $\frac{9}{21} = \frac{3}{n}$ 27. $\frac{20}{24} = \frac{5}{n}$ 28. $\frac{12}{32} = \frac{n}{8}$ 29. $\frac{3}{30} = \frac{n}{10}$ 30. $\frac{15}{36} = \frac{5}{n}$

31. $\frac{3}{4} = \frac{n}{16}$ 32. $\frac{10}{25} = \frac{2}{n}$ 33. $\frac{6}{54} = \frac{1}{n}$ 34. $\frac{2}{3} = \frac{n}{18}$ 35. $\frac{4}{5} = \frac{n}{25}$

36. $\frac{5}{10} = \frac{1}{n}$ 37. $\frac{6}{10} = \frac{3}{n}$ 38. $\frac{3}{10} = \frac{n}{100}$ 39. $\frac{75}{100} = \frac{3}{n}$ ★40. $\frac{550}{1{,}000} = \frac{11}{n}$

You know that decimals and fractions can be written for the same numbers. Write the fractions that make these equations true.

41. $0.3 = n$ 42. $0.03 = n$ 43. $0.79 = n$ 44. $0.001 = n$ 45. $0.103 = n$

If cross products are equal, then the fractions are equivalent.

$\frac{2}{3}$ ● $\frac{40}{60}$

2×60 ● 3×40

$120 = 120$ True

The cross products are equal, and so the fractions are equivalent.

$\frac{2}{3}$ ● $\frac{24}{39}$

2×39 ● 3×24

$78 \neq 72$

The cross products are not equal, and so the fractions are not equivalent.

Write = or ≠.

46. $\frac{1}{3}$ ● $\frac{4}{12}$ 47. $\frac{6}{7}$ ● $\frac{5}{6}$ 48. $\frac{3}{4}$ ● $\frac{75}{100}$ 49. $\frac{2}{3}$ ● $\frac{3}{4}$ 50. $\frac{9}{11}$ ● $\frac{11}{13}$

PROBLEM SOLVING • APPLICATIONS

51. I am equivalent to $\frac{5}{10}$. My denominator is 2. What number am I?

52. I am equivalent to $\frac{3}{8}$. My numerator is 9. What number am I?

Suppose n is a whole number greater than 0.

★53. What whole number is equal to $\frac{n}{n}$?

★54. What whole number is equal to $\frac{3n}{n}$?

Lowest Terms

The fractions $\frac{4}{12}$, $\frac{2}{6}$, and $\frac{1}{3}$ are equivalent fractions.

Divide both terms of $\frac{4}{12}$ by their common factor 2.

$$\frac{4}{12} = \frac{4 \div 2}{12 \div 2} = \frac{2}{6}$$

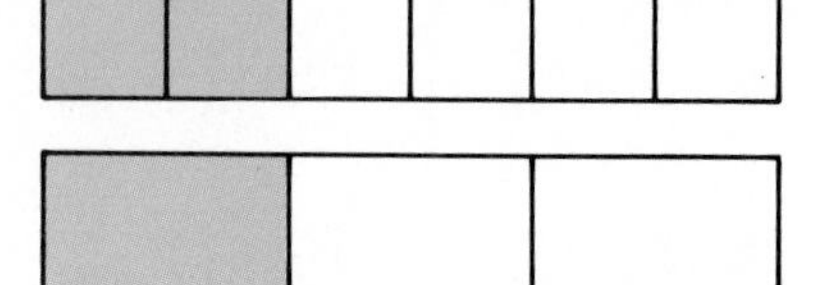

Divide both terms of $\frac{4}{12}$ by their common factor 4.

$$\frac{4}{12} = \frac{4 \div 4}{12 \div 4} = \frac{1}{3}$$

The fraction $\frac{1}{3}$ is in **lowest terms.** A fraction is in lowest terms when the numerator and the denominator have no common factor other than 1.

Write $\frac{12}{18}$ as a fraction in lowest terms.

Step 1 Find the greatest common factor of 12 and 18. 6 is the GCF. → Factors of 12: 1, 2, 3, 4, (6), 12
Factors of 18: 1, 2, 3, (6), 9, 18

Step 2 Divide the numerator and the denominator by 6. → $\frac{12}{18} = \frac{12 \div 6}{18 \div 6} = \frac{2}{3}$

$\frac{2}{3}$ is the fraction in lowest terms.

> ***To find the lowest terms for a fraction $\frac{a}{b}$, divide a and b by their GCF.***

Here are two different fractions. Which is in lowest terms? Which is not in lowest terms? $\frac{6}{8}$ $\frac{5}{9}$

Practice • Write the fractions in lowest terms.

1. $\frac{8}{12}$ **2.** $\frac{4}{6}$ **3.** $\frac{6}{15}$ **4.** $\frac{2}{5}$ **5.** $\frac{10}{12}$

6. $\frac{9}{16}$ **7.** $\frac{10}{15}$ **8.** $\frac{4}{10}$ **9.** $\frac{6}{20}$ **10.** $\frac{100}{200}$

Mixed Practice • Write the fractions in lowest terms.

11. $\frac{4}{8}$ **12.** $\frac{12}{15}$ **13.** $\frac{9}{24}$ **14.** $\frac{1}{6}$ **15.** $\frac{6}{18}$

16. $\frac{18}{20}$ **17.** $\frac{20}{25}$ **18.** $\frac{60}{72}$ **19.** $\frac{28}{38}$ **20.** $\frac{10}{14}$

Write the fractions in lowest terms.

21. $\frac{18}{24}$ 22. $\frac{10}{21}$ 23. $\frac{30}{40}$ 24. $\frac{24}{36}$ 25. $\frac{35}{50}$

26. $\frac{16}{20}$ 27. $\frac{15}{45}$ 28. $\frac{11}{66}$ 29. $\frac{70}{140}$ 30. $\frac{150}{300}$

31. $\frac{8}{10}$ 32. $\frac{5}{10}$ 33. $\frac{7}{10}$ 34. $\frac{30}{100}$ ★ 35. $\frac{780}{1{,}000}$

Copy and complete.

★ 36. $\frac{7}{10} = \frac{?}{20} = \frac{?}{100} = \frac{?}{200}$

★ 37. $\frac{32}{64} = \frac{?}{16} = \frac{?}{4} = \frac{?}{2}$

Write as whole numbers.

38. $\frac{10}{2}$ 39. $\frac{5}{1}$ 40. $\frac{18}{3}$ 41. $\frac{6}{1}$ 42. $\frac{7}{1}$

★ 43. If n is any whole number, what does $\frac{n}{1}$ equal?

★ 44. If a and b are even numbers (not zero), is $\frac{a}{b}$ a fraction in lowest terms? Explain your answer.

PROBLEM SOLVING • APPLICATIONS

45. There are 36 students in the school band. Every day 24 of them practice for an hour. What fractional part of the band practices an hour a day?

46. Only 8 of the 36 band members practice for 30 minutes a day. What fractional part of the band practices only 30 minutes a day?

47. What part of an hour is 30 minutes?

48. What part of an hour is 15 minutes?

49. What part of an hour is 20 minutes?

★ 50. What part of two hours is 40 minutes?

★ 51. What part of a day is 10 minutes?

★ 52. What part of a day is 2 hours 30 minutes?

★ 53. Is the month of April exactly $\frac{1}{12}$ of a 365-day year?

Comparing Fractions

One cup is $\frac{1}{3}$ full. The other cup is $\frac{2}{3}$ full. Which is greater, $\frac{1}{3}$ or $\frac{2}{3}$?

You know that $\frac{2}{3} > \frac{1}{3}$. It is easy to compare fractions that have the same denominator. The fraction with the greater numerator names the greater number.

How can you compare fractions that have different denominators?

Write the fractions as equivalent fractions with the same denominator. You can use the **least common denominator (LCD).**

Write <, =, or >: $\frac{5}{6} \bullet \frac{3}{4}$.

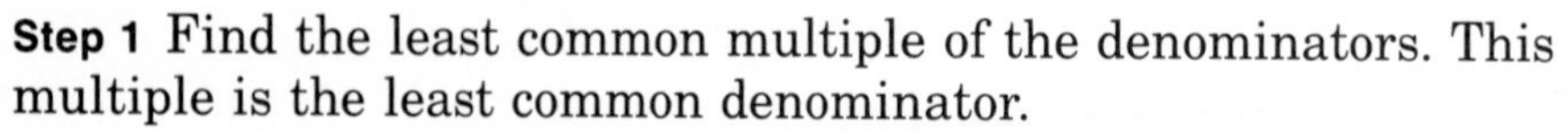

Step 1 Find the least common multiple of the denominators. This multiple is the least common denominator.

Multiples of 6: 6, 12, 18
Multiples of 4: 4, 8, 12 ⟵ 12 is the LCM.

Step 2 Write the fractions as equivalent fractions with the same denominator. Use 12 as the least common denominator.

$\frac{5}{6} = \frac{n}{12}$ $\times 2$ $\qquad \frac{5}{6} = \frac{2 \times 5}{2 \times 6} = \frac{10}{12}$

$\frac{3}{4} = \frac{n}{12}$ $\times 3$ $\qquad \frac{3}{4} = \frac{3 \times 3}{3 \times 4} = \frac{9}{12}$

Since $\frac{10}{12} > \frac{9}{12}$, then $\frac{5}{6} > \frac{3}{4}$.

Practice • Write the fractions as equivalent fractions. Use the least common denominator.

1. $\frac{3}{5}, \frac{2}{3}$ **2.** $\frac{1}{2}, \frac{4}{7}$ **3.** $\frac{1}{4}, \frac{2}{9}$ **4.** $\frac{2}{3}, \frac{7}{9}$ **5.** $\frac{3}{8}, \frac{5}{6}$

Write <, =, or >.

6. $\frac{5}{7} \bullet \frac{6}{7}$ **7.** $\frac{7}{12} \bullet \frac{11}{12}$ **8.** $\frac{7}{8} \bullet \frac{3}{4}$ **9.** $\frac{1}{3} \bullet \frac{1}{4}$ **10.** $\frac{2}{3} \bullet \frac{7}{9}$

Mixed Practice • Write the fractions as equivalent fractions. Use the least common denominator.

11. $\frac{2}{3}, \frac{1}{4}$
12. $\frac{5}{6}, \frac{7}{8}$
13. $\frac{3}{4}, \frac{4}{5}$
14. $\frac{5}{6}, \frac{17}{20}$
15. $\frac{1}{3}, \frac{2}{9}$
16. $\frac{3}{5}, \frac{4}{7}$
17. $\frac{1}{3}, \frac{1}{5}$
18. $\frac{5}{8}, \frac{2}{9}$
19. $\frac{7}{20}, \frac{9}{30}$
20. $\frac{1}{2}, \frac{2}{3}$

Write $<$, $=$, or $>$.

21. $\frac{2}{5}$ ● $\frac{4}{5}$
22. $\frac{7}{9}$ ● $\frac{2}{9}$
23. $\frac{1}{2}$ ● $\frac{3}{7}$
24. $\frac{2}{3}$ ● $\frac{4}{9}$
25. $\frac{5}{6}$ ● $\frac{3}{8}$
26. $\frac{3}{4}$ ● $\frac{5}{9}$
27. $\frac{1}{3}$ ● $\frac{3}{4}$
28. $\frac{7}{20}$ ● $\frac{3}{10}$
29. $\frac{1}{2}$ ● $\frac{5}{10}$
30. $\frac{4}{5}$ ● $\frac{23}{30}$
31. $\frac{4}{9}$ ● $\frac{4}{5}$
32. $\frac{1}{4}$ ● $\frac{1}{5}$
33. $\frac{1}{10}$ ● $\frac{1}{8}$
34. $\frac{9}{14}$ ● $\frac{4}{7}$
★ 35. $\frac{33}{98}$ ● $\frac{164}{490}$

Write the fractions in order from least to greatest.

36. $\frac{2}{3}, \frac{3}{4}, \frac{5}{6}$
37. $\frac{1}{2}, \frac{3}{8}, \frac{2}{5}$
38. $\frac{1}{2}, \frac{2}{3}, \frac{3}{5}$
★ 39. $\frac{2}{3}, \frac{5}{6}, \frac{5}{7}, \frac{5}{8}$
★ 40. $\frac{7}{12}, \frac{3}{4}, \frac{8}{9}, \frac{5}{6}, \frac{7}{8}$
★ 41. $\frac{11}{12}, \frac{9}{10}, \frac{7}{8}, \frac{5}{6}, \frac{3}{4}$

PROBLEM SOLVING • APPLICATIONS

42. Which is longer, $\frac{1}{3}$ of a foot or $\frac{1}{4}$ of a foot?

43. Which is worth more, $\frac{7}{10}$ of a dollar or $\frac{3}{4}$ of a dollar?

44. Which is less, $\frac{2}{3}$ of a yard or $\frac{3}{4}$ of a yard?

★ 45. $a > 0$ and $a < b$. Which is less, $\frac{1}{a}$ or $\frac{1}{b}$?

Skills Maintenance

1. $7\overline{)224}$
2. $9\overline{)792}$
3. $6\overline{)1,824}$
4. $8\overline{)17,168}$
5. $10\overline{)9,650}$
6. $70\overline{)420}$
7. $80\overline{)3,600}$
8. $37\overline{)2,960}$
9. $51\overline{)6,681}$
10. $125\overline{)87,500}$

Fractions and Mixed Numbers

This drawing shows that $\frac{4}{4} = 1$.

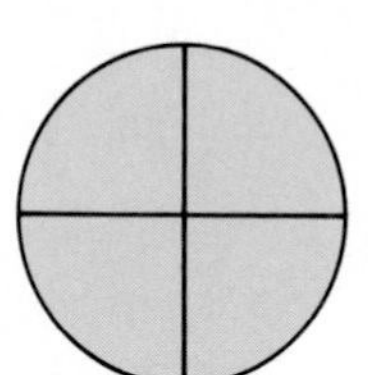

This drawing shows that $\frac{5}{4} = 1 + \frac{1}{4}$.
The **mixed number** $1\frac{1}{4}$ means $1 + \frac{1}{4}$.

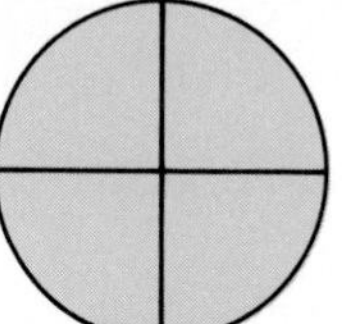

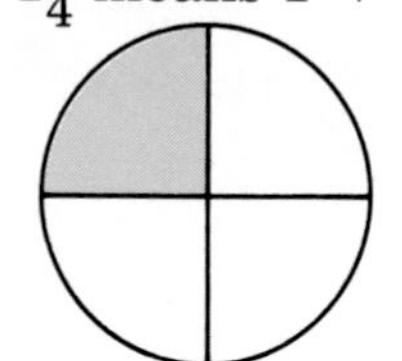

On this number line, the spaces from 0 to 1, 1 to 2, and 2 to 3 have been divided into fourths. You can see that $\frac{5}{4} = 1\frac{1}{4}$ and that $\frac{7}{4} = 1\frac{3}{4}$. Fractions such as $\frac{5}{4}$ and $\frac{7}{4}$ are **improper fractions.** The numerator of an improper fraction is greater than or equal to the denominator.

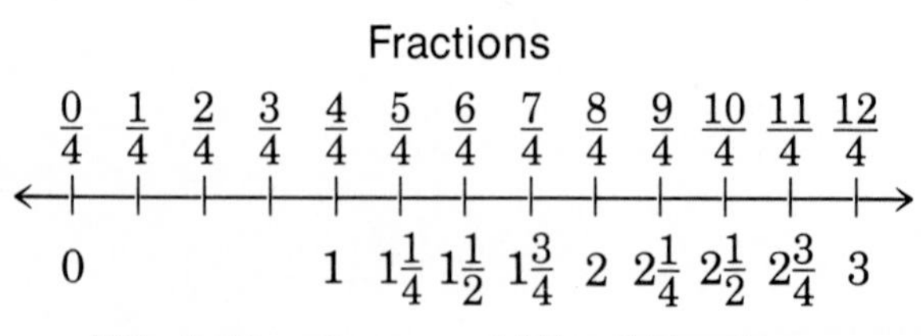

Find a mixed number for $\frac{15}{4}$.

Step 1 Divide the numerator by the denominator.

$$4\overline{)15} = 3 \qquad \begin{array}{r} 15 \\ -12 \\ \hline 3 \end{array}$$

Step 2 Show the remainder as a fraction. The remainder is the numerator. The divisor is the denominator.

$$4\overline{)15} = 3\tfrac{3}{4} \qquad \begin{array}{r} 15 \\ -12 \\ \hline 3 \end{array}$$

Write a fraction for $2\frac{1}{4}$. **Think:** $2\frac{1}{4} \rightarrow 2 + \frac{1}{4} \rightarrow \frac{8}{4} + \frac{1}{4} = \frac{9}{4}$.

Here is another way to write a fraction for $2\frac{1}{4}$. The denominator is 4.

You must find the numerator.

Step 1 Multiply the denominator and the whole number. $2\frac{1}{4}$ (×)

$4 \times 2 = 8$

Step 2 Add the numerator. $2\frac{1}{4}$ (+)

$8 + 1 = 9$

Step 3 Write the fraction. $2\frac{1}{4} = \frac{9}{4}$

Practice • Write as fractions.

1. $1\frac{1}{2}$ **2.** $1\frac{2}{3}$ **3.** $3\frac{4}{5}$ **4.** $2\frac{4}{7}$ **5.** $6\frac{2}{5}$ **6.** $4\frac{3}{10}$

Write as mixed numbers. Use lowest terms for the fractions.

7. $\frac{5}{2}$ **8.** $\frac{17}{4}$ **9.** $\frac{4}{3}$ **10.** $\frac{13}{5}$ **11.** $\frac{14}{6}$ **12.** $\frac{23}{8}$

Mixed Practice • Write as fractions.

13. $4\frac{1}{7}$ **14.** $6\frac{5}{6}$ **15.** $8\frac{1}{2}$ **16.** $2\frac{3}{4}$ **17.** $9\frac{5}{9}$ **18.** $10\frac{4}{9}$

Write as mixed numbers. Use lowest terms for the fractions.

19. $\frac{18}{5}$ **20.** $\frac{10}{8}$ **21.** $\frac{27}{6}$ **22.** $\frac{29}{9}$ **23.** $\frac{19}{4}$ ★**24.** $\frac{270}{100}$

Write as whole numbers.

25. $\frac{6}{6}$ **26.** $\frac{12}{2}$ **27.** $\frac{16}{4}$ **28.** $\frac{20}{2}$ **29.** $\frac{12}{1}$ **30.** $\frac{50}{10}$

Copy and complete.

31. $1 = \frac{n}{4}$ **32.** $2 = \frac{n}{4}$ **33.** $1 = \frac{n}{5}$ **34.** $3 = \frac{n}{5}$ **35.** $6 = \frac{n}{10}$

Write $<$, $=$, or $>$.

36. $1\frac{3}{8}$ ● $\frac{9}{8}$ **37.** $\frac{8}{5}$ ● $1\frac{3}{5}$ **38.** $2\frac{1}{4}$ ● $\frac{11}{4}$ ★**39.** 3.1 ● $\frac{16}{5}$

PROBLEM SOLVING • APPLICATIONS

40. Elena has $2\frac{3}{5}$ dollars. Steve has $2\frac{1}{2}$ dollars. Who has more money?

★**41.** Aretha works 3.4 hours. Paul works $3\frac{1}{2}$ hours. Who works longer? How many minutes longer?

Midchapter Review

Make the fractions equivalent.

1. $\frac{1}{4} = \frac{n}{8}$ **2.** $\frac{3}{5} = \frac{n}{15}$ **3.** $\frac{18}{24} = \frac{3}{n}$

Write in lowest terms.

4. $\frac{8}{16}$ **5.** $\frac{32}{40}$

Write $<$, $=$, or $>$.

6. $\frac{2}{5}$ ● $\frac{1}{5}$ **7.** $\frac{3}{4}$ ● $\frac{9}{12}$ **8.** $\frac{5}{6}$ ● $\frac{7}{8}$

Write as mixed numbers.

9. $\frac{13}{10}$ **10.** $\frac{17}{8}$

Adding Fractions

Jan glued two pieces of wood together. One piece was $\frac{5}{16}$ inch thick and the other was $\frac{3}{16}$ inch thick. What was the total thickness?

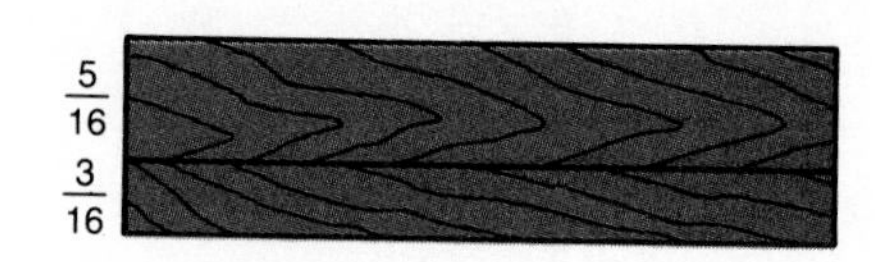

$\frac{5}{16} + \frac{3}{16} = n$

Step 1 The denominators are the same. Add the numerators. Use the common denominator.

$$\begin{array}{r} \frac{5}{16} \\ + \frac{3}{16} \\ \hline \end{array}$$

Step 2 Write the answer in lowest terms.

$$\frac{8}{16} = \frac{1}{2}$$

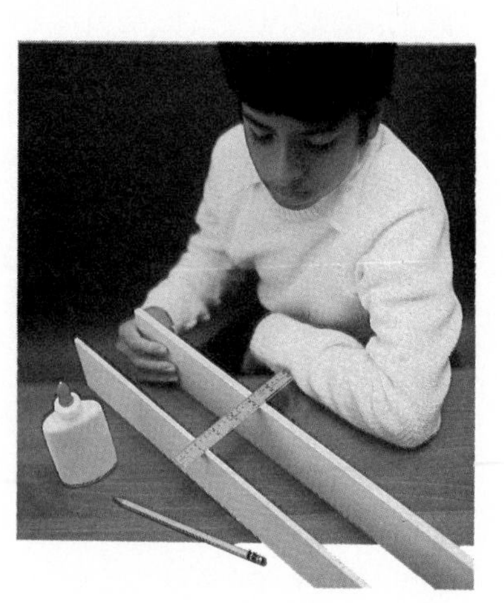

The total thickness was $\frac{1}{2}$ inch.

The example can also be worked in equation form.

$$\frac{5}{16} + \frac{3}{16} = \frac{8}{16}$$
$$= \frac{1}{2}$$

In variables: $\frac{a}{c} + \frac{b}{c} = \frac{a+b}{c}$

To add fractions that have the same denominator, add the numerators. Use the common denominator. Then write the answer in lowest terms when necessary.

Sometimes you must find the sum of two fractions that have different denominators.

Add: $\frac{7}{12} + \frac{5}{8}$.

Step 1 Write the fractions as equivalent fractions with the same denominator. Use the LCD (least common denominator).

$$\begin{array}{rl} \frac{7}{12} = & \frac{14}{24} \\ + \frac{5}{8} = & \frac{15}{24} \\ \hline \end{array}$$

Step 2 Add.

$$\begin{array}{rl} \frac{7}{12} = & \frac{14}{24} \\ + \frac{5}{8} = & \frac{15}{24} \\ \hline & \frac{29}{24} \end{array}$$

Step 3 Since $\frac{29}{24} > 1$, write the answer as a mixed number.

$$\begin{array}{rl} \frac{7}{12} = & \frac{14}{24} \\ + \frac{5}{8} = & \frac{15}{24} \\ \hline & \frac{29}{24} = 1\frac{5}{24} \end{array}$$

Practice • Add. Write the answers in lowest terms.

1. $\frac{2}{7} + \frac{3}{7}$

2. $\frac{1}{2} + \frac{2}{5}$

3. $\frac{5}{12} + \frac{5}{12}$

4. $\frac{2}{3} + \frac{3}{4}$

5. $\frac{3}{8} + \frac{1}{2}$

6. $\frac{3}{10} + \frac{7}{10}$

7. $\frac{3}{4} + \frac{9}{10}$

8. $\frac{5}{6} + \frac{7}{8}$

9. $\frac{5}{8} + \frac{1}{3}$

10. $\frac{9}{10} + \frac{9}{10}$

Mixed Practice • Add. Write the answers in lowest terms.

11. $\frac{3}{8} + \frac{4}{8}$

12. $\frac{1}{10} + \frac{5}{6}$

13. $\frac{3}{4} + \frac{7}{10}$

14. $\frac{1}{4} + \frac{1}{3}$

15. $\frac{3}{12} + \frac{5}{12}$

16. $\frac{7}{10} + \frac{1}{10}$

17. $\frac{2}{9} + \frac{5}{12}$

18. $\frac{3}{5} + \frac{1}{20}$

19. $\frac{1}{4} + \frac{5}{6}$

20. $\frac{4}{5} + \frac{4}{5}$

21. $\frac{4}{15} + \frac{3}{5}$

22. $\frac{5}{8} + \frac{1}{3}$

23. $\frac{3}{7} + \frac{5}{12}$

24. $\frac{4}{5} + \frac{1}{10}$

25. $\frac{5}{8} + \frac{3}{8}$

26. $\frac{1}{10} + \frac{3}{10} + \frac{7}{10}$

27. $\frac{2}{3} + \frac{1}{6} + \frac{1}{2}$

28. $\frac{3}{16} + \frac{1}{2} + \frac{3}{8}$

★ 29. $\frac{2}{5} + \frac{1}{4} + \frac{1}{3}$

★ 30. $\frac{1}{4} + \frac{2}{5} + \frac{1}{6}$

Solve the equations.

31. $\frac{3}{16} + \frac{5}{16} = n$

32. $\frac{1}{5} + \frac{1}{4} = n$

33. $\frac{2}{5} + \frac{7}{8} = n$

34. $\frac{9}{10} + \frac{1}{2} = n$

35. $\frac{3}{4} + \frac{3}{4} = n$

★ 36. $\frac{4}{5} + \frac{2}{3} + \frac{5}{8} = n$

PROBLEM SOLVING • APPLICATIONS

37. Sanji spends $\frac{3}{4}$ hour doing yard work and $\frac{1}{2}$ hour cleaning the cellar. What is the total time spent on these jobs?

★ 38. Tara spends $\frac{1}{2}$ dollar on a card and $\frac{1}{5}$ dollar on a stamp. What part of a dollar does she spend on these two items? How many cents is this?

Adding Mixed Numbers

One day Kathy worked $1\frac{1}{2}$ hours on a science project. The next day she worked $2\frac{1}{4}$ hours to finish the project. How many hours did she work on the project?

$1\frac{1}{2} + 2\frac{1}{4} = n$

Step 1 Rewrite the example using the LCD.

$$\begin{array}{r} 1\frac{1}{2} = 1\frac{2}{4} \\ +2\frac{1}{4} = 2\frac{1}{4} \\ \hline \end{array}$$

Step 2 Add. The sum $3\frac{3}{4}$ is in lowest terms.

$$\begin{array}{r} 1\frac{1}{2} = 1\frac{2}{4} \\ +2\frac{1}{4} = 2\frac{1}{4} \\ \hline 3\frac{3}{4} \end{array}$$

Kathy worked $3\frac{3}{4}$ hours in all.

Add: $3\frac{5}{6} + 1\frac{3}{4}$.

Step 1 Rewrite the example using the LCD.

$$\begin{array}{r} 3\frac{5}{6} = 3\frac{10}{12} \\ +1\frac{3}{4} = 1\frac{9}{12} \\ \hline \end{array}$$

Step 2 Add.

$$\begin{array}{r} 3\frac{5}{6} = 3\frac{10}{12} \\ +1\frac{3}{4} = 1\frac{9}{12} \\ \hline 4\frac{19}{12} \end{array}$$

Step 3 Write the answer as a mixed number in lowest terms.

$\frac{19}{12} = 1\frac{7}{12}$ $\quad 4 + 1\frac{7}{12} = 5\frac{7}{12}$

$$\begin{array}{r} 3\frac{5}{6} = 3\frac{10}{12} \\ +1\frac{3}{4} = 1\frac{9}{12} \\ \hline 4\frac{19}{12} = 5\frac{7}{12} \end{array}$$

More Examples

$$\begin{array}{r} 3\frac{1}{8} \\ +2\frac{5}{8} \\ \hline 5\frac{6}{8} = 5\frac{3}{4} \end{array}$$

$$\begin{array}{r} 5\frac{1}{2} \\ +1\frac{1}{2} \\ \hline 6\frac{2}{2} = 7 \end{array}$$

$$\begin{array}{r} 2\frac{1}{3} = 2\frac{4}{12} \\ 3\frac{1}{6} = 3\frac{2}{12} \\ +\ \frac{5}{12} = \frac{5}{12} \\ \hline 5\frac{11}{12} \end{array}$$

$$\begin{array}{r} 6\frac{2}{5} = 6\frac{12}{30} \\ 1\frac{1}{3} = 1\frac{10}{30} \\ +1\frac{1}{2} = 1\frac{15}{30} \\ \hline 8\frac{37}{30} = 9\frac{7}{30} \end{array}$$

Practice • Add. Write the answers in lowest terms.

1. $\begin{array}{r} 2\frac{1}{5} \\ +1\frac{3}{5} \\ \hline \end{array}$ **2.** $\begin{array}{r} 3\frac{3}{8} \\ +2\frac{1}{4} \\ \hline \end{array}$ **3.** $\begin{array}{r} 2\frac{7}{10} \\ +\ \frac{7}{10} \\ \hline \end{array}$ **4.** $\begin{array}{r} 2\frac{1}{2} \\ +3\frac{1}{3} \\ \hline \end{array}$ **5.** $\begin{array}{r} 8\frac{7}{10} \\ +2 \\ \hline \end{array}$

6. $2\frac{3}{4} + 5\frac{1}{5}$

7. $4\frac{4}{9} + 7\frac{1}{3}$

8. $4\frac{9}{20} + 2\frac{3}{20}$

9. $3\frac{3}{5} + 7\frac{2}{3}$

10. $4\frac{5}{8} + \frac{5}{6}$

Mixed Practice • Add. Write the answers in lowest terms.

11. $6\frac{7}{20} + 1\frac{5}{20}$

12. $2\frac{3}{4} + 1\frac{1}{6}$

13. $3\frac{1}{4} + 4\frac{1}{7}$

14. $3 + 9\frac{1}{4}$

15. $10\frac{2}{3} + 2\frac{1}{5}$

16. $2\frac{5}{10} + 2\frac{5}{8}$

17. $\frac{2}{3} + 2\frac{1}{2}$

18. $5\frac{3}{4} + 4\frac{1}{12}$

19. $4\frac{5}{16} + 3\frac{7}{16}$

20. $2\frac{6}{7} + 3\frac{3}{14}$

21. $9\frac{1}{2} + 6\frac{8}{9}$

22. $7\frac{3}{7} + 2$

23. $2\frac{3}{5} + 6\frac{3}{10}$

24. $5\frac{1}{8} + \frac{5}{8}$

25. $\frac{7}{8} + \frac{5}{6}$

26. $\frac{7}{8} + 2\frac{1}{8} + \frac{3}{8}$

27. $3\frac{9}{10} + 2\frac{9}{10} + 1\frac{7}{10}$

28. $3\frac{1}{3} + 4\frac{5}{6} + \frac{1}{12}$

★ 29. $2\frac{2}{5} + 1\frac{1}{2} + \frac{3}{4}$

★ 30. $1\frac{2}{3} + 3\frac{3}{4} + 5\frac{3}{5}$

Solve the equations.

31. $4\frac{1}{8} + \frac{5}{8} = n$

32. $2\frac{1}{6} + 3\frac{1}{4} = n$

33. $3\frac{1}{5} + 8\frac{3}{5} = n$

34. $12\frac{9}{10} + 11\frac{3}{8} = n$

35. $\frac{9}{10} + \frac{7}{9} = n$

36. $2\frac{7}{9} + 4\frac{1}{6} = n$

★ 37. $n + 5\frac{1}{3} + 2\frac{1}{6} + 1\frac{1}{2} = 41$

★ 38. $7\frac{1}{2} + 5\frac{1}{10} + 4\frac{2}{5} + n = 102$

PROBLEM SOLVING • APPLICATIONS

39. Wyatt is making fruit punch for the annual fund-raising show at his school. He pours $1\frac{5}{8}$ cups of juice into a bowl. Then he pours $1\frac{1}{2}$ cups of water into the bowl. How much liquid is in the bowl?

★ 40. Toni made decorations for a school show. She worked $1\frac{1}{3}$ hours on Monday afternoon, $\frac{3}{4}$ hour on Tuesday afternoon, and $1\frac{4}{5}$ hours on Wednesday afternoon. How many hours did she work in all?

PROBLEM SOLVING • STRATEGIES

Sensible Answers

When you write an answer, be sure it makes sense in the situation. For example, in division situations you often need to decide if it is sensible to express a remainder as a fraction.

Problem 1

One bus route is 26 miles long. The bus makes 20 stops along the route. The stops are equally spaced. How far apart are they?

$$\begin{array}{r} 1\frac{6}{20} = 1\frac{3}{10} \\ 20\overline{)26} \\ \underline{20} \\ 6 \end{array}$$

It is possible to have part of a mile. So the remainder can be shown in a fraction. The stops are $1\frac{3}{10}$ miles apart.

Problem 2

A dispatcher knows that 230 people will need buses between 5:00 P.M. and 6:00 P.M. Each bus can carry 52 people. How many buses should be available?

$$\begin{array}{r} 4 \text{ r}22 \\ 52\overline{)230} \\ \underline{208} \\ 22 \end{array}$$

It is not possible to have only part of a bus available, and so the answer must be either 4 or 5 buses.

4 buses are not enough. 5 buses should be available.

Solve.

1. A bus makes 10 stops along a coastal route that is 27 miles long. The stops along this route are equally spaced. How far apart are they?

2. The bus company is planning a new route. It will be 46 miles long. The company wants the stops to be no farther apart than 6 miles. How many stops after the starting point should be planned?

Be sure your answer makes sense in the problem situation.

3. Bus tokens cost $.80. Alice has $3.00. How many tokens can she buy?

4. Seth has $4.15. How many bus tokens can he buy if tokens cost $.80 each?

5. A new bus can carry 64 people. On one route 230 people ride buses. How many new buses will be needed to serve this route?

6. On one route the dispatcher sends out 8 buses every hour. How many minutes should there be between buses?

7. Steve has a part-time job with a bus company. He works 4 days a week. His total working time is 18 hours per week. What is the average number of hours that he works per day?

8. Steve's brother Gil has a part-time job as a salesperson in an insurance office. Gil works on Monday, Tuesday, Wednesday, and Thursday for a total of 21 hours. He does not work in the office any other day of the week. What is the average number of hours that Gil works per day?

Decide if you can express the remainder as a fraction to answer the question.

9. The Community Club is planning a special bus trip. There will be 287 people going on the trip. Each bus can carry 64 people. How many buses are needed?

10. Toni is planning a party. She decides that she will spend no more than $5.00 on a special fruit drink. If the fruit drink costs 95¢ per bottle, how many bottles can she buy?

11. Toni needs 36 frankfurters. They come 10 in a pack. How many packs should she buy?

★ 12. On Saturday morning Jim rides his bicycle for $2\frac{1}{4}$ hours. On Saturday afternoon he rides for $1\frac{3}{4}$ hours. In all, he rides a total of 27 miles. What is the average distance that he rides per hour?

★ 13. On Friday, Ann works $2\frac{1}{2}$ hours as a waitress. On Saturday, she works $5\frac{1}{2}$ hours as a waitress. She earns a total of $44.00 on these two days. What is the average amount of money that she earns per hour?

Subtracting Fractions

Arnie has $\frac{9}{10}$ dollar. He spends $\frac{3}{10}$ dollar. What part of a dollar does he have left?

$$\frac{9}{10} - \frac{3}{10} = n$$

Step 1 The denominators are the same. Subtract the numerators. Use the common denominator.

Step 2 Write the answer in lowest terms.

$$\begin{array}{r} \frac{9}{10} \\ -\frac{3}{10} \\ \hline \frac{6}{10} = \frac{3}{5} \end{array}$$

Arnie has $\frac{3}{5}$ dollar left.

The example can also be worked in equation form.

$$\frac{9}{10} - \frac{3}{10} = \frac{6}{10}$$
$$= \frac{3}{5}$$

In variables: $\frac{a}{c} - \frac{b}{c} = \frac{a - b}{c}$

> ***To subtract fractions that have the same denominator, subtract the numerators. Use the common denominator. Then write the answer in lowest terms when necessary.***

Subtract: $\frac{7}{8} - \frac{2}{3}$.

Step 1 The denominators are not the same. Write the fractions as equivalent fractions, using the LCD.

$$\begin{array}{r} \frac{7}{8} = \frac{21}{24} \\ -\frac{2}{3} = \frac{16}{24} \\ \hline \end{array}$$

Step 2 Subtract. The difference $\frac{5}{24}$ is in lowest terms.

$$\begin{array}{r} \frac{7}{8} = \frac{21}{24} \\ -\frac{2}{3} = \frac{16}{24} \\ \hline \frac{5}{24} \end{array}$$

More Examples

$$\begin{array}{r} \frac{5}{6} = \frac{5}{6} \\ -\frac{1}{2} = \frac{3}{6} \\ \hline \frac{2}{6} = \frac{1}{3} \end{array} \qquad \begin{array}{r} \frac{3}{4} = \frac{15}{20} \\ -\frac{3}{10} = \frac{6}{20} \\ \hline \frac{9}{20} \end{array} \qquad \begin{array}{r} \frac{2}{3} = \frac{10}{15} \\ -\frac{1}{5} = \frac{3}{15} \\ \hline \frac{7}{15} \end{array}$$

Practice • Subtract. Write the answers in lowest terms.

1. $\frac{7}{8} - \frac{5}{8}$
2. $\frac{9}{10} - \frac{3}{10}$
3. $\frac{5}{6} - \frac{2}{3}$
4. $\frac{1}{2} - \frac{2}{5}$
5. $\frac{7}{10} - \frac{3}{5}$
6. $\frac{5}{9} - \frac{1}{3}$
7. $\frac{9}{10} - \frac{2}{15}$
8. $\frac{7}{8} - \frac{1}{4}$
9. $\frac{1}{2} - \frac{1}{5}$
10. $\frac{8}{15} - \frac{2}{15}$

Mixed Practice • Subtract. Write the answers in lowest terms.

11. $\frac{2}{3} - \frac{1}{2}$
12. $\frac{1}{2} - \frac{4}{11}$
13. $\frac{11}{12} - \frac{7}{12}$
14. $\frac{19}{20} - \frac{2}{5}$
15. $\frac{7}{8} - \frac{2}{9}$
16. $\frac{7}{16} - \frac{5}{16}$
17. $\frac{3}{4} - \frac{1}{3}$
18. $\frac{4}{5} - \frac{5}{8}$
19. $\frac{3}{4} - \frac{2}{7}$
20. $\frac{11}{20} - \frac{3}{20}$
21. $\frac{11}{12} - \frac{1}{4}$
22. $\frac{3}{7} - \frac{1}{6}$
23. $\frac{5}{8} - \frac{1}{3}$
24. $\frac{5}{6} - \frac{1}{6}$
★ 25. $\frac{2}{3} - \frac{5}{40}$

Solve the equations.

26. $\frac{15}{32} - \frac{7}{32} = n$
27. $\frac{7}{10} - \frac{1}{4} = n$
28. $\frac{7}{8} - \frac{1}{5} = n$
29. $\frac{11}{12} - \frac{1}{3} = n$
30. $\frac{5}{6} - \frac{1}{10} = n$
31. $\frac{11}{15} - \frac{1}{15} = n$
32. $\left(\frac{5}{8} + \frac{1}{8}\right) - \frac{1}{2} = n$
33. $\frac{4}{7} - \left(\frac{9}{14} - \frac{1}{7}\right) = n$
34. $\frac{3}{4} - \left(\frac{3}{8} - \frac{1}{16}\right) = n$

★ 35. $x + \frac{1}{3} = \frac{5}{6}$
★ 36. $a - \frac{11}{20} = \frac{3}{10}$
★ 37. $y - \frac{1}{4} = \frac{2}{3}$

PROBLEM SOLVING • APPLICATIONS

38. One route from Bill's house to the library is $\frac{7}{10}$ mile long. Another route is $\frac{4}{5}$ mile long. How much longer is the second route?

★ 39. Before a trip a gas tank was about $\frac{3}{4}$ full. After the trip the gas tank was about $\frac{1}{3}$ full. How much gas was used on the trip?

Subtracting Mixed Numbers and Whole Numbers

In some examples with mixed numbers, you can subtract without regrouping. In other examples you must regroup before you can subtract.

Subtract: $6\frac{3}{8} - 1\frac{1}{8}$.

Step 1 $\frac{3}{8} > \frac{1}{8}$, and so you can subtract without regrouping.

$$\begin{array}{r} 6\frac{3}{8} \\ -1\frac{1}{8} \\ \hline 5\frac{2}{8} \end{array}$$

Step 2 Write the answer in lowest terms.

$$\begin{array}{r} 6\frac{3}{8} \\ -1\frac{1}{8} \\ \hline 5\frac{2}{8} = 5\frac{1}{4} \end{array}$$

Subtract: $6\frac{1}{8} - 1\frac{3}{8}$.

Step 1 $\frac{1}{8} < \frac{3}{8}$, and so you need to regroup.

$6\frac{1}{8} = 5 + 1\frac{1}{8}$
$= 5 + \frac{9}{8}$, or $5\frac{9}{8}$

$$\begin{array}{r} 6\frac{1}{8} = 5\frac{9}{8} \\ -1\frac{3}{8} = 1\frac{3}{8} \\ \hline \end{array}$$

Step 2 Subtract. Write the answer in lowest terms.

$$\begin{array}{r} 6\frac{1}{8} = 5\frac{9}{8} \\ -1\frac{3}{8} = 1\frac{3}{8} \\ \hline 4\frac{6}{8} = 4\frac{3}{4} \end{array}$$

More Examples

$$\begin{array}{r} 8\frac{5}{6} \\ -3\frac{1}{6} \\ \hline 5\frac{4}{6} = 5\frac{2}{3} \end{array} \qquad \begin{array}{r} 7\frac{9}{10} \\ -1 \\ \hline 6\frac{9}{10} \end{array} \qquad \begin{array}{r} 9 = 8\frac{5}{5} \\ -4\frac{2}{5} = 4\frac{2}{5} \\ \hline 4\frac{3}{5} \end{array} \qquad \begin{array}{r} 6 = 5\frac{4}{4} \\ -5\frac{1}{4} = 5\frac{1}{4} \\ \hline \frac{3}{4} \end{array}$$

Practice • Subtract. Write the answers in lowest terms.

1. $\begin{array}{r} 3\frac{4}{5} \\ -1\frac{1}{5} \\ \hline \end{array}$
2. $\begin{array}{r} 3\frac{1}{5} \\ -1\frac{4}{5} \\ \hline \end{array}$
3. $\begin{array}{r} 6\frac{5}{8} \\ -2\frac{3}{8} \\ \hline \end{array}$
4. $\begin{array}{r} 7\frac{1}{3} \\ -4 \\ \hline \end{array}$
5. $\begin{array}{r} 7 \\ -4\frac{1}{3} \\ \hline \end{array}$
6. $\begin{array}{r} 8\frac{5}{6} \\ -3\frac{1}{6} \\ \hline \end{array}$
7. $\begin{array}{r} 10 \\ -1\frac{1}{2} \\ \hline \end{array}$
8. $\begin{array}{r} 8 \\ -7\frac{2}{3} \\ \hline \end{array}$
9. $\begin{array}{r} 5\frac{1}{4} \\ -1\frac{3}{4} \\ \hline \end{array}$
10. $\begin{array}{r} 12\frac{3}{10} \\ -10\frac{7}{10} \\ \hline \end{array}$

Mixed Practice • Subtract. Write the answers in lowest terms.

11. $4\frac{3}{10} - 2\frac{1}{10}$

12. $4\frac{1}{10} - 2\frac{3}{10}$

13. $10 - 4\frac{4}{7}$

14. $3\frac{2}{5} - 1\frac{1}{5}$

15. $3\frac{1}{5} - 1\frac{2}{5}$

16. $6\frac{3}{4} - 1$

17. $6 - 1\frac{3}{4}$

18. $8\frac{1}{12} - 2\frac{5}{12}$

19. $5\frac{3}{4} - 1\frac{1}{4}$

20. $5\frac{1}{4} - 1\frac{3}{4}$

21. $4\frac{1}{3} - 3\frac{2}{3}$

22. $15\frac{9}{10} - \frac{3}{10}$

23. $12 - 1\frac{1}{8}$

24. $7\frac{3}{8} - 1\frac{7}{8}$

25. $8 - 6\frac{2}{3}$

26. $\frac{9}{10} - \frac{5}{6}$

27. $15\frac{4}{9} - 3\frac{1}{9}$

28. $8\frac{2}{3} - 6\frac{2}{3}$

29. $4\frac{1}{6} - 1\frac{5}{6}$

★ 30. $3\frac{1}{100} - 2\frac{23}{100}$

Solve the equations.

31. $7 - 3\frac{4}{5} = n$

32. $8\frac{5}{6} - 7\frac{5}{6} = n$

33. $4\frac{5}{8} - 1\frac{1}{8} = n$

34. $\frac{5}{12} - \frac{1}{3} = n$

35. $5\frac{1}{16} - 1\frac{7}{16} = n$

36. $3\frac{2}{5} - 2\frac{4}{5} = n$

★ 37. $\left(3\frac{1}{4} + 2\frac{1}{8}\right) - 1\frac{5}{8} = n$

★ 38. $\left(5 - 1\frac{3}{10}\right) + \left(6\frac{1}{4} - 4\frac{3}{4}\right) = n$

PROBLEM SOLVING • APPLICATIONS

39. By bus a trip from Greenview to the state capital takes $5\frac{1}{3}$ hours. By train the trip takes $4\frac{2}{3}$ hours. How much shorter is the train trip?

★ 40. By car the trip takes $4\frac{1}{2}$ hours. By plane the trip takes 55 minutes. How much shorter is the plane trip?

Practicing Subtraction with Mixed Numbers

How much more is $3\frac{3}{4}$ pounds than $2\frac{1}{2}$ pounds?

$3\frac{3}{4} - 2\frac{1}{2} = n$

Step 1 Rewrite the example using the LCD.

$$\begin{array}{r} 3\frac{3}{4} = 3\frac{3}{4} \\ -2\frac{1}{2} = 2\frac{2}{4} \\ \hline \end{array}$$

Step 2 $\frac{3}{4} > \frac{2}{4}$. Subtract:

$$\begin{array}{r} 3\frac{3}{4} = 3\frac{3}{4} \\ -2\frac{1}{2} = 2\frac{2}{4} \\ \hline 1\frac{1}{4} \end{array}$$

$3\frac{3}{4}$ pounds is $1\frac{1}{4}$ pounds more than $2\frac{1}{2}$ pounds.

Subtract: $6\frac{1}{2} - 1\frac{2}{3}$.

Step 1 Rewrite the example using the LCD.

$$\begin{array}{r} 6\frac{1}{2} = 6\frac{3}{6} \\ -1\frac{2}{3} = 1\frac{4}{6} \\ \hline \end{array}$$

Step 2 $\frac{3}{6} < \frac{4}{6}$, and so you need to regroup.

$6\frac{3}{6} = 5\frac{9}{6}$

$$\begin{array}{r} 6\frac{1}{2} = 6\frac{3}{6} = 5\frac{9}{6} \\ -1\frac{2}{3} = 1\frac{4}{6} = 1\frac{4}{6} \\ \hline \end{array}$$

Step 3 $\frac{9}{6} > \frac{4}{6}$ Subtract.

$$\begin{array}{r} 6\frac{1}{2} = 6\frac{3}{6} = 5\frac{9}{6} \\ -1\frac{2}{3} = 1\frac{4}{6} = 1\frac{4}{6} \\ \hline 4\frac{5}{6} \end{array}$$

More Examples

$$\begin{array}{r} 5\frac{3}{4} = 5\frac{9}{12} \\ -1\frac{1}{6} = 1\frac{2}{12} \\ \hline 4\frac{7}{12} \end{array}$$

$$\begin{array}{r} 8\frac{3}{10} = 8\frac{3}{10} = 7\frac{13}{10} \\ -2\frac{3}{5} = 2\frac{6}{10} = 2\frac{6}{10} \\ \hline 5\frac{7}{10} \end{array}$$

$$\begin{array}{r} 3\frac{3}{5} = 3\frac{12}{20} = 2\frac{32}{20} \\ -2\frac{3}{4} = 2\frac{15}{20} = 2\frac{15}{20} \\ \hline \frac{17}{20} \end{array}$$

Practice • Subtract. Write the answers in lowest terms.

1. $3\frac{2}{3} - 1\frac{1}{2}$
2. $7\frac{3}{8} - 1\frac{3}{4}$
3. $5\frac{1}{3} - 1\frac{1}{6}$
4. $9\frac{2}{3} - \frac{3}{8}$
5. $7\frac{1}{6} - 6\frac{3}{4}$
6. $3\frac{1}{6} - 1\frac{1}{2}$
7. $9\frac{1}{10} - 5\frac{3}{5}$
8. $6\frac{3}{8} - 5\frac{1}{6}$
9. $2\frac{5}{6} - 1\frac{8}{9}$
10. $4\frac{5}{8} - 2\frac{9}{10}$

Mixed Practice • Subtract. Write the answers in lowest terms.

11. $3\frac{1}{6} - 1\frac{3}{4}$
12. $9\frac{7}{10} - 5\frac{4}{5}$
13. $10\frac{11}{12} - 7\frac{3}{4}$
14. $6\frac{2}{3} - 1\frac{1}{3}$
15. $4\frac{3}{16} - 1\frac{1}{4}$
16. $7\frac{7}{8} - 1\frac{3}{8}$
17. $4\frac{5}{6} - 2\frac{1}{3}$
18. $5\frac{1}{5} - 4\frac{1}{4}$
19. $12 - 8\frac{1}{6}$
20. $\frac{7}{8} - \frac{3}{4}$
21. $9\frac{1}{6} - 4\frac{5}{9}$
22. $10\frac{3}{8} - 7\frac{7}{8}$
23. $15\frac{1}{7} - 6\frac{2}{3}$
24. $5\frac{9}{10} - 1\frac{1}{2}$
25. $3 - 2\frac{3}{10}$
26. $2\frac{3}{8} - 1\frac{5}{8}$
27. $8\frac{1}{3} - 2\frac{5}{9}$
28. $9\frac{1}{4} - 3\frac{2}{5}$
29. $\frac{2}{3} - \frac{1}{2}$
★ 30. $8\frac{3}{10} - 1\frac{7}{12}$

Solve the equations.

31. $4\frac{1}{4} - 3\frac{1}{3} = n$
32. $6\frac{1}{2} - 2\frac{4}{5} = n$
33. $5\frac{7}{8} - 1\frac{3}{4} = n$
34. $6\frac{9}{10} - 5\frac{1}{100} = n$
35. $9\frac{1}{10} - 8\frac{3}{10} = n$
36. $2\frac{7}{100} - 1\frac{1}{100} = n$
★ 37. $\left(2\frac{1}{2} + 3\frac{1}{4}\right) - 5\frac{1}{8} = n$
★ 38. $\left(8\frac{1}{6} - 2\frac{3}{4}\right) - \left(2\frac{1}{6} + 1\frac{2}{3}\right) = n$

Estimate. Is the answer greater than 3? Answer *yes* or *no*.

★ 39. $\frac{5}{6} + \frac{2}{3} + \frac{9}{19}$
★ 40. $\frac{6}{5} + \frac{3}{2} + \frac{100}{99}$
★ 41. $4\frac{1}{6} - 1\frac{9}{10}$

PROBLEM SOLVING • APPLICATIONS

42. It takes $9\frac{1}{3}$ minutes to walk from the campground to the fishing pier. It only takes $2\frac{3}{4}$ minutes to go by boat. How much longer does it take if you walk?

★ 43. You walk to the pier in $9\frac{3}{4}$ minutes. You stay there $3\frac{1}{2}$ minutes. Then you walk back to camp in $9\frac{7}{10}$ minutes. What is the total time away from camp?

Skills Maintenance

Find the greatest common factor.

1. 18, 24
2. 15, 50
3. 40, 100
4. 45, 60
5. 24, 60
6. 56, 63
7. 38, 40
8. 48, 96

PROBLEM SOLVING • STRATEGIES

Multistep Problems

Tara lives $1\frac{1}{5}$ miles from school.

Beth lives $\frac{9}{10}$ of a mile from school.

How much longer is Tara's round trip than Beth's?

It is helpful to analyze a problem that has more than one step.

Think: First find the distance in Tara's round trip. Then find the distance in Beth's round trip. Then subtract.

Step 1 Add $1\frac{1}{5}$ and $1\frac{1}{5}$.

$$\begin{array}{r} 1\frac{1}{5} \\ +1\frac{1}{5} \\ \hline 2\frac{2}{5} \end{array}$$

Tara's round trip is $2\frac{2}{5}$ miles.

Step 2 Add $\frac{9}{10}$ and $\frac{9}{10}$.

$$\begin{array}{l} \frac{9}{10} \\ +\frac{9}{10} \\ \hline \frac{18}{10} = 1\frac{8}{10} = 1\frac{4}{5} \end{array}$$

Beth's round trip is $1\frac{4}{5}$ miles.

Step 3 Find the difference between $2\frac{2}{5}$ and $1\frac{4}{5}$.

$$\begin{array}{rcr} 2\frac{2}{5} & = & 1\frac{7}{5} \\ -1\frac{4}{5} & = & 1\frac{4}{5} \\ \hline & & \frac{3}{5} \end{array}$$

Tara's round trip is $\frac{3}{5}$ of a mile greater than Beth's round trip.
Can the problem be solved another way? Explain.

Solve.

1. Alana works $2\frac{1}{4}$ hours on Monday and $3\frac{1}{2}$ on Tuesday. Janine works $1\frac{1}{4}$ hours on Monday and $3\frac{1}{3}$ hours on Tuesday. How much less time does Janine work than Alana?

2. Suna has a board $4\frac{2}{3}$ feet long. She cuts two pieces from it. One piece is $\frac{5}{6}$ of a foot long. The other piece is $1\frac{1}{2}$ feet long. How much of the board is left?

3. A play with two acts is $1\frac{11}{12}$ hours long. The first act is $\frac{5}{6}$ hour long and the intermission is $\frac{1}{4}$ hour long. How long is the second act?

4. At a school exhibit, $\frac{1}{4}$ of the exhibit will be artwork and $\frac{1}{5}$ will be sculpture. The rest will be craftwork. What fractional part of the exhibit will be craftwork?

Analyze the problem and decide which operations you must use.

5. Keith uses $\frac{3}{10}$ of his earnings for school expenses and $\frac{1}{5}$ of his earnings for recreation. He saves the rest. What fractional part of his earnings does he save?

6. Yoko lives $1\frac{3}{4}$ miles from school. Claire lives $1\frac{2}{3}$ miles from school. How much shorter is Claire's round trip than Yoko's?

7. At one football game there were about 23,700 people. At the next game, there were about 4,000 more people than at the first game. About how many people were at the two games?

8. At one baseball game, there were about 21,500 people. At the next game there were about 3,800 fewer people than at the first game. About how many people were at the two games?

9. In a five-mile race, $\frac{1}{4}$ of the runners finished in less than 30 minutes. Within 30 to 40 minutes, $\frac{2}{5}$ of the runners finished. The rest of the runners did not finish. What fractional part of the runners did not finish?

Check the computation in each step.

★ 10. One afternoon Renee works 3 hours at \$3.75 per hour. In the evening she babysits and earns \$2.25 per hour for 5 hours. How much less than \$25 does she earn?

★ 11. Jesse has \$2.50 on Saturday morning as he leaves for his job. He works 4 hours and is paid \$3.85 per hour. He spends \$1.50 for busfare and \$2.95 for food that day. How much money does he have at the end of the day?

★ 12. Fran and Dinah each bowl three games. Fran bowls 146, 172, and 147. Dinah bowls 167, 153, and 94. How much less is Dinah's average than Fran's?

CHAPTER 7

REVIEW

Write the fractions. (pp. 162–163)

1. three-fourths **2.** one-eighth **3.** six-tenths **4.** four-fifths

Write as fractions or whole numbers. (pp. 162–163)

5. $4 \div 5$ **6.** $7 \div 10$ **7.** $\frac{9}{9}$ **8.** $\frac{6}{3}$ **9.** $\frac{15}{5}$

Make the fractions equivalent. (pp. 164–165)

10. $\frac{5}{6} = \frac{n}{12}$ **11.** $\frac{2}{3} = \frac{n}{21}$ **12.** $\frac{15}{21} = \frac{5}{n}$ **13.** $\frac{4}{9} = \frac{n}{36}$ **14.** $\frac{4}{40} = \frac{1}{n}$

Write the fractions in lowest terms. (pp. 166–167)

15. $\frac{5}{10}$ **16.** $\frac{12}{20}$ **17.** $\frac{9}{15}$ **18.** $\frac{15}{40}$ **19.** $\frac{16}{36}$

Write $<$, $=$, or $>$. (pp. 168–169) **20.** $\frac{2}{3} \bullet \frac{3}{4}$ **21.** $\frac{5}{6} \bullet \frac{7}{10}$ **22.** $\frac{8}{15} \bullet \frac{5}{8}$ **23.** $\frac{2}{3} \bullet \frac{8}{12}$

Write as fractions. (pp. 170–171) **24.** $3\frac{1}{2}$ **25.** $4\frac{3}{10}$ **26.** $6\frac{2}{5}$ **27.** $8\frac{1}{4}$ **28.** $5\frac{2}{3}$

Add. Write the answers in lowest terms. (pp. 172–175)

29. $\frac{1}{10} + \frac{7}{10}$ **30.** $\frac{3}{8} + \frac{1}{6}$ **31.** $1\frac{5}{12} + 3\frac{3}{4}$ **32.** $3\frac{2}{3} + 4\frac{2}{15}$ **33.** $1\frac{1}{3} + 4\frac{5}{6} + 2\frac{2}{9}$

Subtract. Write the answers in lowest terms. (pp. 178–183)

34. $\frac{8}{9} - \frac{4}{9}$ **35.** $\frac{1}{2} - \frac{2}{5}$ **36.** $3\frac{7}{20} - 1\frac{1}{10}$ **37.** $5 - 2\frac{5}{9}$ **38.** $3\frac{1}{3} - 1\frac{5}{8}$

Solve the equations. (pp. 174–175, 178–183)

39. $2\frac{7}{8} + 2\frac{5}{6} = n$ **40.** $\frac{1}{2} - \frac{1}{3} = n$ **41.** $8\frac{2}{5} - 2\frac{7}{8} = n$

42. A bus makes 8 stops along a route that is 15 miles long. The stops are equally spaced. How far apart are they? (pp. 176–177)

43. Tess cuts 2 pieces from a board $5\frac{1}{4}$ feet long. One piece is $1\frac{1}{2}$ feet long. The other piece is $\frac{2}{3}$ of a foot long. How much is left? (pp. 184–185)

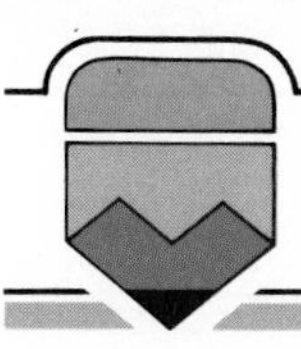

PROJECT

Stock Market

By buying shares of **stock** in a company you become a part owner of that company.

Stock prices are listed each day in the business section of most newspapers. The dollar value of a share of stock is shown as a whole number or a mixed number.

Highest and lowest prices over past 52 weeks.

Highest and lowest prices for today.

Difference between Yesterday's closing price and Today's closing price. + means the price went up. − means the price went down.

Abbreviation of company name.

Closing price for the day.

STOCKS

52 weeks High	52 weeks Low	Stock	High	Low	Close	Net Chg.
$32\frac{1}{9}$	$24\frac{1}{2}$	AAC	$30\frac{1}{4}$	$29\frac{3}{8}$	$30\frac{1}{8}$	$+\frac{1}{8}$
$16\frac{1}{2}$	$9\frac{3}{4}$	Amr	$13\frac{7}{8}$	13	$13\frac{3}{8}$	$-\frac{1}{4}$
$12\frac{7}{8}$	$5\frac{1}{4}$	Apl	$8\frac{1}{8}$	$7\frac{3}{4}$	$7\frac{7}{8}$	. . .
56	$45\frac{3}{8}$	ARA	$49\frac{1}{2}$	$48\frac{1}{4}$	$48\frac{3}{8}$	-1
$27\frac{3}{4}$	$19\frac{1}{8}$	Ast	22	$21\frac{1}{8}$	$21\frac{3}{4}$	$+\frac{3}{8}$
$32\frac{1}{4}$	$24\frac{1}{2}$	ATC	$30\frac{1}{4}$	$29\frac{3}{4}$	$30\frac{1}{8}$	$+\frac{1}{8}$

1. Today's low for one share of ARA is $48\frac{1}{4}$. What is today's closing price for one share of ARA?

2. What is today's high price for one share of Amr?

3. What is the difference between the 52-week high and low prices for one share of Apl?

4. Compute yesterday's closing price for one share of Ast.

5. Find the stock tables in a newspaper. Pretend that you buy one share of 3 different stocks. Use the closing price when you buy. Record your purchases in a chart. Pretend that you sell the stocks at the end of a week. Use the closing price when you sell. Compute your profit or loss.

Stock	Buy	Sell	Profit or Loss (+) (−)

CHAPTER 7

TEST

Write the fractions.

1. five-twelfths **2.** two-sevenths **3.** nine-tenths **4.** four-sixths

Write as fractions or whole numbers.

5. $3 \div 10$ **6.** $2 \div 5$ **7.** $\frac{5}{5}$ **8.** $\frac{8}{4}$ **9.** $\frac{12}{3}$

Make the fractions equivalent.

10. $\frac{1}{5} = \frac{n}{15}$ **11.** $\frac{3}{4} = \frac{n}{20}$ **12.** $\frac{6}{7} = \frac{12}{n}$ **13.** $\frac{3}{8} = \frac{n}{40}$ **14.** $\frac{15}{18} = \frac{5}{n}$

Write the fractions in lowest terms.

15. $\frac{6}{10}$ **16.** $\frac{10}{25}$ **17.** $\frac{20}{36}$ **18.** $\frac{18}{54}$ **19.** $\frac{27}{45}$

Write <, =, or >. **20.** $\frac{7}{12}$ ● $\frac{1}{2}$ **21.** $\frac{2}{3}$ ● $\frac{9}{10}$ **22.** $\frac{6}{9}$ ● $\frac{2}{3}$ **23.** $\frac{5}{12}$ ● $\frac{1}{4}$

Write as fractions. **24.** $2\frac{1}{4}$ **25.** $7\frac{2}{5}$ **26.** $3\frac{5}{6}$ **27.** $4\frac{1}{3}$ **28.** $6\frac{5}{8}$

Add. Write the answers in lowest terms.

29. $\frac{5}{12} + \frac{1}{12}$ **30.** $\frac{3}{5} + \frac{1}{3}$ **31.** $4\frac{5}{8} + 2\frac{3}{4}$ **32.** $1\frac{5}{9} + 3\frac{5}{6}$ **33.** $3\frac{3}{10} + 2\frac{1}{4} + 2\frac{2}{5}$

Subtract. Write the answers in lowest terms.

34. $\frac{5}{8} - \frac{3}{8}$ **35.** $\frac{9}{10} - \frac{2}{5}$ **36.** $4\frac{7}{8} - 3\frac{2}{3}$ **37.** $8 - 1\frac{5}{6}$ **38.** $7\frac{3}{5} - 4\frac{3}{4}$

Solve the equations.

39. $6\frac{7}{12} + 1\frac{1}{4} = n$ **40.** $\frac{14}{15} - \frac{2}{3} = n$ **41.** $7 - 1\frac{4}{9} = n$

42. Dave works 10 hours in 4 days. He works the same number of hours each day. How long does he work each day?

43. Cora cuts 2 pieces from a roll of wire $8\frac{1}{6}$ feet long. One piece is $3\frac{3}{4}$ feet long. The other piece is $1\frac{1}{2}$ feet long. How much wire is left?

ENRICHMENT

Flowcharts

A **flowchart** is a diagram that shows the steps used in doing something. These symbols are used in a flowchart.

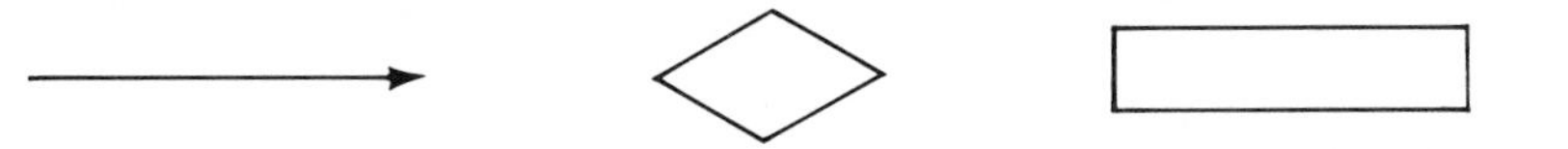

Points to the next direction. Asks a question. Gives a direction. START or STOP.

This flowchart tells you how to add fractions. Read the flowchart.

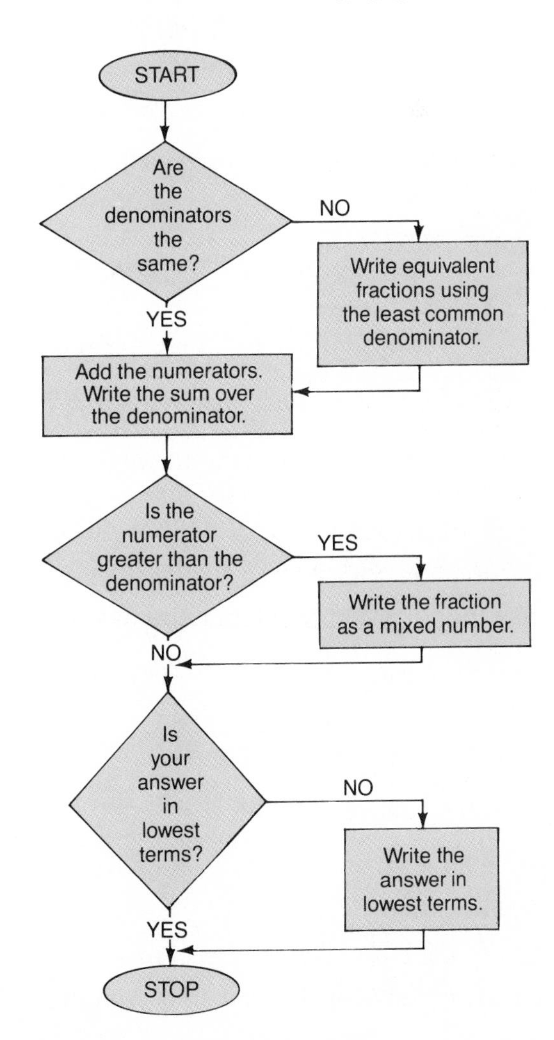

1. If your answer to the first question in the flowchart is YES, what do you do next?
2. If your answer is NO, what do you do?
3. If your answer to the second question is YES, what do you do next?
4. If your answer is NO, what do you do?
5. If your answer to the third question is YES, what do you do next?
6. If your answer is NO, what do you do?

Make a flowchart

7. for subtracting fractions.
8. for solving: $64 + 28 = n$.
9. for writing a fraction in lowest terms.
10. for comparing $\frac{5}{8}$ and $\frac{7}{10}$ to decide which is greater.
11. for comparing 0.73 and 0.72 to decide which is greater.

CALCULATOR

Deciding to Use the Calculator

Sometimes it may be simpler to work a problem in your head or on paper than to use a calculator.

Subtract $5\frac{1}{4}$ from $9\frac{3}{4}$. You could turn your calculator on, push  ,

and write the first part of the answer: 4. Then you could push   

and write the answer, 2, over 4, rewriting the fraction in lowest terms: $\frac{1}{2}$. The total answer is $4\frac{1}{2}$. But it would be simpler if you could work the problem without using the calculator at all.

Subtract. Write the answers in lowest terms.

1. $\frac{4}{5} - \frac{3}{5}$
2. $6\frac{8}{10} - 2\frac{3}{5}$
3. $\frac{7}{4} - \frac{3}{2}$
4. $7\frac{5}{6} - 2\frac{2}{6}$
5. $\frac{856}{999} - \frac{784}{999}$
6. $\frac{4}{2} - \frac{3}{3}$

7. On how many of those problems did you use the calculator?

In other cases, it may be easy to work with large numbers once the problem has been rewritten. If you rewrite $999 - 998 + 856 - 855 + 433 - 432$ as $(999 - 998) + (856 - 855) + (433 - 432)$, you can see that the problem is $1 + 1 + 1$. You do not need a calculator for that.

Simplify the following problems and calculate.

8. $15{,}000 + 150 - 149 + 836 - 835 + 4{,}305 - 3{,}306 - 15{,}000 =$ ___?___
9. $\frac{15}{3} - \frac{84}{42} - \frac{27}{27} + \frac{48}{12} - \frac{25}{25} - \frac{98}{98} =$ ___?___
10. $98 + 97 + 96 + 95 - 98 - 97 - 96 =$ ___?___
11. $35 + 36 + 37 + 38 + 39 + 40 + 41 =$ ___?___
12. $\frac{9{,}357}{2{,}222} - \frac{7{,}468}{4{,}444} - \frac{4{,}826}{8{,}888} =$ ___?___
13. On how many of the last five problems did you use the calculator?

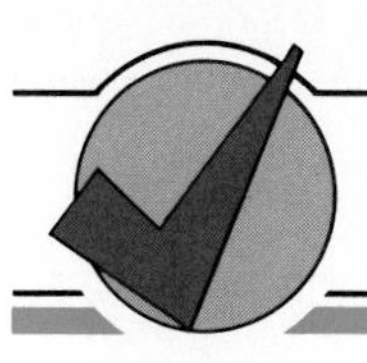

SKILLS MAINTENANCE

Chapters 1 Through 7

Choose the correct answers.

1. Write <, =, or >.

3.407 ● 3.470

A. >
B. <
C. =
D. not here

2. Add.

$$\begin{array}{r} 29{,}036 \\ 4{,}981 \\ +15{,}657 \\ \hline \end{array}$$

A. 49,664
B. 49,574
C. 49,674
D. not here

3. Subtract.

$$\begin{array}{r} 462.854 \\ -\ 72.658 \\ \hline \end{array}$$

A. 390.196
B. 390.296
C. 380.196
D. not here

4. Multiply.

$$\begin{array}{r} 240 \\ \times\ 50 \\ \hline \end{array}$$

A. 1,200
B. 10,000
C. 12,000
D. not here

5. Divide.

$25\overline{)75{,}250}$

A. 31
B. 301
C. 3,000
D. not here

6. Solve.

$n - 84 = 252$

A. $n = 168$
B. $n = 336$
C. $n = 3$
D. not here

7. Find the prime factorization of 54.

A. 2×3^3
B. $2^2 \times 3^2$
C. $2^2 \times 3^3$
D. not here

8. Find the LCM of 8 and 14.

A. 28
B. 112
C. 56
D. not here

9. Multiply.

0.09×0.013

A. 1.17
B. 0.927
C. 0.00117
D. not here

10. Find an equivalent fraction in lowest terms.

$\frac{20}{35}$

A. $\frac{4}{5}$
B. $\frac{4}{7}$
C. $\frac{2}{3}$
D. not here

11. Add.

$$\begin{array}{r} \frac{2}{3} \\ +\frac{2}{5} \\ \hline \end{array}$$

A. $\frac{4}{5}$
B. $1\frac{1}{15}$
C. $1\frac{1}{5}$
D. not here

12. Subtract.

$$\begin{array}{r} \frac{5}{6} \\ -\frac{1}{3} \\ \hline \end{array}$$

A. $\frac{2}{3}$
B. $\frac{4}{5}$
C. $\frac{1}{2}$
D. not here

Choose the correct answers.

13. Adoette earns $5\frac{1}{2}$ dollars on Monday and $4\frac{3}{4}$ dollars on Tuesday. How much money does Adoette earn in these two days?

A. $10\frac{1}{2}$ dollars **B.** $10\frac{1}{4}$ dollars
C. $9\frac{9}{10}$ dollars **D.** not here

14. Brian works $2\frac{3}{4}$ hours on Monday and $2\frac{1}{2}$ hours on Tuesday. Ron works $1\frac{2}{3}$ hours on Monday and $3\frac{3}{4}$ hours on Tuesday. How much more time does Ron work than Brian?

A. $\frac{1}{3}$ hour **B.** $\frac{1}{2}$ hour
C. $\frac{1}{6}$ hour **D.** not here

15. Mrs. Mosley is 3 times as old as her son Ted. If Mrs. Mosley is 42 years old, how old is her son Ted?

A. 21 **B.** 14
C. 13 **D.** not here

16. The Mohansic School is having a puppet show. Tickets for adults cost $2.50. Tickets for children cost $1.25. What is the total cost of 2 adult tickets and 3 children's tickets?

A. $3.75 **B.** $6.75
C. $8.75 **D.** not here

17. Rosie's Gift Shop is having a sale. She offers $15 off the price of any item selling for $25 or more. What is the sale price of a tea set?

A. $40 **B.** $10
C. $15 **D.** not here

18. The Kane family paid a moving company $1,488 when they moved. The moving company charges $48 per hour. How many hours did it take to move the Kanes?

A. 21 hours **B.** 31 hours
C. 32 hours **D.** not here

19. Kevin worked 3.9 hours on Friday and 4.5 hours on Saturday. He earns $3.75 an hour. How much money did he earn in the two days?

A. $14.63 **B.** $15.88
C. $31.50 **D.** not here

20. Nishi earns $72 in three days while working at a part-time job. She works 5 hours on Monday, 4 hours on Tuesday, and 3 hours on Wednesday. How much does Nishi earn per hour?

A. $6 **B.** $8.64
C. $8 **D.** not here

Fractions: Multiplication and Division

CHAPTER 8

Multiplying Fractions • Understanding a Shortcut • Multiplying Whole Numbers and Mixed Numbers • Problem Solving: Using Graphs • Reciprocals • Dividing by Fractions • Dividing by Whole Numbers • Using Mixed Numbers in Division • Fractions and Decimals • Repeating Decimals • Problem Solving: Using Estimates • Operation Properties and Density

Multiplying Fractions

A play area takes up $\frac{3}{4}$ of a park. Baseball fields occupy $\frac{1}{2}$ of the play area. What fractional part of the park is used for baseball fields?

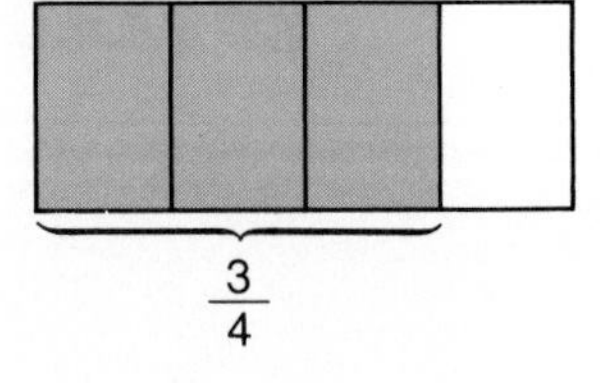

$\frac{1}{2}$ of $\frac{3}{4} = n$

You can make a drawing to find the answer.

The drawing shows that $\frac{1}{2}$ of $\frac{3}{4} = \frac{3}{8}$.

Baseball fields occupy $\frac{3}{8}$ of the park.

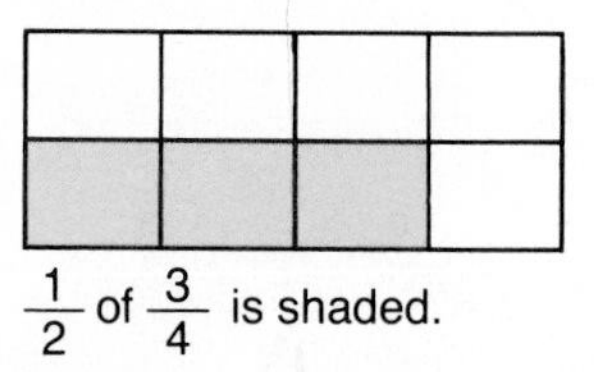

$\frac{1}{2}$ of $\frac{3}{4}$ is shaded.

$\frac{3}{8}$ is shaded.

You can also multiply fractions.

$\frac{1}{2}$ of $\frac{3}{4}$ → $\frac{1}{2} \times \frac{3}{4}$

Step 1 Multiply the numerators.
$1 \times 3 = 3$

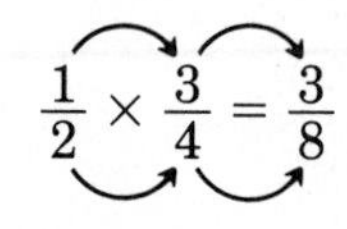

Step 2 Multiply the denominators.
$2 \times 4 = 8$

> ***To multiply fractions, multiply the numerators and multiply the denominators. In variables:*** $\frac{a}{b} \times \frac{c}{d} = \frac{a \times c}{b \times d}$

After you multiply, you may need to rewrite the product in lowest terms.

$$\frac{4}{5} \times \frac{1}{4} = \frac{4}{20} = \frac{1}{5}$$

Practice • Make a drawing to find each answer.

1. $\frac{1}{2}$ of $\frac{1}{2} = n$ **2.** $\frac{1}{3}$ of $\frac{2}{5} = n$ **3.** $\frac{3}{4}$ of $\frac{1}{5} = n$

Multiply. Write the answers in lowest terms.

4. $\frac{1}{2} \times \frac{1}{3}$ **5.** $\frac{1}{3} \times \frac{3}{4}$ **6.** $\frac{2}{5} \times \frac{1}{4}$ **7.** $\frac{5}{6} \times \frac{2}{5}$

8. $\frac{3}{8} \times \frac{4}{5}$ **9.** $\frac{3}{4} \times \frac{1}{9}$ **10.** $\frac{1}{2} \times \frac{1}{4}$ **11.** $\frac{1}{4} \times \frac{2}{3}$

Mixed Practice • Multiply. Write the answers in lowest terms.

12. $\frac{1}{4} \times \frac{4}{5}$ **13.** $\frac{1}{10} \times \frac{1}{2}$ **14.** $\frac{2}{5} \times \frac{1}{2}$ **15.** $\frac{1}{6} \times \frac{3}{4}$

16. $\frac{5}{9} \times \frac{9}{10}$ **17.** $\frac{1}{6} \times \frac{1}{2}$ **18.** $\frac{2}{3} \times \frac{1}{6}$ **19.** $\frac{2}{3} \times \frac{3}{8}$

20. $\frac{4}{5} \times \frac{5}{7}$ **21.** $\frac{5}{8} \times \frac{5}{8}$ **22.** $\frac{4}{7} \times \frac{7}{8}$ **23.** $\frac{3}{10} \times \frac{5}{6}$

24. $\frac{5}{9} \times \frac{3}{4}$ **25.** $\frac{7}{10} \times \frac{2}{5}$ **26.** $\frac{3}{4} \times \frac{2}{3}$ **27.** $\frac{4}{5} \times \frac{1}{8}$

28. $\frac{2}{3} \times \frac{1}{8}$ **29.** $\frac{3}{4} \times \frac{8}{9}$ **30.** $\frac{3}{5} \times \frac{1}{5}$ **31.** $\frac{7}{9} \times \frac{3}{5}$

32. $\frac{3}{10} \times \frac{2}{3}$ **33.** $\frac{7}{8} \times \frac{4}{5}$ **34.** $\frac{2}{9} \times \frac{3}{8}$ **35.** $\frac{1}{10} \times \frac{2}{5}$

36. $\frac{2}{5} \times \frac{5}{18}$ **37.** $\frac{3}{10} \times \frac{7}{10}$ **38.** $\frac{9}{10} \times \frac{1}{3}$ **39.** $\frac{7}{8} \times \frac{1}{7}$

40. $\frac{1}{10} \times \frac{1}{10}$ ★ **41.** $\frac{1}{10} \times \frac{1}{10} \times \frac{1}{10}$ ★ **42.** $\frac{3}{4} \times \frac{1}{3} \times \frac{5}{6}$ ★ **43.** $\frac{2}{3} \times \frac{3}{5} \times \frac{1}{4}$

When you multiply a number by 1, the product is that number. This is how you find equivalent fractions. You use different names for 1.

$$1 \times \frac{2}{3} = \frac{2}{3}$$

$$\downarrow \quad \downarrow \quad \downarrow$$

$$\frac{4}{4} \times \frac{2}{3} = \frac{8}{12}$$

What name for 1 do you use to make the sentence true?

44. $\frac{n}{n} \times \frac{1}{2} = \frac{3}{6}$ **45.** $\frac{n}{n} \times \frac{4}{5} = \frac{8}{10}$ ★ **46.** $\frac{n}{n} \times \frac{7}{10} = \frac{70}{100}$ ★ **47.** $\frac{n}{n} \times \frac{3}{10} = \frac{300}{1,000}$

PROBLEM SOLVING • APPLICATIONS

48. Angelo spends $\frac{7}{10}$ of an hour practicing basketball in the park. He spends $\frac{2}{3}$ of that time practicing lay-up shots. What fractional part of an hour does he spend practicing lay-up shots?

49. Ron takes $\frac{9}{10}$ of a dollar to the park. He spends $\frac{8}{9}$ of this money for refreshments. What fractional part of a dollar does he spend for refreshments?

★ **50.** Claire spends $\frac{1}{3}$ of a day at the park. She spends $\frac{1}{4}$ of this time in the play area. What fractional part of a day does she spend in the play area? What fractional part of a day does she spend in other sections of the park?

Understanding a Shortcut

Study this multiplication example.

$$\frac{5}{8} \times \frac{2}{3} = \frac{10}{24} = \frac{5}{12}$$

$$\frac{10 \div 2}{24 \div 2} = \frac{5}{12}$$

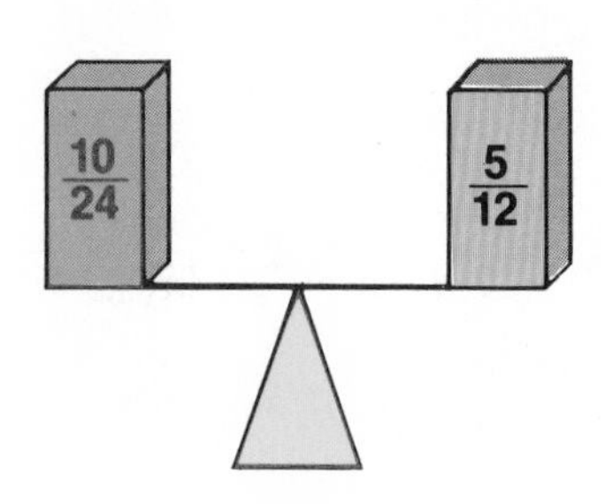

To find the product in lowest terms, you divide both terms of $\frac{10}{24}$ by the common factor, 2.

You can divide a numerator and a denominator by a common factor before you multiply. Here is the same example with the division done first.

Step 1 2 is a common factor of 2 and 8. Divide each by 2. $2 \div 2 = 1 \quad 8 \div 2 = 4$ → $\frac{5}{\underset{4}{\cancel{8}}} \times \frac{\overset{1}{\cancel{2}}}{3}$

Step 2 Multiply. $\frac{5 \times 1}{4 \times 3} = \frac{5}{12}$ → $\frac{5}{\underset{4}{\cancel{8}}} \times \frac{\overset{1}{\cancel{2}}}{3} = \frac{5}{12}$

Dividing by common factors before you multiply is a shortcut in some examples. If you divide by each common factor before you multiply, the multiplication gives the product in lowest terms.

Multiply: $\frac{9}{10} \times \frac{5}{6}$.

Step 1 3 is a common factor of 9 and 6. Divide each by 3. $9 \div 3 = 3 \quad 6 \div 3 = 2$ → $\frac{\overset{3}{\cancel{9}}}{10} \times \frac{5}{\underset{2}{\cancel{6}}}$

Step 2 5 is a common factor of 5 and 10. Divide each by 5. $5 \div 5 = 1 \quad 10 \div 5 = 2$ → $\frac{\overset{3}{\cancel{9}}}{\underset{2}{\cancel{10}}} \times \frac{\overset{1}{\cancel{5}}}{\underset{2}{\cancel{6}}}$

Step 3 Multiply. $\frac{3 \times 1}{2 \times 2} = \frac{3}{4}$ → $\frac{\overset{3}{\cancel{9}}}{\underset{2}{\cancel{10}}} \times \frac{\overset{1}{\cancel{5}}}{\underset{2}{\cancel{6}}} = \frac{3}{4}$

More Examples

$\frac{7}{2} \times \frac{1}{3} = \frac{7}{6}$ $\qquad$ $\frac{8}{\underset{1}{\cancel{3}}} \times \frac{\overset{1}{\cancel{3}}}{5} = \frac{8}{5} = 1\frac{3}{5}$ $\qquad$ $\frac{3}{\underset{2}{\cancel{4}}} \times \frac{\overset{3}{\cancel{6}}}{7} \times \frac{3}{2} = \frac{27}{28}$

Practice • Multiply. Write the answers in lowest terms.

1. $\frac{3}{5} \times \frac{1}{3}$
2. $\frac{3}{8} \times \frac{6}{7}$
3. $\frac{4}{5} \times \frac{5}{6}$
4. $\frac{3}{8} \times \frac{4}{9}$
5. $\frac{2}{9} \times \frac{3}{8}$
6. $\frac{10}{3} \times \frac{1}{2}$
7. $\frac{1}{6} \times \frac{9}{10}$
8. $\frac{3}{2} \times \frac{10}{9} \times \frac{1}{2}$

Mixed Practice • Multiply. Write the answers in lowest terms.

9. $\frac{1}{4} \times \frac{4}{5}$
10. $\frac{3}{5} \times \frac{10}{7}$
11. $\frac{5}{8} \times \frac{6}{5}$
12. $\frac{7}{8} \times \frac{4}{7}$
13. $\frac{2}{7} \times \frac{1}{4}$
14. $\frac{3}{4} \times \frac{5}{6}$
15. $\frac{2}{3} \times \frac{3}{7}$
16. $\frac{1}{2} \times \frac{2}{3} \times \frac{1}{4}$
17. $\frac{4}{9} \times \frac{9}{8}$
18. $\frac{8}{9} \times \frac{3}{4}$
19. $\frac{2}{35} \times \frac{7}{8}$
20. $\frac{5}{16} \times \frac{4}{5}$
21. $\frac{5}{6} \times \frac{2}{15}$
22. $\frac{2}{3} \times \frac{9}{10}$
23. $\frac{1}{2} \times \frac{2}{3}$
24. $\frac{5}{3} \times \frac{9}{10}$
25. $\frac{3}{10} \times \frac{4}{15}$
26. $\frac{9}{7} \times \frac{7}{8}$
27. $\frac{2}{3} \times \frac{6}{5}$
28. $\frac{1}{7} \times \frac{2}{5}$
29. $\frac{5}{7} \times \frac{7}{10}$
30. $\frac{1}{8} \times \frac{4}{5}$
31. $\frac{5}{8} \times \frac{1}{10}$
32. $\frac{2}{3} \times \frac{3}{4} \times \frac{3}{2}$
33. $\frac{5}{8} \times \frac{8}{3}$
34. $\frac{1}{3} \times \frac{6}{5}$
35. $\frac{4}{5} \times \frac{3}{2}$
36. ★ $\frac{49}{50} \times \frac{15}{98}$

Solve the equations.

37. $\frac{1}{2} + \frac{1}{8} = n$
38. $\frac{1}{2} - \frac{1}{8} = n$
39. $\frac{1}{2} \times \frac{1}{8} = n$
40. $\frac{1}{10} \times \frac{5}{6} \times \frac{2}{3} = n$
41. ★ $\frac{4}{5} \times \frac{5}{4} \times \frac{99}{100} = n$
42. ★ $\frac{3}{5} \times \frac{5}{3} \times \frac{97}{100} \times \frac{100}{97} = n$

Write <, =, or >.

43. $\frac{2}{3} \times \frac{1}{4}$ ● $\frac{1}{4}$
44. ★ $\frac{5}{5} \times \frac{4}{3}$ ● $\frac{4}{3}$
45. ★ $\frac{4}{5} \times \frac{4}{3}$ ● $\frac{4}{3}$

PROBLEM SOLVING • APPLICATIONS

46. Phil's weekly pay is equal to $\frac{4}{5}$ of Karen's weekly pay. Who has the greater pay?

47. ★ Ann's weekly pay is equal to $\frac{7}{6}$ of Karen's weekly pay. Who has the greater pay?

48. ★ Is multiplication of fractions commutative? Is it associative? Write six examples that support each answer.

Multiplying Whole Numbers and Mixed Numbers

There are 12 eggs in a carton of 1 dozen.

How many eggs are there in $\frac{5}{6}$ of a dozen?

$\frac{5}{6} \times 12 = n$

Step 1 Write the whole number as a fraction, $\frac{12}{1}$. $\quad \frac{5}{6} \times \frac{12}{1}$

Step 2 Multiply. $\quad \frac{5}{6} \times \frac{12}{1} = \frac{60}{6}$

Step 3 Since $\frac{60}{6} = 10$, write the whole number as the answer. $\quad \frac{5}{6} \times \frac{12}{1} = \frac{60}{6} = 10$

You can also divide by a common factor before you multiply.

$$\frac{5}{\cancel{6}_1} \times \frac{\cancel{12}^2}{1} = \frac{10}{1} = 10$$

Multiply: $1\frac{1}{2} \times 3\frac{3}{4}$.

Step 1 Write the mixed numbers as fractions. $\quad \frac{3}{2} \times \frac{15}{4}$

Step 2 Multiply. $\quad \frac{3}{2} \times \frac{15}{4} = \frac{45}{8}$

Step 3 Write a mixed number for the answer. $\quad \frac{3}{2} \times \frac{15}{4} = \frac{45}{8} = 5\frac{5}{8}$

More Examples

$$\frac{4}{5} \times 1\frac{3}{8} = \frac{\cancel{4}^1}{5} \times \frac{11}{\cancel{8}_2} = \frac{11}{10} = 1\frac{1}{10}$$

$$8 \times 2\frac{1}{2} = \frac{\cancel{8}^4}{1} \times \frac{5}{\cancel{2}_1} = \frac{20}{1} = 20$$

Practice • Multiply. Write the answers in lowest terms.

1. $\frac{3}{4} \times 12$ **2.** $10 \times \frac{1}{5}$ **3.** $4 \times 1\frac{1}{2}$ **4.** $3 \times \frac{2}{9}$

5. $2\frac{1}{4} \times \frac{2}{3}$ **6.** $\frac{7}{10} \times 100$ **7.** $3\frac{1}{4} \times 1\frac{1}{2}$ **8.** $6\frac{2}{3} \times 1\frac{1}{10}$

Mixed Practice • Multiply. Write the answers in lowest terms.

9. $\frac{5}{6} \times 18$ **10.** $20 \times \frac{1}{2}$ **11.** $12 \times \frac{1}{6}$ **12.** $4 \times \frac{3}{10}$

13. $\frac{7}{8} \times 4$ **14.** $1\frac{1}{3} \times \frac{1}{4}$ **15.** $\frac{2}{5} \times 3\frac{1}{2}$ **16.** $\frac{1}{3} \times 15$

17. $1\frac{1}{4} \times 1\frac{1}{3}$ **18.** $2\frac{1}{4} \times 1\frac{1}{9}$ **19.** $3\frac{2}{5} \times 10$ **20.** $2\frac{2}{5} \times 2\frac{2}{3}$

21. $4 \times 2\frac{4}{5}$ **22.** $3\frac{1}{3} \times 1\frac{1}{10}$ **23.** $7\frac{7}{10} \times 5$ **24.** $1\frac{5}{6} \times 4\frac{1}{11}$

25. $\frac{1}{2} \times \frac{3}{4} \times 8$ **26.** $\frac{2}{5} \times \frac{1}{4} \times 10$ ★**27.** $\frac{1}{2} \times 100 \times \frac{1}{2}$ ★**28.** $2\frac{1}{2} \times \frac{2}{5} \times \frac{3}{3}$

★**29.** $1\frac{1}{2} \times 2\frac{2}{3} \times 3\frac{1}{4}$ ★**30.** $1\frac{4}{5} \times 1\frac{5}{9} \times 3\frac{1}{2} \times \frac{4}{7}$

Solve the equations.

31. $6 \times \frac{1}{6} = n$ **32.** $\frac{2}{3} \times \frac{3}{2} = n$ **33.** $2\frac{3}{4} \times \frac{4}{11} = n$ **34.** $\frac{9}{10} \times 1\frac{1}{9} = n$

You know that $6 \times (10 + 2) = (6 \times 10) + (6 \times 2)$.
The distributive property also applies to mixed numbers and fractions.
To multiply $6 \times 4\frac{1}{2}$, you can think of $4\frac{1}{2}$ as $4 + \frac{1}{2}$, multiply each addend by 6, and then add.

Find the products.

35. $5 \times 8\frac{1}{5}$ **36.** $4 \times 9\frac{3}{4}$ ★**37.** $8 \times 12\frac{1}{10}$ ★**38.** $9 \times 25\frac{2}{3}$

PROBLEM SOLVING • APPLICATIONS

39. How many eggs are there in $\frac{3}{4}$ of a dozen?

40. How many eggs are there in $1\frac{5}{6}$ dozen?

★**41.** A day is 24 hours. How many hours are there in $8\frac{5}{8}$ days?

★**42.** A mile is 5,280 feet. How much less than 20,000 feet is $3\frac{3}{4}$ miles?

Skills Maintenance

Round to the nearest

whole number. **1.** 12.3 **2.** 8.51 **3.** 9.921 **4.** 25.487

hundredth. **5.** 1.236 **6.** 3.521 **7.** 6.005 **8.** 8.997

PROBLEM SOLVING • STRATEGIES

Using Graphs

Sometimes the information in a graph will be shown as fractions. You may need to compute using the fractions.

How Carol Uses Her Earnings

Clothing	Food	Recreation	Savings	School Supplies	All Other Expenses
$\frac{1}{5}$	$\frac{1}{4}$	$\frac{3}{20}$	$\frac{1}{10}$	$\frac{3}{25}$	$\frac{9}{50}$

This **divided-bar graph** shows how Carol uses the money she earns. For example, it shows that Carol spends $\frac{1}{5}$ of her money on clothing.

If Carol earns \$116.42 per month, about how much does she spend on clothing?

\$116.42 can be written as 116.42.

$$\frac{1}{5} \times 116.42 = n$$

$$\frac{1}{5} \times \frac{116.42}{1} = n$$

$$\frac{116.42}{5} = n$$

Is multiplying by $\frac{1}{5}$ like dividing by 5?

This example shows the value for n.

$$5\overline{)116.420} = 23.284 \approx 23.28 \longleftarrow \$23.28$$

To the nearest dollar, Carol spends \$23 per month on clothing.

Solve.

1. About how much money does Carol spend on food?
2. About how much money does Carol spend on recreation?

Round to the nearest dollar to give your answer.

3. About how much of her earnings does Carol save?
4. About how much money does Carol spend on school supplies?
5. Which expense uses the greatest fractional part of her money?
6. About how much money is used in the All Other Expenses category?

This graph shows how the Forbes family uses its yearly income. The yearly income of the Forbes family is $26,500 (after taxes).

Food	Clothing	Shelter	Recreation	Medical Expenses	All Other Expenses
$\frac{33}{100}$	$\frac{9}{100}$	$\frac{3}{10}$	$\frac{2}{25}$	$\frac{1}{20}$	$\frac{3}{20}$

7. About how much money does the Forbes family use for food?

8. About how much money does the Forbes family use for recreation?

9. About how much money does the Forbes family use for clothing?

Use fractions with denominators of 100 to answer the questions in problems 10–12.

10. How many hundredths of the budget is used for shelter?

11. How many hundredths of the budget is used for recreation?

12. What fractional part of the budget is used for food, clothing, and shelter?

★ **13.** About how much more money is used for food than for shelter?

★ **14.** About how much more money is used for clothing than for medical expenses?

Reread the problem to be sure you understand the question.

★ **15.** The Forbeses use $\frac{4}{5}$ of their medical expenses for doctors' and dentists' bills not covered by insurance. The rest is used for prescriptions from the pharmacy. About how much money is used for prescriptions from the pharmacy?

Reciprocals

Two numbers whose product is 1 are **reciprocals.**

$$\frac{2}{5} \times \frac{5}{2} = \frac{10}{10} = 1 \qquad \frac{1}{4} \times 4 = \frac{1}{4} \times \frac{4}{1} = \frac{4}{4} = 1$$

$\frac{2}{5}$ and $\frac{5}{2}$ are reciprocals. $\frac{1}{4}$ and 4 are reciprocals.

There is an easy way to find the reciprocal of a fraction such as $\frac{3}{8}$.

Exchange the numerator and the denominator.

Fraction	Reciprocal
$\frac{3}{8}$	$\frac{8}{3}$

$\frac{3}{8}$ and $\frac{8}{3}$ are reciprocals.

Check: $\frac{3}{8} \times \frac{8}{3} = \frac{24}{24} = 1$

To find the reciprocal of a whole number or a mixed number, first write the number as a fraction.

Find these reciprocals. 10 $\qquad 2\frac{1}{4}$

Step 1 Rewrite each number as a fraction. → $\frac{10}{1} \qquad \frac{9}{4}$

Step 2 Exchange the numerator and the denominator. → $\frac{10}{1} \to \frac{1}{10} \qquad \frac{9}{4} \to \frac{4}{9}$

10 and $\frac{1}{10}$ are reciprocals.

$\frac{10}{1} \times \frac{1}{10} = \frac{10}{10} = 1$

$2\frac{1}{4}$ and $\frac{4}{9}$ are reciprocals.

$2\frac{1}{4} \times \frac{4}{9} = \frac{9}{4} \times \frac{4}{9} = \frac{36}{36} = 1$

The number 1 is its own reciprocal, since $1 \times 1 = 1$.

The number 0 has no reciprocal. No matter what number is substituted for n in this equation, the product will be 0. The equation has no solution.

$$0 \times n \stackrel{?}{=} 1$$

Practice • Find the reciprocal of each number.

1. $\frac{1}{3}$ **2.** 5 **3.** $\frac{7}{4}$ **4.** $1\frac{2}{3}$ **5.** $\frac{9}{10}$

6. 1 **7.** $\frac{3}{8}$ **8.** $\frac{5}{2}$ **9.** $2\frac{7}{10}$ **10.** 15

Mixed Practice • Find the reciprocal of each number.

11. $\frac{7}{10}$ 12. $\frac{4}{5}$ 13. 6 14. $\frac{1}{2}$ 15. $\frac{8}{3}$

16. $\frac{7}{8}$ 17. 2 18. $\frac{1}{8}$ 19. 7 20. $\frac{12}{11}$

21. $1\frac{1}{4}$ 22. $2\frac{1}{3}$ 23. $3\frac{3}{5}$ 24. $4\frac{1}{2}$ 25. $6\frac{1}{10}$

26. 18 27. $\frac{1}{20}$ 28. $2\frac{1}{16}$ ★29. $2\frac{99}{100}$ ★30. $3\frac{499}{500}$

Solve the equations.

31. $\frac{5}{6} \times n = 1$ 32. $8 \times n = 1$ 33. $\frac{1}{5} \times n = 1$

34. $n \times \frac{3}{8} = 1$ 35. $n \times 5\frac{7}{10} = 1$ 36. $n \times 1 = 1$

★37. $0.5 \times n = 1$ ★38. $0.25 \times n = 1$ ★39. $1.1 \times n = 1$

PROBLEM SOLVING • APPLICATIONS

40. The Ruggio family uses $\frac{1}{4}$ of a pound of butter each day. How many days does it take for the Ruggio family to use 1 pound?

41. Hakan has $2\frac{1}{2}$ dollars. He spends $\frac{2}{5}$ of this money. How much money does he spend?

★42. If $\frac{a}{b}$ is less than 1, is its reciprocal less than 1, or is it greater than 1?

★43. If $\frac{a}{b}$ is greater than 1, is its reciprocal less than 1, or is it greater than 1?

Midchapter Review

Multiply. Write the answers in lowest terms.

1. $\frac{3}{5} \times \frac{1}{2}$ 2. $\frac{1}{8} \times \frac{4}{9}$ 3. $\frac{5}{6} \times \frac{8}{15}$ 4. $\frac{7}{12} \times \frac{9}{14}$ 5. $6 \times \frac{3}{5}$

6. $\frac{5}{8} \times 16$ 7. $\frac{5}{9} \times 3\frac{3}{10}$ 8. $2\frac{1}{7} \times 14$ 9. $4\frac{1}{2} \times 2\frac{2}{5}$ 10. $3\frac{3}{5} \times 2\frac{7}{9}$

Find the reciprocal of each number.

11. 8 12. $\frac{2}{3}$ 13. $3\frac{1}{4}$ 14. $\frac{1}{6}$ 15. $9\frac{1}{8}$

Dividing by Fractions

4 oranges are divided into half-oranges.
How many half-oranges are there?
From the picture, the answer is 8.

$$4 \div \frac{1}{2} = 8.$$

Since there are 2 half-oranges in each of 4 oranges, you can also multiply: $4 \times 2 = 8$.

The division sentence and the multiplication sentence have the same answer.

$$4 \div \frac{1}{2} = 4 \times 2 = 8$$

($\frac{1}{2}$ and 2: reciprocals)

Dividing by $\frac{1}{2}$ and multiplying by its reciprocal give the same answer.

How many eighth-inches are there in $\frac{3}{4}$ inch?

6 eighth-inches

inches 1

$\frac{3}{4}$ inch

From the picture, the answer is 6.

$$\frac{3}{4} \div \frac{1}{8} = 6$$

You can also multiply by the reciprocal of the divisor.

$$\frac{3}{4} \times \frac{8}{1} = \frac{24}{4} = 6 \longrightarrow \frac{3}{4} \div \frac{1}{8} = \frac{3}{4} \times \frac{8}{1} = \frac{24}{4} = 6$$

($\frac{1}{8}$ and $\frac{8}{1}$: reciprocals)

> ***To divide by a number, multiply by its reciprocal. In variables:*** $\frac{a}{b} \div \frac{c}{d} = \frac{a}{b} \times \frac{d}{c}$

More Examples

$$\frac{3}{2} \div \frac{2}{9} = \frac{3}{2} \times \frac{9}{2} = \frac{27}{4} = 6\frac{3}{4}$$

($\frac{2}{9}$ and $\frac{9}{2}$: reciprocals)

$$\frac{1}{12} \div \frac{2}{3} = \frac{1}{12} \times \frac{3}{2} = \frac{3}{24} = \frac{1}{8}$$

($\frac{2}{3}$ and $\frac{3}{2}$: reciprocals)

Practice • Divide. Write the answers in lowest terms.

1. $3 \div \frac{1}{2}$ **2.** $\frac{3}{4} \div \frac{1}{16}$ **3.** $\frac{5}{2} \div \frac{1}{2}$ **4.** $2 \div \frac{1}{4}$ **5.** $\frac{2}{3} \div \frac{5}{6}$

6. $\frac{5}{8} \div \frac{5}{4}$ **7.** $\frac{1}{3} \div \frac{5}{6}$ **8.** $2 \div \frac{1}{3}$ **9.** $\frac{4}{7} \div \frac{1}{2}$ **10.** $4 \div \frac{2}{3}$

Mixed Practice • Divide. Write the answers in lowest terms.

11. $2 \div \frac{1}{4}$ **12.** $\frac{3}{4} \div \frac{1}{8}$ **13.** $5 \div \frac{1}{2}$ **14.** $\frac{3}{8} \div \frac{1}{16}$ **15.** $\frac{1}{8} \div \frac{1}{2}$

16. $\frac{1}{2} \div \frac{3}{4}$ **17.** $5 \div \frac{1}{4}$ **18.** $\frac{1}{3} \div \frac{1}{9}$ **19.** $\frac{5}{8} \div \frac{3}{4}$ **20.** $\frac{7}{10} \div \frac{2}{5}$

21. $\frac{1}{10} \div \frac{1}{5}$ **22.** $\frac{5}{6} \div \frac{2}{3}$ **23.** $\frac{3}{10} \div \frac{1}{5}$ **24.** $\frac{1}{2} \div \frac{3}{10}$ **25.** $\frac{5}{8} \div \frac{1}{4}$

26. $\frac{7}{2} \div \frac{3}{4}$ **27.** $\frac{5}{4} \div \frac{1}{8}$ **28.** $\frac{5}{2} \div \frac{3}{8}$ **29.** $\frac{1}{2} \div \frac{1}{3}$ **30.** $6 \div \frac{2}{3}$

31. $\frac{3}{10} \div \frac{1}{15}$ **32.** $\frac{9}{10} \div \frac{3}{10}$ **33.** $3 \div \frac{3}{4}$ **34.** $\frac{1}{8} \div \frac{5}{8}$ **35.** $\frac{3}{8} \div \frac{3}{4}$

36. $2 \div \frac{1}{10}$ **37.** $\frac{1}{10} \div \frac{1}{100}$ ★**38.** $\frac{1}{10} \div \frac{1}{1{,}000}$ ★**39.** $\frac{1}{100} \div \frac{1}{1{,}000}$ ★**40.** $\frac{7}{10} \div \frac{7}{1{,}000}$

Solve the equations.

41. $\frac{1}{2} + \frac{1}{5} = n$ **42.** $\frac{1}{2} - \frac{1}{5} = n$ **43.** $\frac{1}{2} \times \frac{1}{5} = n$

44. $\frac{1}{2} \div \frac{1}{5} = n$ ★**45.** $0.75 \times n = 1$ ★**46.** $4.5 \times n = 1$

★**47.** $n + \left(\frac{3}{4} + \frac{1}{8}\right) = 1\frac{1}{2}$ ★**48.** $n - \left(\frac{1}{5} + \frac{1}{10}\right) = \frac{19}{20}$ ★**49.** $\left(\frac{1}{3} \div \frac{1}{5}\right) \times \frac{3}{5} = n$

PROBLEM SOLVING • APPLICATIONS

50. How many $\frac{1}{4}$ inches are there in $\frac{1}{2}$ inch?

51. How many $\frac{1}{8}$ inches are there in $\frac{1}{2}$ inch?

52. How many $\frac{1}{16}$ inches are there in $\frac{3}{4}$ inch?

★**53.** How many times as great as $\frac{1}{8}$ of a pound is $\frac{3}{4}$ of a pound?

★**54.** Steve, Tony, and Len are brothers. Steve can jump $5\frac{1}{2}$ feet. Tony can jump $\frac{2}{3}$ as far as Steve. Len can jump $\frac{3}{4}$ as far as Tony. How many feet can Len jump?

★**55.** Helena, Alexandra, and Melanie are sisters. Helena is $17\frac{1}{4}$ years old. Alexandra's age is $\frac{8}{9}$ of Helena's age. Melanie's age is $\frac{6}{7}$ of Alexandra's age. How old will Melanie be on her next birthday?

Dividing by Whole Numbers

A group of 6 people share $\frac{3}{4}$ of a watermelon equally. How much will each person receive?

$\frac{3}{4} \div 6 = n$

Step 1 Write the whole number as a fraction, $\frac{6}{1}$.

$\frac{3}{4} \div \frac{6}{1}$

Step 2 Rewrite as a multiplication example.

$\frac{3}{4} \div \frac{6}{1} = \frac{3}{4} \times \frac{1}{6}$

Step 3 Multiply. Write the answer in lowest terms.

$\frac{3}{4} \div \frac{6}{1} = \frac{3}{4} \times \frac{1}{6} = \frac{3}{24} = \frac{1}{8}$

Each person will receive $\frac{1}{8}$ of the watermelon.

Check by multiplying: $6 \times \frac{1}{8} = \frac{6}{8} = \frac{3}{4}$.

After you rewrite a division example as a multiplication example, you can use the shortcut in multiplication.

$$\frac{3}{4} \div 6 = \frac{3}{4} \div \frac{6}{1}$$

$$= \frac{\overset{1}{\cancel{3}}}{4} \times \frac{1}{\underset{2}{\cancel{6}}} = \frac{1}{8}$$

More Examples

$$\frac{8}{5} \div 2 = \frac{8}{5} \div \frac{2}{1}$$

$$= \frac{\overset{4}{\cancel{8}}}{5} \times \frac{1}{\underset{1}{\cancel{2}}} = \frac{4}{5}$$

$$\frac{21}{4} \div 3 = \frac{21}{4} \div \frac{3}{1}$$

$$= \frac{\overset{7}{\cancel{21}}}{4} \times \frac{1}{\underset{1}{\cancel{3}}} = \frac{7}{4} = 1\frac{3}{4}$$

Practice • Divide. Write the answers in lowest terms.

1. $\frac{8}{9} \div 2$ **2.** $\frac{1}{2} \div 4$ **3.** $\frac{2}{5} \div 10$ **4.** $\frac{9}{4} \div 6$ **5.** $\frac{14}{3} \div 4$

6. $\frac{1}{8} \div 4$ **7.** $\frac{5}{6} \div 5$ **8.** $\frac{6}{7} \div 3$ **9.** $\frac{7}{10} \div 14$ **10.** $\frac{9}{2} \div 6$

Mixed Practice • Divide. Write the answers in lowest terms.

11. $\frac{1}{2} \div 8$
12. $\frac{4}{9} \div 2$
13. $\frac{8}{5} \div 4$
14. $\frac{4}{5} \div 6$
15. $\frac{5}{8} \div \frac{1}{8}$
16. $\frac{7}{3} \div 2$
17. $\frac{9}{10} \div 3$
18. $6 \div \frac{1}{2}$
19. $\frac{6}{7} \div 4$
20. $\frac{9}{10} \div 12$
21. $\frac{8}{11} \div 8$
22. $\frac{18}{7} \div 2$
23. $\frac{2}{3} \div 4$
24. $\frac{3}{4} \div 12$
25. $3 \div \frac{3}{10}$
26. $\frac{1}{6} \div 2$
27. $\frac{9}{4} \div 4$
28. $4 \div \frac{3}{5}$
★ 29. $\frac{11}{10} \div 10$
★ 30. $\frac{7}{100} \div 10$

Solve the equations. Look for a pattern.

31. $1 \div \frac{1}{5} = n$
32. $1 \div \frac{3}{2} = n$
33. $1 \div \frac{10}{7} = n$
34. $1 \div \frac{5}{3} = n$
35. $1 \div \frac{7}{4} = n$
36. $1 \div \frac{9}{5} = n$

★ 37. If 1 is divided by a number $\frac{a}{b}$, what is the quotient?

Solve the equations.

38. $\left(\frac{1}{2} + \frac{1}{4}\right) \div 4 = n$
39. $\left(1\frac{3}{8} + 1\frac{5}{8}\right) \div \frac{1}{5} = n$

★ 40. $\left(\frac{5}{6} \times \frac{6}{5}\right) \times n = \frac{3}{4}$
★ 41. $\frac{2}{3} \times \frac{1}{4} \times n = 5$

PROBLEM SOLVING • APPLICATIONS

42. Marcia is making 6 sandwiches from $\frac{3}{4}$ pound of roast beef. How much roast beef is on each sandwich?

43. How many $\frac{1}{4}$-pound portions can be made from 2 pounds of potato salad?

44. How many $\frac{1}{4}$-pound hamburgers can be made from 3 pounds of ground beef?

★ 45. Marcia buys 3 pounds of ground beef. She uses $1\frac{1}{4}$ pounds in a lasagna recipe. How many $\frac{1}{4}$-pound hamburgers can be made from the rest of the ground beef?

Using Mixed Numbers in Division

Paul is packaging $4\frac{1}{2}$ trays of rolls. If $\frac{3}{4}$ of a tray will fill 1 package, how many packages can Paul fill?

$4\frac{1}{2} \div \frac{3}{4} = n$

Step 1 Write the mixed number as a fraction. $\frac{9}{2} \div \frac{3}{4}$

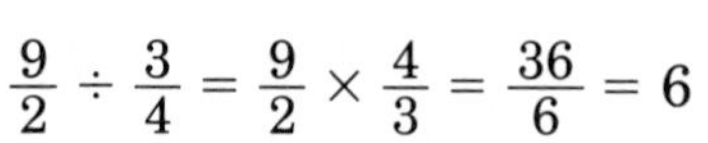

Step 2 Rewrite as a multiplication example. $\frac{9}{2} \div \frac{3}{4} = \frac{9}{2} \times \frac{4}{3}$

Step 3 Multiply. Since $\frac{36}{6} = 6$, write the answer as 6. $\frac{9}{2} \div \frac{3}{4} = \frac{9}{2} \times \frac{4}{3} = \frac{36}{6} = 6$

Paul can fill 6 packages.

Divide: $2\frac{2}{3} \div 1\frac{2}{5}$.

Step 1 Write the mixed numbers as fractions. $\frac{8}{3} \div \frac{7}{5}$

Step 2 Rewrite as a multiplication example. $\frac{8}{3} \div \frac{7}{5} = \frac{8}{3} \times \frac{5}{7}$

Step 3 Multiply. Write a mixed number for the answer. $\frac{8}{3} \div \frac{7}{5} = \frac{8}{3} \times \frac{5}{7} = \frac{40}{21} = 1\frac{19}{21}$

More Examples

$\frac{3}{4} \div 1\frac{1}{2} = \frac{3}{4} \div \frac{3}{2} = \frac{\overset{1}{\cancel{3}}}{\underset{2}{\cancel{4}}} \times \frac{\overset{1}{\cancel{2}}}{\underset{1}{\cancel{3}}} = \frac{1}{2}$

$3\frac{5}{8} \div 2\frac{1}{4} = \frac{29}{8} \div \frac{9}{4} = \frac{29}{\underset{2}{\cancel{8}}} \times \frac{\overset{1}{\cancel{4}}}{9} = \frac{29}{18} = 1\frac{11}{18}$

Practice • Divide. Write the answers in lowest terms.

1. $1\frac{1}{2} \div \frac{3}{8}$ **2.** $3\frac{1}{3} \div \frac{5}{6}$ **3.** $\frac{5}{8} \div 1\frac{1}{4}$ **4.** $\frac{7}{8} \div 3\frac{1}{2}$ **5.** $10 \div 3\frac{1}{3}$

6. $1\frac{1}{2} \div 4\frac{1}{2}$ **7.** $5 \div 1\frac{1}{4}$ **8.** $2\frac{1}{2} \div 1\frac{1}{2}$ **9.** $3\frac{1}{4} \div 1\frac{3}{8}$ **10.** $2\frac{1}{2} \div 100$

Mixed Practice • Divide. Write the answers in lowest terms.

11. $1\frac{1}{4} \div \frac{5}{8}$ **12.** $2\frac{3}{4} \div \frac{11}{12}$ **13.** $\frac{7}{8} \div 1\frac{3}{4}$ **14.** $\frac{4}{5} \div 1\frac{1}{10}$ **15.** $6 \div 2\frac{2}{3}$

16. $8 \div 2\frac{1}{2}$ **17.** $4\frac{4}{5} \div 2$ **18.** $\frac{1}{3} \div 3\frac{1}{3}$ **19.** $2\frac{1}{4} \div 2\frac{2}{5}$ **20.** $1\frac{1}{8} \div 6\frac{3}{4}$

21. $15\frac{5}{8} \div 3\frac{1}{8}$ **22.** $1\frac{3}{8} \div 8\frac{1}{4}$ **23.** $5\frac{5}{7} \div 2\frac{1}{2}$ **24.** $10 \div 3\frac{3}{4}$ ★ **25.** $3\frac{1}{3} \div 14\frac{2}{7}$

Solve the equations.

26. $33\frac{1}{3} \div 100 = n$ **27.** $66\frac{2}{3} \div 100 = n$ **28.** $16\frac{2}{3} \div 100 = n$

29. $12\frac{1}{2} \div 100 = n$ **30.** $25 \div 100 = n$ **31.** $37\frac{1}{2} \div 100 = n$

32. $50 \div 100 = n$ **33.** $62\frac{1}{2} \div 100 = n$ **34.** $75 \div 100 = n$

★ **35.** $133\frac{1}{3} \div 100 = n$ ★ **36.** $116\frac{2}{3} \div 100 = n$ ★ **37.** $137\frac{1}{2} \div 100 = n$

A **complex fraction** has a fraction or a mixed number for the numerator, for the denominator, or for both.

Complex Fraction

$$\frac{\frac{3}{4}}{\frac{2}{3}}$$

$\frac{\frac{3}{4}}{\frac{2}{3}}$ means $\frac{3}{4} \div \frac{2}{3}$. You can simplify the fraction by dividing.

$$\frac{3}{4} \div \frac{2}{3} = \frac{3}{4} \times \frac{3}{2} = \frac{9}{8} = 1\frac{1}{8}$$

Simplify.

38. $\frac{\frac{1}{2}}{\frac{1}{4}}$ **39.** $\frac{4}{\frac{2}{5}}$ **40.** $\frac{\frac{1}{3}}{6}$ **41.** $\frac{\frac{3}{8}}{\frac{3}{4}}$ ★ **42.** $\frac{1\frac{1}{2}}{4\frac{1}{2}}$

PROBLEM SOLVING • APPLICATIONS

43. Valerie has a board that is $12\frac{3}{4}$ feet long. She cuts it into sections that are $2\frac{1}{8}$ feet long each. How many sections are there?

44. Valerie earns $24\frac{3}{4}$ dollars for $5\frac{1}{2}$ hours of work in a part-time job. How much does she earn per hour?

★ **45.** How much would Valerie earn for $17\frac{1}{2}$ hours of work at the same rate per hour?

Fractions and Decimals

The decimal 0.3 and the fraction $\frac{3}{10}$ name the same number. 0.27 and $\frac{27}{100}$ name the same number.

Sometimes you need to write a fraction or a mixed number for a decimal such as 0.75 or 2.800.

Think: $0.75 = \frac{75}{100}$.

Then write the answer in lowest terms.

$$0.75 = \frac{75}{100} = \frac{3}{4}$$

Think: $2.800 = 2\frac{800}{1{,}000}$.

Then write the answer in lowest terms.

$$2.800 = 2\frac{800}{1{,}000} = 2\frac{4}{5}$$

When a fraction has a denominator that is a power of 10, it is easy to write the decimal. $\frac{3}{100} = 0.03$

To write a decimal for a fraction such as $\frac{3}{8}$, you can divide the numerator by the denominator. $\frac{a}{b} \longrightarrow b\overline{)a}$

Find the decimal for $\frac{3}{8}$.
Divide 3 by 8.
Remember that 3 = 3.0 = 3.00 = 3.000.
Divide until the remainder is 0.
The decimal 0.375 is called a **terminating decimal**.

$$\begin{array}{r} 0.375 \\ 8\overline{)3.000} \\ -2\,4 \\ \hline 60 \\ -56 \\ \hline 40 \\ -40 \\ \hline 0 \end{array}$$

$\frac{3}{8} = 0.375$

More Examples

$\frac{7}{4} \longrightarrow 4\overline{)7.00}$ with quotient 1.75

$\frac{7}{4} = 1.75$

$1\frac{3}{4}$, $\frac{3}{4} \longrightarrow 4\overline{)3.00}$ with quotient 0.75

Since $\frac{3}{4} = 0.75$,
then $1\frac{3}{4} = 1.75$.

$\frac{3}{500} \longrightarrow$
$$\begin{array}{r} 0.006 \\ 500\overline{)3.000} \\ -3\,000 \\ \hline 0 \end{array}$$

$\frac{3}{500} = 0.006$

Note that $\frac{7}{4} = 1\frac{3}{4} = 1.75$.

Practice • Write as fractions, whole numbers, or mixed numbers in lowest terms.

1. 0.2 **2.** 0.15 **3.** 0.250 **4.** 7.60 **5.** 8.000 **6.** 3.0007

Write as decimals.

7. $\frac{9}{100}$ **8.** $\frac{3}{10}$ **9.** $\frac{1}{2}$ **10.** $\frac{3}{40}$ **11.** $\frac{13}{5}$ **12.** $1\frac{5}{8}$

Mixed Practice • Write as fractions, whole numbers, or mixed numbers in lowest terms.

13. 0.80 **14.** 0.4 **15.** 0.11 **16.** 4.00 **17.** 0.750 **18.** 5.900

19. 0.55 **20.** 1.5 **21.** 0.010 **22.** 2.95 ★**23.** 0.0004 ★**24.** 0.00007

Write as decimals.

25. $\frac{1}{10}$ **26.** $\frac{15}{100}$ **27.** $\frac{1}{100}$ **28.** $1\frac{3}{1,000}$ **29.** $\frac{25}{1,000}$ **30.** $2\frac{75}{100}$

31. $\frac{1}{4}$ **32.** $\frac{2}{5}$ **33.** $\frac{7}{20}$ **34.** $\frac{19}{25}$ **35.** $\frac{9}{5}$ **36.** $\frac{7}{8}$

37. $2\frac{1}{8}$ **38.** $3\frac{9}{50}$ **39.** $2\frac{7}{40}$ ★**40.** $2\frac{18}{250}$ ★**41.** $\frac{487}{5,000}$ ★**42.** $\frac{2,113}{2,000}$

Write $<$, $=$, or $>$.

43. $\frac{1}{2}$ ● 0.4 **44.** $1\frac{1}{2}$ ● 1.5 ★**45.** $\frac{3}{8}$ ● 0.35 ★**46.** $\frac{5}{16}$ ● 0.32

PROBLEM SOLVING • APPLICATIONS

Write decimals for the fractions.

47. About $\frac{3}{4}$ of the population of the United States lives in metropolitan areas.

48. Each year about $\frac{1}{5}$ of the population moves to a new residence.

Solve.

★**49.** If the population of the United States is about 230 million people, about how many people move each year?

★**50.** In 1790 there were only 3.9 million people in the United States. In 1800 there were 5.3 million people. The population in 1800 was about how many times as great as the population in 1790? Give your answer to the nearest tenth.

Skills Maintenance

Find the least common multiple.

1. 3, 4 **2.** 6, 8 **3.** 2, 5 **4.** 3, 6 **5.** 10, 100

6. 3, 7 **7.** 10, 12 **8.** 12, 15 **9.** 2, 3, 4 **10.** 3, 6, 9

Repeating Decimals

Find a decimal for $\frac{3}{11}$.

Divide 3 by 11.

Note how the remainders 8 and 3 repeat as you divide. The digits 2 and 7 in the quotient also repeat endlessly.

$$\begin{array}{r} 0.2727 \\ 11\overline{)3.0000} \\ \underline{-2\,2} \\ 80 \\ \underline{-77} \\ 30 \\ \underline{-22} \\ 80 \\ \underline{-77} \\ 3 \end{array}$$

0.2727 . . . is a **repeating decimal**. The three dots indicate that the pattern continues; the digits 2 and 7 repeat. The decimal 0.2727 . . . can be written in a shorter way, as shown below.

$\frac{3}{11} = 0.\overline{27}$ ⟵ The bar is used to show the digits that repeat.

Here are more examples.

$\frac{1}{3} \longrightarrow$
$$\begin{array}{r} 0.33 \\ 3\overline{)1.00} \\ \underline{-\ 9} \\ 10 \\ \underline{-\ 9} \\ 1 \end{array}$$

$\frac{1}{6} \longrightarrow$
$$\begin{array}{r} 0.166 \\ 6\overline{)1.000} \\ \underline{-\ 6} \\ 40 \\ \underline{-36} \\ 40 \\ \underline{-36} \\ 4 \end{array}$$

$\frac{1}{3} = 0.\overline{3}$

$\frac{1}{6} = 0.1\overline{6}$ ⟵ The bar is over the 6 only.

Sometimes you round to get a decimal that is approximately equal to a fraction. To the nearest hundredth, the decimal for $\frac{1}{6}$ is 0.17.

Practice • Write the fractions as decimals. Use a bar to show a repeating decimal.

1. $\frac{5}{6}$ **2.** $\frac{2}{3}$ **3.** $\frac{2}{9}$ **4.** $\frac{2}{15}$ **5.** $\frac{1}{12}$ **6.** $\frac{15}{11}$

Write the fractions as decimals. Round to the nearest hundredth.

7. $\frac{2}{3}$ **8.** $\frac{7}{6}$ **9.** $\frac{5}{9}$ **10.** $\frac{7}{15}$ **11.** $\frac{5}{12}$ **12.** $\frac{19}{9}$

Mixed Practice • Write as decimals. Use a bar to show a repeating decimal.

13. $\frac{5}{9}$ **14.** $\frac{7}{12}$ **15.** $\frac{5}{18}$ **16.** $\frac{7}{3}$ **17.** $\frac{9}{11}$ **18.** $\frac{11}{6}$

19. $\frac{7}{30}$ **20.** $\frac{2}{45}$ **21.** $\frac{1}{18}$ **22.** $\frac{26}{9}$ **23.** $\frac{7}{90}$ **24.** $\frac{13}{36}$

25. $\frac{17}{9}$ **26.** $\frac{19}{12}$ **27.** $\frac{11}{18}$ **28.** $\frac{1}{11}$ **29.** $\frac{601}{600}$ ★**30.** $1\frac{166}{333}$

Write as decimals. Round to the nearest hundredth.

31. $\frac{5}{3}$ **32.** $\frac{11}{6}$ **33.** $\frac{5}{36}$ **34.** $\frac{50}{9}$ **35.** $\frac{47}{45}$ **36.** $\frac{13}{12}$

37. $1\frac{1}{3}$ **38.** $2\frac{1}{6}$ **39.** $1\frac{11}{12}$ ★**40.** $\frac{103}{90}$ ★**41.** $3\frac{76}{99}$ ★**42.** $1\frac{599}{600}$

Write the fractions as terminating decimals or as repeating decimals.

43. $\frac{3}{40}$ **44.** $\frac{23}{12}$ **45.** $\frac{17}{3}$ **46.** $\frac{113}{250}$ **47.** $\frac{11}{6}$ ★**48.** $\frac{3,725}{180}$

Write $<$, $=$, or $>$.

★**49.** $0.60 \bullet 0.\overline{6}$ ★**50.** $1.011 \bullet 1.\overline{01}$ ★**51.** $0.3 \bullet \frac{1}{3}$

Solve the equations.

52. $1\frac{2}{3} + 1\frac{1}{2} = n$ **53.** $1\frac{2}{3} - 1\frac{1}{2} = n$ **54.** $1\frac{2}{3} \times 1\frac{1}{2} = n$

55. $1\frac{2}{3} \div 1\frac{1}{2} = n$ ★**56.** $n - 1\frac{1}{2} = 1\frac{2}{3}$ ★**57.** $\left(\frac{1}{4} \div \frac{1}{5}\right) \div \frac{1}{6} = n$

PROBLEM SOLVING • APPLICATIONS

Find each player's batting average. To find a player's batting average, divide the number of hits by the number of times at bat. Give each average to the nearest thousandth.

Player	Number of Hits	Times at Bat	Batting Average
58. Robert	6	22	?
59. Marcia	8	29	?
60. Carlos	5	17	?
61. Donna	15	46	?
62. Johnny	12	38	?

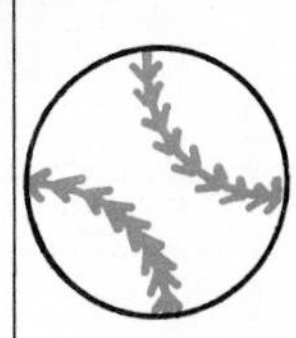

63. Rewrite the batting averages in order, from greatest to least.

64. Who had the best average?

★**65.** In one season a major league ballplayer had an average of .300. If he was at bat 450 times, how many hits did he have?

PROBLEM SOLVING • STRATEGIES

Using Estimates

When you work with mixed numbers and fractions, you can use an estimate as a check for a careless error.

A fox can run $\frac{2}{3}$ of a mile in a minute. At this rate how far will it run in $3\frac{1}{4}$ minutes?

$$3\frac{1}{4} \times \frac{2}{3} = n$$

Keith multiplied and obtained this answer:

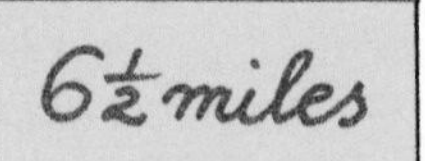

Anne multiplied and obtained this answer:

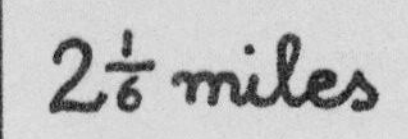

Use a "rough" estimate to check.

$3\frac{1}{4} < 4$ and $\frac{2}{3} < 1$

So $3\frac{1}{4} \times \frac{2}{3}$ must be less than 4×1, or 4. Keith's answer must be incorrect.

Here is another way to estimate roughly.

$3\frac{1}{4}$ is close to 3.

$\frac{2}{3}$ is close to 1.

So $3\frac{1}{4} \times \frac{2}{3}$ must be close to 3×1, or 3. Anne's answer seems possible.

Multiply to see if her answer is correct.

Solve.

1. A dragonfly can fly $\frac{5}{6}$ of a mile in 1 minute. At this rate how far will it fly in $4\frac{3}{5}$ minutes?

2. An owl can fly $4\frac{2}{3}$ miles in 7 minutes. How far can it fly in 1 minute?

3. A whale can swim $3\frac{2}{3}$ miles in 11 minutes. How far can it swim in 1 minute?

4. A dolphin can swim $\frac{5}{12}$ of a mile in 1 minute. How far can it swim in $8\frac{2}{5}$ minutes?

5. Jessie works in an aquarium. She works $2\frac{3}{4}$ hours each day. How many hours does she work in 5 days?

A rough estimate can help you decide if your answer is possible.

6. Bill works in a pet shop. He works 18 hours in 4 days. How many hours does he work per day?

7. Bill is paid $3\frac{3}{5}$ dollars per hour at his job. How much money does he earn for $4\frac{1}{2}$ hours' work?

8. Jessie is paid $4\frac{1}{5}$ dollars per hour at her job. How much money is she paid for $2\frac{1}{2}$ hours' work?

Use multiplication and division to check each other.

9. Bill can run $2\frac{1}{2}$ miles in 15 minutes. What is his average speed in miles per minute?

★ 10. What is Bill's average speed in feet per minute?

★ 11. Jessie can run 2 miles in $10\frac{2}{3}$ minutes. What is her average speed in feet per minute?

★ 12. If a dolphin can swim $\frac{5}{12}$ of a mile in a minute, how many seconds will it take to swim 1 mile?

★ 13. Can a person run a mile faster than a dolphin can swim a mile? Use a reference library to find out the record for a mile run by a person.

CHAPTER 8

REVIEW

Multiply. Write the answers in lowest terms. (pp. 194–199)

1. $\frac{1}{5} \times \frac{2}{3}$ **2.** $\frac{7}{10} \times \frac{3}{5}$ **3.** $\frac{3}{8} \times \frac{4}{9}$ **4.** $\frac{3}{4} \times \frac{5}{6}$ **5.** $\frac{5}{6} \times 10$

6. $\frac{9}{10} \times 25$ **7.** $6 \times \frac{5}{12}$ **8.** $2\frac{2}{5} \times \frac{5}{8}$ **9.** $4\frac{1}{3} \times 1\frac{1}{2}$ **10.** $2\frac{3}{4} \times 3\frac{1}{3}$

Find the reciprocal of each number. (pp. 202–203)

11. $\frac{5}{8}$ **12.** 7 **13.** $\frac{1}{3}$ **14.** $3\frac{1}{3}$ **15.** $5\frac{3}{4}$

Divide. Write the answers in lowest terms. (pp. 204–209)

16. $\frac{2}{3} \div \frac{1}{2}$ **17.** $\frac{7}{8} \div \frac{3}{4}$ **18.** $6 \div \frac{3}{4}$ **19.** $\frac{5}{6} \div \frac{2}{9}$ **20.** $\frac{5}{8} \div 20$

21. $\frac{7}{10} \div 14$ **22.** $\frac{6}{7} \div \frac{7}{18}$ **23.** $1\frac{3}{8} \div \frac{1}{6}$ **24.** $6\frac{2}{3} \div 1\frac{5}{9}$ **25.** $6\frac{3}{5} \div 1\frac{7}{8}$

Write as fractions, whole numbers, or mixed numbers in lowest terms. (pp. 210–211)

26. 0.70 **27.** 0.8 **28.** 0.15 **29.** 9.00 **30.** 0.250 **31.** 5.600

Write as decimals. (pp. 210–211)

32. $\frac{9}{10}$ **33.** $\frac{3}{100}$ **34.** $\frac{3}{5}$ **35.** $\frac{13}{20}$ **36.** $\frac{5}{8}$ **37.** $2\frac{7}{25}$

Write as decimals. Use a bar to show a repeating decimal. (pp. 212–213)

38. $\frac{2}{3}$ **39.** $\frac{5}{6}$ **40.** $\frac{7}{9}$ **41.** $\frac{3}{11}$ **42.** $\frac{7}{6}$ **43.** $\frac{4}{3}$

44. The deep end of a swimming pool is $3\frac{1}{2}$ times as deep as the shallow end. The shallow end is $2\frac{3}{4}$ feet deep. What is the depth of the deep end? (pp. 214–215)

45. Toshi runs $2\frac{1}{4}$ laps in 12 minutes. What is her average speed in laps per minute? (pp. 214–215)

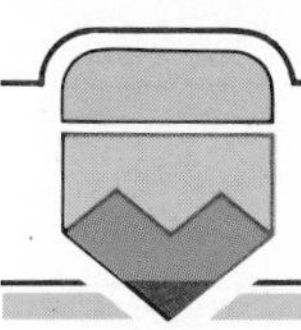

PROJECT

Using Recipes

Sometimes recipes need to be changed when you are preparing more or less food than the recipe suggests.

Alison is using this recipe to prepare dinner for guests.

ORIENTAL CHICKEN AND VEGETABLES

2 pounds chicken cutlets
1 teaspoon paprika
1 clove of garlic, chopped
½ teaspoon salt
¼ teaspoon pepper
2 tablespoons salad oil
2 tablespoons cornstarch
3 tablespoons soy sauce
1 medium onion, thinly sliced
2 medium green peppers, thinly sliced
¾ cup celery, chopped
1½ cups chicken broth
3 medium tomatoes, cut into wedges
4 cups cooked rice

MAKES 4 SERVINGS

Cut chicken into thin strips. Season chicken with paprika, garlic, salt, and pepper. Sauté in oil for 1 minute. Add onion, green pepper, celery, and half of the chicken broth. Cover and cook for 1½ minutes. Combine the remaining chicken broth, cornstarch, and soy sauce. Mix well. Add broth mixture to skillet, stirring well. Add tomatoes. Cook 1 minute. Serve over rice.

The recipe makes 4 servings. Alison wants to make 8 servings. She must multiply the amount of each ingredient in the recipe by 2.

chicken: 2×2 pounds $= 4$ pounds
paprika: 2×1 teaspoon $= 2$ teaspoons
salt: $2 \times \frac{1}{2}$ teaspoon $= 1$ teaspoon

How much of each ingredient does Alison need?

1. pepper
2. salad oil
3. soy sauce
4. onion
5. green pepper
6. celery
7. chicken broth
8. rice

How much chicken broth would you need to make

9. 2 servings?
10. 14 servings?

11. Find a recipe for one of your favorite fish, chicken, or vegetable dishes. Write two problems that involve changing the amounts of the ingredients (to prepare less or more of the food than the recipe suggests). Solve the problems yourself. Then ask a friend to check your answers.

CHAPTER 8

TEST

Multiply. Write the answers in lowest terms.

1. $\frac{7}{8} \times \frac{1}{3}$ **2.** $\frac{3}{4} \times \frac{3}{5}$ **3.** $\frac{9}{10} \times \frac{3}{7}$ **4.** $\frac{4}{5} \times \frac{1}{2}$ **5.** $6 \times \frac{1}{8}$

6. $\frac{2}{3} \times 12$ **7.** $\frac{7}{10} \times 5$ **8.** $3\frac{1}{5} \times 1\frac{3}{8}$ **9.** $6\frac{3}{4} \times 1\frac{5}{9}$ **10.** $6\frac{2}{3} \times 4\frac{3}{4}$

Find the reciprocal of each number.

11. 9 **12.** $\frac{7}{8}$ **13.** $\frac{1}{7}$ **14.** $4\frac{2}{9}$ **15.** $6\frac{2}{3}$

Divide. Write the answers in lowest terms.

16. $\frac{1}{6} \div \frac{1}{4}$ **17.** $\frac{2}{5} \div \frac{3}{10}$ **18.** $\frac{2}{5} \div \frac{5}{6}$ **19.** $10 \div \frac{5}{8}$ **20.** $15 \div \frac{3}{4}$

21. $\frac{4}{9} \div 12$ **22.** $\frac{5}{6} \div 15$ **23.** $\frac{7}{9} \div \frac{2}{3}$ **24.** $3\frac{3}{4} \div 4\frac{1}{5}$ **25.** $9\frac{1}{2} \div 2\frac{1}{4}$

Write as fractions, whole numbers, or mixed numbers in lowest terms.

26. 0.30 **27.** 0.2 **28.** 0.25 **29.** 1.15 **30.** 0.65 **31.** 2.750

Write as decimals.

32. $\frac{3}{10}$ **33.** $\frac{9}{100}$ **34.** $\frac{1}{2}$ **35.** $\frac{17}{25}$ **36.** $\frac{3}{8}$ **37.** $3\frac{9}{20}$

Write as decimals. Use a bar to show a repeating decimal.

38. $\frac{1}{6}$ **39.** $\frac{5}{9}$ **40.** $\frac{9}{11}$ **41.** $\frac{5}{12}$ **42.** $\frac{13}{11}$ **43.** $\frac{13}{3}$

44. Tara is paid $4\frac{1}{2}$ dollars per hour at her job. How much money is she paid for $3\frac{1}{2}$ hours' work?

45. Vince runs $3\frac{3}{4}$ laps in 20 minutes. What is his average speed in laps per minute?

ENRICHMENT

Operation Properties and Density

You know that $\frac{5}{2} = 2\frac{1}{2} = 2.5$ and $\frac{1}{3} = 0.\overline{3}$. If a and b are whole numbers (and $b \neq 0$), $\frac{a}{b}$ can always be written as a terminating or a repeating decimal. So, if you investigate properties of fractions, you are really investigating properties of such decimals too.

Replace the variables in each equation with different fractions (or decimals).

Is the equation true for all the replacements you try?

Is there any replacement that makes the equation false?

If there is no replacement that makes the equation false, then the equation shows a property of fractions and decimals.

Addition	Multiplication
Commutative Property	**Commutative Property**
$a + b = b + a$	$ab = ba$
Associative Property	**Associative Property**
$(a + b) + c = a + (b + c)$	$(ab)c = a(bc)$
Property of Zero	**Property of One**
$a + 0 = a$	$1a = a$

Distributive Property

$a(b + c) = ab + ac$

Study these sentences.

$\frac{1}{8} < \frac{1}{4}$ and $\frac{1}{4} < \frac{1}{2}$

$b < a$ and $a < c$

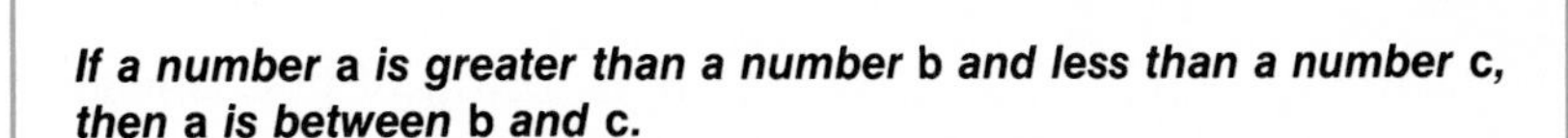

If a number* a *is greater than a number* b *and less than a number* c*, then* a *is between* b *and* c*.

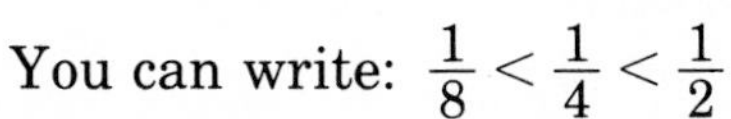

You can write: $\frac{1}{8} < \frac{1}{4} < \frac{1}{2}$ $\qquad$ $b < a < c$

Read: $\frac{1}{4}$ is between $\frac{1}{8}$ and $\frac{1}{2}$. $\qquad$ Read: a is between b and c.

1. Is there a number between $\frac{1}{8}$ and $\frac{1}{4}$?

Add $\frac{1}{8}$ and $\frac{1}{4}$. Then divide the sum by 2.

Is $\frac{3}{16}$ the quotient?

Is $\frac{3}{16}$ between $\frac{1}{8}$ and $\frac{1}{4}$?

$$\left(\frac{1}{8} + \frac{1}{4}\right) \div 2 = n$$
$$\left(\frac{1}{8} + \frac{2}{8}\right) \div 2 = n$$
$$\frac{3}{8} \div 2 = n$$
$$\frac{3}{16} = n$$

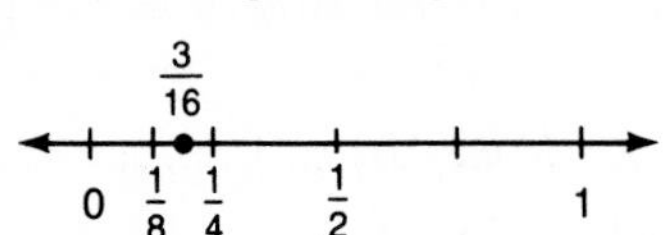

2. Find a number that is between $\frac{1}{4}$ and $\frac{3}{16}$. Use the equation at the right.

$$\left(\frac{1}{4} + \frac{3}{16}\right) \div 2 = x$$

Find a number between

3. $\frac{1}{2}$ and $\frac{1}{3}$.

4. $\frac{1}{2}$ and $\frac{5}{12}$.

5. $\frac{1}{2}$ and $\frac{11}{24}$.

6. $\frac{199}{100}$ and $\frac{200}{100}$.

7. $\frac{199}{100}$ and $\frac{399}{200}$.

8. $\frac{199}{100}$ and $\frac{797}{400}$.

9. Find five numbers between $\frac{499}{500}$ and $\frac{500}{500}$.

When you add two numbers and then divide by 2, you are finding the average of the two numbers. The average of two different numbers is always greater than one number and less than the other.

Between any two fractions, there is always another fraction.

Since there are an **infinite** (unlimited) number of fractions between any two fractions such as $\frac{1}{2}$ and $\frac{1}{4}$, it is said that the fractions are **dense**. The set of fractions has the property of **density**.

10. Now think of 0, 1, 2, 3, . . .; that is, think of just the set of whole numbers. (Imagine that fractions and decimals have not been invented.) The number 1 is between 0 and 2. But is there any whole number between 1 and 2? Is there any whole number between 99 and 100? The set of whole numbers does not have the property of density.

COMPUTER

Machine Language

Computer software contains both instructions and data. *Instructions* process data; *data* are used by instructions. Instructions are executed in a strict *sequence of control*. Data may be retrieved, stored, or displayed in *any* sequence. Instructions and data must be kept separate in computers.

Each byte in computer storage has a *numerical address*. In a 32K computer (remember, K = 1,024 bytes), addresses would go from 00000 to 32767.

All instructions have *operation codes,* shortened to *op-codes.*

Two types of *add instructions* illustrate machine language.

OP-CODE	INSTRUCTION
AA	Add from Addresses given
AL	Add from Literals given

AA 1000,1001 means "add the numbers that are found in the two addresses 1000 and 1001."

AL 1000,1001 means "add the numbers 1000 and 1001."
Literal means "take this number as data."

In the first instruction, addresses tell the computer where to get the data that must be processed. In the second instruction, the data are part of the instruction itself. These are two very simple examples of machine language.

Copy and complete the sentences.

1. ______________ are excecuted in a strict sequence of control.
2. ______________ are retrieved or stored in any sequence.
3. All instructions have ______________, shortened to ______________.
4. Op-code ______________ means "add from literals given."
5. Op-code ______________ means "add from addresses given."
6. Literal means ______________.
7. AA 1010,1101 means ______________.
8. AL 1111,0101 means ______________.
9. The instructions above are simple examples of ______________.

SKILLS MAINTENANCE

Chapters 1 Through 8

Choose the correct answers.

1. Multiply.

$$\begin{array}{r} 35.6 \\ \times 5.18 \\ \hline \end{array}$$

A. 1,844.08
B. 184.408
C. 18.4408
D. not here

2. Divide.

$62\overline{)48{,}962}$

A. 789 r44
B. 799 r4
C. 689 r44
D. not here

3. Solve.

$x + 33 = 70$

A. $x = 33$
B. $x = 103$
C. $x = 37$
D. not here

4. Solve.

$\frac{b}{6} = 12$

A. $b = 2$ **B.** $b = 72$
C. $b = 6$ **D.** not here

5. Solve.

$3\frac{5}{12} + 2\frac{1}{3} = n$

A. $n = 5\frac{3}{4}$ **B.** $n = 5\frac{1}{2}$
C. $n = 5\frac{2}{3}$ **D.** not here

6. Solve.

$6 - 2\frac{3}{7} = n$

A. $n = 4\frac{3}{7}$ **B.** $n = 3\frac{4}{7}$
C. $n = 3\frac{3}{7}$ **D.** not here

7. Multiply. Write the answer in lowest terms.

$\frac{5}{6} \times \frac{2}{3}$

A. $\frac{3}{5}$ **B.** $\frac{7}{9}$
C. $\frac{5}{9}$ **D.** not here

8. Find the reciprocal of $\frac{7}{10}$.

A. $\frac{1}{7}$ **B.** $\frac{10}{7}$
C. $\frac{1}{10}$ **D.** not here

9. Divide. Write the answer in lowest terms.

$\frac{4}{15} \div \frac{1}{3}$

A. $\frac{4}{5}$ **B.** $\frac{4}{45}$
C. $\frac{3}{5}$ **D.** not here

10. Kate has a board $4\frac{1}{2}$ meters long. She cuts it into pieces that are $\frac{3}{4}$ meter long. How many pieces are there?

A. $5\frac{1}{4}$ **B.** 6
C. $3\frac{3}{4}$ **D.** not here

11. Larry works $5\frac{3}{4}$ hours each day. How many hours does he work in 6 days?

A. $11\frac{3}{4}$ hours **B.** $30\frac{3}{4}$ hours
C. $34\frac{1}{2}$ hours **D.** not here

Ratio and Proportion

Ratio • Ratio and Proportion • Rates • Scale Drawing • Problem Solving: Unit Prices • Ratios and Functions

Ratio

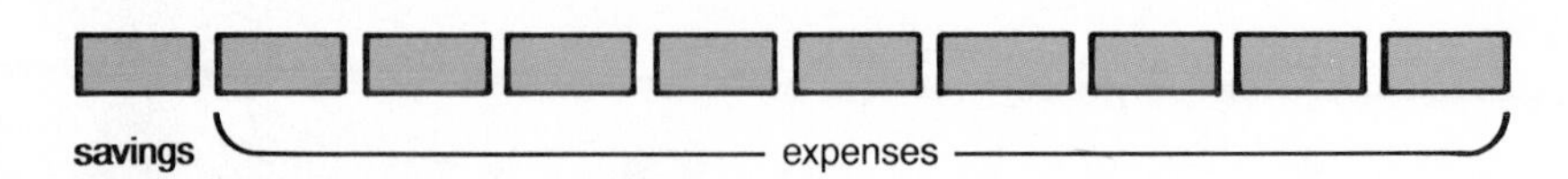

Ratio is a method of comparing numbers.

Ann earns $10 per week doing yard work.
She saves $1 per week. She uses $9 for her weekly expenses.

The ratio of Ann's savings to her expenses is 1 to 9.
Here are three ways to show the ratio.

1 to 9 1:9 $\frac{1}{9}$ ← Read each ratio as "1 to 9."

In the ratio $\frac{1}{9}$, 1 is the **first term** of the ratio. 9 is the **second term.**

This table shows the amounts that Ann saves and spends during a period of four weeks.

	1 week	2 weeks	3 weeks	4 weeks
Savings (in dollars)	1	2	3	4
Expenses (in dollars)	9	18	27	36

During this period, the ratio of her savings to her expenses remains the same. $\frac{1}{9}$, $\frac{2}{18}$, $\frac{3}{27}$, and $\frac{4}{36}$ are **equal ratios**. The ratio $\frac{1}{9}$ is in **lowest terms**.

From the ratio $\frac{1}{9}$, you know that Ann saves one-ninth as much as she spends.

You can use what you have learned about fractions in working with equal ratios.

$$\frac{1}{9} = \frac{2}{18} \quad (\times 2)$$

$$\frac{4}{36} = \frac{1}{9} \quad (\div 4)$$

To find an equal ratio, you can multiply or divide each term of a ratio by the same number (not zero).

In all, Ann earns $10 per week. She saves $1.
The ratio of her earnings to savings is 10:1, or $\frac{10}{1}$.
This means that she earns 10 times as much as she saves.

The ratio of Ann's savings to her earnings is $\frac{1}{10}$.
This means that Ann saves one-tenth as much as she earns.

Practice • Write the ratios in fraction form, $\frac{a}{b}$.

1. red stripes to white stripes
2. white stripes to red stripes
3. red stripes to all the stripes
4. white stripes to all the stripes

5. 1 to 4 6. 8 to 1 7. 3:8 8. 7:2

Write equal ratios in lowest terms.

9. $\frac{3}{6}$ 10. $\frac{12}{16}$

Mixed Practice • Write the ratios in fraction form, $\frac{a}{b}$.

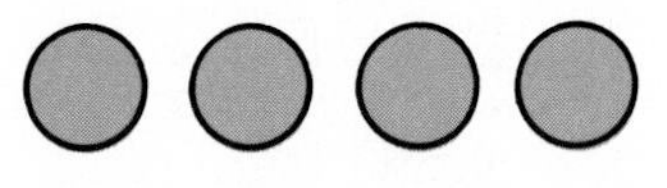
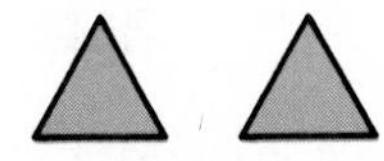

11. circles to triangles
12. triangles to circles
13. circles to all the figures
14. triangles to all the figures

15. 3 to 5 16. 4 to 3 17. 6 to 1 18. 1 to 5

19. 2:9 20. 11:4 21. 1:7 22. 1:1

Write equal ratios in lowest terms.

23. $\frac{2}{6}$ 24. $\frac{5}{10}$ 25. $\frac{9}{12}$ 26. $\frac{12}{20}$ 27. $\frac{75}{100}$

28. $\frac{80}{100}$ 29. $\frac{23}{100}$ ★30. $\frac{51}{100}$ ★31. $\frac{240}{100}$ ★32. $\frac{650}{100}$

PROBLEM SOLVING • **APPLICATIONS**

33. Bonita earns $13 per week. She saves $3 per week. What is the ratio of her savings to her earnings?

34. What is the ratio of Bonita's earnings to her savings?

★ 35. Taro said, "The ratio of my savings to my earnings is $\frac{3}{20}$." List five different pairs of numbers that tell how much Taro could have saved and earned.

Ratio and Proportion

Each roll of this film will give you 12 pictures. The ratio is 1 to 12. No matter how many rolls you buy, this ratio will remain the same.

Rolls	1	2	3	4
Pictures	12	24	36	48
Ratio of Rolls to Pictures	$\frac{1}{12}$	$\frac{2}{24}$	$\frac{3}{36}$	$\frac{4}{48}$

A **proportion** is an equation stating that two ratios are equal.

number of rolls → 2, number of pictures → 24; $\frac{2}{24} = \frac{3}{36}$; 3 ← number of rolls, 36 ← number of pictures

If the cross products are equal, then the proportion is true.

$$\frac{2}{24} = \frac{3}{36}$$

$3 \times 24 = 2 \times 36$

$72 = 72$ True

The cross products are equal, and so the proportion is true.

$$\frac{2}{24} = \frac{3}{36}$$

$$\frac{2}{24} = \frac{5}{64}$$

$5 \times 24 = 2 \times 64$

$120 = 128$ False

The cross products are not equal, and so the proportion is not true.

$$\frac{2}{24} \neq \frac{5}{64}$$

Practice • Is each proportion true? Compare the cross products. Then write *yes* or *no*.

1. $\frac{3}{4} = \frac{15}{20}$ **2.** $\frac{5}{8} = \frac{10}{20}$ **3.** $\frac{12}{9} = \frac{16}{11}$ **4.** $\frac{12}{10} = \frac{18}{15}$

Write = or ≠.

5. $\frac{2}{3}$ ● $\frac{10}{15}$ **6.** $\frac{4}{5}$ ● $\frac{8}{9}$ **7.** $\frac{15}{12}$ ● $\frac{25}{20}$ **8.** $\frac{7}{1}$ ● $\frac{98}{14}$

Mixed Practice • Is each proportion true? Compare the cross products. Then write *yes* or *no*.

9. $\frac{4}{5} = \frac{8}{10}$ **10.** $\frac{7}{8} = \frac{14}{15}$ **11.** $\frac{4}{6} = \frac{6}{8}$ **12.** $\frac{3}{6} = \frac{5}{10}$

13. $\frac{3}{4} = \frac{5}{8}$ **14.** $\frac{6}{8} = \frac{9}{12}$ **15.** $\frac{7}{9} = \frac{12}{16}$ **16.** $\frac{4}{20} = \frac{6}{30}$

17. $\frac{3}{9} = \frac{5}{15}$ **18.** $\frac{5}{4} = \frac{4}{3}$ **19.** $\frac{6}{9} = \frac{16}{24}$ **20.** $\frac{3}{2} = \frac{12}{8}$

Write = or ≠.

21. $\frac{4}{7}$ ● $\frac{12}{21}$ **22.** $\frac{2}{6}$ ● $\frac{5}{15}$ **23.** $\frac{3}{5}$ ● $\frac{6}{8}$ **24.** $\frac{6}{30}$ ● $\frac{8}{40}$

25. $\frac{12}{16}$ ● $\frac{18}{24}$ **26.** $\frac{6}{8}$ ● $\frac{5}{9}$ **27.** $\frac{4}{10}$ ● $\frac{8}{20}$ **28.** $\frac{10}{12}$ ● $\frac{25}{30}$

29. $\frac{9}{12}$ ● $\frac{10}{11}$ **30.** $\frac{3}{15}$ ● $\frac{7}{35}$ **31.** $\frac{5}{3}$ ● $\frac{6}{5}$ **32.** $\frac{15}{18}$ ● $\frac{25}{30}$

33. $\frac{21}{14}$ ● $\frac{6}{4}$ **34.** $\frac{15}{12}$ ● $\frac{50}{45}$ **35.** $\frac{90}{30}$ ● $\frac{54}{18}$ ★ **36.** $\frac{220}{100}$ ● $\frac{5.5}{2.5}$

PROBLEM SOLVING • APPLICATIONS

37. The ratio of rolls of film to the number of pictures is 1 to 12. Will 5 rolls of film give you 60 pictures?

38. Will 7 rolls give you 90 pictures?

★ **39.** How many rolls are needed for 216 pictures?

★ **40.** While Helmut was on vacation, he took 36 pictures. Only 30 of the pictures came out well. In lowest terms, what is the ratio of the pictures that *did not* come out well to the pictures that *did* come out well?

Skills Maintenance

1. 6.2 + 3.9 **2.** 7.03 + 6.19 **3.** 12.01 + 3 + 6.2951

4. 0.1 + 15.95 **5.** 0.008 + 1.72 **6.** 126.4 + 0.6234 + 15 + 9

7. 8.4 − 1.7 **8.** 12.75 − 1.08 **9.** 6 − 1.248

10. 12.3 − 1.05 **11.** 14 − 13.67 **12.** 100 − 0.01

Solving Proportions

To make a fruit punch, you mix 2 cans of apple juice with every 3 cans of grape juice. How many cans of apple juice do you need to mix with 9 cans of grape juice?

You can write a proportion to help you solve this problem.

Think: The ratio of cans of apple juice to cans of grape juice is 2 to 3. 2 cans is to 3 cans as n cans is to 9 cans.

Step 1
Write the proportion. → $\frac{2}{3} = \frac{n}{9}$

Step 2
Use cross products.
$3 \times n = 2 \times 9$ ⟶ $3n = 18$

Step 3
Solve the equation. ⟶ $\frac{3n}{3} = \frac{18}{3}$

$n = 6$ You need 6 cans of apple juice.

To make orange-grapefruit juice, you can use a recipe that calls for 1.5 cans of orange juice for every 3 cans of grapefruit juice. How many cans of grapefruit juice do you need to mix with 2 cans of orange juice?

Step 1
Write the proportion. → $\frac{1.5}{3} = \frac{2}{n}$

Step 2
Use cross products.
$3 \times 2 = 1.5 \times n$ ⟶ $6 = 1.5n$

Step 3
Solve the equation. ⟶ $\frac{6}{1.5} = \frac{1.5n}{1.5}$

$4 = n$ You need 4 cans of grapefruit juice.

Practice • Solve the proportions.

1. $\frac{3}{4} = \frac{n}{32}$
2. $\frac{8}{9} = \frac{40}{n}$
3. $\frac{8}{6} = \frac{n}{21}$
4. $\frac{10}{n} = \frac{15}{3}$
5. $\frac{n}{12} = \frac{15}{18}$
6. $\frac{6}{4.5} = \frac{n}{3}$
7. $\frac{2.4}{n} = \frac{1}{5}$
8. $\frac{4}{5} = \frac{14}{n}$

Mixed Practice • Solve the proportions.

9. $\frac{n}{12} = \frac{9}{16}$ 10. $\frac{4}{n} = \frac{18}{27}$ 11. $\frac{14}{16} = \frac{n}{40}$ 12. $\frac{5}{13} = \frac{n}{26}$

13. $\frac{10}{3} = \frac{n}{12}$ 14. $\frac{90}{100} = \frac{n}{30}$ 15. $\frac{15}{n} = \frac{35}{42}$ 16. $\frac{16}{n} = \frac{40}{35}$

17. $\frac{14}{24} = \frac{21}{n}$ 18. $\frac{n}{30} = \frac{16}{20}$ 19. $\frac{5}{4} = \frac{n}{20}$ 20. $\frac{16}{6} = \frac{n}{9}$

21. $\frac{n}{12} = \frac{15}{20}$ 22. $\frac{20}{n} = \frac{8}{6}$ 23. $\frac{30}{20} = \frac{n}{8}$ 24. $\frac{21}{6} = \frac{70}{n}$

25. $\frac{6}{8} = \frac{9}{n}$ 26. $\frac{n}{12} = \frac{10}{5}$ 27. $\frac{8}{5} = \frac{n}{3.75}$ 28. $\frac{2}{3.5} = \frac{5}{n}$

29. $\frac{4.8}{6.0} = \frac{8}{n}$ 30. $\frac{1.40}{n} = \frac{7}{4}$ 31. $\frac{1.25}{5} = \frac{n}{9}$ ★ 32. $\frac{0.17}{1.92} = \frac{n}{24.0}$

Solve. Write each answer as a mixed number in lowest terms.

★ 33. $\frac{1}{8} = \frac{n}{100}$ ★ 34. $\frac{7}{8} = \frac{n}{100}$ ★ 35. $\frac{1}{3} = \frac{n}{100}$ ★ 36. $\frac{2}{3} = \frac{n}{100}$

PROBLEM SOLVING • APPLICATIONS

Tad makes pineapple-grapefruit juice. He uses 2 cans of pineapple juice for every 3.5 cans of grapefruit juice.

37. How many cans of pineapple juice does Tad need to mix with 7 cans of grapefruit juice?

38. How many cans of grapefruit juice does Tad need to mix with 5 cans of pineapple juice?

The small gear makes 7 turns for every 5 turns of the large gear.

39. How many turns will the large gear make if the small gear makes 35 turns?

★ 40. How many turns will the small gear make if the large gear makes 42.5 turns?

Midchapter Review

Write = or ≠.

1. $\frac{10}{15}$ ● $\frac{8}{20}$ 2. $\frac{9}{11}$ ● $\frac{7}{8}$ 3. $\frac{8}{12}$ ● $\frac{14}{21}$ 4. $\frac{7}{49}$ ● $\frac{4}{28}$

Solve.

5. $\frac{9}{13} = \frac{n}{52}$ 6. $\frac{n}{12} = \frac{15}{20}$ 7. $\frac{4.5}{n} = \frac{18}{12}$ 8. $\frac{2}{3.99} = \frac{n}{19.95}$

Rates

Sunflower seeds sell at a rate of 3 bags for \$2.39. You buy 5 bags. What will they cost?

Think: bags → $\frac{3}{2.39}$ cost → $\frac{5}{n}$ \$2.39 can be written as 2.39.

The ratios must be equal.

Step 1
Write the proportion.

$$\frac{3}{2.39} = \frac{5}{n}$$

Step 2
Use cross products.
$5 \times 2.39 = 3 \times n$

$$11.95 = 3n$$

Step 3
Solve the equation.

$$\frac{11.95}{3} = \frac{3n}{3}$$

$$3.983 = n$$

Since a store always rounds parts of a cent upward, round to the next whole cent. The 5 bags will cost \$3.99.

Mr. Ramirez drives 168 kilometers in 2.4 hours. At this rate, how far will he drive in 5 hours?

Think: kilometers → $\frac{168}{2.4}$ hours → $\frac{n}{5}$

Step 1
Write the proportion. $\frac{168}{2.4} = \frac{n}{5}$

Step 2
Use cross products. $2.4n = 840$
$2.4 \times n = 168 \times 5$

Step 3
Solve the equation. $\frac{2.4n}{2.4} = \frac{840}{2.4}$

$$n = 350$$

Mr. Ramirez will drive 350 kilometers.

Practice • What will they cost?

1. 3 for 75¢
   You buy 8.
2. 5 for 79¢
   You buy 10.
3. 4 for \$1.63
   You buy 10.

How many do you buy?

4. 5 for 82¢
   You spend \$1.64.
5. 2 for 39¢
   You spend \$2.73.
6. 7 for \$1.00
   You spend \$8.00.

Mixed Practice • What do they cost?

7. 5 for 65¢
   You buy 12.

8. 6 for 87¢
   You buy 4.

9. 3 for \$1.49
   You buy 14.

10. 6 for \$1.95
    You buy 15.

11. 8 for \$2.49
    You buy 20.

12. 5 for \$7.75
    You buy 3.

Find the times.

13. 360 km in 4 hours
    How long to travel
    684 km?

14. 210 km in 3 hours
    How long to travel
    651 km?

15. 130 km in 2 hours
    How long to travel
    812.5 km?

Find the distances.

16. 950 km in 10 hours
    How far in 12 hours?

17. 272 km in 4 hours
    How far in 6.3 hours?

18. 623 km in 7 hours
    How far in 9.4 hours?

PROBLEM SOLVING • APPLICATIONS

19. The price of tomato juice is 4 cans for \$1.00. Eric buys 15 cans. How much does he spend?

20. Small cans of tomato sauce are 5 for \$2.39. Beth spends \$7.17. How many cans of tomato sauce does she buy?

21. Large cans of tomato paste are 2 for \$1.69. Cobb buys 5 cans. How much does he spend?

22. Mrs. Akada drives 196 kilometers in 2.8 hours. At this rate, how far will she drive in 7 hours?

23. Mark can ride his bike at a speed of 15 kilometers per hour. At this rate, how far can he travel in 5 hours?

24. Denise jogged 6 kilometers in 1 hour. How far can she jog in 3 hours?

★ 25. The price of tomato soup is 4 cans for \$1.29. If Eva has \$3.93 to spend, how many cans of tomato soup can she buy?

★ 26. Mr. Wagner can drive 238 kilometers in 3.5 hours. To the nearest hour, how long will it take to drive 140 kilometers?

Skills Maintenance

1. 2.5×3.5
2. 9.1×6.04
3. 0.3×0.2
4. 1.4×0.003
5. $2\overline{)5.38}$
6. $6\overline{)1.5}$
7. $5\overline{)1.4}$
8. $12\overline{)0.36}$

Scale Drawing

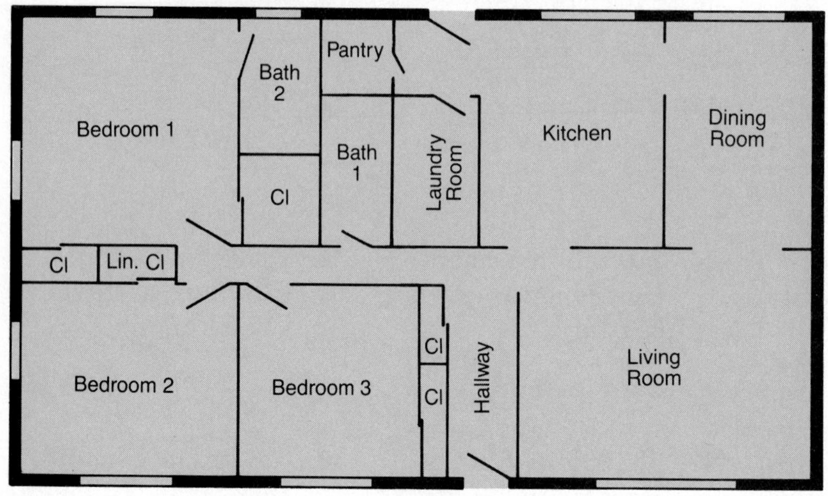

This is a **scale drawing** of a ranch house.
Every 2 centimeters in the scale drawing represent 3 meters in the house.

Measure the drawing of the living room. It is 4 centimeters long. Use a proportion to find the actual length of the living room.

length on drawing (cm) → 2, 4 ← length on drawing (cm)
actual length (m) → 3, n ← actual length (m)

$$\frac{2}{3} = \frac{4}{n}$$
$$2n = 12$$
$$n = 6$$

The actual length of the living room is 6 meters.

The width of a patio that is to be attached to the house is 4.5 meters.

Use a proportion to find the width of the patio on the scale drawing.

width on drawing (cm) → 2, n ← width on drawing (cm)
actual width (m) → 3, 4.5 ← actual width (m)

$$\frac{2}{3} = \frac{n}{4.5}$$
$$3n = 9$$
$$n = 3$$

The width of the patio on the scale drawing is 3 centimeters.

Practice • Find the actual dimensions of the rooms.

1. dining room **2.** kitchen **3.** bedroom 1 **4.** laundry

5. A basement playroom is 9 meters long. Using the scale 2 cm = 3 m, find the length of the drawing of the playroom.

Mixed Practice • Find the actual dimensions of the rooms.

6. bedroom 2
7. pantry
8. bedroom 3
9. bath 1

Here is a scale drawing of the first floor of a school.

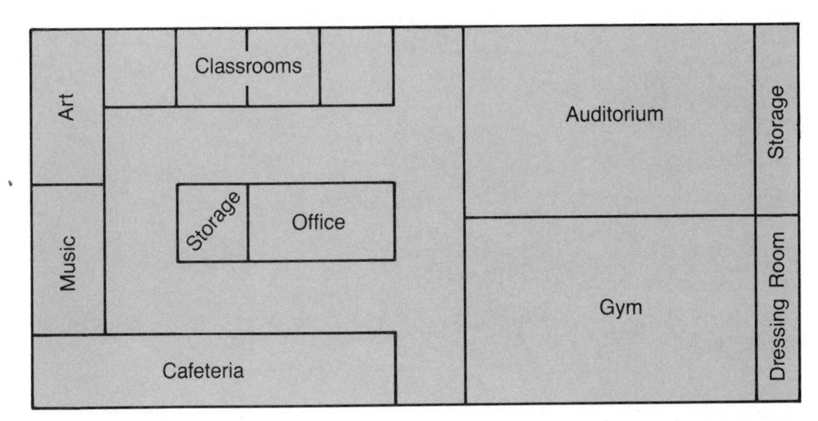

Use the lengths on the drawing to find the actual dimensions of the rooms.

10. office
11. cafeteria
12. auditorium
13. music room

14. Find the actual length of the school.

15. Find the actual width of the school.

PROBLEM SOLVING • APPLICATIONS

Below are the actual dimensions of four rectangular rooms. What would be their dimensions on a scale drawing if the scale 1 cm = 2.5 m were used?

16. a room 5 m by 5 m
17. a room 10 m by 7.5 m

18. a room 6.25 m by 3.75 m
19. a room 8.125 m by 5.625 m

★ 20. Draw each of the rooms in problems 16–19. Use the scale 1 cm = 2.5 m.

★ 21. What do you think the ideal apartment or house would look like? Make a scale drawing of it. Include as many details as you want. Be sure to mark the scale you are using on the drawing.

PROBLEM SOLVING • STRATEGIES

Unit Prices: Choosing a Method

Sometimes you can solve the same problem in different ways.

One store sells 4 bottles of apple juice for \$1.84. Another store sells a pack of 6 bottles of the same apple juice for \$2.55. Which is the better buy?

To find the better buy, you compare **unit prices**. The unit price is the price of 1 item. In this problem the unit price is the price of 1 bottle.

Method 1 Use ratio and proportion.

Think: The ratio $\frac{4}{1.84}$ must be equal to $\frac{1}{x}$.

$$\frac{4}{1.84} = \frac{1}{x}$$

$$4x = 1.84$$
$$x = 0.46$$

Think: The ratio $\frac{6}{2.55}$ must be equal to $\frac{1}{y}$.

$$\frac{6}{2.55} = \frac{1}{y}$$

$$6y = 2.55$$
$$y = 0.425$$
$$y \approx 0.43$$

The 4 bottles have a unit price of \$.46 per bottle.
The 6 bottles have a unit price of \$.425, or about \$.43, per bottle.
The pack of 6 bottles is the better buy.

Method 2 Use division.

A quick way to find the unit price is to divide the total cost by the number of units.

$$\frac{\textbf{Total Cost}}{\textbf{Number of Units}} = \textbf{Unit Price}$$

$$4\overline{)1.84} = 0.46 \qquad 6\overline{)2.550} = 0.425 \approx 0.43$$

\$.43 is less than \$.46, and so the pack of 6 bottles is the better buy.

Find the prices. Round the unit price to the nearest cent whenever necessary.

1. 5 raisin bars for 75¢

2. 8 waffles for 98¢

The unit price is the price of 1 item.

3. 10 frankfurters for $1.40

4. 12 oranges for $1.42

5. 3 cans of juice for $1.60

6. 24 cans of soup for $12.45

In problems 7–12 find the unit prices of the items. Then tell which is the better buy.

7. A package of 6 hamburger rolls for 60¢ or a package of 8 hamburger rolls for 64¢

8. A package of 12 dinner rolls for $1.38 or a package of 6 dinner rolls for $.66

Find the unit prices by whichever method you think is easier.

9. 2 liters of milk for $1.16 or 1 liter of milk for $.59

10. A box of 12 plastic garbage bags for $1.80 or a box of 20 plastic garbage bags for $2.59

11. A 6-pack of muffins for $1.25 or a 4-pack for $.80

★ 12. 3 cans of orange juice for $2.11 or 4 cans of orange juice for $2.86

★ 13. One store sells steak at a unit price of $3.10 per kilogram. Another store sells steak at a unit price of $3.15 per kilogram. Is the steak at $3.10 per kilogram necessarily a better buy? Write at least two reasons that explain your answer.

CHAPTER 9

REVIEW

Write the ratios in fraction form, $\frac{a}{b}$. (pp. 224–225)

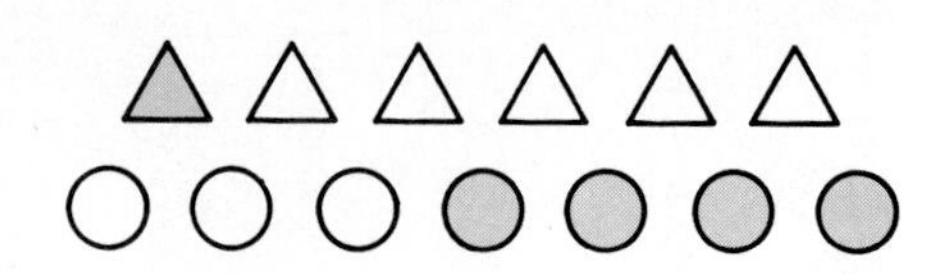

1. triangles to circles
2. blue circles to white circles
3. blue triangles to all the triangles
4. 1 to 5
5. 8:11

Write equal ratios in lowest terms. (pp. 224–225)

6. $\frac{8}{10}$
7. $\frac{4}{12}$
8. $\frac{12}{20}$
9. $\frac{14}{49}$

Write = or ≠. (pp. 226–227)

10. $\frac{1}{3}$ ● $\frac{5}{15}$
11. $\frac{7}{9}$ ● $\frac{14}{16}$
12. $\frac{3}{20}$ ● $\frac{12}{80}$
13. $\frac{5}{13}$ ● $\frac{20}{78}$

Solve the proportions. (pp. 228–229)

14. $\frac{4}{9} = \frac{n}{45}$
15. $\frac{2}{n} = \frac{6}{30}$
16. $\frac{4}{10} = \frac{n}{15}$
17. $\frac{5}{n} = \frac{10}{26}$
18. $\frac{n}{3} = \frac{40}{12}$
19. $\frac{12}{15} = \frac{n}{30}$
20. $\frac{15}{n} = \frac{30}{20}$
21. $\frac{24}{6} = \frac{32}{n}$
22. $\frac{n}{8} = \frac{15}{20}$
23. $\frac{8}{17} = \frac{n}{4.25}$
24. $\frac{2.60}{n} = \frac{3}{6}$
25. $\frac{4.50}{10} = \frac{9}{n}$

26. Pens sell at a rate of 8 for $1.20. You buy 14. What will the total cost be? (pp. 230–231)

27. Mr. Furillo drives 273 kilometers in 3.5 hours. At this rate how far will he drive in 5 hours? (pp. 230–231)

This is a scale drawing of a bedroom. (pp. 232–233)

28. Find the actual length of the room.

29. Find the actual width of the room.

Scale: 1 cm = 2.5 m

30. The local supermarket sells 6 oranges for 96¢. What is the unit price? (pp. 234–235)

31. Which is the better buy: 6 pencils for $1.30 or 8 pencils for $1.59? (pp. 234–235)

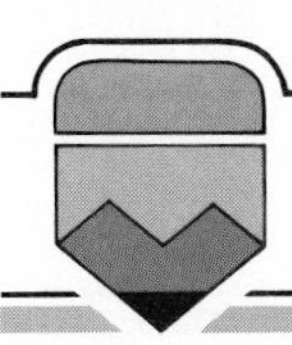

PROJECT

Investigating Ratios and Rates

Ratios are used in many different ways.

Sometimes ratios are used to compare two lengths, two weights, or two other similar types of measurement.

Suppose you want to compare 2 centimeters to 3 meters. You cannot say that the ratio is 2:3, or $\frac{2}{3}$, since that would mean that 2 centimeters is two-thirds as long as 3 meters.

To compare 2 centimeters to 3 meters, you must express both measurements in the same unit of measure.

3 meters = 300 centimeters
The ratio of 2 centimeters to 300 centimeters is $\frac{2}{300}$, or $\frac{1}{150}$.

2 cm

Ratios are also used in rates. A rate is often a comparison that involves different types of measurements. For example, Mrs. Jedson drives 325 kilometers on 25 liters of gasoline. She drives 13 kilometers per 1 liter of gasoline.

"325 kilometers per 25 liters of gasoline" and "13 kilometers per 1 liter of gasoline" (or "13 kilometers per liter") are examples of a rate. Note the different types of measurements (distance, amount of gasoline) involved in the rate.

The ratios $\frac{325}{25}$ and $\frac{13}{1}$ can be written for this rate.

distance ⟶ $\frac{325}{25} = \frac{13}{1}$
gasoline usage ⟶

Write the ratios in lowest terms.

See the tables on pages 276 and 282 if you need help with these units of measure.

1. 1 cm to 1 m
2. 50 cm to 1 m
3. 1 g to 1 kg
4. 100 g to 1 kg
5. 500 g to 2 kg
6. 800 g to 4 kg
7. Sven walks 9 kilometers in 2 hours. Complete the following phrases to write his rate of speed in two ways.

   ? kilometers per 2 hours   ? kilometers per hour

8. Look in newspapers or magazines for five examples of rates that are comparisons of different types of measurements.

CHAPTER 9

TEST

Write the ratios in fraction form, $\frac{a}{b}$.

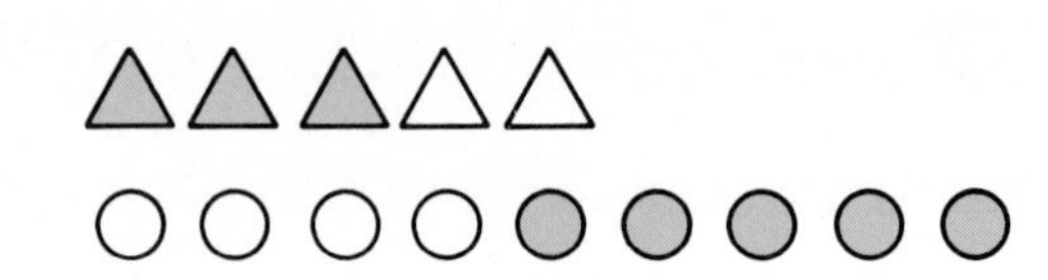

1. triangles to circles

2. blue triangles to white triangles

3. white circles to all the circles

4. 1 to 7

5. 4:15

Write equal ratios in lowest terms.

6. $\frac{3}{6}$ 7. $\frac{8}{12}$ 8. $\frac{12}{15}$ 9. $\frac{28}{42}$

Write = or ≠.

10. $\frac{3}{5}$ ● $\frac{9}{15}$ 11. $\frac{7}{10}$ ● $\frac{28}{50}$ 12. $\frac{7}{3}$ ● $\frac{49}{25}$ 13. $\frac{15}{18}$ ● $\frac{25}{30}$

Solve the proportions.

14. $\frac{1}{6} = \frac{n}{30}$ 15. $\frac{7}{2} = \frac{14}{n}$ 16. $\frac{n}{5} = \frac{16}{40}$ 17. $\frac{6}{n} = \frac{4}{28}$

18. $\frac{5}{12} = \frac{20}{n}$ 19. $\frac{n}{6} = \frac{40}{12}$ 20. $\frac{26}{18} = \frac{n}{9}$ 21. $\frac{21}{n} = \frac{14}{32}$

22. $\frac{9}{36} = \frac{n}{14}$ 23. $\frac{3.8}{n} = \frac{10}{4}$ 24. $\frac{4.5}{12} = \frac{n}{4}$ 25. $\frac{5}{8} = \frac{9.4}{n}$

26. Pads sell at a rate of 4 for $1.88. You buy 10. What is the total cost?

27. Mrs. Jessup drives 185 kilometers in 2.5 hours. At this rate how far will she drive in 6 hours?

This is a scale drawing of a jumbo jet.

28. Find the actual length of the jet.

29. Find the actual wingspan of the jet.

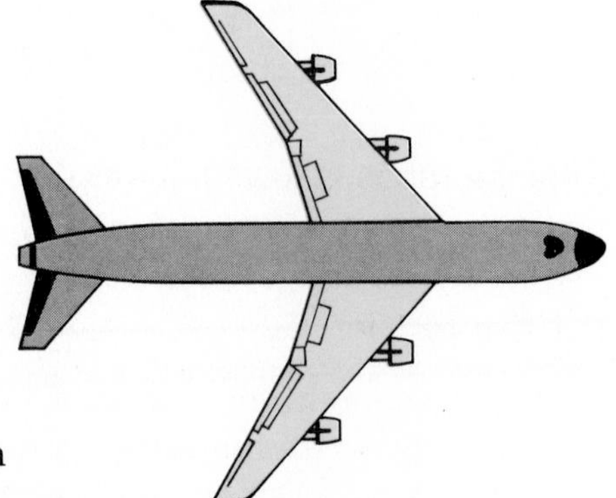

Scale: 1 cm = 11.5 m

30. A supermarket sells 3 cans of vegetable soup for $1.77. What is the unit price?

31. Which is the better buy: a package of 4 waffles for 57¢ or a package of 6 waffles for 80¢?

ENRICHMENT

Ratios and Functions

You remember that an equation such as $x + y = 6$ is a rule for a function.

The solutions for $x + y = 6$ are ordered pairs of numbers. For each value of x, there is just one value of y. The table below shows the function; as x increases, y decreases. (Look back at page 79 if you want to reread the earlier discussion of functions.)

rule → $x + y = 6$

x	0	1	2	3	4	5	6
y	6	5	4	3	2	1	0

← table of pairs of numbers that are solutions for $x + y = 6$

Suppose that sometimes the rule for a function is not given in equation form. Delia and Evan played a function game. For every number x Delia named, Evan named a number y that followed this rule: The ratio of y to x is 3:2.

The table below shows some pairs of numbers in this game.

	x	2	4	6	8	10
Delia →	x	2	4	6	8	10
Evan →	y	3	6	9	12	15

The ratio of y to x is 3:2.

$$\frac{3}{2} = \frac{6}{4} = \frac{9}{6} = \frac{12}{8} = \frac{15}{10}$$

If you divide the value of y by the value of x, you always get the same quotient.

$\frac{3}{2} = 1.5 \quad \frac{6}{4} = 1.5 \quad \frac{9}{6} = 1.5 \quad \frac{12}{8} = 1.5 \quad \frac{15}{10} = 1.5$

The rule for this function can be given in equation form as $y = 1.5x$ or $y = 1\frac{1}{2}x$.

Use ratio to write an English sentence that is a rule for each function. Then write the rule in equation form.

1.

x	4	8	12	16	20
y	5	10	15	20	25

2.

x	5	10	15	20	25
y	2	4	6	8	10

3.

x	1	2	3	4	5
y	10	20	30	40	50

4.

x	10	20	30	40	50
y	8	16	24	32	40

5.

x	16	24	32	40	48
y	2	3	4	5	6

6.

x	10	15	20	25	30
y	32	48	64	80	96

7. Make a table that shows the function with this rule: The ratio of y to x is 11:4.

COMPUTER

Computer Switches

Switches carry electric current. If the current is on, the bit is on, or 1. If the current is off, the bit is off, or 0. There are three basic types of switches.

The NOT rule of logic is used by the *NOT switch*: Input flows IN from the left and OUT to the right.

IN NOT OUT

The AND rule of logic is used by the *AND switch*: Input flows down from top to bottom.

IN IN AND OUT

The OR rule of logic is used by the *OR switch*: Input flows down from top to bottom.

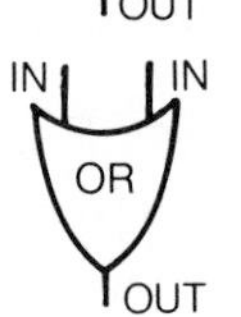

These switches are connected to form a *binary adder*, shown on the next page.

Dots, ┿, show where circuit lines are connected. The same current goes in two directions. Where lines cross without dots, ┼, currents continue in straight lines. Lines are not connected at these points.

Recall the binary addition facts: $\begin{array}{r} 0 \\ +0 \\ \hline 0 \end{array}$ $\quad \begin{array}{r} 0 \\ +1 \\ \hline 1 \end{array}$ $\quad \begin{array}{r} 1 \\ +0 \\ \hline 1 \end{array}$ $\quad \begin{array}{r} 1 \\ +1 \\ \hline 10 \end{array}$

The binary sum of 1 and 1 produces a *carry bit* of 1.

Add using binary addition. Count how many carries each problem has.

1. $\begin{array}{r} 101 \\ +101 \\ \hline \end{array}$, ? carries

2. $\begin{array}{r} 1111 \\ +1111 \\ \hline \end{array}$, ? carries

3. $\begin{array}{r} 1010 \\ +\ 101 \\ \hline \end{array}$, ? carries

In general a binary number can receive a carry from the next lower place and pass a carry to the next higher place. This is the same as in decimal addition: The tens place can receive a ten regrouped from the ones place and can pass a regrouped hundred to the hundreds place.

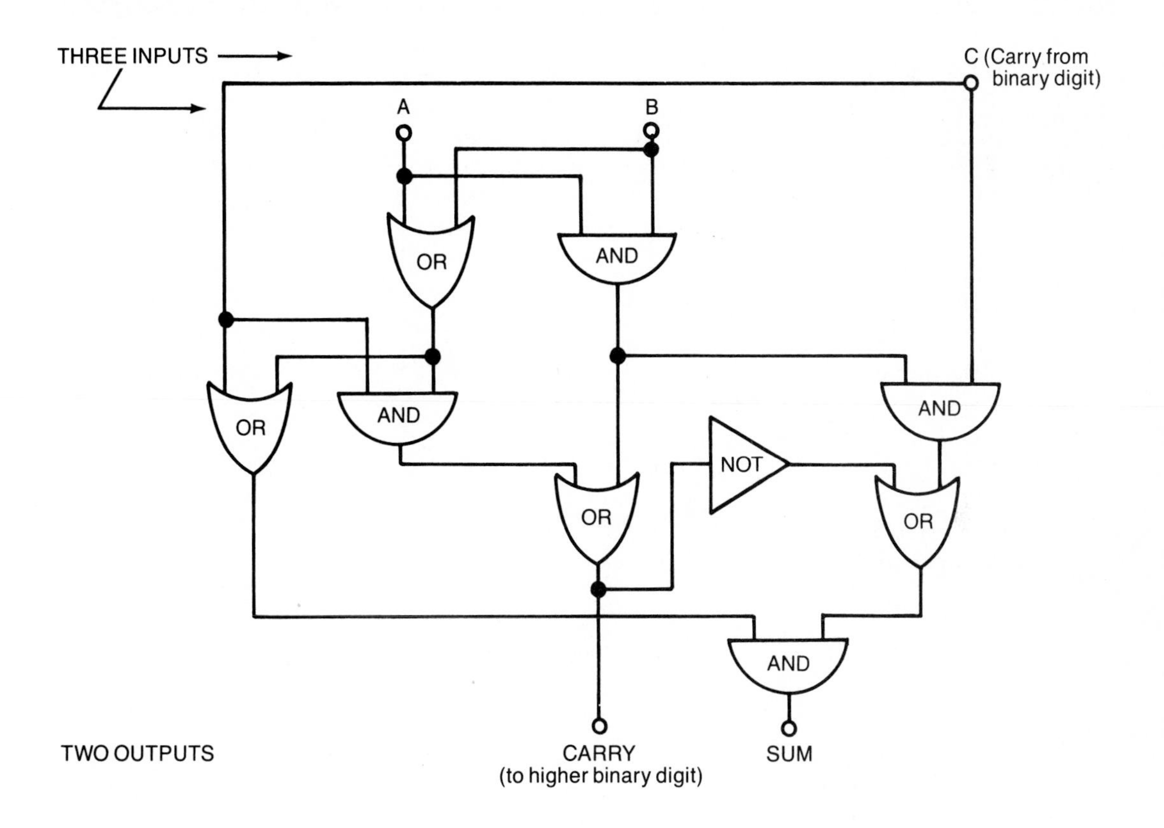

Follow the circuits to find the sum bit and the carry bit.

4. A = 0, B = 0, C = 1

SUM = __?__, CARRY = __?__

5. A = 1, B = 0, C = 1

SUM = __?__, CARRY = __?__

6. A = 1, B = 1, C = 0

SUM = __?__, CARRY = __?__

7. A = 0, B = 1, C = 1

SUM = __?__, CARRY = __?__

8. A = 0, B = 1, C = 0

SUM = __?__, CARRY = __?__

9. A = 1, B = 1, C = 1

SUM = __?__, CARRY = __?__

10. A = 1, B = 0, C = 0

SUM = __?__, CARRY = __?__

11. What is the only possible remaining combination and what are the answers?

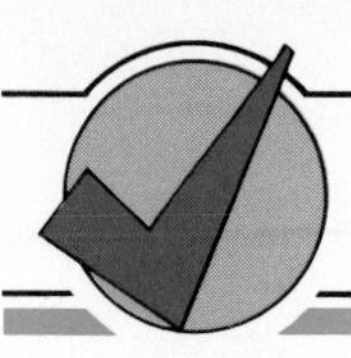

SKILLS MAINTENANCE

Chapters 1 Through 9

Choose the correct answers.

1. Divide.

$46\overline{)52{,}679}$

A. 1,145 r9
B. 145 r9
C. 1,144 r45
D. not here

2. Solve.

$x - 16 = 25$

A. $x = 41$
B. $x = 9$
C. $x = 400$
D. not here

3. Add.

$$\begin{array}{r} 237.6 \\ +\ 45.87 \\ \hline \end{array}$$

A. 272.47
B. 283.47
C. 282.47
D. not here

4. Multiply.

$$\begin{array}{r} 30.86 \\ \times\ 45.7 \\ \hline \end{array}$$

A. 1,410.302
B. 1,400.302
C. 1,410.203
D. not here

5. Solve.

$5\frac{1}{2} - 4\frac{2}{3} = n$

A. $n = 1\frac{5}{6}$
B. $n = 10\frac{1}{6}$
C. $n = \frac{5}{6}$
D. not here

6. Divide. Write the answer in lowest terms.

$\frac{7}{10} \div \frac{3}{8}$

A. $1\frac{13}{15}$
B. $1\frac{3}{5}$
C. $\frac{21}{80}$
D. not here

7. Find the LCM of 12 and 20.

A. 6 **B.** 32
C. 60 **D.** not here

8. Solve the proportion.

$\frac{14}{n} = \frac{21}{54}$

A. $n = 36$ **B.** $n = 54$
C. $n = 28$ **D.** not here

9. I sell 10 books for \$5.50. You buy 7. What will they cost?

A. \$4.50 **B.** \$3.85
C. \$3.25 **D.** not here

Find the unit price. Round to the nearest cent if necessary.

10. A store sells 4 containers of fruit punch for \$3.58.

A. \$.90 **B.** \$.89
C. \$.88 **D.** not here

11. The market sells 8 bars of soap for \$2.98.

A. \$.39 **B.** \$.35
C. \$.36 **D.** not here

Percent

CHAPTER 10

Percent, Ratio, and Proportion • Percents, Decimals, and Fractions • Problem Solving: Using a Percent Formula • Discount and Sales Tax • Simple Interest • Circle Graph and Percent • Problem Solving: Choosing a Method • Compound Interest • Finding the Percent of Increase or Decrease

Percent and Ratio

Percent (%) means "per hundred." You can think of a percent as a ratio that has a second term of 100.

In a town election in Green Ridge, there were two candidates.

Carson received 92% of the total vote. This means that the ratio of Carson's vote to the total vote was 92:100, or $\frac{92}{100}$. Carson received 92 out of every 100 votes.

Weekly News-Record

It's a Landslide!

Carson 92% Jordan 8%

Jordan received 8% of the total vote. This means that the ratio of Jordan's vote to the total vote was 8:100, or $\frac{8}{100}$. Jordan received 8 out of every 100 votes.

During recent years, the population of Green Ridge has been increasing rapidly. The present population is 125% of the population in 1980. This means that the ratio of the present population to the 1980 population is 125:100, or $\frac{125}{100}$. For every 100 people in Green Ridge in 1980, there are 125 people now.

Any ratio, such as $\frac{1}{5}$ or $\frac{3}{2}$, can be expressed as a percent. First find an equal ratio with 100 as the second term. Here are some examples.

$$\frac{1}{5} = \frac{n}{100}$$

$$5n = 100$$
$$n = 20$$

$$\text{So } \frac{1}{5} = \frac{20}{100}$$
$$= 20\%$$

$$\frac{3}{2} = \frac{n}{100}$$

$$2n = 300$$
$$n = 150$$

$$\text{So } \frac{3}{2} = \frac{150}{100}$$
$$= 150\%$$

Practice • Write each percent as a ratio with a second term of 100.

1. 7%
2. 11%
3. 50%
4. 130%

Write as percents.

5. 3 per 100
6. $\frac{18}{100}$
7. 25:100
8. 90 out of 100
9. $\frac{1}{2}$
10. $\frac{3}{4}$
11. $\frac{2}{5}$
12. $\frac{7}{5}$

Mixed Practice • Write each percent as a ratio with a second term of 100.

13. 9%
14. 5%
15. 23%
16. 35%
17. 60%
18. 99%
19. 110%
20. 170%

Write as percents.

21. 8 per 100
22. $\frac{15}{100}$
23. 39:100
24. 90 out of 100
25. $\frac{1}{100}$
26. $\frac{27}{100}$
27. 45:100
28. 82 out of 100
29. $\frac{1}{4}$
30. $\frac{3}{20}$
31. $\frac{7}{10}$
32. $\frac{1}{50}$
33. $\frac{3}{25}$
34. $\frac{9}{10}$
35. $\frac{13}{10}$
36. $\frac{7}{4}$

★ 37. $\frac{2}{2}$

★ 38. $\frac{5}{2}$

★ 39. $\frac{3}{1}$

★ 40. $\frac{8}{1}$

PROBLEM SOLVING • APPLICATIONS

41. The present population of Maplecrest is 90% of the 1980 population. Is the population greater today than it was in 1980?

42. The present population of Oakview is 110% of the 1980 population. Is the population greater today than it was in 1980?

43. In a town election in Amesville, 65% of the registered voters actually voted. What percent of the registered voters did not vote?

★ 44. In an election for mayor in Newton, a candidate named Smithers received 37% of the votes that were cast. A candidate named Davis received 34% of the votes that were cast. Could Smithers and Davis have been the only two candidates for mayor? Explain your answer.

Percent and Proportion

There are 120 students who use the computer laboratory.
This graph shows the percents of students from different grades.

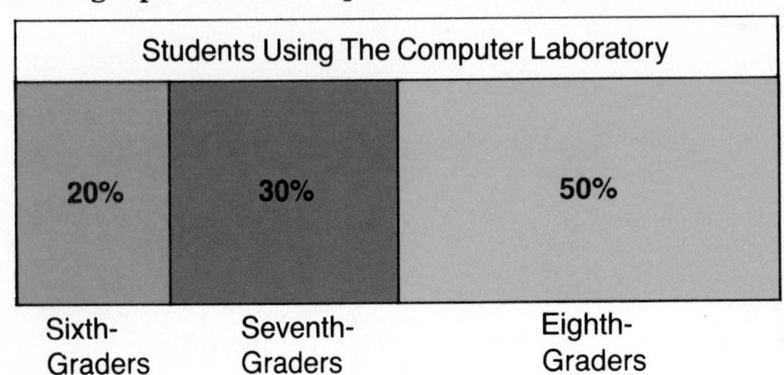

Seventh-graders are 30% $\left(\frac{30}{100}\right)$ of the student body.
How many seventh-graders use the computer laboratory?
You can use a proportion to solve the problem.
Let n stand for the number of seventh-graders.
The ratio of n to the total number, 120, must be equal to the ratio $\frac{30}{100}$.

seventh-graders → $\frac{n}{120}$ ← total number of students $\qquad \frac{30}{100}$

Step 1 Write a proportion. $\quad \frac{n}{120} = \frac{30}{100}$

Step 2 Use cross products. $\quad 100n = 3{,}600$

Step 3 Solve the proportion. $\quad n = 36$

Of the 120 students, 36 are seventh-graders.

More Examples

What number is 50% of 120?

$$\frac{n}{120} = \frac{50}{100}$$
$$100n = 6{,}000$$
$$n = 60$$

What number is 20% of 120?

$$\frac{n}{120} = \frac{20}{100}$$
$$100n = 2{,}400$$
$$n = 24$$

Practice • Solve the proportion.

1. $\frac{n}{200} = \frac{25}{100}$ **2.** $\frac{n}{80} = \frac{50}{100}$ **3.** $\frac{n}{250} = \frac{10}{100}$ **4.** $\frac{n}{75} = \frac{8}{100}$

Use your work from exercises 1–2 to answer these questions.

5. What number is 25% of 200?

6. What number is 50% of 80?

7. There are 35 students in the History Club. If 20% of them are seventh-graders, how many are seventh-graders?

Mixed Practice • Solve the proportion.

8. $\frac{n}{300} = \frac{15}{100}$

9. $\frac{n}{50} = \frac{10}{100}$

10. $\frac{n}{160} = \frac{25}{100}$

11. $\frac{n}{80} = \frac{35}{100}$

12. $\frac{n}{150} = \frac{4}{100}$

13. $\frac{n}{30} = \frac{4}{100}$

14. $\frac{n}{40} = \frac{5}{100}$

15. $\frac{n}{800} = \frac{30}{100}$

16. $\frac{n}{350} = \frac{20}{100}$

17. $\frac{n}{90} = \frac{50}{100}$

★ **18.** $\frac{n}{1{,}000{,}000} = \frac{1}{100}$

★ **19.** $\frac{n}{1{,}000{,}000} = \frac{99}{100}$

Use your work from exercises 16–19 to answer these questions.

20. What number is 20% of 350?

21. What number is 50% of 90?

★ **22.** What number is 1% of 1,000,000?

★ **23.** What number is 99% of 1,000,000?

Solve the proportion.

★ **24.** What number is 10% of 70?

★ **25.** What number is 80% of 50?

★ **26.** What number is 100% of 5?

★ **27.** What number is 130% of 500?

PROBLEM SOLVING • APPLICATIONS

28. There are 40 students in the Science Club. How many are seventh-graders?

29. How many are eighth-graders?

★ **30.** How many fewer sixth-graders than seventh-graders are in the Science Club?

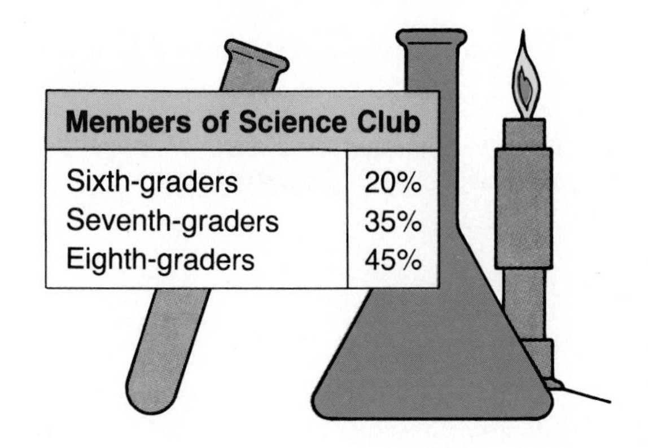

Members of Science Club	
Sixth-graders	20%
Seventh-graders	35%
Eighth-graders	45%

Skills Maintenance

Write the decimals.

1. 30 hundredths

2. 15 hundredths

3. 9 hundredths

4. 3 hundredths

5. 251 thousandths

6. 87 thousandths

7. 3 thousandths

8. 5 thousandths

Percents and Decimals

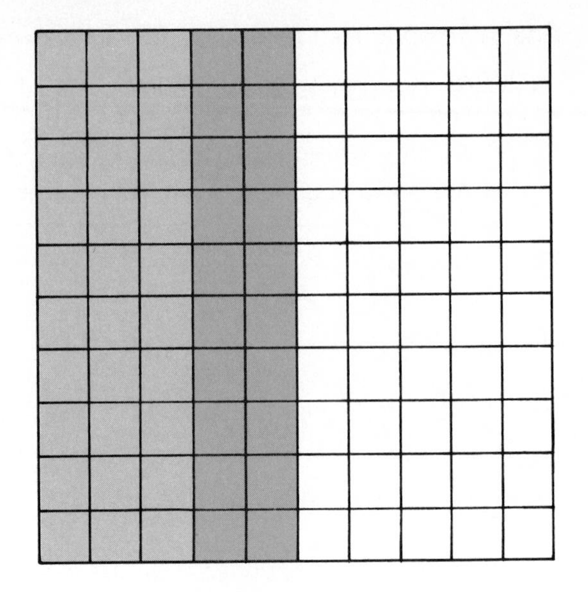

30 of the 100 small squares are blue.
30% of the drawing is blue.

You can also use a decimal to tell about the blue part. The drawing is divided into hundredths.
30 hundredths is blue. 0.30 is blue.

30% = 0.30 (or 0.3)

20% of the drawing is green.
20 hundredths is green.
20% = 0.20 (or 0.2)

Do you see an easy way to change a percent to a decimal?

> ***To write a decimal for a percent, move the decimal point two places to the left. Omit the percent sign.***

17% = .17.% = 0.17
103% = 1.03.% = 1.03
12.5% = .12.5% = 0.125

80% = .80.% = 0.80
3% = . 3.% = 0.03
2.5% = . 2.5% = 0.025

You reverse the procedure to write a percent for a decimal.

> ***To write a percent for a decimal, move the decimal point two places to the right. Write the percent sign.***

0.65 = 0.65.% = 65%
1.08 = 1.08.% = 108%
0.375 = 0.37.5% = 37.5%

0.90 = 0.90.% = 90%
0.08 = 0.08.% = 8%
0.075 = 0.07.5% = 7.5%

Practice • Write as decimals.

1. 29% **2.** 75% **3.** 7% **4.** 12.5% **5.** 175%

Write as percents.

6. 0.80 **7.** 0.08 **8.** 0.99 **9.** 1.35 **10.** 0.015

Mixed Practice • Write as decimals.

11. 13% **12.** 72% **13.** 40% **14.** 3% **15.** 94%

16. 1% **17.** 85% **18.** 5% **19.** 8% **20.** 80%

21. 37.5% **22.** 6.5% **23.** 18.6% **24.** 1.8% **25.** 99.9%

26. 105% **27.** 143% **28.** 198% **29.** 201% ★ **30.** 4,000%

Write as percents.

31. 0.70 **32.** 0.07 **33.** 0.28 **34.** 0.91 **35.** 0.06

36. 0.65 **37.** 0.14 **38.** 0.01 **39.** 0.40 **40.** 0.98

41. 1.03 **42.** 1.50 **43.** 1.85 **44.** 1.07 **45.** 2.00

★ **46.** 0.375 ★ **47.** 4.50 ★ **48.** 0.034 ★ **49.** 0.005 ★ **50.** 0.0003

Write as decimals in tenths.

51. 10% **52.** 80% **53.** 100% **54.** 150% ★ **55.** 970%

Think of this small square as 0.01, or 1%, of a large square. Half of this hundredth is yellow. $\frac{1}{2}$ of 1%, or $\frac{1}{2}$%, is yellow. The magnifying glass shows that the small square is divided into ten equal parts. $\frac{5}{10}$ of 1%, or $\frac{5}{10}$%, is yellow.

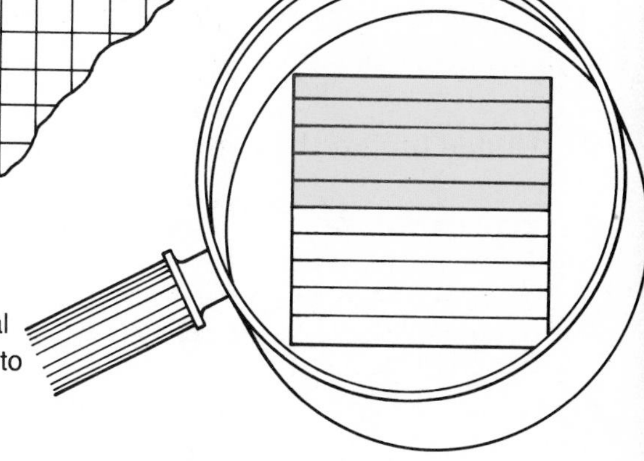

$\frac{1}{2}\% = \frac{5}{10}\% = 0.5\% = 0.005$

Move the decimal point two places to the left.

Write as decimals.

★ **56.** 0.2% ★ **57.** 0.25% ★ **58.** $\frac{75}{100}$% ★ **59.** $\frac{3}{4}$% ★ **60.** $\frac{4}{5}$%

PROBLEM SOLVING • APPLICATIONS

61. The human body is 18% carbon. Hydrogen makes up 10%, and 65% is oxygen. Write these percents as decimals.

★ **62.** Is the human body composed only of carbon, hydrogen, and oxygen? How do you know that your answer is correct?

Percents and Fractions

100 students are asked which season they like best. This table gives the answers in percents.

Favorite Season	
Spring	13%
Summer	47%
Fall	25%
Winter	15%

You can write a fraction for a percent. Use a fraction with a denominator of 100.

$13\% = \frac{13}{100}$ $\qquad$ $47\% = \frac{47}{100}$

Sometime you need to show the fraction in lowest terms.

$25\% = \frac{25}{100} = \frac{1}{4}$ $\qquad$ $15\% = \frac{15}{100} = \frac{3}{20}$

You can also write percents for fractions. It is easy when the denominator is 100 or a factor of 100.

$\frac{1}{100} = 1\%$ $\qquad$ $\frac{39}{100} = 39\%$ $\qquad$ $\frac{3}{5} = \frac{60}{100} = 60\%$

To find the percent for any fraction, you can divide the numerator by the denominator to find the decimal. Then you can write the percent.

Divide to find the percent for $\frac{3}{5}$. $\qquad$ $\begin{array}{r} 0.60 \\ 5\overline{)3.00} \end{array}$ $\qquad$ $0.60 = 60\%$

Sometimes the division does not terminate in the hundredths place, and you need to continue the division. Study these examples.

Find the percent for $\frac{1}{8}$. $\longrightarrow$ $\begin{array}{r} 0.1\ 2\ 5 \\ 8\overline{)1.0^{2}0^{4}0} \end{array}$

$\frac{1}{8}$ can also be expressed as $12\frac{1}{2}\%$. $\qquad$ $\frac{1}{8} = 0.125 = 12.5\%$

Find the percent for $\frac{2}{3}$. $\longrightarrow$ $\begin{array}{r} 0.6\ 6\frac{2}{3} \\ 3\overline{)2.0^{2}0} \end{array}$

The remainder 2 will keep repeating. Show the remainder in a fraction. $\qquad$ $\frac{2}{3} = 0.66\frac{2}{3} = 66\frac{2}{3}\%$

Practice • Write as fractions, whole numbers, or mixed numbers. Show the answers in lowest terms.

1. 9% $\qquad$ **2.** 30% $\qquad$ **3.** 60% $\qquad$ **4.** 100% $\qquad$ **5.** 120%

Write as percents.

6. $\frac{3}{100}$ **7.** $\frac{49}{100}$ **8.** $\frac{7}{10}$ **9.** $\frac{3}{8}$ **10.** $\frac{13}{10}$

Mixed Practice • Write as fractions, whole numbers, or mixed numbers in lowest terms.

11. 40% **12.** 50% **13.** 35% **14.** 1% **15.** 80%

16. 90% **17.** 96% **18.** 175% **19.** 200% ★**20.** 950%

Write as percents.

21. $\frac{41}{100}$ **22.** $\frac{5}{100}$ **23.** $\frac{3}{10}$ **24.** $\frac{1}{5}$ **25.** $\frac{1}{2}$

26. $\frac{3}{4}$ **27.** $\frac{5}{8}$ **28.** $\frac{1}{3}$ **29.** $\frac{1}{12}$ **30.** $\frac{7}{8}$

31. $\frac{130}{100}$ **32.** $\frac{17}{10}$ **33.** $1\frac{35}{100}$ ★**34.** $1\frac{3}{4}$ ★**35.** $2\frac{1}{8}$

36. Copy and complete this table of fractions, decimals, and percents.

Fraction	Decimal	Percent
$\frac{1}{4}$	0.25	25%
$\frac{2}{4}$	?	?
$\frac{3}{4}$	?	?
$\frac{4}{4}$	?	?

37. Make a table of fractions, decimals, and percents for $\frac{1}{3}, \frac{2}{3}, \frac{3}{3}, \ldots, \frac{6}{3}$.

★ **38.** Make a table of fractions, decimals, and percents for $\frac{1}{6}, \frac{2}{6}, \frac{3}{6}, \ldots, \frac{6}{6}$.

PROBLEM SOLVING • APPLICATIONS

39. Ben takes 100 free throws in a practice session. He makes 76 baskets. What percent of the throws are baskets?

★ **40.** Lori makes 7 out of 8 free throws during a game. What percent is this?

Midchapter Review

Write percents for the ratios.

1. 3 per 100 **2.** $\frac{1}{4}$

Write as ratios.

3. 43% **4.** 7%

Write as decimals.

5. 71% **6.** 185%

Write as fractions.

7. 15% **8.** 56%

Finding the Percent of a Number

The Johnsons paid \$9,560 for their new car. The first year they owned it, the car depreciated (lost value) 25%. How much less was the car worth after one year?

Think:

25% of \$9,560 is how much?

25% of \$9,560 $= n$

$0.25 \times 9{,}560 = n$

Use the decimal 0.25 instead of 25%. Use × for "of."

Step 1 Write the equation. → $0.25 \times 9{,}560 = n$

Step 2 Multiply to solve. →

$$\begin{array}{r} 9{,}560 \\ \times \quad 0.25 \\ \hline 47800 \\ 19120 \\ \hline 2{,}390.00 \end{array}$$

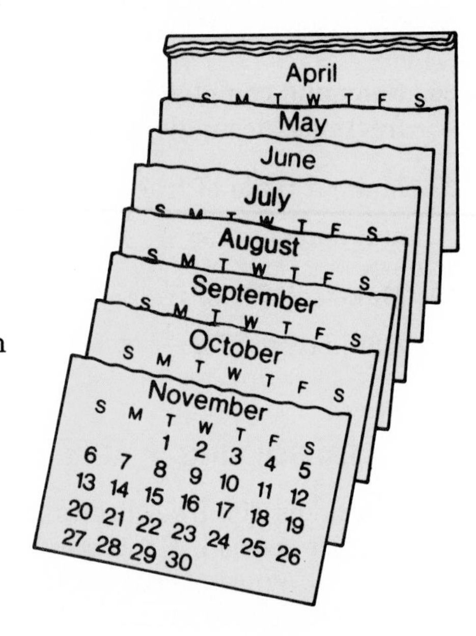

The car depreciated \$2,390.

The same example can be done using a fraction in place of 25%.

You know that $25\% = \frac{25}{100} = \frac{1}{4}$.

25% of \$9,560 $= n$ → $\frac{1}{4} \times 9{,}560 = n$

$$\frac{9{,}560}{4} = n$$

$$2{,}390 = n$$

Which seems easier to you, using 0.25 or using $\frac{1}{4}$?

More Examples

3% of 150 $= n$

$0.03 \times 150 = n$

$4.5 = n$

107% of 15 $= n$

$1.07 \times 15 = n$

$16.05 = n$

50% of 80 $= n$

$50\% = \frac{50}{100} = \frac{1}{2}$

$\frac{1}{2} \times 80 = n$

$40 = n$

Practice • Solve.

1. 14% of 200 = n
2. 36% of 150 = n
3. 10% of 80 = n
4. 50% of 38 = n
5. 7% of 60 = n
6. 43% of 74 = n

Mixed Practice • Solve.

7. 15% of 300 = n
8. 28% of 250 = n
9. 20% of 60 = n
10. 40% of 70 = n
11. 25% of 50 = n
12. 6% of 80 = n
13. 9% of 36 = n
14. 50% of 90 = n
15. 32% of 90 = n
16. 7% of 145 = n
17. 15% of 650 = n
18. 49% of 50 = n
19. 25% of 460 = n
20. 3% of 600 = n
21. 99% of 2,000 = n
22. 29% of 102 = n
23. 14% of 16 = n
24. 34% of 95 = n
25. 8% of 82 = n
26. 51% of 256 = n
27. 50% of 50 = n
28. 19% of 3,400 = n
29. 84% of 6,500 = n
30. 95% of 3,600 = n

★ 31. 100% of 60 = n

★ 32. 125% of 80 = n

★ 33. 175% of 120 = n

★ 34. 250% of 8.2 = n

★ 35. 300% of 12.4 = n

★ 36. 280% of 32 = n

★ 37. 3.5% of 100 = n

★ 38. 0.5% of 300 = n

★ 39. 0.9% of 15 = n

Write <, =, or >.

★ 40. (80% of 50) + (20% of 50) ● 100% of 50

★ 41. (75% of 200) + (15% of 200) ● 80% of 200

PROBLEM SOLVING • APPLICATIONS

42. The Gearings paid $10,500 for their new car. The first year they owned it, the car depreciated 21%. How much less was the car worth after one year?

43. How much money was the Gearings' car worth after one year?

44. A certain used car is worth $3,500 today. It will depreciate 20% over the next year. How much less will it be worth then?

★ 45. Another used car is worth $2,750 today. It will depreciate 12% over the next year. How much will the car be worth then?

Finding the Percent One Number Is of Another

On a test Jeff answers 20 of the 25 questions correctly. What percent of the test questions does he answer correctly?

Think:
What percent of 25 is 20?
$n\%$ of 25 is 20.
$n \times 25 = 20$

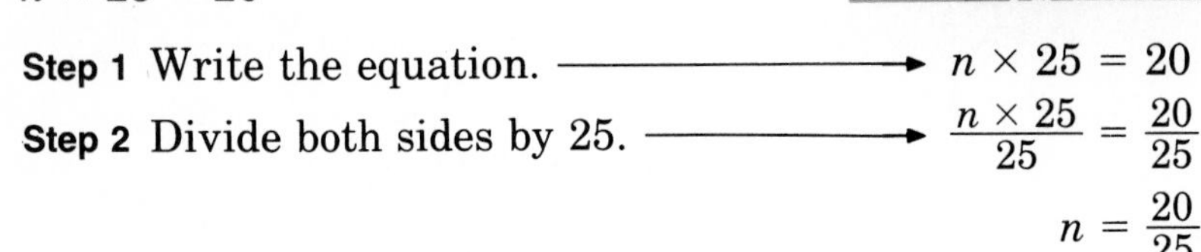

Step 1 Write the equation. → $n \times 25 = 20$

Step 2 Divide both sides by 25. → $\frac{n \times 25}{25} = \frac{20}{25}$

$n = \frac{20}{25}$

Step 3 Write a decimal for the quotient. → $n = 0.80$

$0.80 = 80\%$. Jeff answers 80% of the questions correctly.

More Examples

What percent of 8 is 5?

$n\%$ of 8 is 5.

$n \times 8 = 5$

$\frac{n \times 8}{8} = \frac{5}{8}$

$n = \frac{5}{8}$

$n = 0.625$

$0.625 = 62.5\%$

So 5 is 62.5% of 8.

1 is what percent of 3? ← This means: What percent of 3 is 1?

$n\%$ of 3 is 1.

$n \times 3 = 1$

$\frac{n \times 3}{3} = \frac{1}{3}$

$n = \frac{1}{3}$

$n = 0.33\frac{1}{3}$

$0.33\frac{1}{3} = 33\frac{1}{3}\%$

So 1 is $33\frac{1}{3}\%$ of 3.

Practice • Answer the questions.

1. What percent of 28 is 7?

2. What percent of 8 is 3?

3. What percent of 90 is 60?

4. 1 is what percent of 20?

Find the percents.

5. $n\%$ of 20 is 3.

6. $n\%$ of 15 is 9.

Mixed Practice • Answer the questions.

7. What percent of 10 is 3?
8. What percent of 48 is 12?
9. What percent of 50 is 35?
10. What percent of 45 is 36?
11. What percent of 20 is 2?
12. What percent of 30 is 27?
13. 9 is what percent of 18?
14. 4 is what percent of 10?
15. 10 is what percent of 40?
16. 60 is what percent of 80?
17. What percent of 8 is 1?
18. What percent of 6 is 2?
19. What percent of 9 is 4?
20. What percent of 200 is 200?
21. What percent of 200 is 150?
★22. What percent of 200 is 300?
★23. What percent of 10 is 12?
★24. What percent of 10 is 25?
★25. 4 is what percent of 800?
★26. 6 is what percent of 1,000?

Find the percents.

27. $n\%$ of 40 is 12.
★28. $n\%$ of 200 is 500.
★29. $n\%$ of 400 is 2.

What percent is the first number of the second?

30. 3, 30
31. 17, 68
32. 9, 27
33. 1, 7
★34. 20, 8

Sometimes you want to round percents.

$\frac{1}{3} = 0.3333\ldots \left(\text{or } 0.33\frac{1}{3}\right)$ To the nearest tenth of a percent: $\frac{1}{3} \rightarrow 33.3\%$.

Find each percent to the nearest tenth of a percent.

★35. 1 is what percent of 6?
★36. 4 is what percent of 11?
★37. 6 is what percent of 27?
★38. 70 is what percent of 90?

PROBLEM SOLVING • APPLICATIONS

Find the test scores in percents.

39. 17 correct out of 25
40. 19 correct out of 20
41. 40 correct out of 50
42. 3 correct out of 4
★43. Bart answers 84% of his test questions correctly. There are 150 questions in all. How many wrong answers does Bart have?

Finding a Number When a Percent of It Is Known

Tania has saved \$33.75 for a cassette player. She says that this is 75% of the cost of the player. How much does the cassette player cost?

Think:

75% of what amount is \$33.75?

75% of n = \$33.75

$0.75 \times n = 33.75$

Step 1

Write the equation. ⟶ $0.75n = 33.75$

Step 2

Divide both sides by 0.75. ⟶ $\frac{0.75n}{0.75} = \frac{33.75}{0.75}$

$n = 45$

The cassette player costs \$45.

More Examples

12% of what number is 24?

$12\% \text{ of } n = 24$

$0.12 \times n = 24$

$\frac{0.12n}{0.12} = \frac{24}{0.12}$

$n = 200$

12% of 200 is 24.

5 is 40% of what number?

This means: 40% of what number is 5?

$40\% \text{ of } n = 5$

$0.40 \times n = 5$

$\frac{0.40n}{0.40} = \frac{5}{0.40}$

$n = 12.5$

5 is 40% of 12.5.

Practice • Answer the questions.

1. 50% of what number is 48?

2. 70% of what number is 42?

3. 20% of what number is 6?

4. 5% of what number is 20?

5. 12 is 20% of what number?

6. 25 is 8% of what number?

Solve.

7. 90% of n = 36 **8.** 15% of n = 21

Mixed Practice • Answer the questions.

9. 10% of what number is 8?
10. 50% of what number is 12?
11. 30% of what number is 21?
12. 75% of what number is 18?
13. 18 is 60% of what number?
14. 12 is 16% of what number?
15. 252 is 42% of what number?
16. 9 is 25% of what number?
17. 80% of what number is 80?
18. 1% of what number is 6?
19. 48% of what number is 24?
20. 51% of what number is 204?
21. 7 is 35% of what number?
22. 21 is 28% of what number?
23. 5 is 40% of what number?
24. 75 is 75% of what number?
25. 10% of what number is 8.65?
26. 4% of what number is 0.3?
★ 27. 10 is 12.5% of what number?
★ 28. 12.5 is 2.5% of what number?
★ 29. 120% of what number is 67.2?
★ 30. 175% of what number is 227.5?
★ 31. 300 is 150% of what number?
★ 32. 99 is 110% of what number?

Solve.

33. 40% of $n = 36$
34. 70% of $n = 210$
35. 110% of $n = 33$
36. 75% of $300 = n$
37. 15% of $60 = n$
38. r% of $40 = 20$
39. r% of $180 = 45$
★ 40. 125% of $n = 375$
★ 41. 7.5% of $n = 6$

PROBLEM SOLVING • APPLICATIONS

42. At a special sale, a television set sells for $84. The owner says this is 60% of the original price. What is the original price?

★ 43. At another sale, a refrigerator sells for $399. The owner says this is 80% of the original price. How much less than $500 is the original price?

Skills Maintenance

1. 10×2.3
2. 100×3.6
3. $1{,}000 \times 15.9$
4. $1{,}000 \times 0.06$
5. $12.4 \div 10$
6. $17.3 \div 100$
7. $26.1 \div 1{,}000$
8. $5 \div 1{,}000$

PROBLEM SOLVING • STRATEGIES

Using a Percent Formula

Often it is useful to think about the way the numbers in problems are related to each other.

Tina wrote these notes about percent.

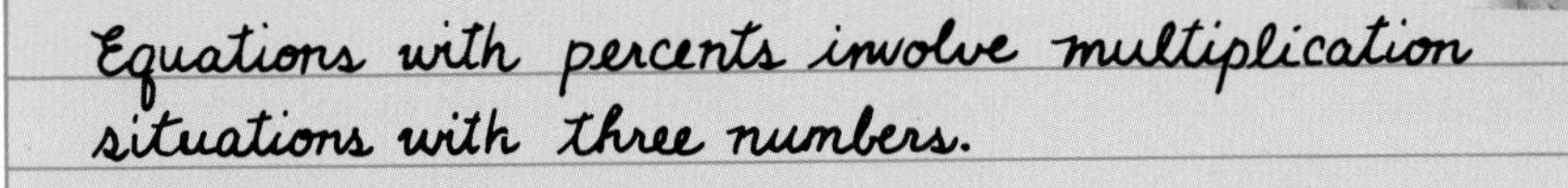
Equations with percents involve multiplication situations with three numbers. $r \times b = p$

r → the rate (a percent)

b → the base (a number that is multiplied by the rate)

p → the product (the result obtained when r and b are multiplied)

The product is sometimes called the percentage.

	rate		base		product, or percentage
Example:	30%	of	200	=	p
	0.30	×	200	=	p
			60	=	p The product, or percentage is 60.

These problems use Tina's equation. Study the problems.

Problem 1

$90\% \times b = p$

Replace b with 240.
Is p greater than b?

$0.90 \times 240 = p$
$216 = p$

Since b is 240
and p is 216,
p is not greater than b.
p is less than b.

Problem 2

$90\% \times b = p$

Replace b with 80.
Is p greater than b?

$0.90 \times 80 = p$
$72 = p$

Since b is 80
and p is 72,
p is not greater than b.
p is less than b.

Use the equation given.
Answer the question.

1. $125\% \times b = p$
Replace b with 240.
Is p greater than b?

2. $99\% \times b = p$
Replace b with 46.50.
Is p greater than b?

Solve.

3. One year the salary for a clerk's job is $12,000. The next year the salary is 107% of that amount. What is the new salary?

Reread the problem.
What does it ask you to find?

4. One year a computer programmer earns $30,000. The next year he earns 120% of that amount. What is his salary then?

5. One year Ahmik earns $1,500. The next year he earns only 80% of that amount. How much does he earn?

6. Suzi said, "This year I earned $1,200. Last year I earned $1,600." This year's earnings are what percent of last year's?

7. Phil said, "This year I earned $800. Last year I earned only $500." This year's earnings are what percent of last year's?

8. Karen earns $900 in a year. She spends 75% of her earnings. How much money does she spend?

9. Frank said, "This year I saved $180. This was 15% of what I earned." How much did he earn?

10. Francine said, "This year I saved $240. This was 37.5% of what I earned." How much did she earn?

Use the equation $r \times b = p$ for problems 11–15.

11. If $r < 100\%$, which of the following is true?

$p < b$ $\quad$ $p = b$ $\quad$ $p > b$

12. If $r > 100\%$, which of the following is true?

$p < b$ $\quad$ $p = b$ $\quad$ $p > b$

Try some values for r and b if you need help.

13. If $r = 100\%$, which of the following is true?

$p < b$ $\quad$ $p = b$ $\quad$ $p > b$

14. Suppose $r = 200\%$. Write an equation that shows the relationship between b and p.

15. Suppose $r = 50\%$. Write an equation that shows the relationship between b and p.

Discount and Sales Tax

A department store advertises a special sale. For one day only, the store will give a discount at a rate of 20%. You want to buy a transistor radio that regularly sells for $49.95. What is the sale price?

A **discount** is an amount that is subtracted from the original cost. The **rate of discount** (the percent) is used to find the amount of the discount and the sale price.

Think: $49.95 − (20% of $49.95) = sale price.

Step 1
Multiply to find the discount.

```
  $49.95
×   0.20
--------
$9.99 00
```

Step 2
Subtract the discount from the original price.

```
  $49.95
−   9.99
--------
  $39.96
```

The sale price of the transistor radio is $39.96.

States and cities need money for the services that they provide. One way to raise money is to charge a sales tax. A **sales tax** is an amount added to the price of something you buy.

Suppose your state charges a sales tax at a rate of 5%. What is the total cost of a book that has a price tag marked $8.99?

Think: $8.99 + (5% of $8.99) = total cost.

Step 1
Find the amount of the tax.
Round to the next whole cent.

```
  $8.99
× 0.05
-------
$.44 95    Tax: $.45
```

Step 2
Add the tax to the price.

```
  $8.99
+   .45
-------
  $9.44
```

The total cost of the book is $9.44.

Practice • Find the amount of the discount and the sale price.

1. Original price: \$45.00
   Discount rate: 10%
2. Original price: \$70.00
   Discount rate: 20%
3. Original price: \$18.50
   Discount rate: 50%

Find the amount of the tax and the total cost.

4. Price: \$7.00
   Sales tax rate: 6%
5. Price: \$12.50
   Sales tax rate: 4%
6. Price: \$5.95
   Sales tax rate: 5%

Mixed Practice • Find the sale price.

7. Original price: \$4.00
   Discount rate: 25%
8. Original price: \$95.00
   Discount rate: 8%
9. Original price: \$25.00
   Discount rate: 15%
10. Original price: \$120.00
    Discount rate: 20%
11. Original price: \$24.50
    Discount rate: 40%
12. ★ Original price: \$8.40
    Discount rate: $33\frac{1}{3}\%$

Find the amount of the tax and the total cost.

13. Price: \$4.00
    Sales tax rate: 5%
14. Price: \$6.95
    Sales tax rate: 6%
15. Price: \$12.00
    Sales tax rate: 8%
16. Price: \$3.99
    Sales tax rate: 2%
17. Price: \$74.50
    Sales tax rate: 7%
18. Price: \$113.00
    Sales tax rate: 5%

Find the total cost.

19. Price: \$41.50
    Sales tax rate: 4%
20. Price: \$18.50
    Sales tax rate: 7%
21. ★ Price: \$0.75
    Sales tax rate: 6%

PROBLEM SOLVING • APPLICATIONS

22. A store has a "15% Off" (15% discount) sale. To find the amount of discount on a \$24 sweater, can you use this equation?

    $$0.15 \times 24 = n$$

    Solve the equation. What is the amount of discount?

23. Keith says he uses this proportion to find 15% of \$24.

    $$\frac{15}{100} = \frac{n}{24}$$

    Solve the proportion. Is the answer the same as the answer you obtained for problem 22?

24. A store has a "20% Off" sale. Is the sale price 80% of the original price? Find the sale price of an item originally priced at \$12.

25. ★ A store has a "20% Off" sale. A sales tax of 4% must be added to the sale price. What is the total amount paid for an item originally priced at \$27?

Simple Interest

Mr. Tedesco wants to borrow money from the bank. He will have to pay interest for the use of the money he borrows.

You can use a formula to compute **simple interest**.

$$I = prt$$

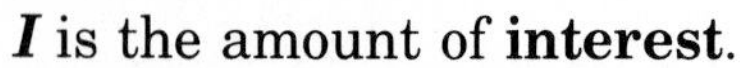

I is the amount of **interest**.
p is the **principal**, or amount of money borrowed.
r is the **rate** (the percent) at which interest is charged per year.
t is the **time** in years for which the money is borrowed.

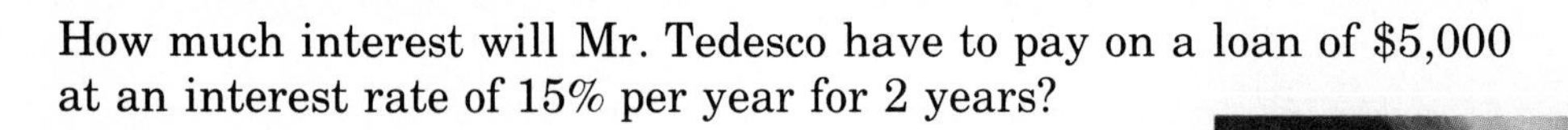

How much interest will Mr. Tedesco have to pay on a loan of $5,000 at an interest rate of 15% per year for 2 years?

Step 1
Write the formula. ⟶ $I = prt$

Step 2
Substitute the numbers you know. ⟶ $I = 5{,}000 \times 0.15 \times 2$

Step 3
Solve the equation. ⟶ $I = 1{,}500$

Mr. Tedesco will have to pay $1,500 in interest.

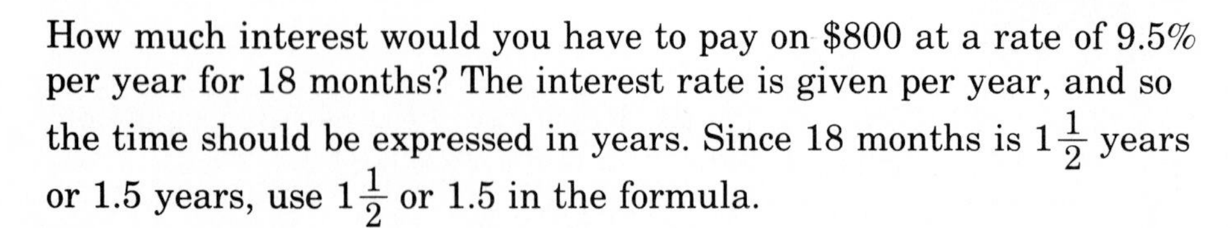

How much interest would you have to pay on $800 at a rate of 9.5% per year for 18 months? The interest rate is given per year, and so the time should be expressed in years. Since 18 months is $1\frac{1}{2}$ years or 1.5 years, use $1\frac{1}{2}$ or 1.5 in the formula.

Step 1
Write the formula. ⟶ $I = prt$

Step 2
Substitute the numbers you know. ⟶ $I = 800 \times 0.095 \times 1.5$

Step 3
Solve the equation. ⟶ $I = 114$

You would have to pay $114 in interest.

Practice • Find the amount of interest.

1. $p = \$400$
   $r = 12\%$
   $t = 1$ year
2. $p = \$600$
   $r = 15\%$
   $t = 2$ years
3. $p = \$850$
   $r = 10\%$
   $t = 1\frac{1}{2}$ years
4. $p = \$1,000$
   $r = 18\%$
   $t = 6$ months
5. Paula borrows \$900 for $2\frac{1}{2}$ years. The rate of interest is 15%. How much interest does she pay?

Mixed Practice • Find the amount of interest.

6. $p = \$500$
   $r = 10\%$
   $t = 1$ year
7. $p = \$2,000$
   $r = 12\%$
   $t = 3$ years
8. $p = \$1,500$
   $r = 14\%$
   $t = 1\frac{1}{2}$ years
9. $p = \$800$
   $r = 10\%$
   $t = 2\frac{1}{2}$ years
10. $p = \$900$
    $r = 15\%$
    $t = 6$ months
11. $p = \$700$
    $r = 14\%$
    $t = 6$ months
12. ★ $p = \$1,200$
    $r = 16.5\%$
    $t = 1\frac{1}{2}$ years
13. ★ $p = \$600$
    $r = 12.5\%$
    $t = \frac{1}{2}$ year

PROBLEM SOLVING • APPLICATIONS

14. Robert borrows \$400 from a loan company for 1 year. The loan company charges 18% interest per year. How much interest will Robert have to pay?
15. Claire borrows \$600 from a bank for 2 years. The bank charges 15% interest per year. How much interest will Claire have to pay?
16. Jim borrows \$700 for 1 year. The bank charges 15% interest per year. How much interest will Jim have to pay?
17. In all, how much money will Jim have to pay at the end of the year to pay off his debt to the bank?
18. ★ Coretta borrows \$500 for 1 year. She pays \$60 in interest. What is the rate of interest?
19. ★ Chen paid \$84 interest on a 2-year loan. The interest rate was 14%. How much was the principal?

Circle Graph and Percent

A **budget** is a plan for using money. Ann uses a **circle graph** to show how she budgets the money she earns in a year.

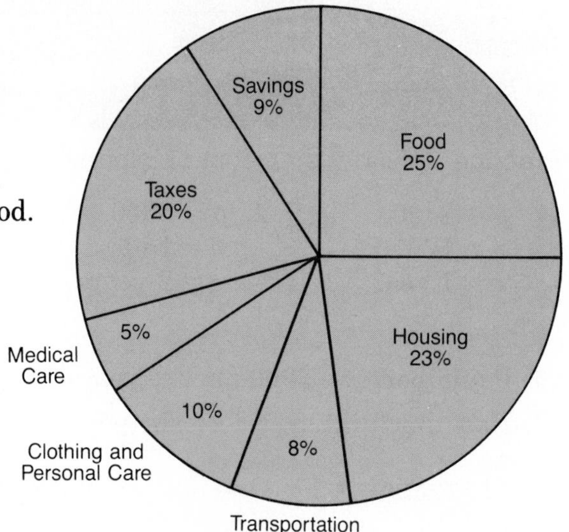

Suppose Ann's yearly income is \$15,000. How much does she plan to spend on food?

We look at the graph and see that Ann plans to spend 25% of her income on food.

25% of \$15,000 = n

$$\begin{array}{r} \$15{,}000 \\ \times \quad 0.25 \\ \hline 75000 \\ 30000 \\ \hline \$3{,}750.00 \end{array}$$

Ann plans to spend \$3,750.00 on food.

Practice • Answer the questions.

1. What is the sum of the percents shown on the graph?
2. On which item does Ann plan to spend the most money?
3. On which item does Ann plan to spend the least money?

How much money does Ann budget for

4. taxes?
5. medical care?
6. transportation?
7. housing?
8. savings?
9. clothing and personal care?

Mixed Practice • Answer the questions.

10. Does Ann plan to spend more money on taxes than on housing?
11. Does Ann plan to save more money than she spends on transportation?

Suppose Ann earns \$20,000 and uses the same percents in her budget.
How much money does she budget for

12. food?
13. housing?
14. clothing and personal care?
15. savings?
16. medical care?
17. transportation?

PROBLEM SOLVING • APPLICATIONS

Study the graph of the Osborne family's budget.

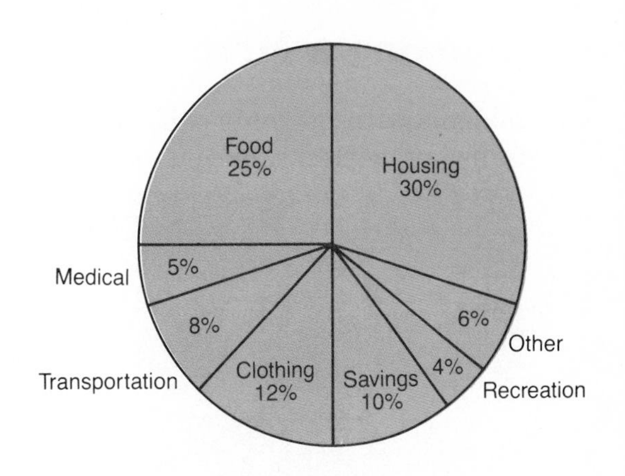

18. What is the sum of the percents shown on the graph?

19. On which item does the Osborne family plan to spend the most money? the least money?

The annual income of the Osborne family is $28,000.00 after taxes. How much money does the Osborne family budget for

20. housing? **21.** food? **22.** savings?

23. clothing? **24.** medical care? **25.** transportation?

★**26.** On which item does the Osborne family plan to spend $1,120?

★**27.** How much more does the Osborne family plan to spend on clothing than on transportation?

★**28.** What is the total amount budgeted for food and housing?

★**29.** What fraction of the total budget is used for housing, food, clothing, and transportation? Write your answer in lowest terms.

In a survey 500 teenagers were asked to name their favorite sports. This circle graph shows the results in percents.

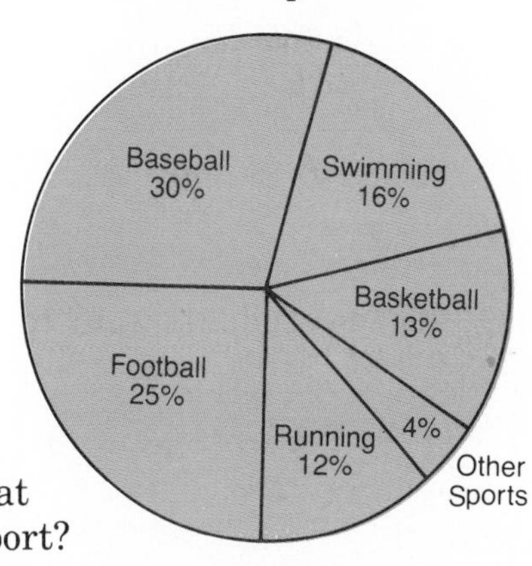

How many teenagers chose

30. basketball? **31.** football?

32. baseball? **33.** running?

★**34.** What is the greatest number of teenagers that might have chosen soccer as their favorite sport?

PROBLEM SOLVING • STRATEGIES

Choosing a Method

Problems with percents can be solved in more than one way. You can use proportions, or you can use equations with decimals or fractions.

There are 210 students in the Washington School. 140 of the students went to the senior play. What percent of the students went to the play?

Method 1

Use a proportion.

To find the percent, use the fact that the ratio $\frac{140}{210}$ is equal to $n\%$, or $\frac{n}{100}$.

$$\frac{140}{210} = \frac{n}{100}$$

$$14{,}000 = 210n$$

$$\frac{14{,}000}{210} = \frac{210n}{210}$$

$$66\tfrac{2}{3} = n$$

So $\frac{66\frac{2}{3}}{100}$ of the students went to the play.

$66\frac{2}{3}\%$ of the students went to the play.

Method 2

Use a decimal.

To find the percent, find the decimal y that solves the equation $y \times 210 = 140$.

$$y \times 210 = 140$$

$$\frac{y \times 210}{210} = \frac{140}{210}$$

$$y = \frac{140}{210} = \frac{2}{3}$$

$$y = 0.66\tfrac{2}{3}$$

$0.66\frac{2}{3} = 66\frac{2}{3}\%$

The answer is the same as the answer using Method 1.

Solve.

1. After the play Simba and Beth eat at a restaurant. Their bill is $10.00. They leave a tip of $1.00. What percent of the bill is the tip?

2. Many people say that a tip should be 15% of the bill. What tip would be 15% of $10.00?

Round tips to the nearest five cents if necessary.

3. What tip would be 15% of a bill of $6.20?

4. What tip would be 15% of a bill of $8.40?

5. One year tickets for the senior play were $4.00 each. The next year the price was $.80 more. The increase ($.80) is what percent of the old price ($4.00)?

6. One year Vernon's costume cost $18.00. The next year, it cost 10% more. What was the increase in cost? What was the new price?

7. Mr. Taylor sells costumes. In addition to his salary, he receives a 5% commission on each sale he makes. If he makes a sale of $400, what is his commission?

8. If Mr. Taylor makes a sale of $1,300, what is his commission?

9. Mrs. Taylor sells business products. In addition to her salary, she receives an 8% commission on each sale she makes. If she makes a sale of $800, what is her commission?

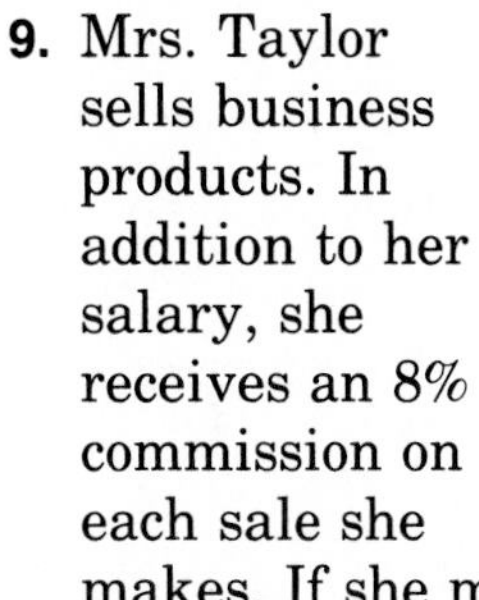

10. One year Mrs. Taylor received commissions totaling $2,400. Since her rate of commission is 8%, what was the amount of her sales that year?

11. Of the 210 students at the Washington School, 126 are girls. What percent of the students are girls?

When you solve a problem with percent, use the method that seems clearer to you.

12. What percent of the students at the Washington School are boys?

★13. Of the students at the Washington School, $83\frac{1}{3}\%$ are over 12 years old. How many are over 12 years old?

★14. What percent of the students are not over 12 years old? What fractional part of the students are not over 12 years old?

CHAPTER 10

REVIEW

Write as percents. (pp. 244–245)

1. 6 per 100
2. $\frac{18}{100}$
3. 46:100
4. $\frac{7}{4}$

Solve the proportion. Then answer the question. (pp. 246–247)

5. $\frac{n}{200} = \frac{25}{100}$

   What number is 25% of 200?

6. $\frac{n}{120} = \frac{5}{100}$

   What number is 5% of 120?

Write as decimals. (pp. 248–249)

7. 32%
8. 8.3%

Write as percents. (pp. 248–249)

9. 0.79
10. 0.015

Write as fractions, whole numbers, or mixed numbers in lowest terms. (pp. 250–251)

11. 3%
12. 60%
13. 34%
14. 25%
15. 125%

Write as percents. (pp. 250–251)

16. $\frac{53}{100}$
17. $\frac{7}{100}$
18. $\frac{9}{10}$
19. $\frac{1}{4}$
20. $\frac{5}{8}$

Solve. (pp. 252–253)

21. 4% of 50 = n
22. 32% of 120 = n
23. 25% of 1,240 = n

Answer the questions. (pp. 254–257)

24. What percent of 40 is 8?
25. 21 is what percent of 300?
26. 40% of what number is 30?
27. 18 is 6% of what number?
28. Paul wants to buy a book that is $10.95. The rate of the sales tax is 6%. What is the total amount that Paul pays? (pp. 260–261)
29. Diana borrows $4,000 for 2 years at 15% simple interest per year. How much interest will Diana have to pay? (pp. 262–263)
30. Gil earns $1,100 in a year. He spends 65% of his earnings. How much money does he spend? (pp. 258–259)

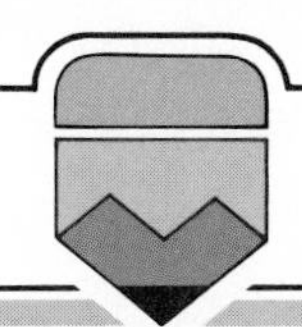

PROJECT

Compound Interest

6%
Compounded Quarterly

The Morgan National Bank pays 6% interest, compounded quarterly.

Compounded quarterly means that the interest is added to the account each 3 months. Then, for the next 3 months, interest is earned on the new principal in the account.

Since 3 months is $\frac{1}{4}$ of a year, the interest for each 3-month period is $\frac{1}{4}$ of 6%, or 1.5%, or 0.015.

Suppose you have $500 in your account on January 1. How much interest will you earn in each quarter? How much money will be in your account at the end of 1 year?

First Quarter

The interest earned is:
0.015 (500) = 7.500
Interest: $7.50

The new principal is:
$500 + $7.50 = $507.50

Second Quarter

The interest earned is:
0.015 (507.50) = 7.6125
Interest: $7.61 (rounded)

The new principal is:
$507.50 + $7.61 = $515.11

Third Quarter

The interest earned is:
0.015 (515.11) = 7.72665
Interest: $7.73 (rounded)

The new principal is:
$515.11 + $7.73 = $522.84

Fourth Quarter

The interest earned is:
0.015 (522.84) = 7.8426
Interest: $7.84 (rounded)

The new principal is:
$522.84 + $7.84 = $530.68

$530.68 is in the account at the end of 1 year.

1. Ms. Alvarez has $1,500 in her account. The bank pays 8% interest per year, compounded quarterly. How much does she have at the end of 1 year?

2. Find out what type of compound interest is paid by a bank in your community. Write a short report telling how much interest you would earn in 1 year if you had $1,000 in the bank on January 1.

CHAPTER 10 TEST

Write as percents. **1.** 3 per 100 **2.** $\frac{27}{100}$ **3.** 58:100 **4.** $\frac{9}{4}$

Solve the proportion. Then answer the question.

5. $\frac{n}{300} = \frac{75}{100}$

What number is 75% of 300?

6. $\frac{n}{150} = \frac{8}{100}$

What number is 8% of 150?

Write as decimals.

7. 4% **8.** 7.35%

Write as percents.

9. 0.11 **10.** 2.05

Write as fractions, whole numbers, or mixed numbers. Show the answers in lowest terms.

11. 7% **12.** 30% **13.** 54% **14.** 80% **15.** 175%

Write as percents.

16. $\frac{49}{100}$ **17.** $\frac{3}{100}$ **18.** $\frac{7}{10}$ **19.** $\frac{2}{5}$ **20.** $\frac{3}{8}$

Solve.

21. 5% of 500 = n **22.** 25% of 104 = n **23.** 98% of 1,000 = n

Answer the questions.

24. What percent of 50 is 6?

25. 32 is what percent of 64?

26. 15% of what number is 9?

27. 106 is 53% of what number?

28. Kathy wants to buy a coat that is selling for $89.00. The rate of the sales tax is 5%. What is the total amount that Kathy pays?

29. Alice borrows $2,500 for 3 years at 12% simple interest per year. How much interest will Alice have to pay?

30. One year a secretary earns $15,000. The next year the salary is 112% of that amount. What is the new salary?

ENRICHMENT

Finding the Percent of Increase or Decrease

Ken is a car salesman. During April he sold 15 cars. During May he sold 18 cars. By what percent did his sales increase from April to May?

The **amount** of the increase from April to May is 3. → $15 + x = 18$ or $18 - 15 = x$

Since the sales in April are being used as the basis for the comparison, you want to answer this question: What percent of 15 is 3?

$$n\% \text{ of } 15 = 3$$
$$n \times 15 = 3$$
$$\frac{n \times 15}{15} = \frac{3}{15}$$
$$n = 0.20$$
$$n = 20\%$$

Ken's sales increased 20% from April to May.

During April Paul sold 16 cars. During May he sold 14 cars. By what percent did his sales decrease from April to May?

The amount of the decrease from April to May is 2. → $16 - y = 14$ or $16 - 14 = y$

Since the sales in April are being used as the basis for the comparison, you want to answer this question: What percent of 16 is 2?

$$n\% \text{ of } 16 = 2$$
$$n \times 16 = 2$$
$$\frac{n \times 16}{16} = \frac{2}{16}$$
$$n = 0.125$$
$$n = 12.5\%$$

Paul's sales decreased 12.5% from April to May.

To find the percent of increase (or decrease), divide the amount of increase (or decrease) by the amount being used as a basis for comparison. Then express the quotient as a percent.

Find the percent of increase or decrease.

1. from 16 to 20
2. from 18 to 27
3. from 20 to 35
4. from 10 to 8
5. from 24 to 12
6. from \$4 to \$5
7. from \$9 to \$6
8. from \$25 to \$15
9. from \$8.40 to \$9.45

CALCULATOR

Sales Tax and Discount

Some calculators have a percent [%] button. If your calculator has a percent button, you can figure sales tax easily. Find 7% of \$4.95. Estimate: $\frac{7}{100}$ of \$5 is about \$.35. Push [4] [·] [9] [5] [×] [7] [%]. Pushing the percent button usually displays the product. With some calculators, you may need to push [=]. The displayed answer is [0.3465].

Always round the tax up to the next whole cent. The tax is \$0.35.

If your calculator has no percent button, change 7% to a decimal: 7% = 0.07.

Push [4] [·] [9] [5] [×] [·] [0] [7] [=]. The answer is the same.

Find the amount of tax to the next whole cent.

1. Price: \$10.10
   Sales tax: 5%
2. Price: \$2.45
   Sales tax: 6%
3. Price: \$93.62
   Sales tax: 7%
4. Price: \$27.99
   Sales tax: 1%
5. Price: \$63.38
   Sales tax: 6%
6. Price: \$72.45
   Sales tax: 0%

You can find the total cost using the calculator. First find the amount of sales tax.

Price: \$580.37 Estimate: $\frac{6}{100}$ of \$600 is about \$36.00.
Sales tax: 6%

Push [5] [8] [0] [·] [3] [7] [×] [6] [%]
(or [×] [·] [0] [6] [=]).

The displayed answer is 34.8222. Round to the next whole cent. Add the dollar sign and write the tax as \$34.83. Then add the price and the tax to find the total cost. Push [5] [8] [0] [·] [3] [7] [+] [3] [4] [·] [8] [3] [=]

Write the total cost as \$615.20.

Find the total cost using the calculator.

7. Price: $448.23
Sales tax: 2%

8. Price: $74.99
Sales tax: 5%

9. Price: $853.59
Sales tax: 0%

10. Price: $22.64
Sales tax: 3%

11. Price: $90.55
Sales tax: 10%

12. Price: $287.63
Sales tax: 4%

13. Price: $89.98
Sales tax: 7%

14. Price: $305.36
Sales tax: 6%

15. Price: $975.40
Sales tax: 8%

You also can find discounts and the sale price using the calculator.

Original price: $85.63 To find the discount:

Discount rate: 15% push [8] [5] [.] [6] [3] [×] [1] [5] [%].

Answer: [12.8445]. Always round the discount up to the next whole cent.

The discount is written as $12.85.

To find the sale price, subtract the discount from the original price.

Push [8] [5] [.] [6] [3] [−] [1] [2] [.] [8] [5] [=].

The sale price is written as $72.78.

Find the sale price.

16. Original price: $58.20
Discount rate: 8%

17. Original price: $12.75
Discount rate: 11%

18. Original price: $34.00
Discount rate: 3%

19. Original price: $99.95
Discount rate: 7%

20. Original price: $46.64
Discount rate: 4%

21. Original price: $29.50
Discount rate: 5%

22. Original price: $22.88
Discount rate: 0%

23. Original price: $40.40
Discount rate: 10%

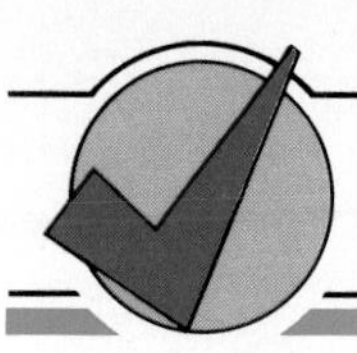

SKILLS MAINTENANCE

Chapters 1 Through 10

Choose the correct answers.

1. Subtract.

$$\begin{array}{r} 139{,}046 \\ -128{,}547 \\ \hline \end{array}$$

A. 110,499
B. 10,499
C. 10,397
D. not here

2. Multiply.

$$\begin{array}{r} 4.76 \\ \times\ 6.4 \\ \hline \end{array}$$

A. 30.464
B. 29.464
C. 304.64
D. not here

3. Write <, =, or >.

$\frac{3}{5} \bullet \frac{8}{15}$

A. >
B. <
C. =
D. not here

4. Solve.

$3\frac{5}{12} + 2\frac{1}{3} = n$

A. $n = 5\frac{1}{2}$
B. $n = 5\frac{2}{3}$
C. $n = 5\frac{3}{4}$
D. not here

5. You travel 180 kilometers in 2.5 hours. At this rate how many hours will it take to travel 288 kilometers?

A. 5 **B.** 4
C. 6 **D.** not here

6. Multiply. Write the answer in lowest terms.

$2\frac{1}{3} \times \frac{7}{8}$

A. $2\frac{1}{24}$ **B.** $\frac{7}{12}$
C. $\frac{7}{24}$ **D.** not here

7. Write $\frac{7}{2}$ as a percent.

A. 350%
B. 300%
C. 250%
D. not here

8. Write the LCM of 12 and 16.

A. 28
B. 192
C. 4
D. not here

9. 25% of what number is 4?

A. 100
B. 16
C. 6
D. not here

10. Ella works at the library on Saturdays. Last year she earned $725. This year she works fewer hours and earns only 75% of that amount. How much does she earn?

A. $543.75 **B.** $534.75
C. $453.75 **D.** not here

11. Mr. Warren sells tools. In addition to his salary, he receives an 8% commission on each sale he makes. If he makes a sale of $125, what is his commission?

A. $16 **B.** $25
C. $10 **D.** not here

Measurement

CHAPTER 11

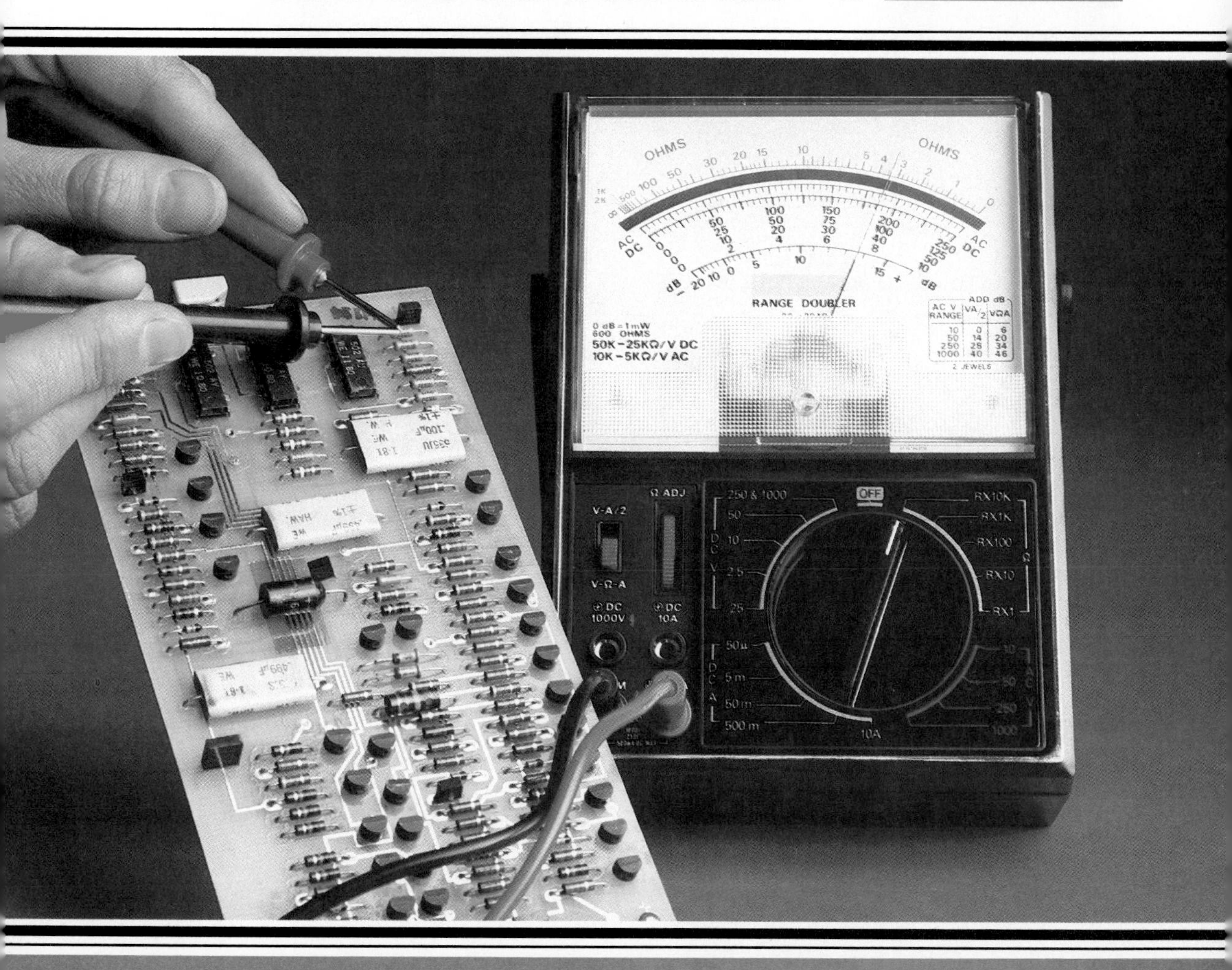

Metric Units of Length • Changing Metric Units • Metric Units of Liquid Capacity and Mass • Problem Solving: Write Your Own Question • Customary Units of Length, Liquid Capacity, and Weight • Time • Problem Solving: Using a Table • Latitude and Longitude • Precision in Measurement

Metric Units of Length

The unit of measure on this ruler is the **centimeter (cm)**.

On this ruler each centimeter is divided into 10 equal parts. Each of the small units of measure is a **millimeter (mm)**.

1 cm = 10 mm   1 mm = 0.1 cm

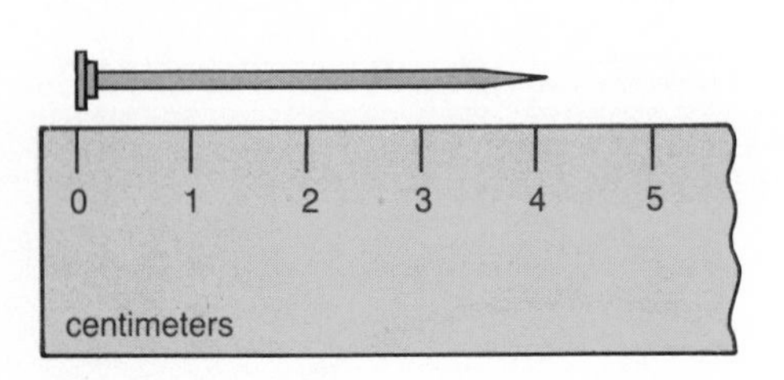

The length of the nail is 4 centimeters to the nearest centimeter.

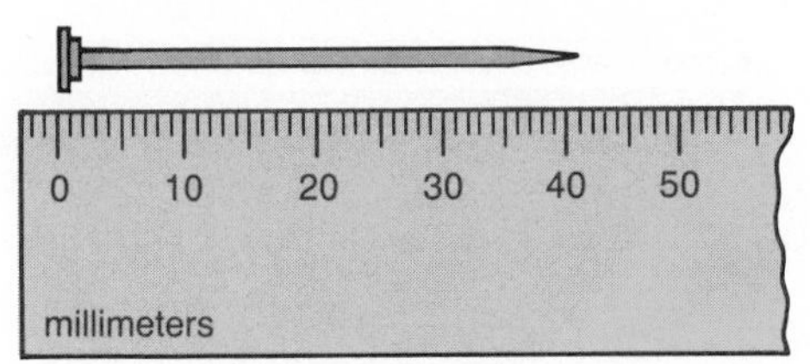

The length of the nail is 41 millimeters to the nearest millimeter.

Estimate the length of this clip in centimeters. Then measure the length.

This table presents information about **metric units** of length.

Kilometer	Hectometer	Dekameter	Meter	Decimeter	Centimeter	Millimeter
km 1,000 m	hm 100 m	dam 10 m	m 1 m	dm 0.1 m	cm 0.01 m	mm 0.001 m

Like the decimal system, the **metric system** is based on 10.

- Each unit is 10 times the next smaller unit.
- Each unit is 0.1 times the next larger unit.

The meter is the basic unit of length in the metric system.
The height of a tennis net is about 1 meter.
1 m = 100 cm   1 m = 1,000 mm

A unit such as the **kilometer (km)** is used to measure long distances.
1 kilometer equals 1,000 meters.

Practice • Estimate the length in centimeters. Then measure.

1. 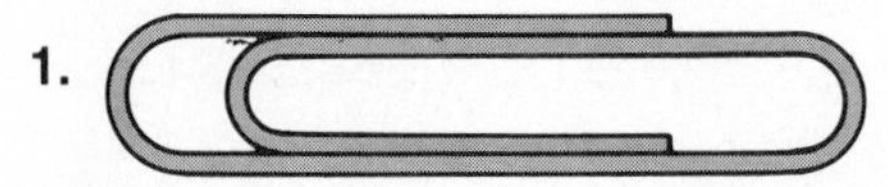

2. 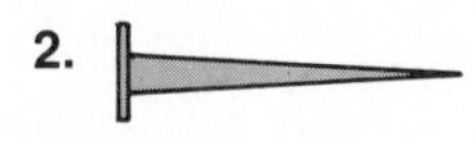

3. Measure the length of the clip in millimeters.

Mixed Practice • Estimate the length in centimeters. Then measure.

4.

5.

Measure in millimeters.

6. the wire in exercise 4

7. the nail in exercise 5

Choose the best estimate.

8. the length of a new pencil **a.** 2 cm **b.** 20 cm **c.** 2 m

9. the width of this book **a.** 19 mm **b.** 19 cm **c.** 19 m

10. the distance from Atlanta to Chicago **a.** 100 cm **b.** 200 m **c.** 1,100 km

11. thickness of a tennis racket string **a.** 1 mm **b.** 1 cm **c.** 1 m

12. height of a basketball player **a.** 1.2 km **b.** 2.1 m **c.** 4.5 mm

Use a ruler to draw a part of a line with the given length.

13. 8 cm **14.** 12 cm **15.** 1 cm ★**16.** 6.8 cm ★**17.** 15.1 cm

18. 26 mm **19.** 35 mm **20.** 7 mm ★**21.** 52.5 mm ★**22.** 60.5 mm

Which unit of measurement would be used to measure the following items? Use km, m, cm, or mm.

23. the width of a guitar string

24. your height

25. the distance between New York City and Dallas

To the nearest centimeter, which of these lengths would be expressed as 73 centimeters?

26. 73.2 cm **27.** 73.8 cm **28.** 73.5 cm **29.** 72.9 cm **30.** 72.5 cm

PROBLEM SOLVING • APPLICATIONS

31. The length of a tennis racket is 68 centimeters. How many centimeters less than 1 meter is this?

32. Adela Youngbear lives 1,275 meters from the tennis court. How much more than 1 kilometer is this?

33. Adela is 172 centimeters tall. How much taller than 1 meter is she?

★**34.** The width of a tennis court is 10.94 meters. What is the width in centimeters?

Changing Metric Units

1 km =	1,000 m
1 hm =	100 m
1 dam =	10 m
1 m =	1 m
1 dm =	0.1 m
1 cm =	0.01 m
1 mm =	0.001 m

The kilometer, the meter, the centimeter, and the millimeter are the metric units of length that are used most often. Study these equivalences and the table.

1 km = 1,000 m

1 m = 100 cm

1 m = 1,000 mm

1 cm = 10 mm

You can use multiplication or division to find equivalent measurements.

9 km = ? m

Think: Kilometers are much larger than meters. There will be more meters.

Since 1 km = 1,000 m, multiply by 1,000.

Multiplying by 1,000 moves the decimal point 3 places to the right.

9 km = 9,000 m

$9 \times 1{,}000 = 9{,}000$

When you change from a larger unit to a smaller unit, multiply.

3,550 m = ? km

Think: Meters are much smaller than kilometers. There will be fewer kilometers.

Since 1,000 m = 1 km, divide by 1,000.

Dividing by 1,000 moves the decimal point 3 places to the left.

3,550 m = 3.550 km

$3{,}550 \div 1{,}000 = 3.550$

When you change from a smaller unit to a larger unit, divide.

More Examples

5.2 cm = ? mm

Centimeters are larger than millimeters. Since 1 cm = 10 mm, multiply by 10.

5.2 cm = 52 mm

75 mm = ? cm

Millimeters are smaller than centimeters. Since 10 mm = 1 cm, divide by 10.

75 mm = 7.5 cm

Practice • Copy and complete.

1. 2 km = ? m **2.** 6 km = ? m **3.** 7.2 m = ? cm **4.** 3 m = ? mm

5. 8 cm = ? mm **6.** 90 mm = ? cm **7.** 115 cm = ? m **8.** 125 mm = ? m

Mixed Practice • Copy and complete.

9. 3 km = ? m
10. 8 km = ? m
11. 9.2 km = ? m
12. 10.5 km = ? m
13. 2 m = ? cm
14. 9 m = ? cm
15. 400 cm = ? m
16. 650 cm = ? m
17. 4 cm = ? mm
18. 7 cm = ? mm
19. 60 mm = ? cm
20. 75 mm = ? cm
21. 2 m = ? mm
22. 8 m = ? mm
23. 3,000 mm = ? m
24. 225 mm = ? m

Which is longer?

25. 5.4 km or 4,500 m
26. 2.8 cm or 30 mm
★27. 3.785 km or 3,875 m
★28. 4.02 m or 4,002 mm

You can use a "metric staircase" to help you to change from one metric unit to another.

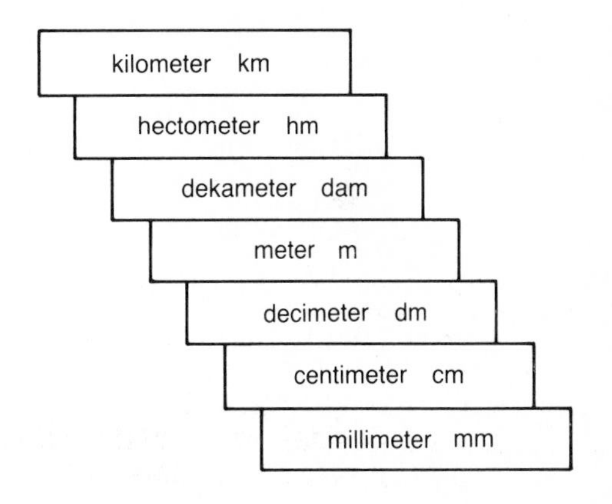

Count the number of stairs you must move to get from one metric unit to another. The decimal point moves as many places as the number of stairs you move.

The decimal point moves to the right as you go down the stairs. It moves to the left as you go up the stairs.

3.1 hm = ? m — Move down 2 stairs.
3.1 hm = 310 m — The decimal point moves 2 places to the right.

63 dm = ? hm — Move up 3 stairs.
63 dm = 0.063 hm — The decimal point moves 3 places to the left.

29. 4.2 cm = ? mm
30. 2.8 m = ? km
31. 1.7 hm = ? m
32. 10,000 m = ? km
★33. 142.1 dam = ? km
★34. 24 dam = ? km

PROBLEM SOLVING • APPLICATIONS

35. John lives 3.5 kilometers from Taft Intermediate School. How many meters is this?

36. Shani has a piece of wire that is 236 centimeters long. How many meters is this?

37. A book is 85 millimeters thick. How many centimeters is this?

★38. Kim walks 1.6 kilometers to the library and then back home. How many meters does she walk?

Metric Units of Liquid Capacity

The milliliter, metric cup, liter, and kiloliter are metric units used to measure liquid capacity.

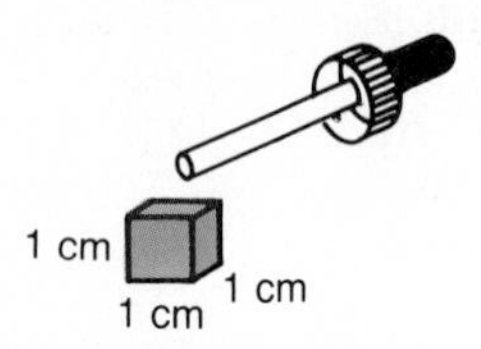

Each edge of the cube is one centimeter long. The volume of the cube is 1 **cubic centimeter**. It takes 1 **milliliter (mL)** of water to fill 1 cubic centimeter.

It takes 250 milliliters of water to fill 1 **metric cup (c)**.

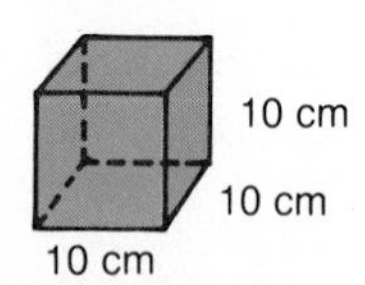

Imagine a cube with edges that are 10 centimeters long. The volume of the cube is 1,000 cubic centimeters. It takes 1,000 milliliters of water to fill the cube. The cube holds 1 **liter (L)** of water.

1,000 mL = 1 L

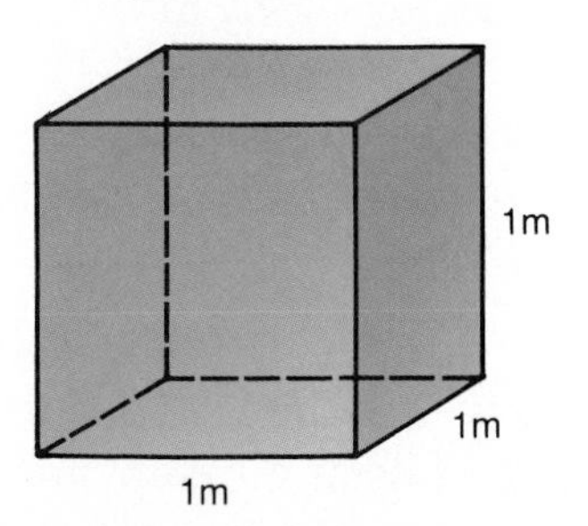

Imagine a cube with edges that are 1 meter long. The volume of the cube is 1 cubic meter. It takes 1,000 liters of water to fill the cube. The cube holds 1 **kiloliter (kL)** of water.

1,000 L = 1 kL

Metric units of liquid capacity follow the same pattern as metric units of length.

Kiloliter	Hectoliter	Dekaliter	Liter	Deciliter	Centiliter	Milliliter
kL 1,000 L	hL 100 L	daL 10 L	L 1 L	dL 0.1 L	cL 0.01 L	mL 0.001 L

Here are two examples that involve equivalent measurements.

5 L = ? mL

To change from a larger unit to a smaller unit, multiply. Since 1 L = 1,000 mL, multiply by 1,000.

5 L = 5,000 mL

$5 \times 1{,}000 = 5{,}000$

280 mL = ? L

To change from a smaller unit to a larger unit, divide. Since 1,000 mL = 1 L, divide by 1,000.

280 mL = 0.280 L

$280 \div 1{,}000 = 0.280$

Practice • Choose the better estimate.

1. 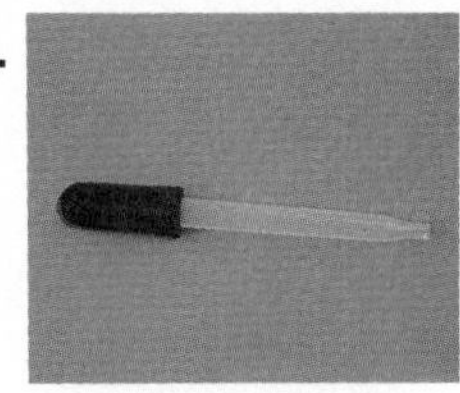
1 mL 1 L

2. 100 mL 1 L

3. 250 mL 2.5 L

4. 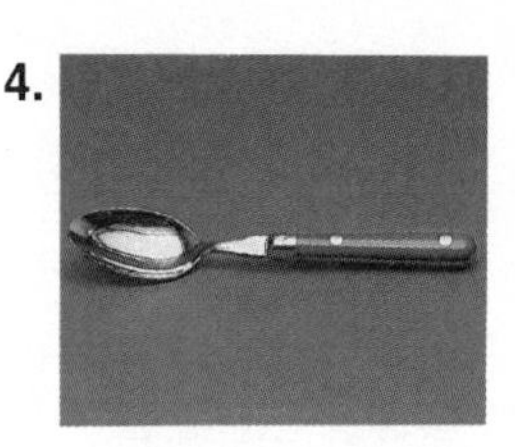
5 mL 5 L

Copy and complete.

5. 2 kL = ? L
6. 3,000 L = ? kL
7. 4 L = ? mL
8. 6,500 mL = ? L

Mixed Practice • Copy and complete.

9. 3 L = ? mL
10. 7 L = ? mL
11. 2,000 mL = ? L
12. 5,400 mL = ? L
13. 2 kL = ? L
14. 3.7 kL = ? L
15. 4,000 L = ? kL
16. 8 L = ? kL
17. 400 mL = ? L
18. 8 mL = ? L
19. 1.4 hL = ? L
20. 3.3 kL = ? L

★21. 0.03 L = ? cL
★22. 56 cL = ? daL
★23. 4,728 kL = ? dL
★24. 0.901 mL = ? kL

Compute.

25. $\begin{array}{r} 3.5\text{ L} \\ 2.7\text{ L} \\ +2.9\text{ L} \\ \hline \end{array}$

26. $\begin{array}{r} 15.25\text{ kL} \\ -\ 8.75\text{ kL} \\ \hline \end{array}$

27. $\begin{array}{r} 7.6\text{ L} \\ \times\ 3 \\ \hline \end{array}$

28. $5\overline{)1.75\text{ L}}$

29. $\begin{array}{r} 5.45\text{ km} \\ +3.65\text{ km} \\ \hline \end{array}$

30. $\begin{array}{r} 12.00\text{ m} \\ -\ 8.76\text{ m} \\ \hline \end{array}$

31. $\begin{array}{r} 8.7\text{ cm} \\ \times\ 4 \\ \hline \end{array}$

32. $3\overline{)11.4\text{ cm}}$

★33. $\begin{array}{r} 9.59\text{ mL} \\ +0.63\text{ mL} \\ \hline \end{array}$

★34. $\begin{array}{r} 40.04\text{ daL} \\ -37.78\text{ daL} \\ \hline \end{array}$

★35. $\begin{array}{r} 12.03\text{ cL} \\ \times\ 8 \\ \hline \end{array}$

★36. $0.7\overline{)26.04\text{ daL}}$

PROBLEM SOLVING • APPLICATIONS

37. How many metric cups will it take to fill a 1-liter jar?

38. A recipe calls for 1.25 liters of milk. How many milliliters is this?

Skills Maintenance

1. $\frac{7}{8} + \frac{5}{8}$
2. $\frac{2}{3} + \frac{1}{6}$
3. $\frac{7}{10} + \frac{9}{20}$
4. $\frac{1}{3} + \frac{4}{5}$
5. $1\frac{1}{9} + \frac{5}{9}$
6. $2\frac{1}{2} + 1\frac{1}{4}$
7. $5\frac{3}{10} + 2\frac{9}{10}$
8. $6\frac{5}{6} + 1\frac{3}{4}$

Metric Units of Mass

The cube measures 1 cubic centimeter. It holds 1 milliliter of water. One milliliter of water has a mass of **1 gram (g)**.

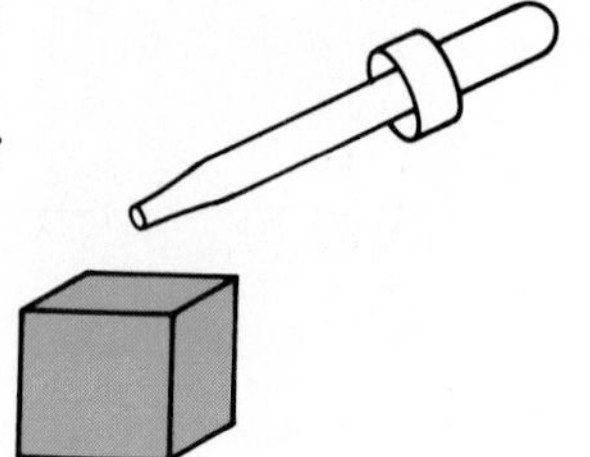

The pitcher holds 1,000 milliliters of juice. The mass of the juice is 1,000 grams, or **1 kilogram (kg)**.

1,000 g = 1 kg

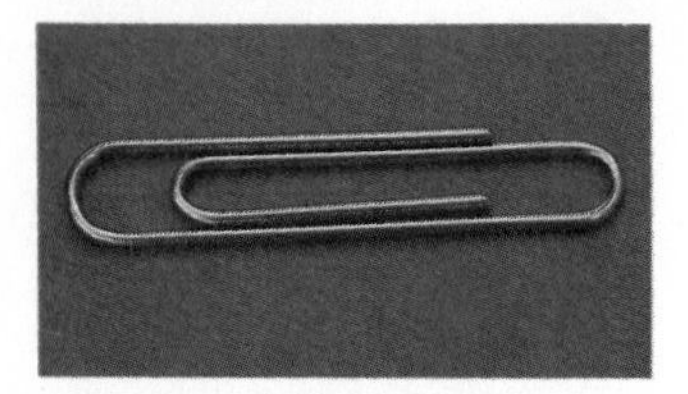

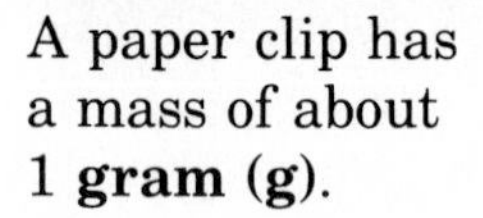

A paper clip has a mass of about 1 **gram (g)**.

A grain of sand has a mass of about 1 **milligram (mg)**.

Your math book has a mass of about 1 **kilogram (kg)**.

Metric units of mass follow the same pattern as metric units of length.

Kilogram	Hectogram	Dekagram	Gram	Decigram	Centigram	Milligram
kg 1,000 g	hg 100 g	dag 10 g	g 1 g	dg 0.1 g	cg 0.01 g	mg 0.001 g

Another metric unit of mass is the **metric ton (t)**, which equals 1,000 kilograms. A baby whale can have a mass of about 10 metric tons, or 10,000 kilograms.

In daily life, units such as the gram and the kilogram are often used as units of mass or *weight*.

Study these examples, which involve equivalent measurements.

3 g = ? mg

To change from a larger unit to a smaller unit, multiply. Since 1 g = 1,000 mg, multiply by 1,000.

3 g = 3,000 mg

$3 \times 1{,}000 = 3{,}000$

400 mg = ? g

To change from a smaller unit to a larger unit, divide. Since 1,000 mg = 1 g, divide by 1,000.

400 mg = 0.400 g

$400 \div 1{,}000 = 0.400$

Practice • Choose the better estimate.

1. 

30 g 3 kg

2. 

14 g 1 kg

3. 

500 g 500 kg

4. 

12 g 1.2 kg

Copy and complete.

5. 1 kg = ? g
6. 5 kg = ? g
7. 2,000 g = ? kg
8. 4,500 g = ? kg
9. 7 g = ? mg
10. 9.2 g = ? mg
11. 5,000 mg = ? g
12. 750 mg = ? g

Mixed Practice • Copy and complete.

13. 6 g = ? mg
14. 7.2 g = ? mg
15. 1,590 mg = ? g
16. 225 mg = ? g
17. 2 kg = ? g
18. 4 kg = ? g
19. 8.2 kg = ? g
20. 3,250 g = ? kg

Compute.

21. $\begin{array}{r} 3.85 \text{ kg} \\ +9.76 \text{ kg} \\ \hline \end{array}$

22. $\begin{array}{r} 10.0 \text{ g} \\ -\ 1.37 \text{ g} \\ \hline \end{array}$

23. $\begin{array}{r} 3.46 \text{ kg} \\ \times\ 4 \\ \hline \end{array}$

★ 24. $6\overline{)12.3 \text{ g}}$

25. $\begin{array}{r} 675 \text{ mg} \\ +518 \text{ mg} \\ \hline \text{g} \end{array}$

★ 26. $\begin{array}{r} 36 \text{ hg} \\ -\ 8 \text{ hg} \\ \hline \text{dag} \end{array}$

★ 27. $\begin{array}{r} 9.4 \text{ dg} \\ \times\ 6 \\ \hline \text{mg} \end{array}$

★ 28. $\begin{array}{r} \text{kg} \\ 7\overline{)9{,}149 \text{ g}} \end{array}$

PROBLEM SOLVING • APPLICATIONS

29. A penny has a mass of about 3 grams. What part of a kilogram does the mass of 100 pennies represent?

30. An empty pitcher has a mass of about 315 grams. When filled with water, the pitcher and the water have a total mass of 950 grams. How many milliliters of water are in the pitcher?

Midchapter Review

1. 5.6 m = ? cm
2. 1,755 mm = ? m
3. 2.7 km = ? m
4. 6 L = ? mL
5. 275 mL = ? L
6. 2,500 mg = ? g
7. 9.2 kg = ? g
8. 1,025 g = ? kg

PROBLEM SOLVING • STRATEGIES

Write Your Own Question

The space shuttle *Columbia* was launched on April 12, 1981, at 7:00 A.M. The *Columbia* returned to Earth about 54 hours after leaving the launchpad.

Which of the following questions can be answered from the information given?

1. Was this the only flight made by *Columbia*?
2. What was the date and time of the *Columbia's* return?
3. How much fuel was used during the flight?
4. How many people worked on the flight?

Question 2 is the only one that can be answered from the information given.

Length of Flight

$$\begin{array}{r} 2 \text{ r}6 \\ 24\overline{)54} \\ \underline{-48} \\ 6 \end{array}$$

The flight took 2 days 6 hours (2d 6h).

The *Columbia* returned on April 14 at about 1:00 P.M.

Time of Return

Launch was April 12 at 7:00 A.M. 2 days 6 hours later is April 14 at 1:00 P.M.

Make up one question that can be answered from the information given. Then answer the question.

1. The space shuttle has 2 solid-fuel rocket boosters. Each rocket booster carries 503,627 kilograms of propellant.
2. The external tank of the space shuttle is 47 meters long. The solid-fuel rocket boosters are 45.46 meters long.

3. The external tank carries liquid oxygen and liquid hydrogen as propellants. The mass of the liquid oxygen is 609,195 kilograms. The mass of the liquid hydrogen is 101,606 kilograms.

4. The length of the *Columbia* is 37.24 meters. The length of the solid-fuel rocket booster is 45.46 meters.

Make sure there is enough data to answer the question that you write.

5. Each solid-fuel rocket booster had consumed about 450,000 kilograms of fuel 2 minutes 12 seconds after lift-off. There are 2 solid-fuel rocket boosters.

6. The solid-fuel rocket boosters were released from the shuttle to fall back to earth 2 minutes 12 seconds after lift-off. Parachutes eased the boosters into the ocean 7 minutes 13 seconds after lift-off.

7. The external tank exhausted its fuel 8 minutes 32 seconds after lift-off. The external tank was released from the shuttle 19 seconds later.

8. The *Columbia's* orbital speed was 28,000 kilometers per hour. It took approximately 1 hour 20 minutes to complete one orbit.

9. About 10 minutes before landing, the *Columbia* was traveling at an altitude of approximately 42 kilometers. The *Columbia* was at an altitude of approximately 25 kilometers $4\frac{1}{2}$ minutes later.

10. At the time of *Columbia's* first voyage into space, Commander John Young was 50 years old. Astronaut Robert Crippen was 43 years old.

11. The *Columbia's* first test flight took place on April 12, 1981, at 7:00 A.M. The *Columbia's* second test flight took place on November 12, 1981, at 10:10 A.M.

Think carefully about possible questions to ask.

★12. Spacecraft have traveled close to the planets in our solar system. On its sunlit side, the planet Mercury has a temperature of 350°C (Celsius). On its dark side, Mercury has a temperature as low as $^-170$°C.

★13. On the Celsius scale, 0°C is the freezing point of water. The average temperature on the surface of Mars is $^-23$°C.

°C
20
10
0
−10
−20
−30
−40

Customary Units of Length

You can measure objects in inches or in parts of an inch.
The length of this clip is 1 inch to the nearest inch.

It is $1\frac{1}{2}$ inches to the nearest $\frac{1}{2}$ inch.

It is $1\frac{1}{4}$ inches to the nearest $\frac{1}{4}$ inch.

It is $1\frac{2}{8}$ inches to the nearest $\frac{1}{8}$ inch.

It is $1\frac{5}{16}$ inches to the nearest $\frac{1}{16}$ inch.

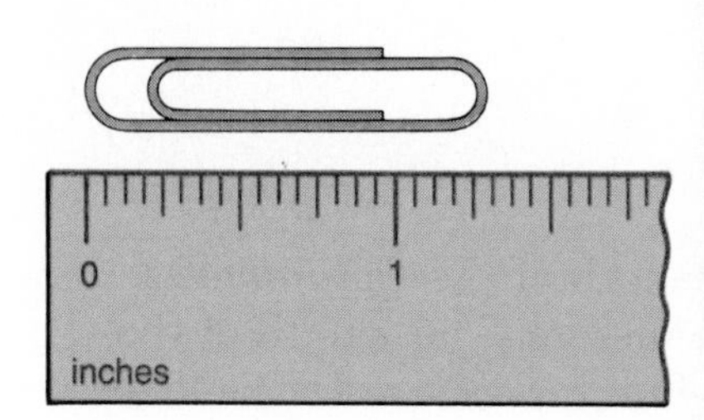

Estimate the length of this ribbon in inches. Then measure the length.

The **inch (in.)**, **foot (ft)**, **yard (yd)**, and **mile (mi)** are **customary units** for measuring length.

The length of a hammer is about 1 foot.
The length of a football field is 100 yards.
The distance from New York City to Washington, D.C., is about 230 miles.
This table shows how customary units are related.

12 inches (in.) = 1 foot (ft)
36 inches (in.) = 1 yard (yd)
3 feet (ft) = 1 yard (yd)
5,280 feet (ft) = 1 mile (mi)
1,760 yards (yd) = 1 mile (mi)

Sometimes you need to find equivalent measurements.

To change from larger units to smaller units, multiply.

2 yd = ? in.

Think: Since 1 yd = 36 in., multiply by 36.

2 yd = 72 in.

$2 \times 36 = 72$

To change from smaller units to larger units, divide.

28 ft = ? yd ? ft

Think: Since 3 ft = 1 yd, divide by 3.

28 ft = 9 yd 1 ft

$28 \div 3 = 9$ r1

Study these examples. Notice the use of the fact that 1 ft = 12 in.

```
  1 ft   9 in.
+ 1 ft  10 in.     19 in. = 1 ft 7 in.
  2 ft  19 in. = 3 ft 7 in.
```

```
  7     18
  8 ft   6 in.  <-- Since 6 in. < 10 in.,
- 3 ft  10 in.      you regroup.
  4 ft   8 in.      8 ft 6 in. = 7 ft 18 in.
```

Practice • Estimate the length in inches.

1.

2.

Measure the wool in exercise 1 to the nearest

3. inch. **4.** $\frac{1}{2}$ inch. **5.** $\frac{1}{4}$ inch. **6.** $\frac{1}{8}$ inch. **7.** $\frac{1}{16}$ inch.

Mixed Practice • Estimate the length in inches.

8.

Measure the wool in exercise 8 to the nearest

9. inch. **10.** $\frac{1}{2}$ inch. **11.** $\frac{1}{4}$ inch. **12.** $\frac{1}{8}$ inch. **13.** $\frac{1}{16}$ inch.

Choose the best estimate.

14. the length of a pen **a.** 1 in. **b.** 6 in. **c.** 20 in.

15. the height of a room **a.** 3 in. **b.** 3 ft **c.** 3 yd

Copy and complete.

16. 3 yd = ? ft **17.** 5 yd = ? ft **18.** 5 yd 2 ft = ? ft

19. 12 ft = ? yd **20.** 18 ft = ? yd **21.** 20 ft = ? yd ? ft

22. 2 ft = ? in. **23.** 4 ft = ? in. **24.** 4 ft 6 in. = ? in.

25. 36 in. = ? ft **26.** 60 in. = ? ft **27.** 68 in. = ? ft ? in.

★**28.** $8\frac{2}{3}$ yd = ? ft ★**29.** $4\frac{3}{4}$ ft = ? in. ★**30.** $\frac{5}{6}$ mi = ? ft

Add or subtract.

31. 1 ft 8 in. + 5 in.

32. 4 yd 1 ft +7 yd 2 ft

33. 15 yd 2 ft 7 in. + 7 yd 2 ft 9 in.

34. 2 ft 3 in. −1 ft 7 in.

★**35.** 4 yd −2 yd 1 ft

★**36.** 9 yd 2 ft 3 in. −4 yd 1 ft 8 in.

PROBLEM SOLVING • APPLICATIONS

37. Seth has a rope 3 yards 2 feet long. How many feet is this?

38. Wendy runs 1,320 yards. What fractional part of a mile is this?

39. Julie has a wooden board that is 4 feet 3 inches long. How many inches is this?

★**40.** Julie cuts a piece 1 foot 9 inches long from the board. How much of the board is left?

Customary Units of Liquid Capacity

The table shows how some units of liquid capacity are related.

2 tablespoons (tbsp)	= 1 fluid ounce (fl. oz)
8 fluid ounces (fl. oz)	= 1 cup (c)
2 cups (c)	= 1 pint (pt)
2 pints (pt)	= 1 quart (qt)
4 quarts (qt)	= 1 gallon (gal)

To change from larger units to smaller units, multiply.

3 gal = ? qt

Think:
Since 1 gal = 4 qt, multiply by 4.

3 gal = 12 qt

$3 \times 4 = 12$

To change from smaller units to larger units, divide.

17 pt = ? qt ? pt

Think:
Since 2 pt = 1 qt, divide by 2.

17 pt = 8 qt 1 pt

$17 \div 2 = 8$ r1

Study the examples below.

$$\begin{array}{r} 1 \text{ gal } 2 \text{ qt} \\ \times \quad 3 \\ \hline 3 \text{ gal } 6 \text{ qt} \end{array} = 4 \text{ gal } 2 \text{ qt}$$

6 qt = 1 gal 2 qt

$$\begin{array}{r} \overset{2}{\cancel{3}} \text{ gal } \overset{5}{\cancel{1}} \text{ qt} \\ -1 \text{ gal } 3 \text{ qt} \\ \hline 1 \text{ gal } 2 \text{ qt} \end{array}$$

Since 1 qt < 3 qt, you regroup.
3 gal 1 qt = 2 gal 5 qt

Practice • Choose the best estimate.

1. the capacity of a soup bowl   a. 1 fl. oz   b. 1 c   c. 1 gal
2. the capacity of a fish tank   a. 5 gal   b. 1 qt   c. 5 c

Copy and complete.

3. 2 gal = ? qt
4. 12 qt = ? gal
5. 13 pt = ? qt ? pt

Mixed Practice • Choose the best estimate.

6. 4 glasses of milk   a. 1 c   b. 1 qt   c. 1 gal
7. the capacity of a car's gas tank   a. 18 pt   b. 18 qt   c. 18 gal

Copy and complete.

8. 5 gal = ? qt
9. 7 gal = ? qt
10. 7 gal 1 qt = ? qt
11. 24 qt = ? gal
12. 32 qt = ? gal
13. 35 qt = ? gal ? qt
14. 2 qt = ? pt
15. 5 qt = ? pt
16. 5 qt 1 pt = ? pt
17. 6 pt = ? qt
18. 16 pt = ? qt
19. 17 pt = ? qt ? pt
20. 3 c = ? fl. oz
21. 6 tbsp = ? fl. oz
22. 6 pt = ? c

★23. $12\frac{1}{2}$ qt = ? pt
★24. $3\frac{3}{4}$ gal = ? qt
★25. $3\frac{1}{2}$ c = ? fl. oz

26. A **half-gallon** is 2 quarts. Which is more, 7 quarts or 3 half-gallons?

★27. How many half-gallons are there in 4 gallons?

Compute.

28. 2 gal 2 qt × 5

29. 3 gal 2 qt − 1 gal 3 qt

30. 2 qt 1 pt + 3 qt 1 pt

31. 1 gal 1 qt × 6

PROBLEM SOLVING • APPLICATIONS

32. How many fluid ounces are there in 1 pint?

33. How many fluid ounces are there in 1 quart?

34. David and Samantha Sanapaw each drink 2 cups of milk a day. How many quarts of milk do they drink in 30 days?

★35. A soup recipe calls for 1 pint of water, $1\frac{1}{2}$ quarts of chicken broth, and 1 cup of cream. How many 8-ounce servings will that make?

Customary Units of Weight

The **ounce (oz)**, the **pound (lb)**, and the **ton (T)** are customary units of weight.

This letter weighs 1 ounce.

This loaf of bread weighs 1 pound.

A small car may weigh 1 ton.

The table shows how customary units of weight are related.

16 ounces (oz) = 1 pound (lb)
2,000 pounds (lb) = 1 ton (T)

To change from larger units to smaller units, what do you do?

3 T = ? lb ← Multiply: 3 × 2,000.
3 T = 6,000 lb

To change from smaller units to larger units, what do you do?

36 oz = ? lb ? oz ← Divide: 36 ÷ 16.
36 oz = 2 lb 4 oz

Alvin has 3 pounds 8 ounces of grapes. He divides them into 2 sections that are equal in weight. How much does each section weigh?

$$3 \text{ lb } 8 \text{ oz} \div 2 = n$$

Step 1
Divide pounds.

```
    1 lb
2)3 lb 8 oz
 -2 lb
  1 lb
```

1 lb 8 oz is how many ounces?

Step 2
Regroup.

```
    1 lb
2)3 lb 8 oz
 -2 lb
  1 lb
       24 oz
```

Step 3
Divide ounces.

```
    1 lb 12 oz
2)3 lb  8 oz
 -2 lb
  1 lb
        24 oz
       -24 oz
            0
```

Each section weighs 1 pound 12 ounces.

Practice • Choose the better estimate.

1. the weight of a hammer **a.** 5 ounces **b.** 5 pounds
2. the weight of a baseball **a.** 1 ounce **b.** 1 pound

Copy and complete.

3. 4 lb = ? oz
4. 96 oz = ? lb
5. 3,000 lb = ? T ? lb

Mixed Practice • Choose the better estimate.

6. the weight of a telephone **a.** 4 ounces **b.** 4 pounds

7. the weight of a truck **a.** 20 pounds **b.** 2 tons

Copy and complete.

8. 3 lb = ? oz **9.** 5 lb = ? oz **10.** 5 lb 4 oz = ? oz

11. 32 oz = ? lb **12.** 80 oz = ? lb **13.** 88 oz = ? lb ? oz

14. 2 T = ? lb **15.** 5 T = ? lb **16.** 5 T 200 lb = ? lb

17. 6,000 lb = ? T **18.** 18,000 lb = ? T **19.** 19,500 lb = ? T ? lb

★**20.** $3\frac{1}{2}$ lb = ? oz ★**21.** $4\frac{5}{8}$ lb = ? oz ★**22.** $2\frac{3}{4}$ T = ? lb

In the customary system, **dry measure** is sometimes used for items such as fruits and vegetables. This table shows equivalences in dry measure.

2 dry pints (pt) = 1 dry quart (qt)
8 dry quarts (qt) = 1 peck (pk)
4 pecks (pk) = 1 bushel (bu)

Copy and complete.

23. 8 dry pints = ? dry quarts **24.** 36 pecks = ? bushels ? pecks

Compute.

25. 2 × 3 lb 9 oz **26.** 5 × 2 T 500 lb **27.** 7 lb 5 oz ÷ 3

28. 3 T 1,000 lb ÷ 4 **29.** 9 ft 11 in. ÷ 7 **30.** 3 gal 3 qt ÷ 5

31.
```
  2 lb 8 oz
 +3 lb 8 oz
```

32.
```
  6 lb
 -1 lb 4 oz
```

33.
```
  3 T   750 lb
 -1 T 1,750 lb
```

PROBLEM SOLVING • APPLICATIONS

34. A large truck carries 14 tons of coal. How many pounds does it carry?

★**35.** Six potatoes weigh $2\frac{5}{8}$ pounds. How many ounces is this?

Skills Maintenance

1. $\frac{9}{10} - \frac{3}{10}$ **2.** $\frac{2}{3} - \frac{1}{12}$ **3.** $\frac{7}{8} - \frac{3}{4}$ **4.** $\frac{3}{4} - \frac{1}{3}$

5. $1\frac{5}{8} - \frac{1}{8}$ **6.** $3\frac{1}{2} - 1\frac{1}{4}$ **7.** $6\frac{2}{5} - 1\frac{4}{5}$ **8.** $5\frac{1}{3} - 4\frac{1}{2}$

Time

This table shows some units of time. These units are used with both metric and customary measurements.

60 seconds (s) = 1 minute (min)
60 minutes (min) = 1 hour (h)
24 hours (h) = 1 day (d)
7 days (d) = 1 week (wk)
365 days (d) = 1 year (yr)*
12 months (mo) = 1 year (yr)
100 years (yr) = 1 century (cen)
*366 days in a leap year

Eli Forbes walks 3 miles a day. It takes him about $1\frac{1}{4}$ hours. How many minutes is this?

$$1\frac{1}{4} \times 60 = n$$

1 hr = 60 min

$$1\frac{1}{4} \times 60 = \frac{5}{\not{4}_1} \times \overset{15}{\not{60}}$$

$$= 75$$

$1\frac{1}{4}$ hours is 75 minutes.

The problem could have been solved using the decimal 1.25. Why will 1.25×60 give the same answer as $1\frac{1}{4} \times 60$?

$$1.25 \times 60 = n$$

Practice • Copy and complete.

1. 4 min = ? s

2. 300 s = ? min

3. 325 s = ? min ? s

Solve.

4. $\frac{1}{4}$ min = ? s

5. $1\frac{1}{2}$ yr = ? mo

6. $2\frac{5}{6}$ d = ? h

Mixed Practice • Copy and complete.

7. 2 wk = ? d

8. 2 wk 3 d = ? d

9. 27 d = ? wk ? d

10. 3 h = ? min

11. 5 h 30 min = ? min

12. 385 min = ? h ? min

13. 4 yr = ? mo

14. 2 yr 6 mo = ? mo

15. 57 mo = ? yr ? mo

Solve.

16. $\frac{3}{4}$ min = ? s

17. $1\frac{5}{6}$ min = ? s

18. $2\frac{1}{10}$ min = ? s

19. $1\frac{1}{4}$ yr = ? mo

20. $2\frac{1}{6}$ yr = ? mo

21. $3\frac{1}{3}$ yr = ? mo

Write your answers as fractions.

22. 8 h = ? d

23. 80 yr = ? cen

★ 24. $1\frac{3}{4}$ d = ? wk

Compute.

25. 3 min 40 s + 2 min 30 s

26. 1 h 40 min 35 s + 2 h 40 min 45 s

27. 5 × 2 wk 3 d

28. 6 min 30 s ÷ 5

PROBLEM SOLVING • APPLICATIONS

29. Jered is 13 years old. His younger brother is 4 years 4 months old. What is the difference between their ages?

30. Lila works $3\frac{1}{2}$ hours on Mondays, Wednesdays, and Fridays. How many hours does she work each week?

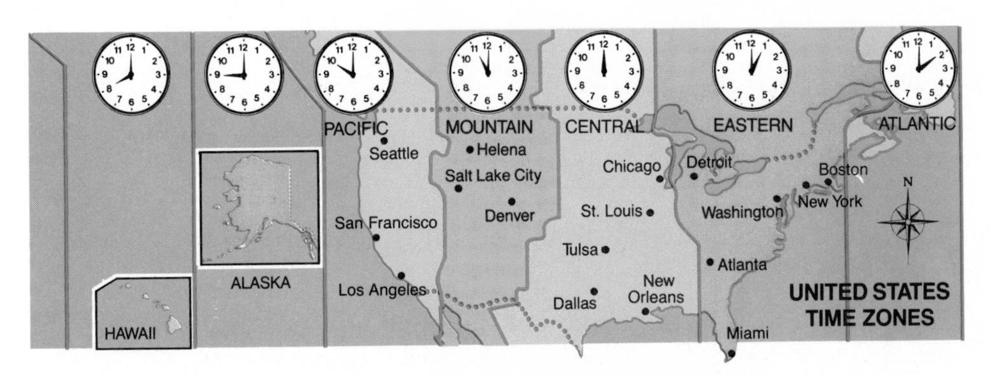

31. This map shows the seven **time zones** in North America. In which time zone is San Francisco?

32. In which time zone is Tulsa?

When it is 10:00 A.M. in San Francisco, it is 11:00 A.M. in Salt Lake City. What time is it in

33. Tulsa?

34. Seattle?

35. Boston?

36. Atlanta?

★ 37. Bob leaves Chicago at 6:35 P.M. (Central Time) on a flight to New York City. The flight takes 2 hours 27 minutes. What time does Bob arrive in New York City (Eastern Time)?

PROBLEM SOLVING • STRATEGIES

Using a Table

Some tables require careful reading of the labels and the "small print."

This table gives the long-distance telephone rates from Central City to several towns.

	DAY RATE 8 A.M. to 5 P.M. Mon.–Fri.		EVENING RATE 5 P.M. to 11 P.M. Mon.–Fri. 8 A.M. to 11 P.M. Weekends		NIGHT RATE 11 P.M to 8 A.M. All Days	
	Initial 2 Mins	Each Add. Min	Initial 2 Mins	Each Add. Min	Initial 1 Min	Each Add. Min
Franklin	$ .90	$.40	$.58	$.26	$.20	$.16
Millbridge	.52	.22	.33	.14	.12	.08
Pleasant Hill	.80	.35	.52	.22	.18	.14
Grifton	.90	.40	.58	.26	.20	.16
Liberty	1.02	.45	.66	.29	.22	.18
Hamilton	.80	.35	.52	.22	.18	.14
Pleasant Grove	1.02	.45	.66	.29	.22	.18
Marshall	1.02	.45	.66	.29	.22	.18

What is the cost of a 4-minute call from Central City to Franklin at 3:00 P.M. on Tuesday?

To find the cost, you look in the section of the table labeled "Day Rate/8 A.M. to 5 P.M. Mon.–Fri." The initial (first) 2 minutes cost \$.90, but this does not mean that 4 minutes cost \$.90 + \$.90. The "Day Rate" section shows that "Each Add. Min." (each additional minute) costs \$.40. So the call will cost \$.90 + 2(\$.40), or \$1.70.

Use the table to solve the problems.

1. Find the cost of a 2-minute call at 11:30 P.M. on Wednesday from Central City to Marshall.

2. Find the cost of a 2-minute call at 9:00 A.M. on Tuesday from Central City to Pleasant Hill.

3. What is the most expensive time to make a long-distance call?

4. Find the cost of a 3-minute call at 8:00 P.M. on Thursday from Central City to Franklin.

What is the cost of

5. a 3-minute call from Central City to Millbridge on Monday at 6:00 P.M.?

6. a 4-minute call from Central City to Grifton on Saturday at 9:00 A.M.?

7. a 3-minute call from Central City to Liberty on Tuesday at 11:30 P.M.?

8. a 7-minute call from Central City to Marshall on Sunday at 7:00 P.M.?

9. a 5-minute call from Central City to Pleasant Grove on Thursday at 7:00 A.M.?

10. a 4-minute call from Central City to Hamilton on Saturday at 10:00 A.M.?

Sometimes you need to obtain data from several sections of a table.

★ 11. Jerry made a 4-minute call from Central City to Grifton at 4:00 P.M. on Tuesday. How much would he have saved by making the same call at 5:10 P.M.?

★ 12. Katherine made a 5-minute call from Central City to Pleasant Grove at 10:30 Thursday evening. How much would she have saved by making the same call 35 minutes later?

Read and reread all the special parts of any table.

★ 13. Serena made a 3-minute call from Central City to Pleasant Grove at 9:00 A.M. on Saturday. How much would she have saved by making the same call at 7:30 A.M. on Saturday?

★ 14. Eric made a call from Central City to Marshall at 2:15 P.M. on Tuesday. The cost of the call is $2.37. How many minutes does the call take?

★ 15. Study the table. Which town do you think is closest to Central City?

CHAPTER 11

REVIEW

Choose the best estimate. (pp. 276–277)

1. the length of a carrot **a.** 3 m **b.** 20 cm **c.** 1 km
2. the height of a football player **a.** 65 mm **b.** 60 cm **c.** 2 m

Copy and complete. (pp. 278–283)

3. 6 km = ? m
4. 3 m = ? cm
5. 20 mm = ? cm
6. 4,600 m = ? km
7. 3.5 cm = ? mm
8. 7 m = ? mm
9. 9,500 m = ? km
10. 6.2 L = ? mL
11. 3,000 mL = ? L
12. 3 kg = ? g
13. 4.1 g = ? mg
14. 275 mg = ? g

Compute. (pp. 276–283)

15. $\begin{array}{r} 4.8 \text{ L} \\ +2.4 \text{ L} \\ \hline \end{array}$

16. $\begin{array}{r} 9.00 \text{ m} \\ -3.75 \text{ m} \\ \hline \end{array}$

17. $4\overline{)10.6 \text{ cm}}$

18. $\begin{array}{r} 2.9 \text{ kg} \\ \times \quad 3 \\ \hline \end{array}$

Choose the best estimate. (pp. 286–287)

19. the length of a hammer **a.** 1 inch **b.** 1 foot **c.** 1 yard
20. the length of an umbrella **a.** 6 inches **b.** 32 inches **c.** 5 yards

Copy and complete. (pp. 286–293)

21. 4 yd = ? ft
22. 15 ft = ? yd
23. 20 in. = ? ft ? in.
24. 12 pt = ? qt
25. 8 qt = ? gal
26. 6,000 lb = ? T
27. 3 lb 4 oz = ? oz
28. 33 d = ? wk ? d
29. 2 min 3 s = ? s

Compute. (pp. 286–293)

30. $\begin{array}{r} 1 \text{ ft } 7 \text{ in.} \\ +6 \text{ ft } 8 \text{ in.} \\ \hline \end{array}$

31. $\begin{array}{r} 6 \text{ gal} \\ -1 \text{ gal } 2 \text{ qt} \\ \hline \end{array}$

32. $2\overline{)5 \text{ lb } 6 \text{ oz}}$

33. $\begin{array}{r} 2 \text{ wk } 4 \text{ d} \\ \times \quad 4 \\ \hline \end{array}$

34. A bag of baking potatoes has a mass of 2.3 kilograms. How many grams is this? (pp. 282–283)

35. Len is 14 years old. His younger sister is 5 years 4 months old. How much older is Len? (pp. 292–293)

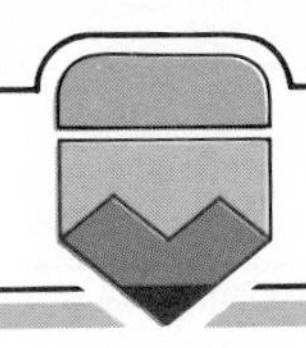

PROJECT

Latitude and Longitude

You can use lines of **latitude** and **longitude** to locate points on a globe or a map.

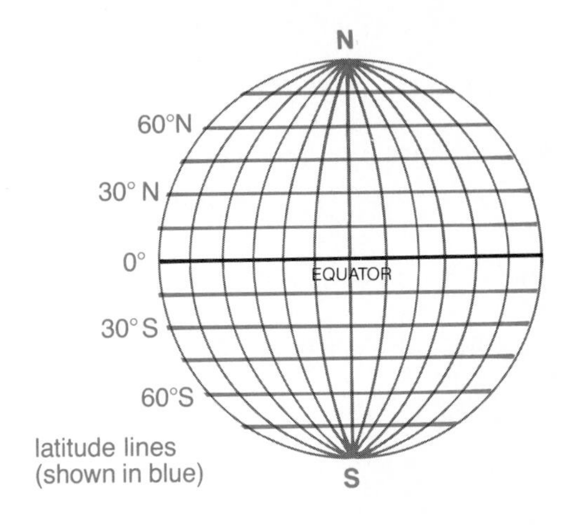

latitude lines (shown in blue)

Latitude lines measure the number of degrees north or south of the equator. A point on the equator has a latitude of 0°.

Longitude lines measure the number of degrees east or west of the **prime meridian**. The prime meridian is the longitude line that runs through Greenwich, England. It has a longitude of 0°.

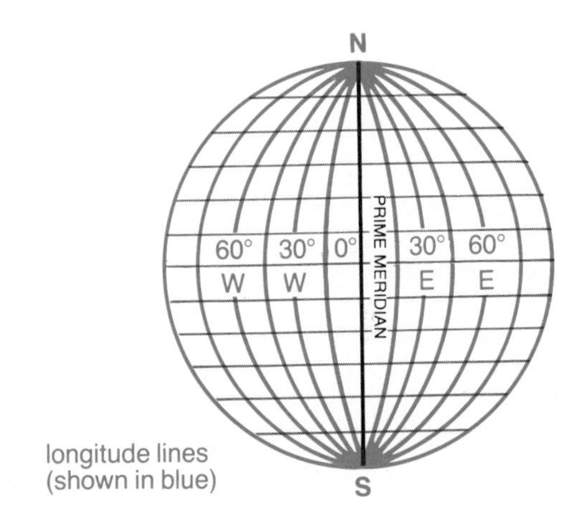

longitude lines (shown in blue)

To give the location of a point on a globe or a map, you name the latitude first and the longitude second.

40°N, 90°E locates a point in China.

Use a globe or an atlas to find the country or body of water at each location.

1. 60°N, 100°W

2. 15°S, 60°E

3. 15°S, 45°W

4. 30°N, 30°W

5. 40°N, 90°W

6. 30°S, 120°W

CHAPTER 11

TEST

Choose the best estimate.

1. the height of a door — a. 5 cm b. 2 m c. 50 mm
2. the distance from Boston (Massachusetts) to Atlanta (Georgia) — a. 2,800 km b. 1,000 mm c. 3,000 cm

Copy and complete.

3. 500 mm = ? cm
4. 7.2 km = ? m
5. 8 m = ? cm
6. 8,500 m = ? km
7. 9 m = ? mm
8. 6.7 cm = ? mm
9. 30 mm = ? cm
10. 6,000 mL = ? L
11. 600 L = ? kL
12. 3 g = ? mg
13. 7,500 g = ? kg
14. 425 mg = ? g

Compute.

15. $\begin{array}{r} 4.3 \text{ L} \\ +3.7 \text{ L} \\ \hline \end{array}$

16. $\begin{array}{r} 16.00 \text{ m} \\ -\ 8.76 \text{ m} \\ \hline \end{array}$

17. $5\overline{)29.5 \text{ cm}}$

18. $\begin{array}{r} 9.5 \text{ kg} \\ \times\ 6 \text{ kg} \\ \hline \end{array}$

Choose the best estimate.

19. the length of a screwdriver — a. 2 feet b. 6 yards c. 8 inches
20. the length of a cane — a. 8 inches b. 3 feet c. 4 yards

Copy and complete.

21. 17 ft = ? yd ? ft
22. 4 yd 1 ft = ? ft
23. 75 in. = ? ft ? in.
24. 3 gal = ? qt
25. 21 qt = ? gal ? qt
26. 9 T = ? lb
27. 3 lb 7 oz = ? oz
28. 6 wk = ? d
29. 465 min = ? h ? min

Compute.

30. $\begin{array}{r} 6 \text{ ft } 10 \text{ in.} \\ +9 \text{ ft } \ \ 4 \text{ in.} \\ \hline \end{array}$

31. $\begin{array}{r} 8 \text{ gal} \\ -2 \text{ gal } 3 \text{ qt} \\ \hline \end{array}$

32. $4\overline{)9 \text{ lb } 4 \text{ oz}}$

33. $\begin{array}{r} 6 \text{ wk } 3 \text{ d} \\ \times \qquad 5 \\ \hline \end{array}$

34. A sack of whole-wheat flour has a mass of 4.5 kilograms. How many grams is this?

35. Lee is 13 years old. Her brother is 3 years 5 months old. How much older is Lee?

ENRICHMENT

Precision in Measurement

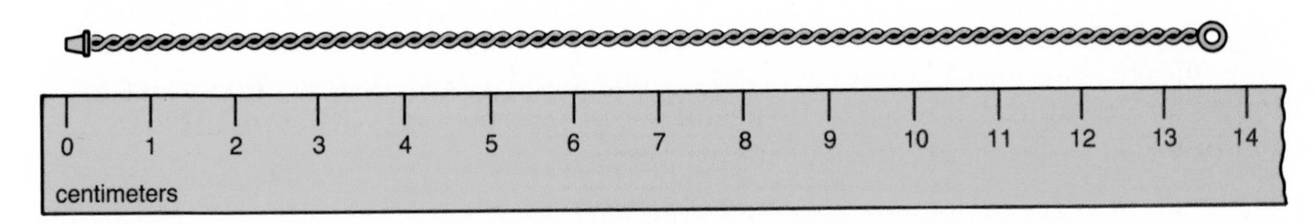

The bracelet is between 13 and 14 centimeters long.
The length is nearer to 14 centimeters than to 13 centimeters.
The length of the bracelet is 14 centimeters to the nearest centimeter.

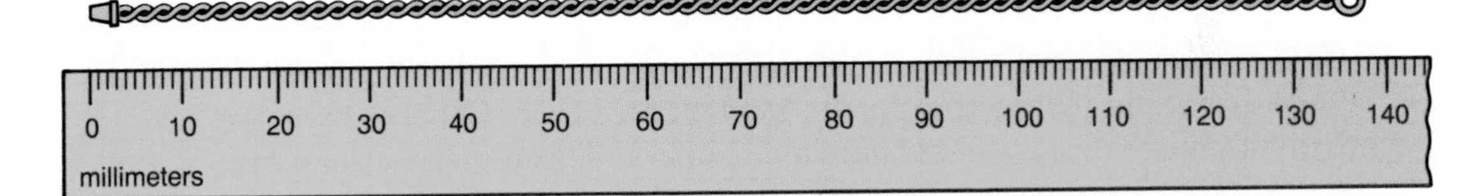

The bracelet is between 137 and 138 millimeters long.
The length of the bracelet is 138 millimeters to the nearest millimeter.

A measurement of 138 millimeters is more **precise** than a measurement of 14 centimeters.

The smaller the unit of measure used, the more precise the measurement is.

Consider these two measurements: 13.8 centimeters and 138 millimeters.
One-tenth of a centimeter is the same as one millimeter.
So 13.8 centimeters is precise to the nearest millimeter.
13.8 centimeters and 138 millimeters show the same precision.

Next consider these two measurements: 12 centimeters and 12.0 centimeters.
12 centimeters is precise to the nearest centimeter.
12.0 centimeters is precise to the nearest millimeter.
12.0 centimeters is the more precise measurement.

Which measurement in the pair is more precise?

1. 10 cm or 102 mm

2. 68 mm or 6 cm

3. 4 cm or 4.0 cm

4. 546 cm or 5.463 m

5. 34.2 mm or 3.4 cm

6. 15 cm or 152 mm

COMPUTER

Computer Instructions

In Chapter 8 you learned about two computer instructions: AA and AL. A computer may have between 15 and many hundreds of instructions. Each individual computer has its own special set of instructions, although all computers use the same types of instructions.

There are *five basic types* of computer instructions.

Calculations: Add, subtract, multiply, and divide.

Logical operations: Process instructions based on NOT, AND, and OR logic.

Bit-test conditions: Determine if a bit is on (1) or off (0).

Control-transfer: Ordinarily, instructions are executed *in sequence*. Control flows from one instruction to the next *in sequence*. Control-transfer instructions change the sequence of control. These instructions are sometimes called *branch* or *jump* instructions.

Input/output: Read data from an input device into storage or from storage out to an output device.

Match each instruction with a letter. Letters can be used more than once.

A. Calculation
B. Logical operation
C. Bit-test condition
D. Control-transfer
E. Input/output
F. Not here

1. Branch to 5000
2. Add 7 and 15
3. Use AND logic
4. Test if bit is on
5. Multiply 77 × 42.5
6. Jump to 735
7. Read floppy disk
8. Use NOT logic
9. Branch to 8745
10. Divide 2000,1000
11. Write on printer
12. Test if bit is off
13. Subtract 888 from 999
14. Read input from Keyboard
15. Punch a card
16. Transfer control to 0

SKILLS MAINTENANCE

Chapters 1 Through 11

Choose the correct answers.

1. Subtract.

$$\begin{array}{r} 7.08 \\ -4.908 \\ \hline \end{array}$$

A. 3.172 **B.** 2.172
C. 2.272 **D.** not here

2. Solve.

$3.407 + 12.006 = ?$

A. 15.413 **B.** 46.070
C. 15.403 **D.** not here

3. Divide.

$0.6\overline{)5.7}$

A. 9 **B.** 0.95
C. 9.5 **D.** not here

4. Multiply. Write the answer in lowest terms.

$\frac{6}{7} \times \frac{2}{3}$

A. $\frac{4}{7}$ **B.** $\frac{4}{9}$
C. $\frac{8}{21}$ **D.** not here

5. Add. Write the answer in lowest terms.

$1\frac{2}{5} + 1\frac{2}{3}$

A. $2\frac{1}{2}$ **B.** $2\frac{4}{15}$
C. $3\frac{1}{15}$ **D.** not here

6. What percent of 75 is 25?

A. 3% **B.** $33\frac{1}{3}\%$
C. $66\frac{2}{3}\%$ **D.** not here

7. Solve the proportion.

$\frac{n}{375} = \frac{24}{250}$

A. $n = 36$ **B.** $n = 24$
C. $n = 48$ **D.** not here

8. Divide. Write the answer in lowest terms.

$\frac{8}{9} \div \frac{1}{6}$

A. $\frac{4}{27}$ **B.** $5\frac{1}{3}$
C. $5\frac{3}{9}$ **D.** not here

9. Complete.

6.4 km = __?__ m

A. 640 **B.** 64
C. 6,400 **D.** not here

10. Compute.

$$\begin{array}{r} 21.00 \text{ cm} \\ -\ 7.79 \text{ cm} \\ \hline \end{array}$$

A. 1.321 cm
B. 13.21 cm
C. 13.31 cm
D. not here

11. Complete.

31 qt = __?__ gal __?__ qt

A. 7 gal 3 qt
B. 6 gal 3 qt
C. 7 gal 2 qt
D. not here

12. Compute.

$$\begin{array}{r} 5 \text{ ft} \quad 8 \text{ in.} \\ +8 \text{ ft} \ \ 11 \text{ in.} \\ \hline \end{array}$$

A. 14 ft 7 in.
B. 14 ft 20 in.
C. 14 ft 6 in.
D. not here

Choose the correct answers.

13. An advertising agency budgeted a TV commercial at $598,675. When the commercial was finished, the actual cost was $687,950. How much over the budget was this?

A. $99,275 **B.** $89,375
C. $89,275 **D.** not here

14. Judy bought 4 tickets for the school bazaar. Each ticket cost $1.75. How much did the 4 tickets cost?

A. $7.00 **B.** $6.80
C. $4.75 **D.** not here

15. Greg has science homework and math homework. It took him 40 minutes to do his science homework and 20 minutes to eat dinner. How much time did he spend doing his homework?

A. 1 hour **B.** 80 minutes
C. 20 minutes **D.** not here

16. The Corner Book Store is having a sale. Lara buys 2 books for $3.98 each. How much change does she receive from a ten-dollar bill?

A. $2.24 **B.** $2.04
C. $3.04 **D.** not here

17. Of the 200 students at the Jefferson School, 112 are girls. What percent are girls?

A. 112% **B.** 50%
C. 56% **D.** not here

18. Muna works $4\frac{1}{2}$ hours on Monday and $2\frac{3}{4}$ hours on Tuesday. How much less than 10 hours does she work on these two days?

A. $7\frac{2}{3}$ hours **B.** $2\frac{3}{4}$ hours
C. $7\frac{1}{4}$ hours **D.** not here

19. Elston can read 8 pages in 6 minutes. At this rate how many pages can he read in 45 minutes?

A. 360 pages **B.** 48 pages
C. 60 pages **D.** not here

20. Amy and Lew each eat a dinner that costs $11.95. They leave a tip of $3.60. How much money do they spend all together?

A. $15.55 **B.** $23.90
C. $27.50 **D.** not here

Geometry

CHAPTER 12

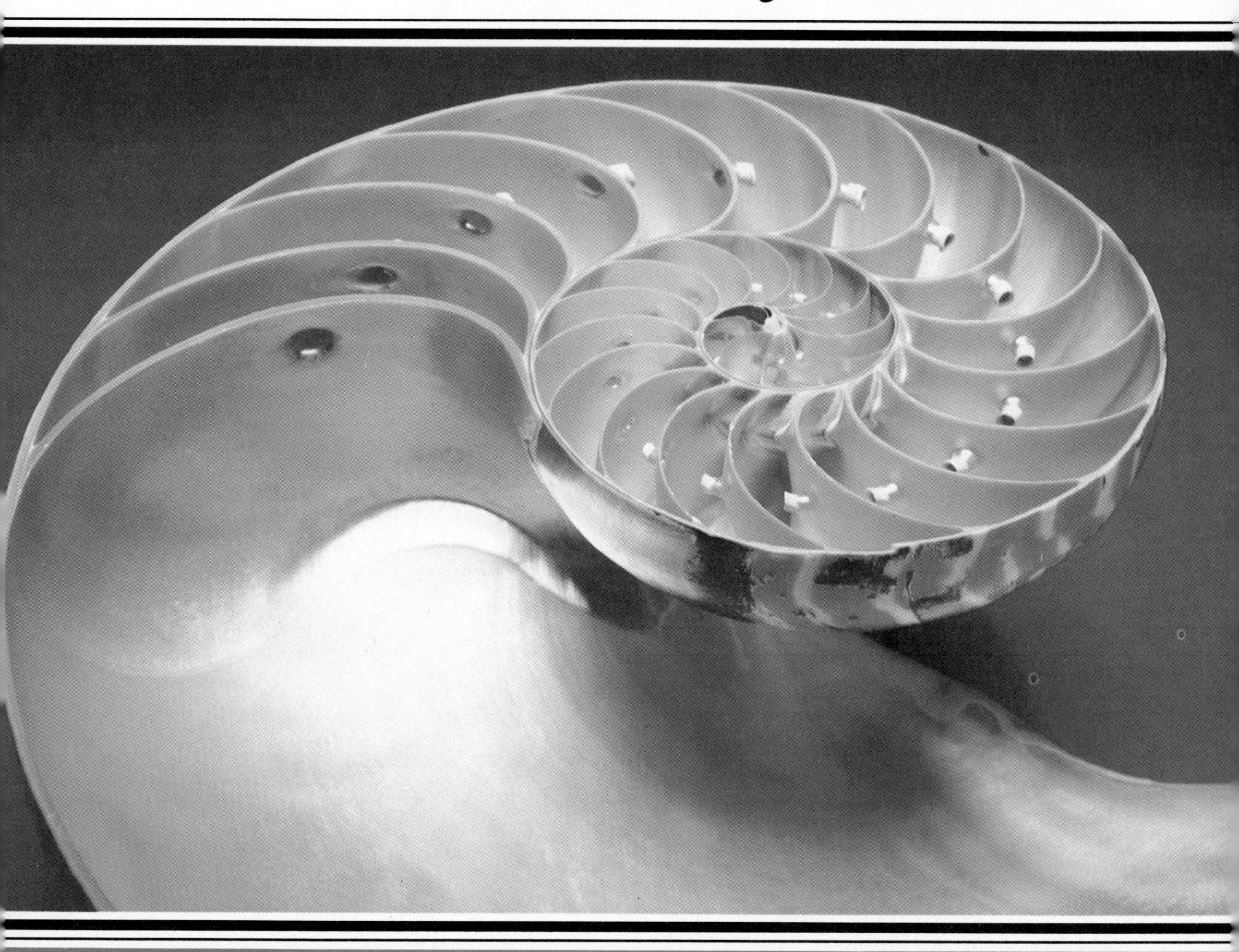

The Vocabulary of Geometry • Angles • Circles • Constructing Congruent Segments and Angles • Bisecting Segments and Angles • Perpendicular and Parallel Lines • Polygons • Congruent Polygons • Symmetry and Reflections • Similar Polygons • Solid Figures • Problem Solving: Using Logic • Exploring Constructions

The Vocabulary of Geometry

A fish tank has many examples of geometric figures.

A **point** is a location. The corners *E* and *F* are examples of points.

A **plane** is a flat surface that has no end.

Points *E*, *F*, and *G* all lie in the same plane. A plane can be named by using three points in it. Find plane *EFG*.

A **line segment** is straight. It has two **endpoints.** Each edge of the tank is an example of a line segment. Find segment *AB*. Its endpoints are *A* and *B*.

The symbol for segment *AB* is $\overline{AB}$. Read: segment AB

Here are some other basic figures in geometry.

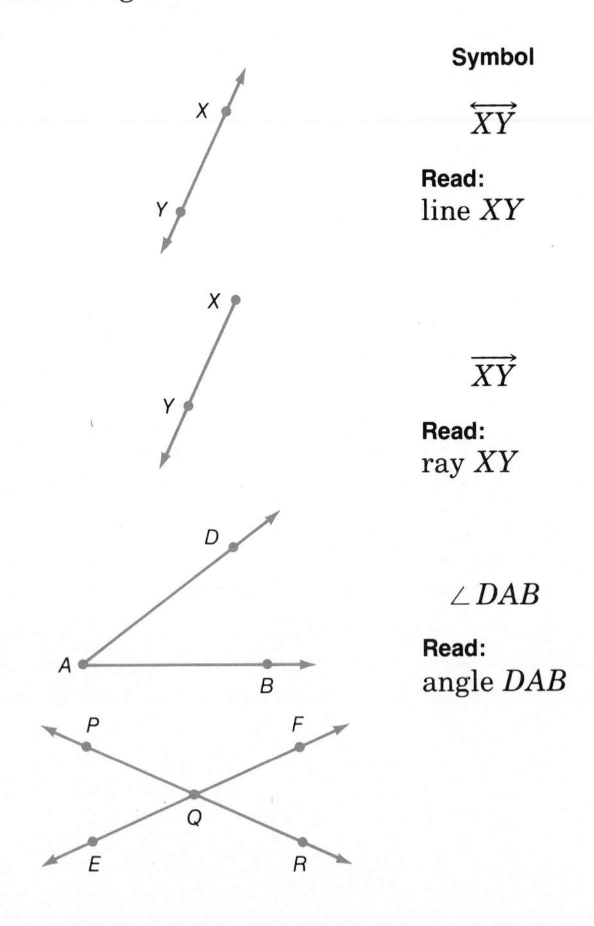

Symbol

A **line** has no endpoints. The arrowheads show that it goes on forever in both directions.

$\overleftrightarrow{XY}$

Read: line *XY*

A **ray** has only one endpoint. It goes on forever in one direction. Ray *XY* has the endpoint *X*. It continues on through *Y*. The arrowhead shows that the ray continues on forever in that direction. In naming a ray, the letter for the endpoint is written first.

$\overrightarrow{XY}$

Read: ray *XY*

Two rays that have the same endpoint form an **angle.** Rays *AD* and *AB* form angle *DAB*. Point *A* is the **vertex** of the angle. The letter for the vertex is written in the middle.

$\angle DAB$

Read: angle *DAB*

In this drawing two lines **intersect** at a point. Name the point of intersection.

Practice • Use this drawing of two intersecting lines.

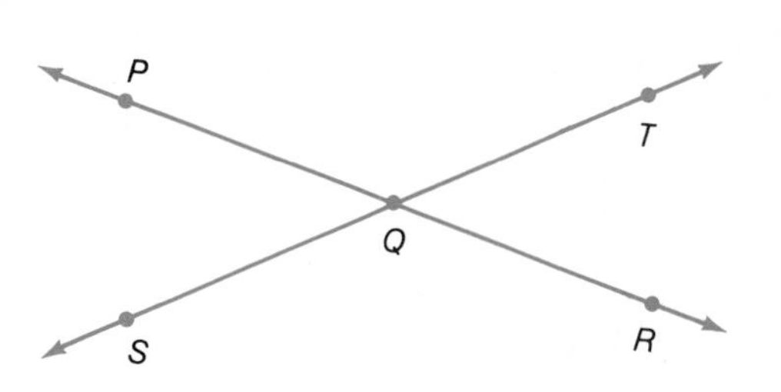

1. Name the point of intersection.
2. Name the two lines.
3. Name two segments on $\overleftrightarrow{PR}$.
4. Name two rays on $\overleftrightarrow{ST}$.
5. Name the angle formed by $\overrightarrow{QP}$ and $\overrightarrow{QT}$.

Mixed Practice • Use the drawing above for exercises 6–10.

6. Name two segments on $\overleftrightarrow{ST}$.
7. Name two rays on $\overleftrightarrow{PR}$.

Name the angle formed by

8. $\overrightarrow{QT}$ and $\overrightarrow{QR}$.
9. $\overrightarrow{QR}$ and $\overrightarrow{QS}$.
10. $\overrightarrow{QS}$ and $\overrightarrow{QP}$.

Draw and label the figures.

11. $\overline{XY}$
12. $\overleftrightarrow{EF}$
13. $\angle BUG$
14. $\overrightarrow{HG}$
15. plane LMN
16. $\angle PAT$
17. $\overrightarrow{GH}$
18. point Z

Use the drawing to do these exercises.

19. Name one plane.
20. Name four lines.
21. Name the point of intersection of $\overleftrightarrow{BC}$ and $\overleftrightarrow{AB}$.
22. Name the lines that intersect at point C.
23. Name the lines that intersect at point D.
24. Name eight segments.
★ 25. Name eight rays.
★ 26. Name seven angles.

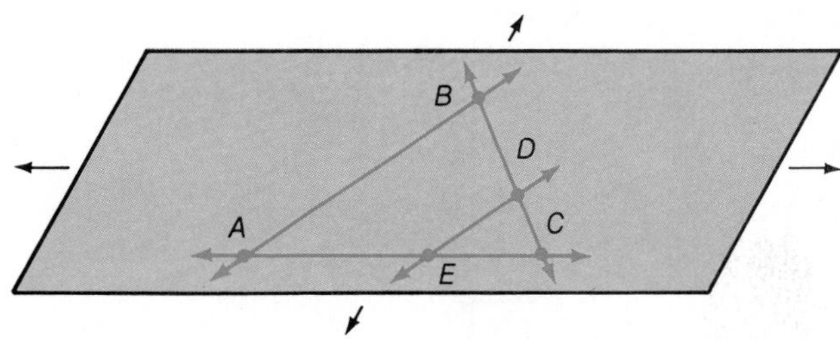

PROBLEM SOLVING • APPLICATIONS

27. Draw a line. Mark 4 points on it: A, B, C, and D. Then name 6 different segments on $\overleftrightarrow{AD}$.
★ 28. Draw a line. Mark 5 points on it: Q, R, S, T, and U. Then name as many segments on $\overleftrightarrow{QU}$ as you can.

Angles

The unit of measure for an angle is a **degree** (1°).

A **protractor** is used to measure angles. It has an inner scale and an outer scale. Place the protractor so that the center mark is on the vertex of the angle. Place the inner 0° mark on one side of the angle. Read the inner scale where the other side crosses the protractor.

The measure of $\angle ABC$ is 70° (not 110°).

$$m\angle ABC = 70°$$

You can also use a protractor to draw angles. Draw $\angle XYZ$ with a measure of 110°. Follow the directions.

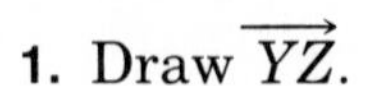

1. Draw $\overrightarrow{YZ}$.
2. Place the protractor so that the center mark is at point Y.
3. Line up the outer 0° mark with $\overrightarrow{YZ}$.
4. Locate point X at the outer 110° mark.
5. Draw $\overrightarrow{YX}$.

Angles are classified by their measures.

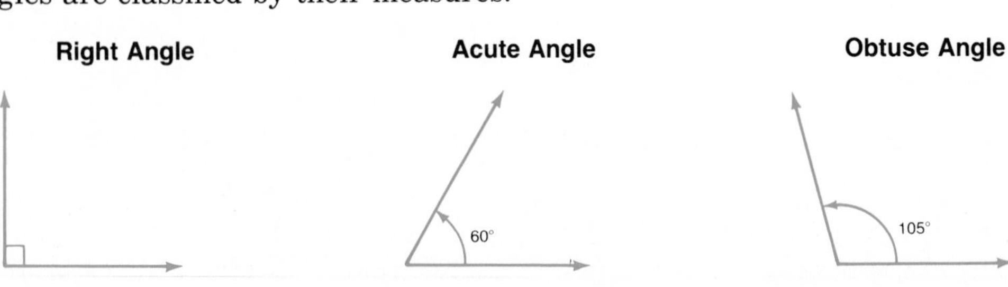

The measure of a **right angle** is 90°.

The measure of an **acute angle** is greater than 0° and less than 90°.

The measure of an **obtuse angle** is greater than 90° and less than 180°.

What kind of angle is $\angle ABC$ near the top of this page?
What kind of angle is $\angle XYZ$?

Practice • Measure each angle. Then write *right, acute,* or *obtuse.*

1. 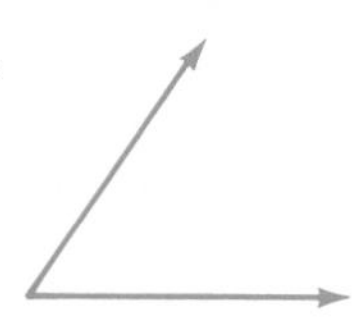

2. 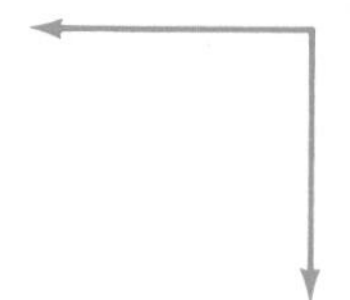

3. 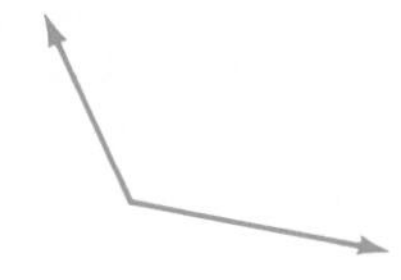

4. 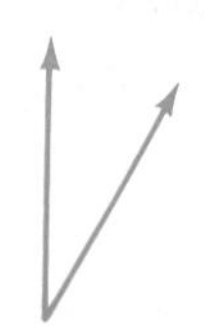

Mixed Practice • Measure each angle. Then write *right, acute,* or *obtuse.*

5. 

6. 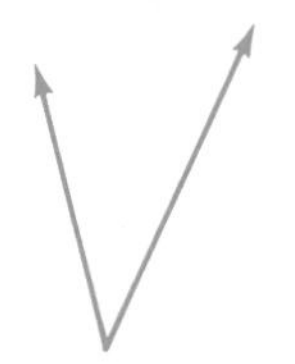

7. 

8. 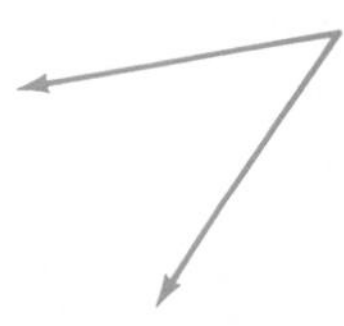

Find the measure of each angle.

9. $m\angle ABE = \underline{\ ?\ }$

10. $m\angle EBF = \underline{\ ?\ }$

11. $m\angle EBG = \underline{\ ?\ }$

12. $m\angle ABG = \underline{\ ?\ }$

13. $m\angle FBH = \underline{\ ?\ }$

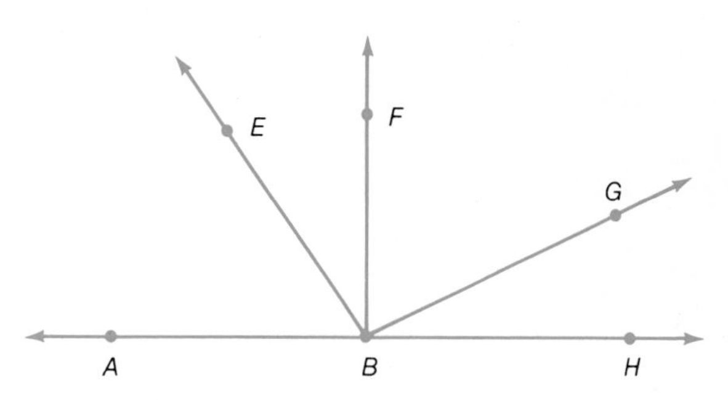

Find the sum of the angle measures.

14. $m\angle ABE + m\angle EBF$

★ **15.** $m\angle HBG + \angle GBF + m\angle FBE + m\angle EBA$

Use a protractor to draw each angle. Label it.

16. $\angle ABC$: 45°
17. $\angle MNO$: 60°
18. $\angle EFG$: 130°
19. $\angle XYZ$: 175°
20. $\angle QRS$: 15°
21. $\angle JKL$: 145°
22. $\angle TUV$: 35°
23. $\angle BCD$: 160°

PROBLEM SOLVING • APPLICATIONS

24. Draw $\angle ABC$ with a measure 10° less than the measure of a right angle. What kind of angle is $\angle ABC$?

25. Draw $\angle MNO$ with a measure 15° more than the measure of a right angle. What kind of angle is $\angle MNO$?

26. Draw $\angle DEF$ with a measure of 70°. Draw $\angle GHI$ with a measure 50° less than the measure of $\angle DEF$. What is the sum of their measures?

★ **27.** Draw $\angle QRS$ with a measure of 40°. Draw $\angle TUV$ with a measure 3.5 times the measure of $\angle QRS$. What is the sum of their measures?

Circles

Point M is the **center** of this **circle.** All the points on the circle are the same distance from the center. A circle is named by its center. This drawing shows circle M.

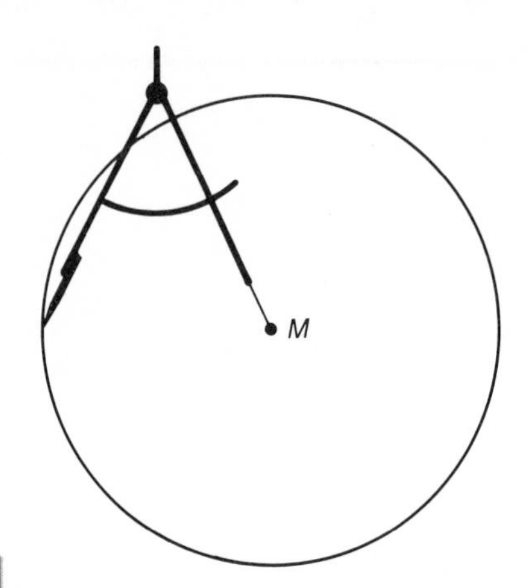

A **compass** can be used to construct a circle or a part of a circle.

Segments related to a circle have special names.

Name	Description	Segment
Radius	A segment with endpoints that are the center of the circle and a point on the circle.	$\overline{AD}$
Chord	A segment with endpoints on the circle.	$\overline{EF}$
Diameter	A chord that passes through the center of the circle.	$\overline{BC}$

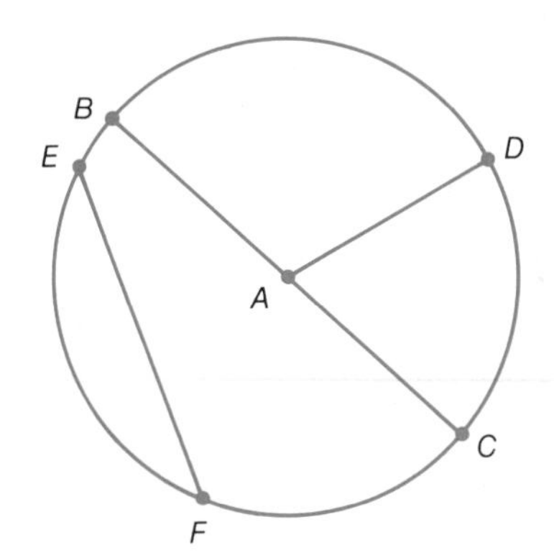

An **arc** is part of a circle. $\overset{\frown}{XZ}$ is an arc. $\frown$ means arc.

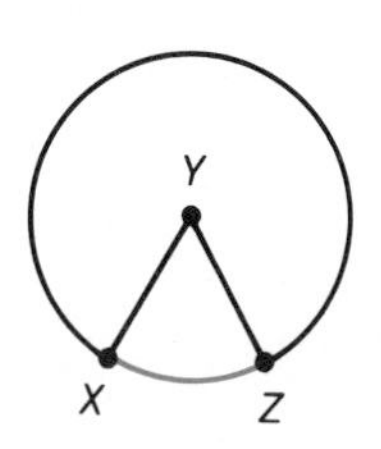

A **central angle** is an angle with its vertex at the center of the circle. $\angle XYZ$ is a central angle.

Practice • Use this drawing for these exercises.

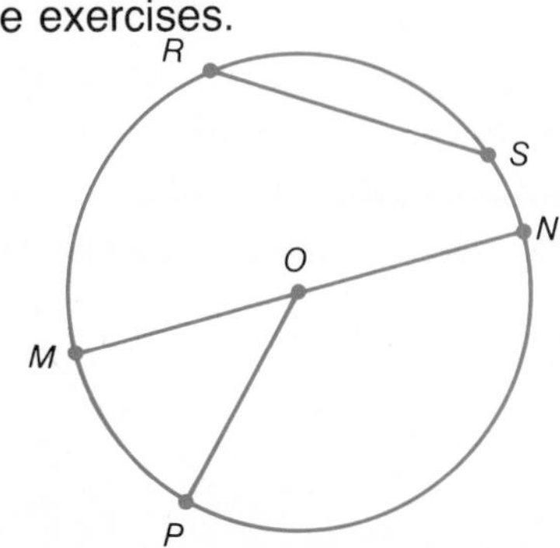

1. Name the circle.
2. Name three radii.
3. Name two chords.
4. Name a diameter.
5. Name three arcs.
6. Name a central angle.

Mixed Practice • Follow these directions.

7. Use a compass to construct circle O.

8. On circle O, draw and label five points A, B, C, D, and E.

For circle O

9. draw and name five radii.

10. draw and name five chords.

11. name five arcs.

12. name five central angles.

Use a compass to construct

13. two circles that intersect in two points.

14. two circles that have the same center.

15. Construct a circle with center W and radius 8 centimeters long. Mark three points, X, Y, and Z, on the circle, as shown. Draw angles XYZ and XWZ. $\angle XYZ$ is an **inscribed angle.** What kind of angle is $\angle XWZ$?

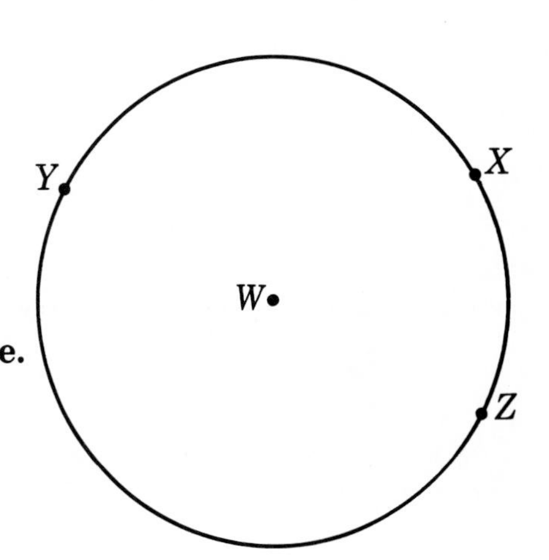

16. Use a protractor to find $m\angle XYZ$ and $m\angle XWZ$. Compare the two measures. What fractional part of $m\angle XWZ$ is $m\angle XYZ$?

★ 17. Construct two circles of different sizes. For each circle
   a. draw an inscribed angle and a central angle with the same arc.
   b. compare the measures of the angles.
   c. tell how the measures of the two angles are related.

PROBLEM SOLVING • APPLICATIONS

18. Draw a segment, $\overline{AB}$, that is 12 centimeters long. Using A as a center, construct a circle with a radius 8 centimeters long. Using B as a center, construct a circle with a radius 8 centimeters long. In how many points do the two circles intersect?

★ 19. Draw a segment, $\overline{XY}$, that is 14 centimeters long. Using X as a center, construct a circle with a radius 7 centimeters long. Using Y as a center, construct a circle with a radius 7 centimeters long. In how many points do the two circles intersect?

Skills Maintenance

1. $\frac{1}{2} \times \frac{1}{4}$
2. $\frac{1}{3} \times \frac{3}{5}$
3. $8 \times \frac{1}{8}$
4. $\frac{5}{6} \times \frac{9}{10}$
5. $\frac{11}{12} \times \frac{8}{11}$
6. $6 \times 1\frac{1}{4}$
7. $\frac{3}{8} \times \frac{5}{9}$
8. $2\frac{1}{2} \times 1\frac{1}{2}$
9. $2\frac{2}{3} \times 4$
10. $3\frac{1}{2} \times 25\frac{1}{7}$

Constructing Congruent Segments and Angles

Congruent segments have the same length. A compass and a straightedge can be used to **construct** a segment congruent to $\overline{AB}$.

Step 1
Draw a ray with endpoint X.

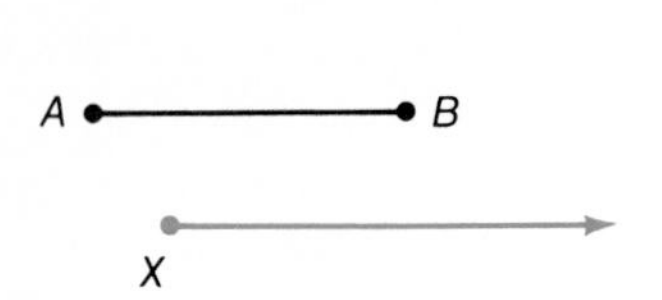

Step 2
Open the compass the length of $\overline{AB}$.

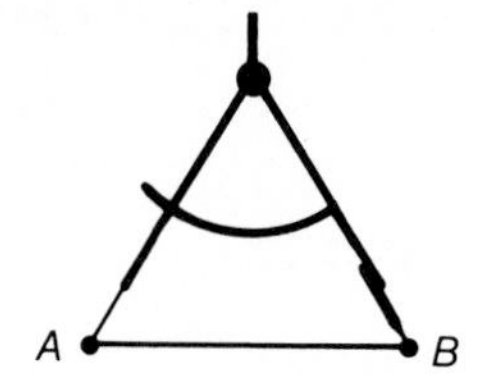

Step 3
Place the compass point at X. Use the same compass opening to mark point Y.

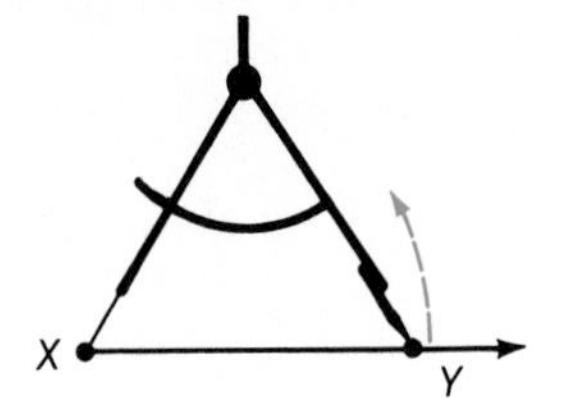

Segment XY is congruent to segment AB. $\overline{XY} \cong \overline{AB}$.
↑ is congruent to

Congruent angles have the same measure. Construct an angle congruent to $\angle ABC$. Use a compass and a straightedge.

Step 1
Draw $\overrightarrow{MN}$.

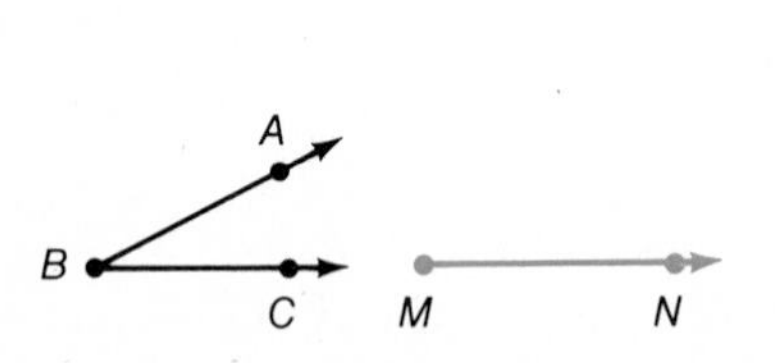

Step 2
Draw an arc through $\angle ABC$ as shown.

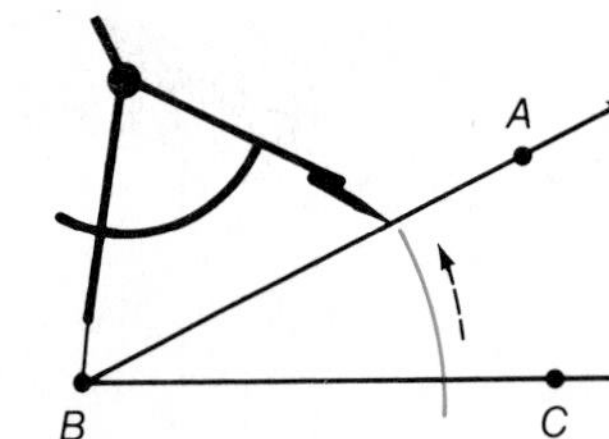

Step 3

Use the same compass opening to draw an arc through $\overrightarrow{MN}$ as shown.

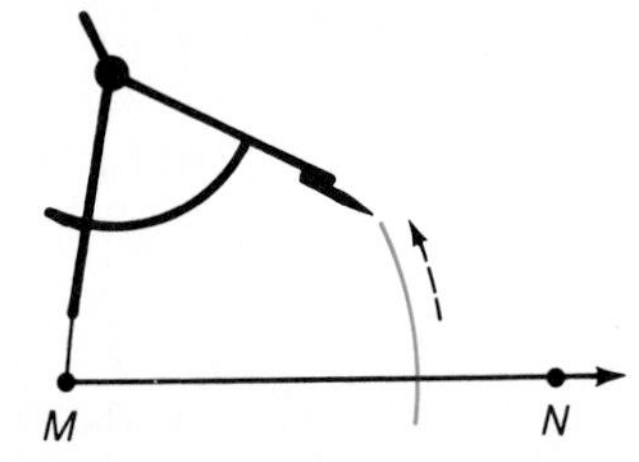

Step 4
Measure the opening of the angle as shown.

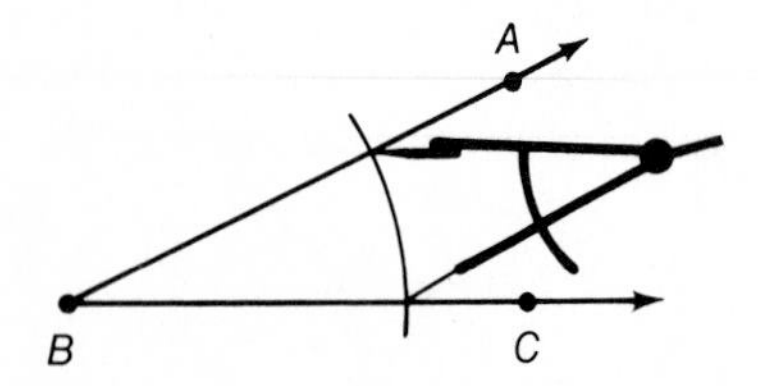

Step 5
Use the same compass opening to locate point O as shown.

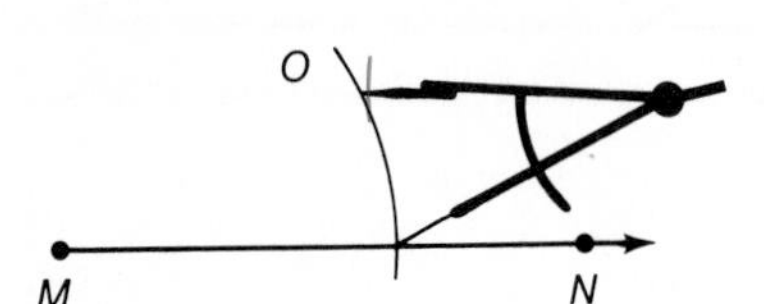

Step 6
Draw $\overrightarrow{MO}$.

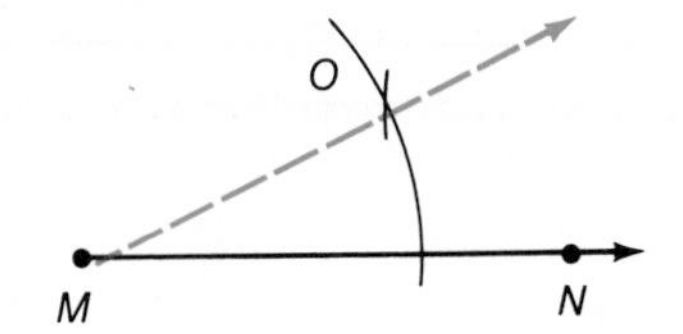

Angle OMN is congruent to angle ABC. $\angle OMN \cong \angle ABC$.

Practice • Trace each figure. Then construct a congruent figure.

1.

2.

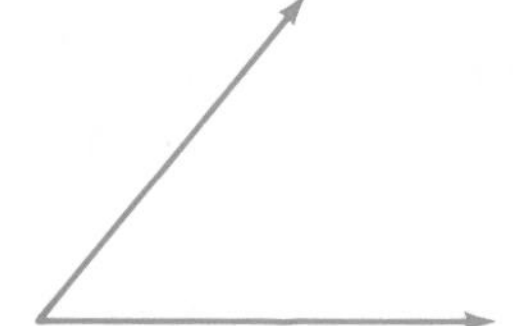

3.

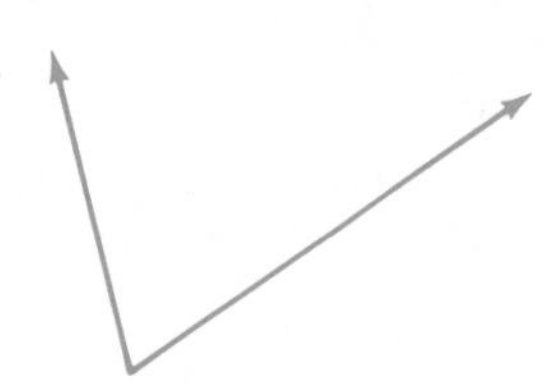

Mixed Practice • Trace each figure. Then construct a congruent figure.

4.

5.

6.

7. Draw three segments. Then construct a segment congruent to each one.

8. Draw three angles. Then construct an angle congruent to each one.

Use a ruler to draw a segment with the given length. Then construct a congruent segment.

9. 5 cm **10.** 3 cm **11.** 9 cm **12.** 6 cm ★ **13.** 7.3 cm

Use a protractor to draw an angle with the given measure. Then construct a congruent angle.

14. 90° **15.** 45° **16.** 75° **17.** 130° ★ **18.** 78°

PROBLEM SOLVING • APPLICATIONS

19. Trace figure XYZ. Then use a compass and a straightedge to construct a figure that is congruent to it. (Hint: Construct a segment congruent to $\overline{XY}$; then construct the angle congruent to $\angle XYZ$; then construct a segment congruent to $\overline{YZ}$.)

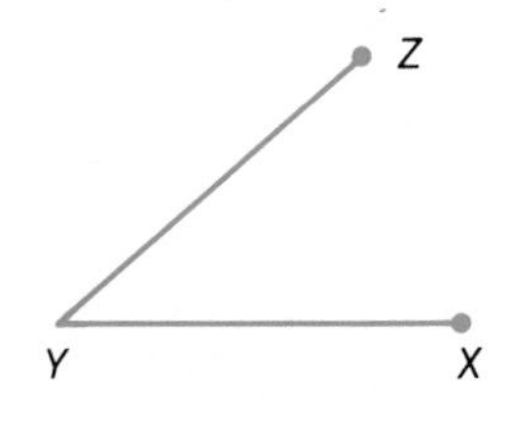

★ **20.** Trace triangle ABC. Then use a compass and a straightedge to construct a triangle that is congruent to triangle ABC. (Hint: Use a method similar to the one in problem 19.)

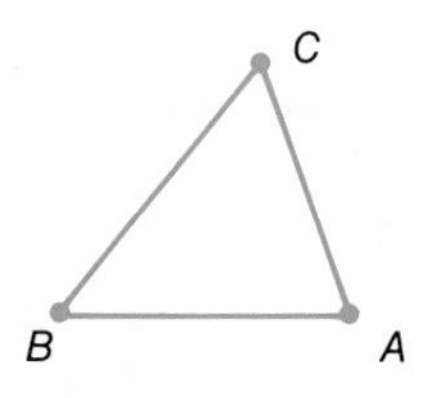

Bisecting Segments and Angles

You can use a compass and a straightedge to **bisect** a segment. To bisect means to divide into two congruent parts. This construction also locates the middle point, or **midpoint,** of the segment.

Step 1
Open the compass to more than half the distance from R to S. Place the compass point on R. Draw an arc as shown.

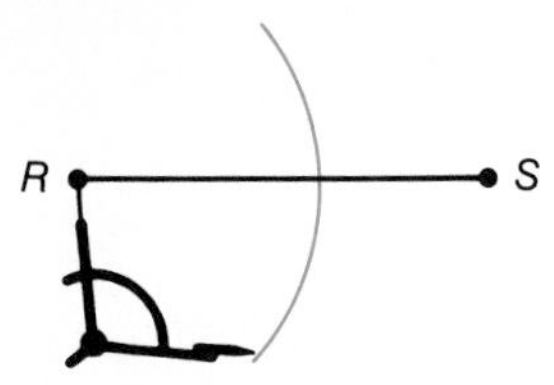

Step 2
Keep the same compass opening. Place the compass point on S. Draw an arc as shown. Label the points of intersection T and U.

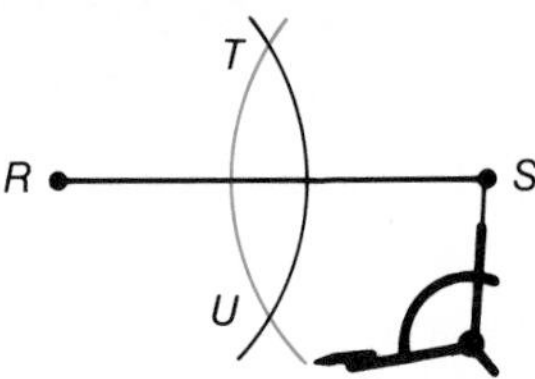

Step 3
Draw $\overleftrightarrow{TU}$. Label M, the point of intersection of $\overleftrightarrow{TU}$ and $\overline{RS}$.

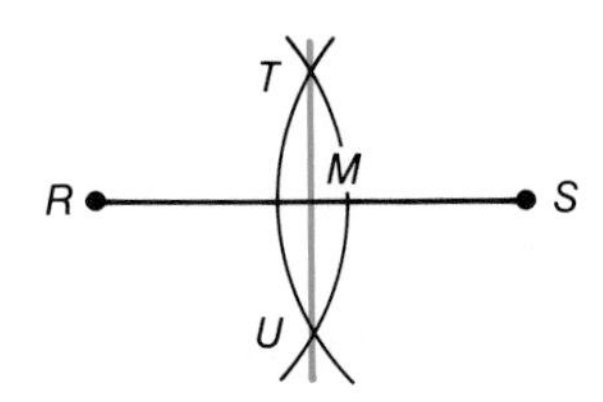

$\overleftrightarrow{TU}$ bisects $\overline{RS}$. $\overline{RM} \cong \overline{MS}$. M is the midpoint of $\overline{RS}$.

You can also use a compass and a straightedge to bisect an angle.

Step 1
Draw an arc through $\angle ABC$, intersecting its sides at two points, E and F.

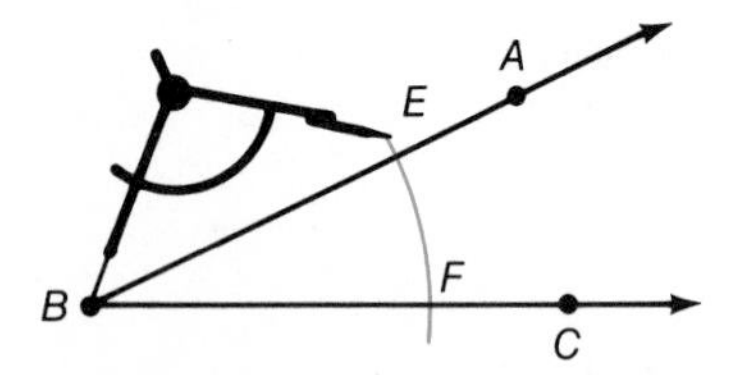

Step 2
Place the compass point on E and draw an arc as shown.

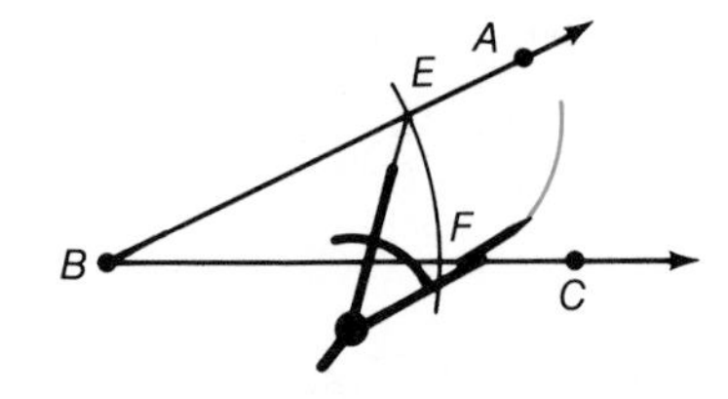

Step 3
Using the same compass opening, place the point on F and draw an arc that intersects the arc drawn in Step 2. Label the point of intersection D.

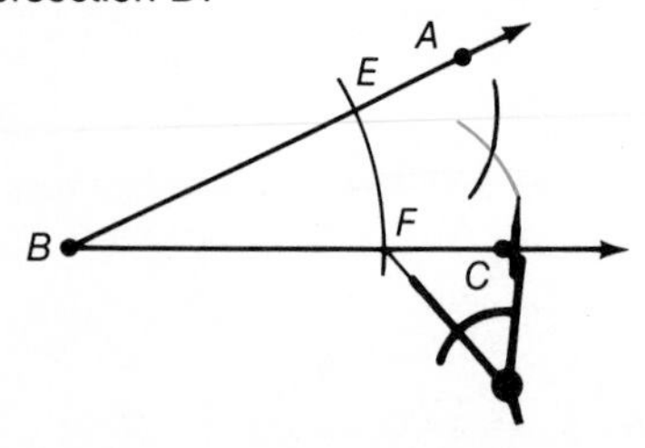

Step 4
Draw $\overrightarrow{BD}$ as shown.

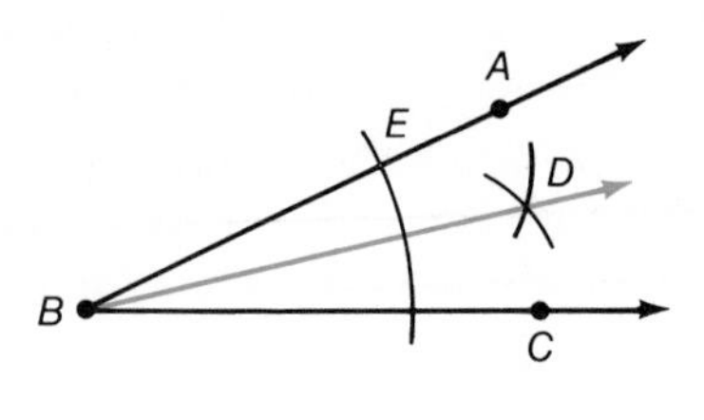

$\angle ABD \cong \angle DBC$. $\overrightarrow{BD}$ is an **angle bisector.**

Practice • Trace each figure. Then use a compass and a straightedge to bisect it.

1.

2.

3.

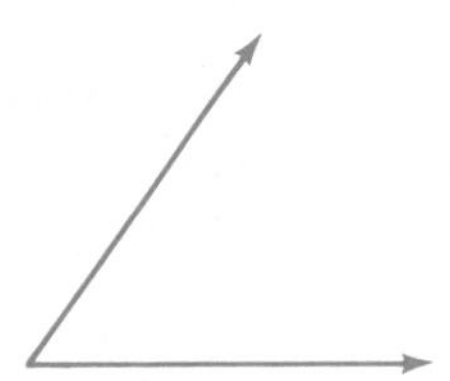

Mixed Practice • Trace each figure. Then use a compass and a straightedge to bisect it.

4.

5.

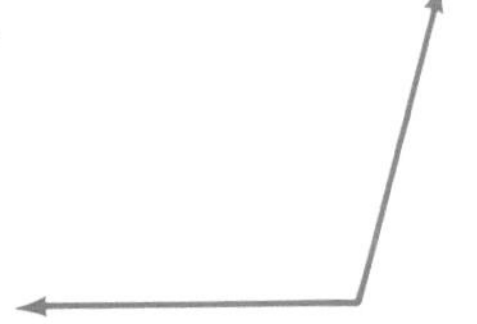

6.

7. Draw three segments. Construct their bisectors.

8. Draw three angles. Construct their bisectors.

Use a ruler to draw a segment with the given length. Then use a compass and a straightedge to bisect it. Check your results with a ruler.

9. 12 cm **10.** 8 cm **11.** 7 cm ★ **12.** 9.8 cm ★ **13.** 112 mm

Use a protractor to draw an angle with the given measure. Then use a compass and a straightedge to bisect it.

14. 70° **15.** 90° **16.** 110° ★ **17.** 124° ★ **18.** 156°

Draw a triangle like the one shown, but make it larger. Using a compass and a straightedge, bisect each angle of the triangle. At how many points do the three angle bisectors intersect?

★ **19.**

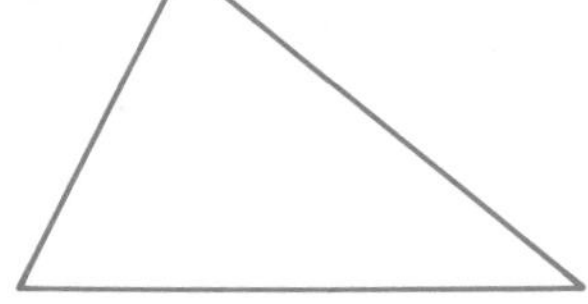

★ **20.**

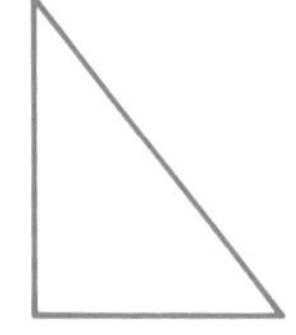

★ **21.**

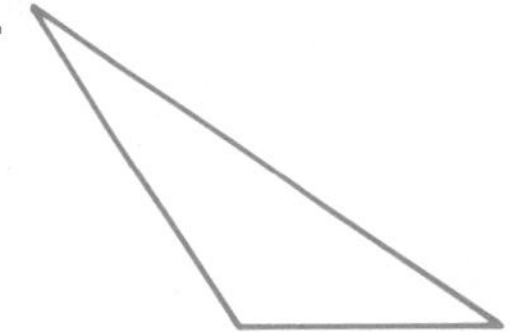

PROBLEM SOLVING • APPLICATIONS

22. $\overline{QR}$ is 17 centimeters long. Point X is the midpoint of $\overline{QR}$. How long is $\overline{XQ}$?

23. $m\angle ABC = 119°$. $\overrightarrow{BR}$ bisects $\angle ABC$. What is the measure of $\angle RBA$?

Angle Relationships

If two lines intersect, two pairs of **vertical angles** are formed. Vertical angles are congruent.

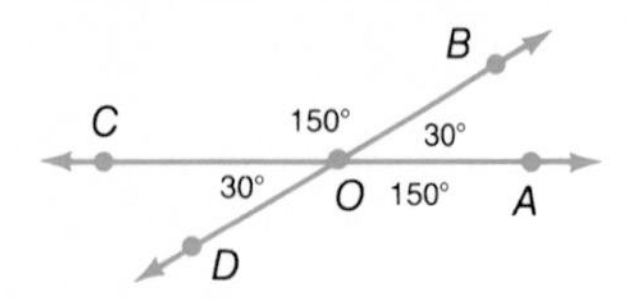

$m\angle AOB = m\angle COD$
$m\angle COB = m\angle AOD$

Angles QRX and XRS are **adjacent angles.** Adjacent angles have a common vertex and a common ray between the other rays.

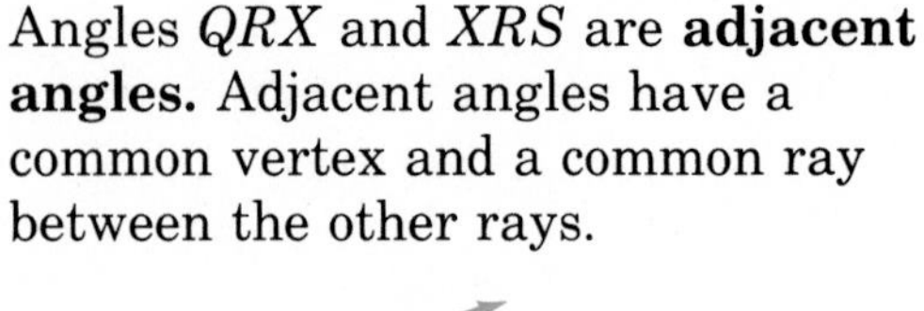

If the sum of the measures of two angles is 90°, they are **complementary angles.**

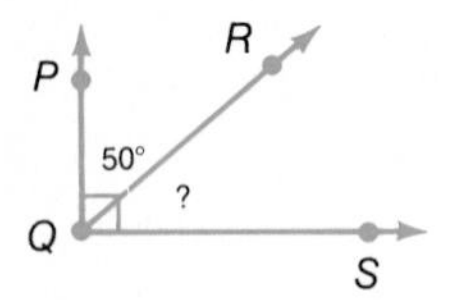

Angle PQS is a right angle. So angles PQR and RQS are complementary.

The measure of $\angle PQR$ is 50°. Find the measure of $\angle RQS$.

$$50 + n = 90$$
$$n = 40$$

The measure of $\angle RQS$ is 40°.

If the sum of the measures of two angles is 180°, they are **supplementary angles.**

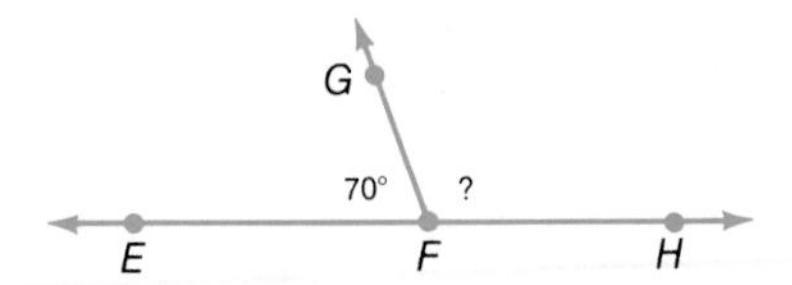

Angle EFH is a **straight angle;** it has a measure of 180°. So angles EFG and GFH are supplementary.

The measure of $\angle EFG$ is 70°. Find the measure of $\angle GFH$.

$$70 + n = 180$$
$$n = 110$$

The measure of $\angle GFH$ is 110°.

Which pair of angles is complementary? Which pair is supplementary?

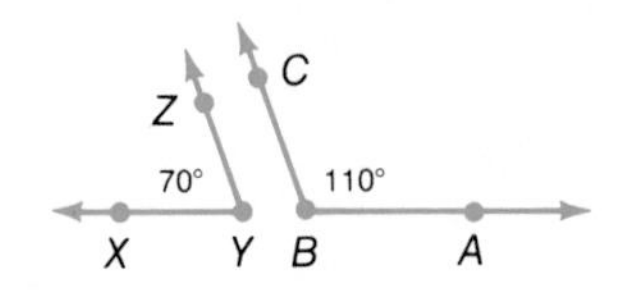

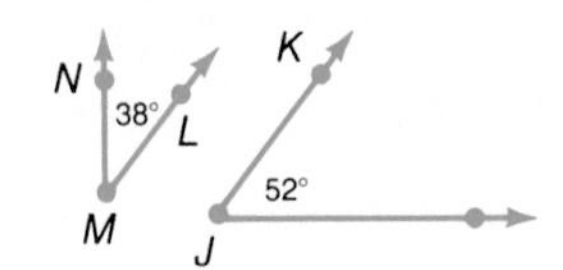

Practice • Use the drawing to do exercises 1–4.

1. Name one pair of vertical angles.
2. Name one pair of adjacent angles.
3. Are angles ABC and CBT complementary?
4. Are angles ABC and CBT supplementary?

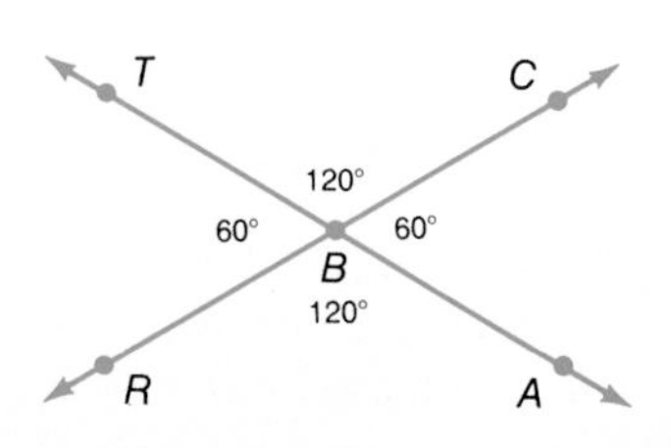

Mixed Practice • Use the drawing to do exercises 5–8.

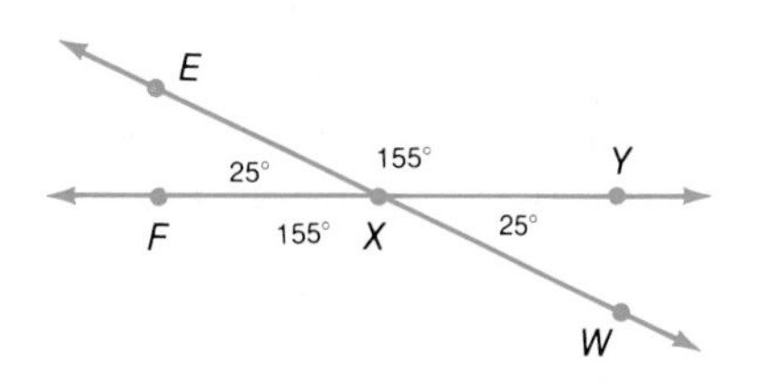

5. Name two pairs of vertical angles.
6. Name two pairs of adjacent angles.
7. Are angles FXE and WXF complementary?
8. Are angles FXE and WXF supplementary?

Use the drawing to do exercises 9–11.

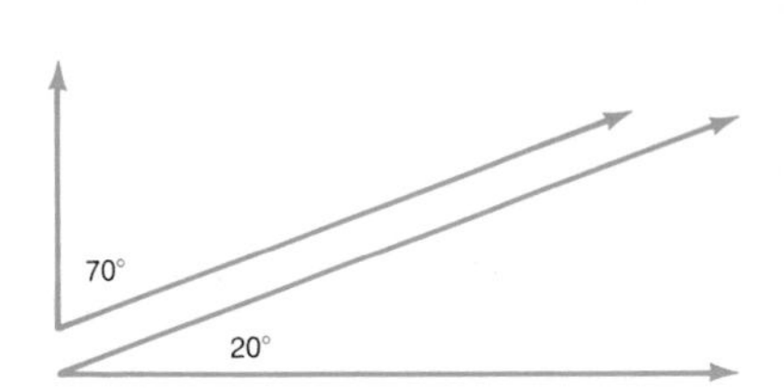

9. Are these two angles complementary?
10. Are these two angles supplementary?
★ 11. Are these two angles adjacent angles? Explain.

The angles are complementary. Find the missing measures.

12. 26°, x 13. 72°, y 14. 57°, n 15. 45°, x ★ 16. n, 89.5°

The angles are supplementary. Find the missing measures.

17. 117°, n 18. 38°, x 19. 65°, y 20. x, 26° ★ 21. 178.5°, x

PROBLEM SOLVING • APPLICATIONS

Use a protractor and a ruler or a straightedge to draw

22. two angles that are supplementary angles but not adjacent angles.
23. two angles that are adjacent angles but not supplementary angles.
24. a pair of vertical angles that are supplementary.

Midchapter Review

Use the diagram with point X in it.

Name

1. three lines.
2. two line segments.
3. an acute angle.
4. a right angle.

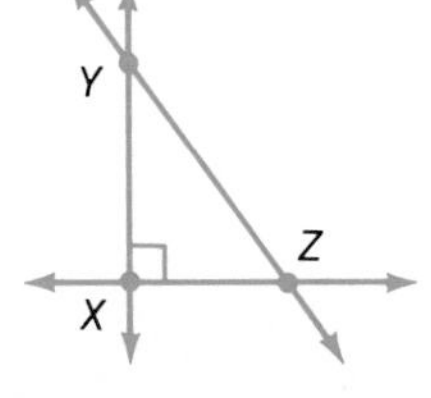

Use the diagram of circle O.

Name

5. three radii.
6. two chords.
7. one diameter.
8. a central angle.

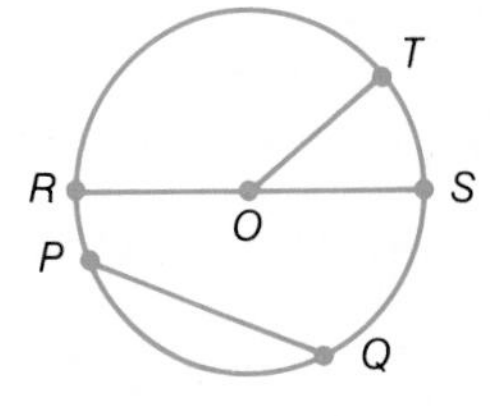

9. Two angles are supplementary: 138°, n. Find the missing measure.

Perpendicular and Parallel Lines

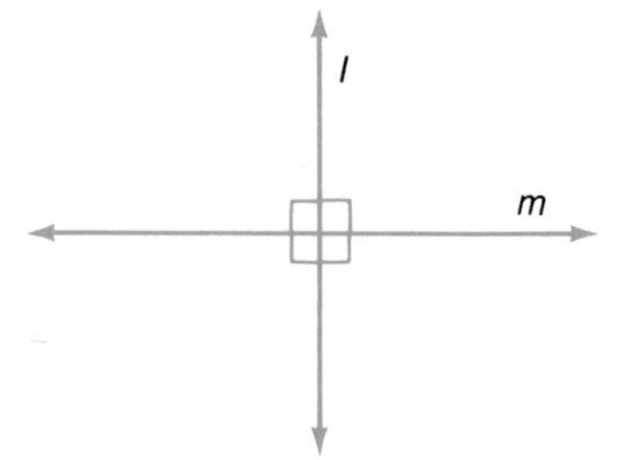

Two lines that intersect to form right angles are **perpendicular lines.** The drawing shows perpendicular lines, named with the small letters l and m.

Write: $l \perp m$.

Read: line l is perpendicular to line m.

How many right angles are formed by l and m?

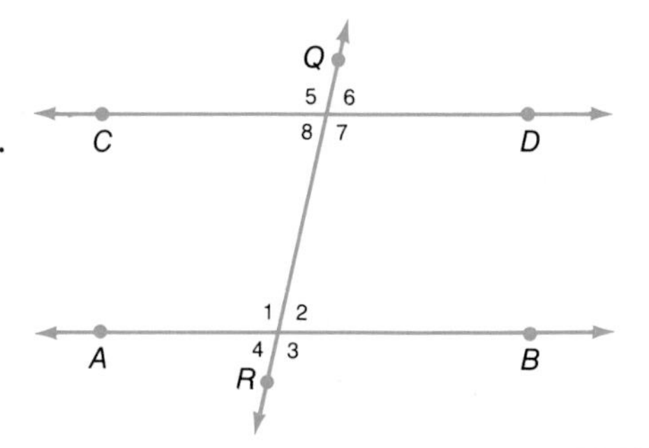

Lines that are in the same plane and never intersect are **parallel lines.**

This drawing shows parallel lines, $\overleftrightarrow{AB}$ and $\overleftrightarrow{CD}$.

Write: $\overleftrightarrow{AB} \parallel \overleftrightarrow{CD}$.

Read: Line AB is parallel to line CD.

$\overleftrightarrow{QR}$ intersects both $\overleftrightarrow{AB}$ and $\overleftrightarrow{CD}$.
$\overleftrightarrow{QR}$ is a **transversal.**

When a pair of parallel lines are intersected by a transversal, pairs of congruent **corresponding angles** are formed.

$\angle 1$ and $\angle 5$ extend above $\overleftrightarrow{AB}$ and $\overleftrightarrow{CD}$ and to the left of the transversal. They are in corresponding positions.

$\angle 1$ and $\angle 5$ are corresponding angles.

$\angle 1 \cong \angle 5$

$\angle 4$ and $\angle 8$ are corresponding angles.
$\angle 4 \cong \angle 8$

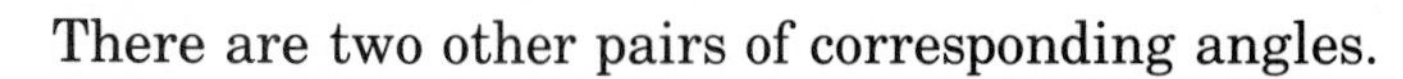

There are two other pairs of corresponding angles.

$\angle 2$ and $\angle 6$
$\angle 2 \cong \angle 6$

$\angle 3$ and $\angle 7$
$\angle 3 \cong \angle 7$

Practice • Are the lines perpendicular? Write *yes* or *no*.

1.

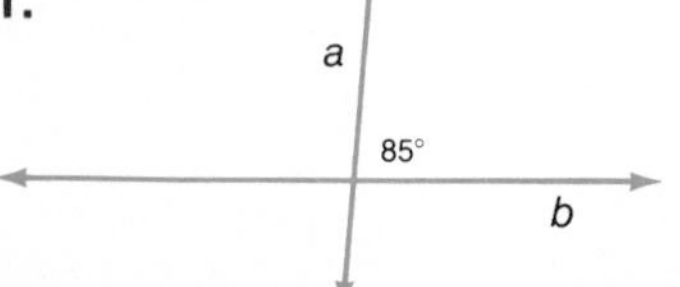

2.

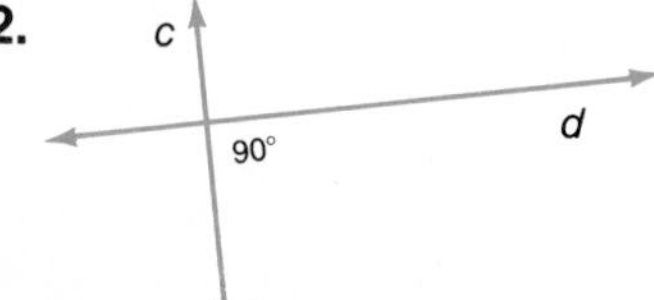

3.

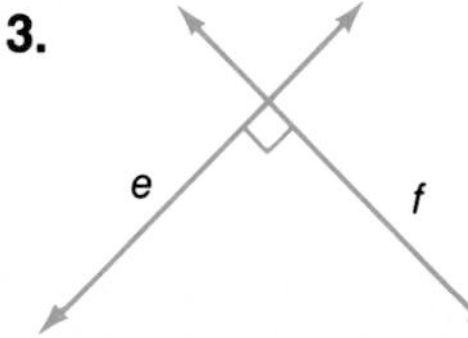

Mixed Practice • Are the lines perpendicular? Write *yes* or *no.*

4.

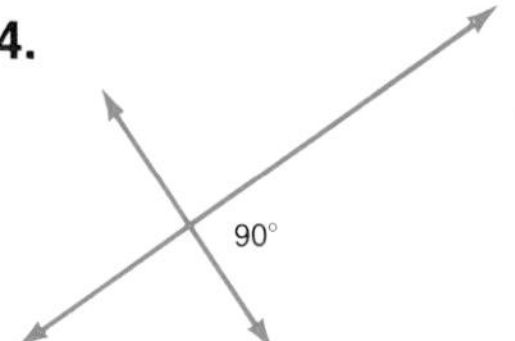

5.

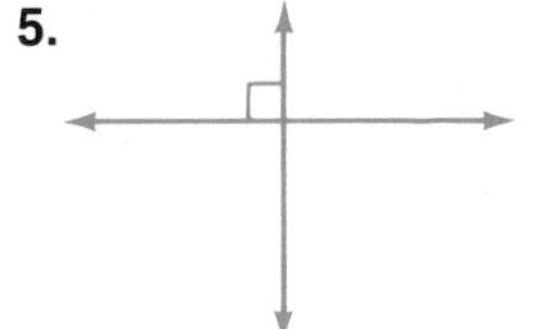

6.

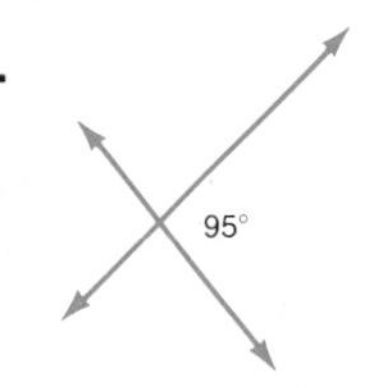

7. Lines c and d are parallel.
Name four pairs of corresponding angles.

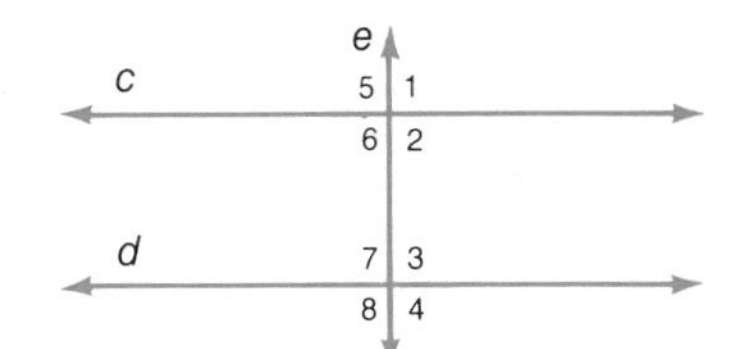

Use your protractor to find the measure of

8. $\angle 1$. **9.** $\angle 8$.

★ **10.** Without using your protractor, write the measure of each of the other angles.

11. Is line e perpendicular to line c? Is line e also perpendicular to line d?

> ***In a plane, if a line is perpendicular to one of two parallel lines, it is perpendicular to the other line too.***

The horizontal lines *a* and *b* are parallel.
Name the corresponding angle.

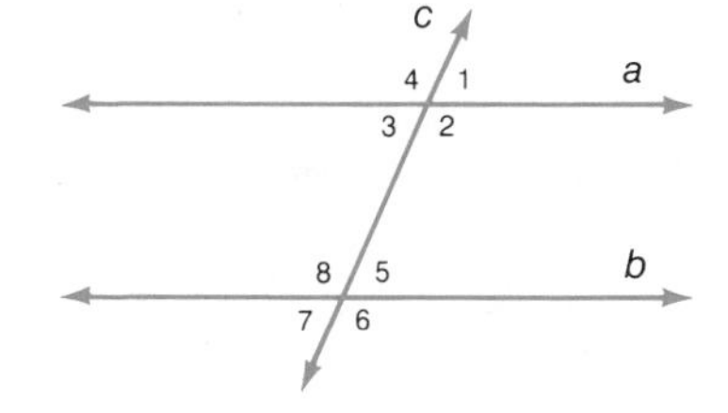

12. $\angle 1$ and $\angle$ ____ **13.** $\angle 2$ and $\angle$ ____

14. $\angle 3$ and $\angle$ ____ **15.** $\angle 4$ and $\angle$ ____

In this figure, $\angle 1$ and $\angle 3$ are vertical angles.
Name the other pairs of vertical angles.

16. $\angle 2$ and $\angle$ ____ **17.** $\angle 5$ and $\angle$ ____ **18.** $\angle 6$ and $\angle$ ____

Use your protractor to find the measure of

19. $\angle 1$. **20.** $\angle 2$. **21.** $\angle 3$. **22.** $\angle 4$.

Without measuring, tell what the measure of each angle is.

★ **23.** $\angle 5$ ★ **24.** $\angle 6$ ★ **25.** $\angle 7$ ★ **26.** $\angle 8$

PROBLEM SOLVING • APPLICATIONS

27. Without measuring, how can you be sure that $\angle 1 \cong \angle 3$?

28. Without measuring, how can you be sure that $m\angle 1 + m\angle 2 = 180°$?

Polygons

A **polygon** has sides that are line segments. The sides meet to form angles. The vertices of the angles are also the vertices of the polygon. Names are given to polygons according to the number of sides and the number of angles they have.

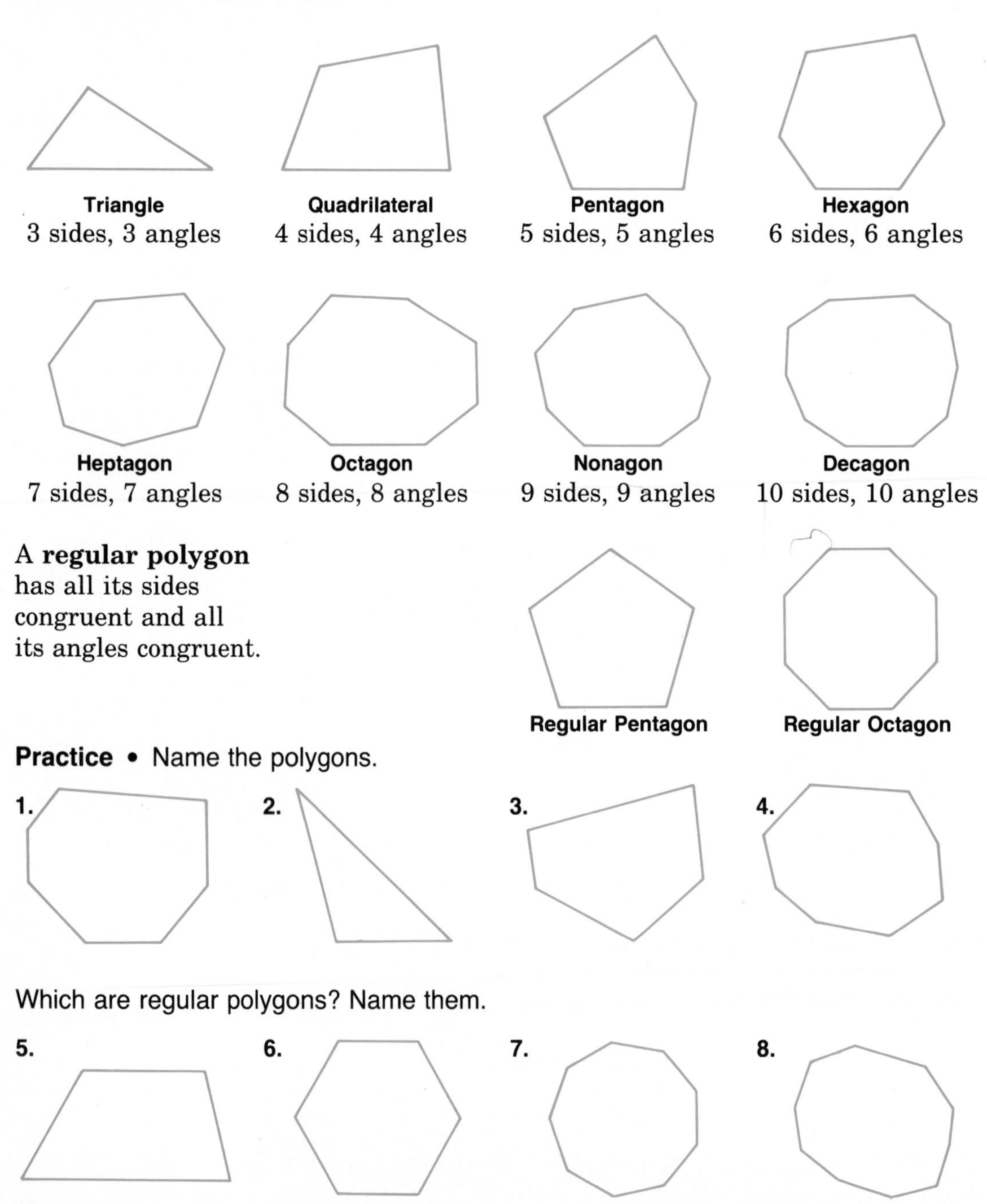

Triangle
3 sides, 3 angles

Quadrilateral
4 sides, 4 angles

Pentagon
5 sides, 5 angles

Hexagon
6 sides, 6 angles

Heptagon
7 sides, 7 angles

Octagon
8 sides, 8 angles

Nonagon
9 sides, 9 angles

Decagon
10 sides, 10 angles

A **regular polygon** has all its sides congruent and all its angles congruent.

Regular Pentagon

Regular Octagon

Practice • Name the polygons.

1. **2.** **3.** **4.**

Which are regular polygons? Name them.

5. **6.** **7.** **8.**

Mixed Practice • Name the polygons.

9. 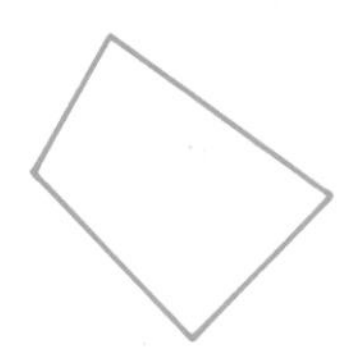

10. 

11. 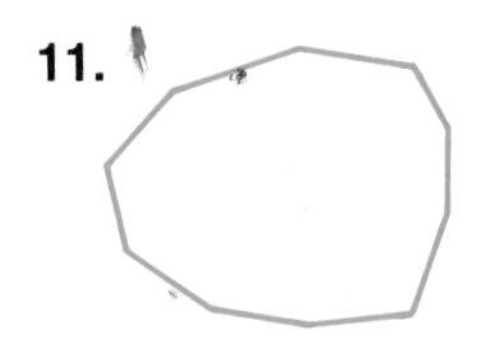

12. 

Which are regular polygons? Name them.

13. 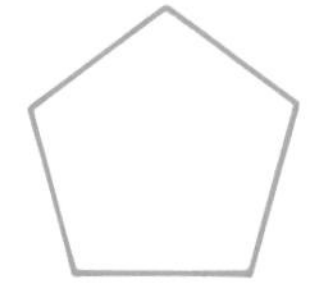

14. 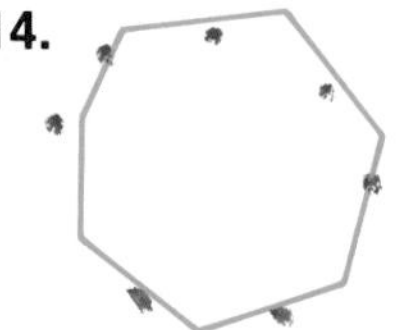

15. 

16. 

A **diagonal** is a line sement that joins the vertices of a polygon but is not a side.

Draw each polygon and all its diagonals. Then complete the table.

	Polygon	Number of Sides	Number of Diagonals
17.	Quadrilateral	4	2
18.	Pentagon		
19.	Hexagon		
20.	Heptagon		
21.	Octagon		

★ 22. Suppose s is the number of sides of a polygon and d is the number of diagonals. Which equation shows the relationship between s and d?

a. $\frac{s}{2} = d$ **b.** $s - 2 = d$

c. $s(s - 3) = d$ **d.** $\frac{s(s - 3)}{2} = d$

★ 23. How many diagonals does a polygon with 100 sides have?

PROBLEM SOLVING • APPLICATIONS

24. Use a compass to construct a circle. Use the same compass opening to mark off six equal arcs, locating points A, B, C, D, E, and F. Draw $\overline{AB}$, $\overline{BC}$, $\overline{CD}$, $\overline{DE}$, $\overline{EF}$, and $\overline{FA}$. Have you constructed a regular polygon? What kind?

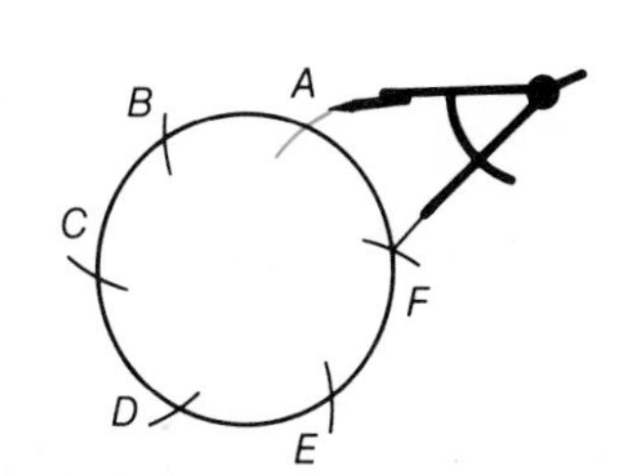

★ 25. As in problem 24, locate six equally spaced points around a circle. Call them A, B, C, D, E, and F. Draw $\overline{AC}$, $\overline{CE}$, and $\overline{EA}$. Have you constructed a regular polygon? What kind?

Triangles

Triangles can be classified according to the lengths of their sides.

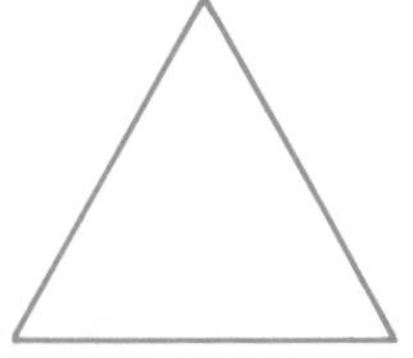

Equilateral Triangle
There are three congruent sides.

Isosceles Triangle
There are at least two congruent sides.

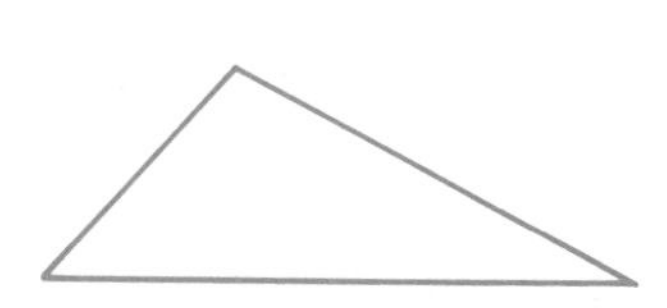

Scalene Triangle
There are no congruent sides.

Triangles can also be classified according to the measures of their angles.

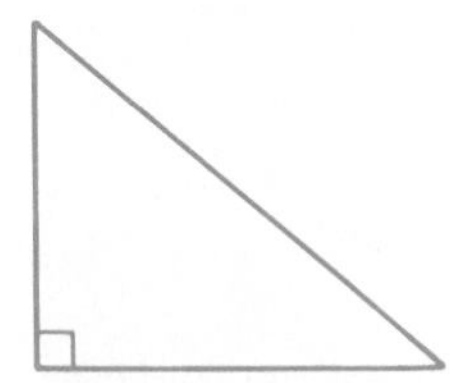

Right Triangle
There is one right angle.

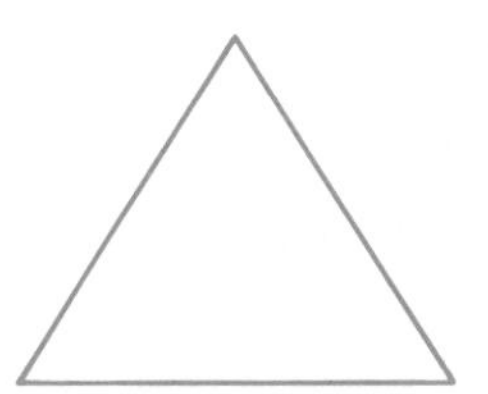

Acute Triangle
There are three acute angles.

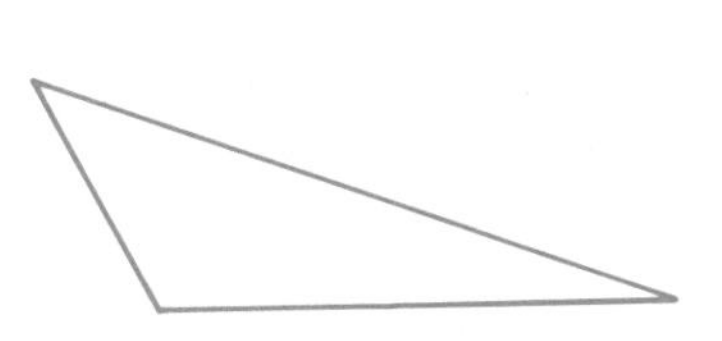

Obtuse Triangle
There is one obtuse angle.

This drawing shows a triangle with the parts of the angles near the vertices cut away. Then the angles are fit together as shown.

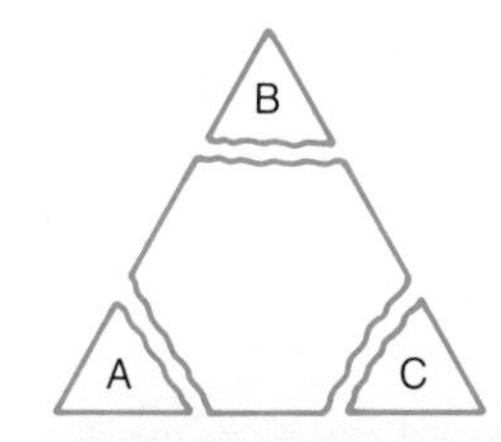

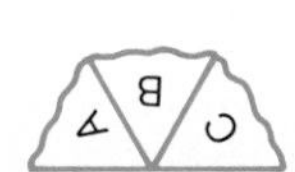

The sides lie along a straight line. The sum of their measures is 180°.

Repeat the experiment with other triangles. Is the sum 180° each time?

The sum of the measures of the angles of a triangle is 180°.

If you know the measures of two angles of a triangle, you can find the measure of the other angle.

$$n + 85° + 72° = 180°$$
$$n + 157° = 180°$$
$$n + 157° - 157° = 180° - 157°$$
$$n = 23°$$

Practice • Measure the lengths of the sides. Then classify each triangle as *equilateral*, *isosceles*, or *scalene*. Some exercises have more than one answer.

1.

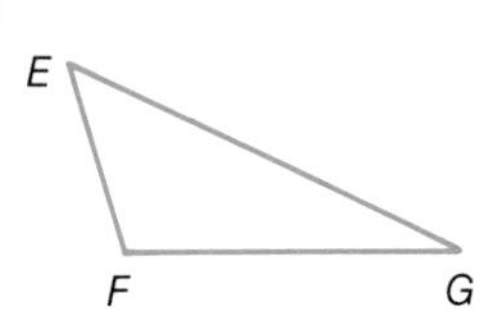

2.

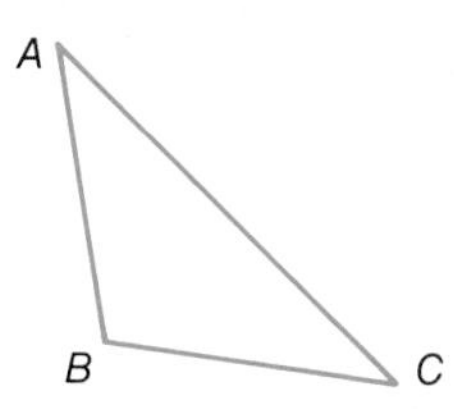

3.

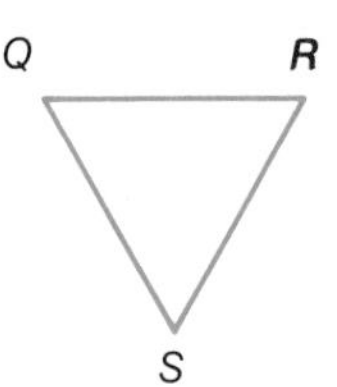

4.

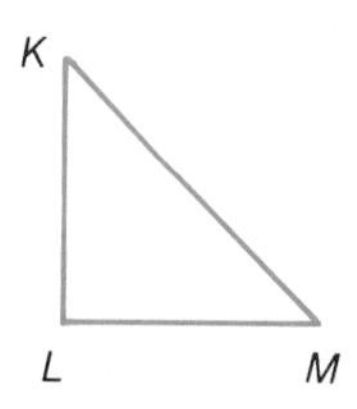

Use a protractor to measure the angles in exercises 1–4. Then classify each triangle as *right*, *acute*, or *obtuse*.

5. triangle EFG **6.** triangle ABC **7.** triangle QRS **8.** triangle KLM

Mixed Practice • Answer these questions.

★ **9.** Is every equilateral triangle also an isosceles triangle?

10. Is every isosceles triangle an equilateral triangle?

Without using a protractor, find the measure of the third angle.

11.

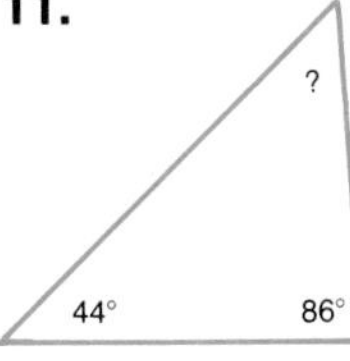

12.

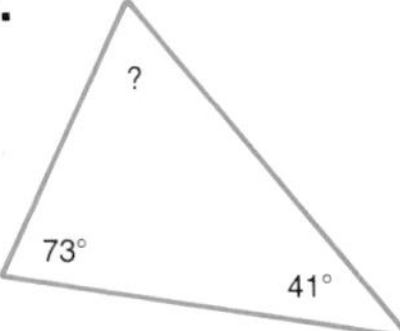

13.

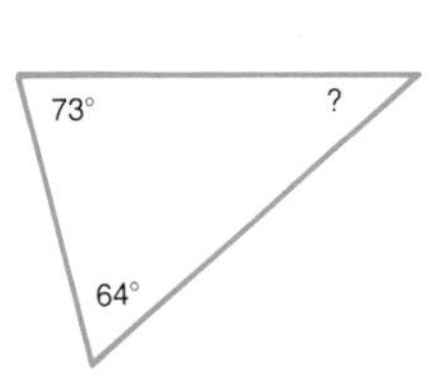

14.

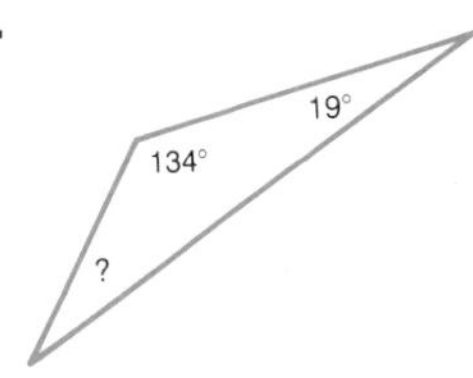

The measures of two angles of a triangle are given. Find the measure of the other angle.

15. $35°, 70°, x$ **16.** $45°, 90°, y$ **17.** $25°, 46°, n$ ★ **18.** $15.5°, x, 74.5°$

PROBLEM SOLVING • APPLICATIONS

Use graph paper and experiment with different drawings. Then decide if it is possible to draw

19. a right triangle that is isosceles.

20. a right triangle that is equilateral.

★ **21.** a triangle with two right angles.

Quadrilaterals

Some quadrilaterals have special names.

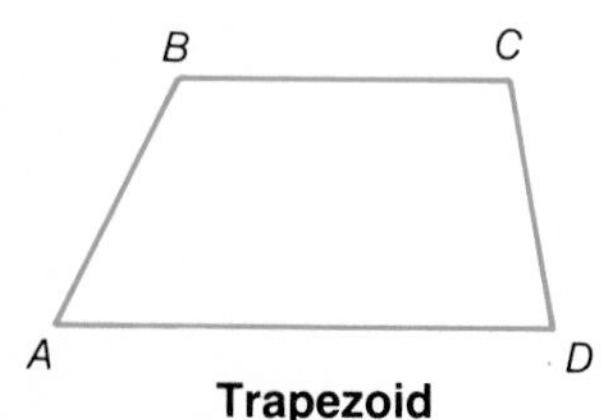

Trapezoid

Two and only two sides are parallel.

$\overline{AD} \parallel \overline{BC}$

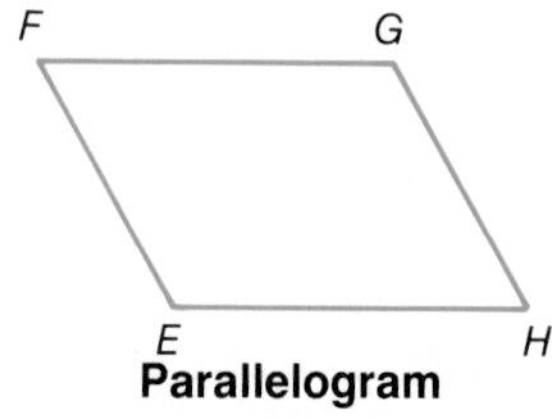

Parallelogram

Opposite sides are parallel and congruent.

$\overline{FE} \parallel \overline{GH}$ $\quad \overline{FE} \cong \overline{GH}$

$\overline{FG} \parallel \overline{EH}$ $\quad \overline{FG} \cong \overline{EH}$

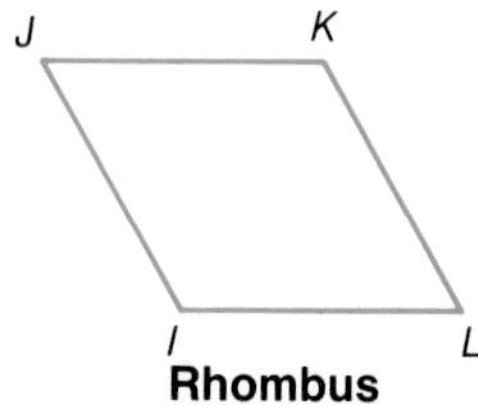

Rhombus

A parallelogram that has four congruent sides.

$\overline{IJ} \cong \overline{JK} \cong \overline{KL} \cong \overline{LI}$

Rectangle

A parallelogram that has four right angles.

Angles M, N, O, and P are right angles.

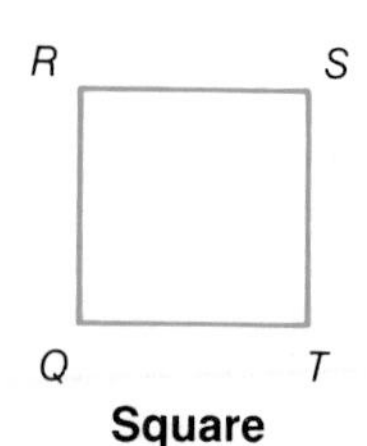

Square

A rectangle that has four congruent sides.

$\overline{QR} \cong \overline{RS} \cong \overline{ST} \cong \overline{TQ}$

Practice • Classify each quadrilateral as a *trapezoid*, *parallelogram*, *rhombus*, *rectangle*, or *square*. List each name that applies to the figure.

1.

2.

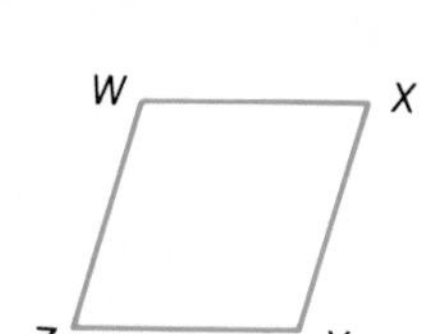

3.

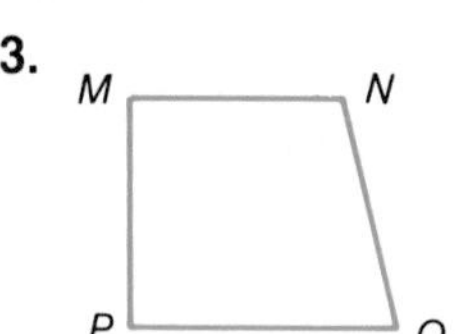

4.

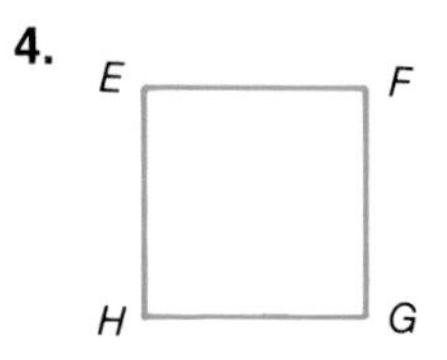

Name the pairs of parallel sides in

5. figure $ABCD$ **6.** figure $WXYZ$ **7.** figure $MNOP$ **8.** figure $EFGH$

Name the congruent sides in

9. figure $ABCD$ **10.** figure $WXYZ$ **11.** figure $MNOP$ **12.** figure $EFGH$

Mixed Practice • Study these figures of a parallelogram and a trapezoid.

This figure is a parallelogram.
$\angle 1$ and $\angle 3$ are **opposite angles**.
$\angle 2$ and $\angle 4$ are opposite angles.

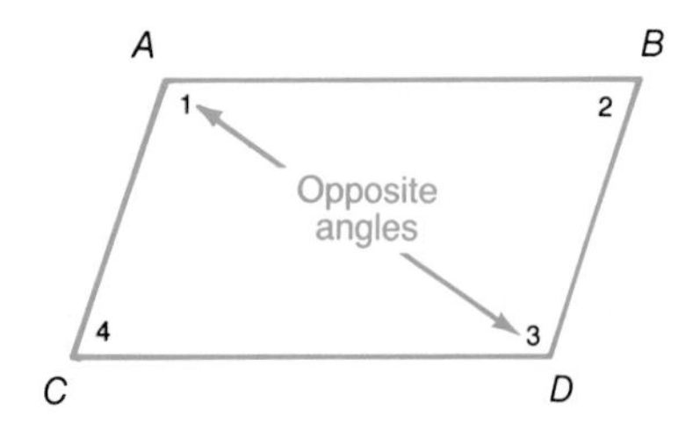

13. Are $\angle 1$ and $\angle 3$ congruent?

14. Are $\angle 2$ and $\angle 4$ congruent?

Opposite angles of a parallelogram are congruent.

15. This trapezoid has its nonparallel sides congruent. It is an **isosceles trapezoid**. Which angles are acute? Which are obtuse? Which angles are congruent?

PROBLEM SOLVING • APPLICATIONS

16. Is every rectangle a square?

17. Is every square a rectangle?

18. Is every rectangle a parallelogram?

19. Is every parallelogram a rectangle?

20. Is every trapezoid a quadrilateral?

21. Is every quadrilateral a trapezoid?

22. Is every square a rhombus?

23. Is every rhombus a square?

24. Draw a quadrilateral. Use a protractor to measure each angle. Find the sum of the measures.

25. Draw five other quadrilaterals. Measure the angles. Find the sum of the measures for each figure.

★ **26.** On graph paper draw a parallelogram that is not a rectangle. Then draw its two diagonals. Is one diagonal longer than the other, or are they equal in length?

★ **27.** Draw five other parallelograms (not rectangles) and their diagonals. In each parallelogram are the diagonals equal in length?

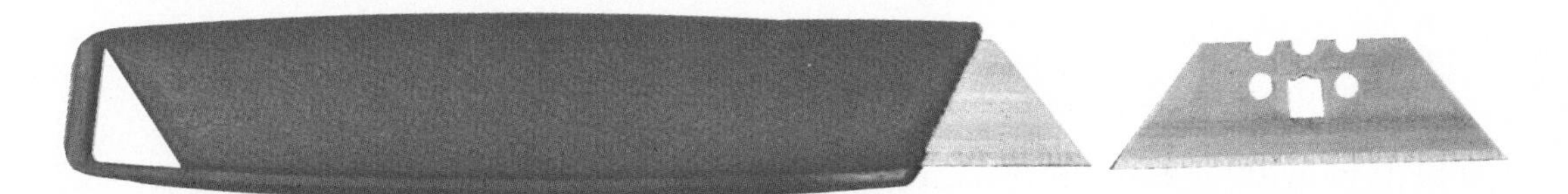

Congruent Polygons

Congruent polygons have the same size and shape. Trace triangle LMN ($\triangle LMN$). Place your triangle above $\triangle RST$ with vertex L on vertex R, vertex M on vertex S, and vertex N on vertex T. Note that your tracing fits $\triangle RST$ exactly.

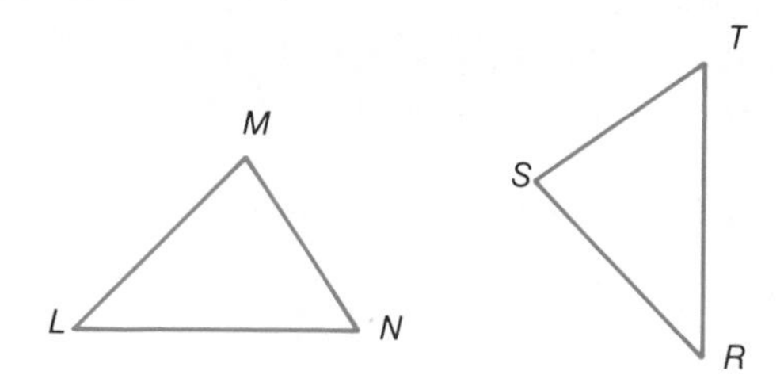

$$\triangle LMN \cong \triangle RST$$

The parts that match are called **corresponding parts**. If the polygons are congruent, then their corresponding parts are also congruent.

Matching vertices

$L \leftrightarrow R$
$M \leftrightarrow S$
$N \leftrightarrow T$

Corresponding sides

$\overline{LM} \cong \overline{RS}$
$\overline{MN} \cong \overline{ST}$
$\overline{NL} \cong \overline{TR}$

Corresponding angles

$\angle L \cong \angle R$
$\angle M \cong \angle S$
$\angle N \cong \angle T$

An angle can be named by its vertex.

If $m\angle L = 30°$, then $m\angle R = 30°$.
If $\overline{LN}$ is 3 centimeters long, then $\overline{RT}$ is also 3 centimeters long.

Practice • $\triangle ABC \cong \triangle DEF$. Complete.

1. $\overline{AB} \cong$ __?__ **2.** $\angle A \cong$ __?__

3. $\overline{BC} \cong$ __?__ **4.** $\angle B \cong$ __?__

5. Suppose $m\angle C = 103°$. What is $m\angle F$?

6. Suppose $m\overline{CA} = 2.5$ centimeters. What is $m\overline{FD}$?

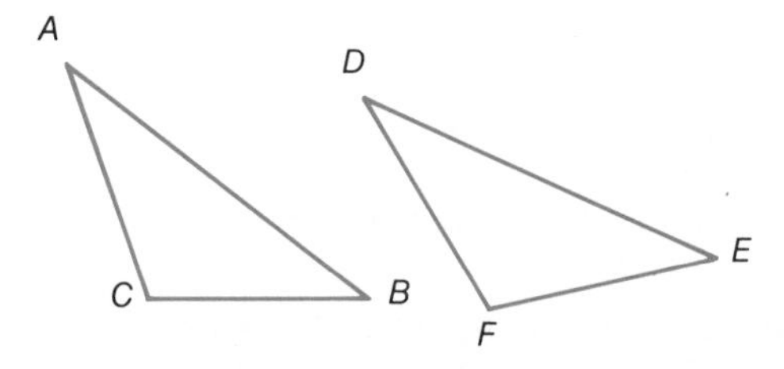

Mixed Practice • $\triangle JKL \cong \triangle PQR$. Complete.

7. $\overline{JK} \cong$ __?__ **8.** $\angle J \cong$ __?__

9. $\overline{JL} \cong$ __?__ **10.** $\angle L \cong$ __?__

11. Suppose $m\angle K = 40°$. What is $m\angle Q$?

12. Suppose $m\overline{KL} = 3.2$ centimeters. What is $m\overline{QR}$?

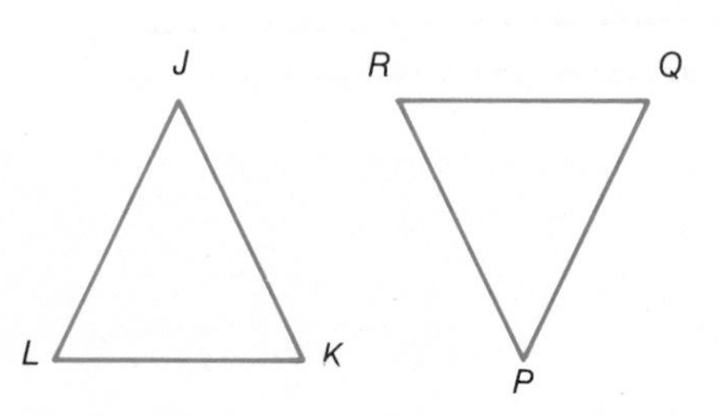

Quadrilaterals *GHJK* and *TUVW* are congruent. Complete.

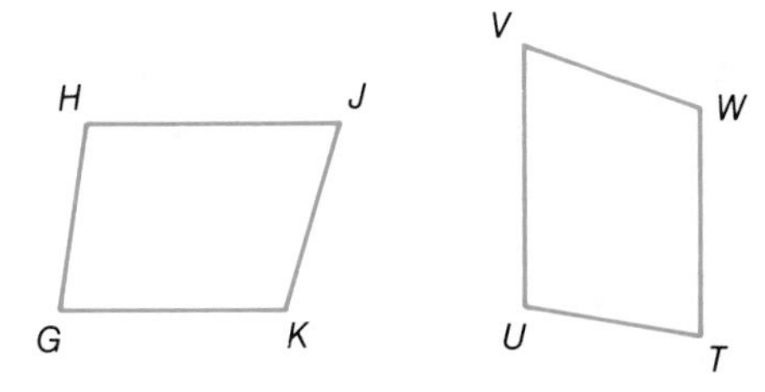

13. $\overline{GH} \cong$ __?__ **14.** $\angle G \cong$ __?__

15. $\overline{HJ} \cong$ __?__ **16.** $\angle H \cong$ __?__

17. $\overline{JK} \cong$ __?__ **18.** $\angle J \cong$ __?__

19. $\overline{KG} \cong$ __?__ **20.** $\angle K \cong$ __?__

Trapezoids *DEFG* and *LMNO* are congruent.

21. $m\angle G = 90°$. What is $m\angle O$?

22. $m\angle E = 102°$. What is $m\angle M$?

★ **23.** Find $m\angle D$ and $m\angle L$.

★ **24.** Find $m\angle F$ and $m\angle N$.

25. Which side of trapezoid *LMNO* is congruent to $\overline{EF}$?

26. Which side of trapezoid *LMNO* is congruent to $\overline{DE}$?

27. Suppose $\overline{GF}$ is 4.8 centimeters long. Name the corresponding part in trapezoid *LMNO* and give its length.

PROBLEM SOLVING • APPLICATIONS

28. Construct a triangle with sides congruent to the segments given.

a __________

b ____________________

c ____________

★ **29.** Construct two more triangles that have *a*, *b*, and *c* as sides. Are each of these triangles congruent to the triangle you constructed in problem 28?

★ **30.** If the three sides of one triangle have the same measures as the three sides of another triangle, are the triangles congruent?

Skills Maintenance

1. $\frac{1}{3} \div \frac{1}{2}$ **2.** $\frac{7}{8} \div \frac{3}{4}$ **3.** $\frac{11}{12} \div \frac{4}{5}$ **4.** $\frac{1}{2} \div \frac{6}{7}$ **5.** $\frac{3}{4} \div 6$

6. $4 \div \frac{1}{2}$ **7.** $3\frac{1}{2} \div 2$ **8.** $2\frac{3}{4} \div 1\frac{1}{2}$ **9.** $6\frac{3}{7} \div 2\frac{1}{4}$ **10.** $10 \div 2\frac{1}{2}$

Symmetry and Reflections

A **line of symmetry** separates a figure in a plane so that one part is an exact **reflection** of the other. The blue line in the figure is a line of symmetry.

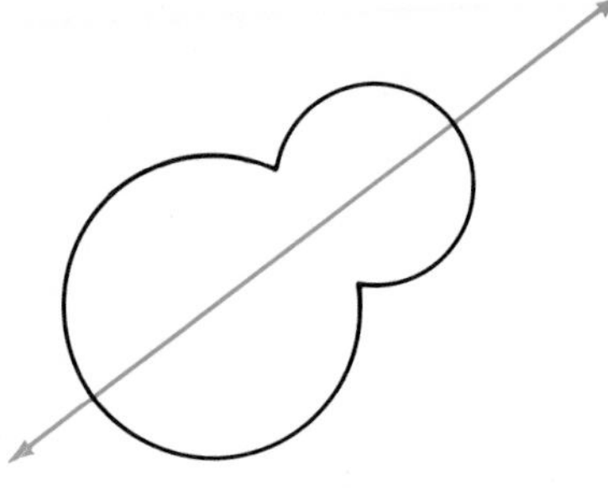

Some figures have no lines of symmetry. Some have one line of symmetry. Some have many lines of symmetry.

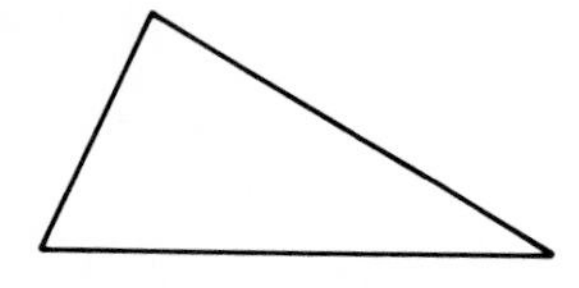

No lines of symmetry

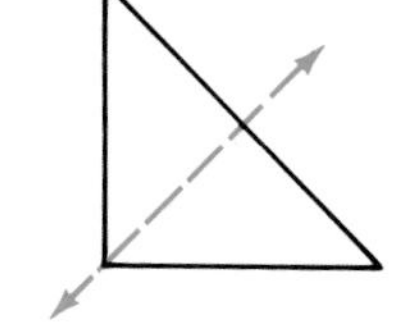

One line of symmetry

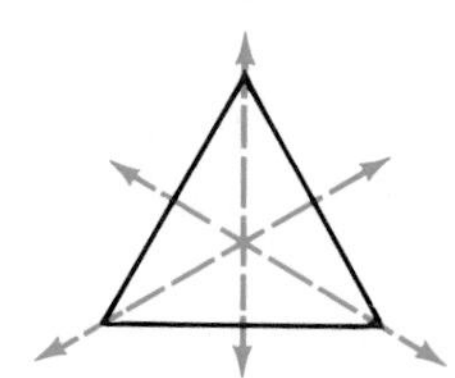

Three lines of symmetry

You can use a mirror to test for a line of symmetry.

Hold a mirror along a line of symmetry (and perpendicular to the plane of the figure). If you see the original figure, the line is a line of symmetry.

This drawing shows a pentagon and its **mirror image**. The dotted line is a line of symmetry for the two figures. If you **flip** the figure along the line of symmetry, you obtain its mirror image.

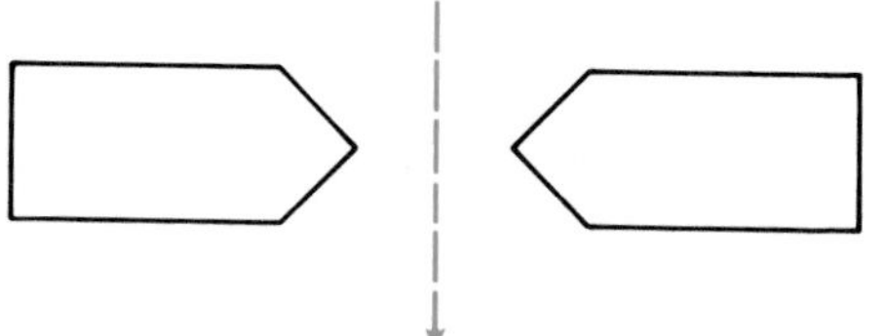

Practice • Each figure has one line of symmetry. Trace the figure. Then draw the line of symmetry.

1.

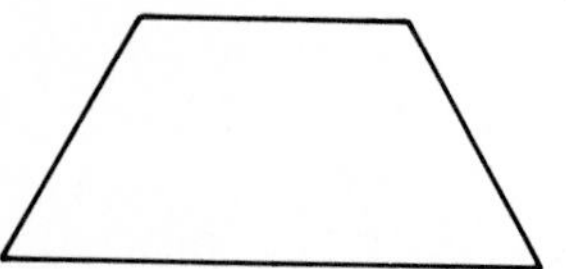

2.

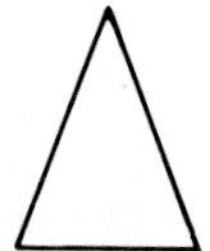

3.

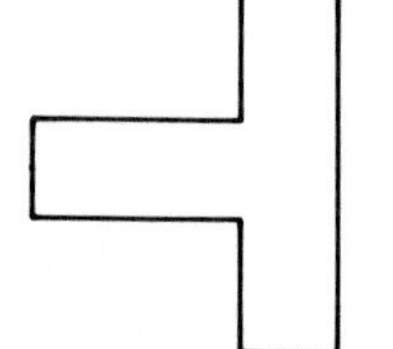

4.

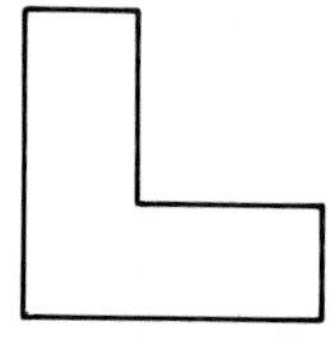

Mixed Practice • Each figure has one line of symmetry. Trace the figure. Then draw the line of symmetry.

5.
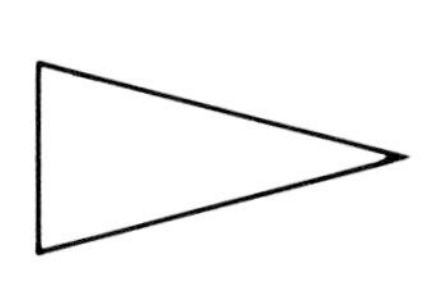

6.

7.

8.
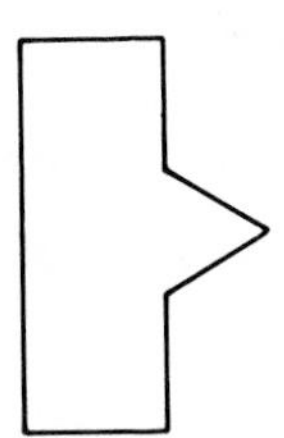

Each figure has more than one line of symmetry. Trace the figure. Then draw the lines of symmetry.

9.
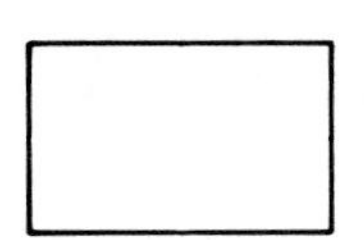

10.

11.
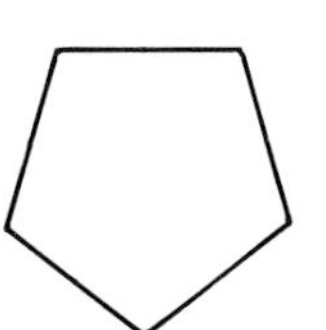

12.
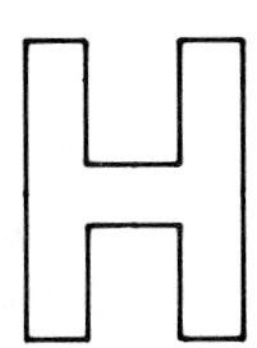

The line of symmetry separates each figure into two congruent figures. Name the corresponding parts.

★**13.**
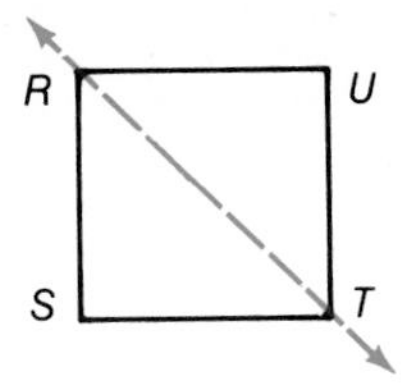

★**14.**
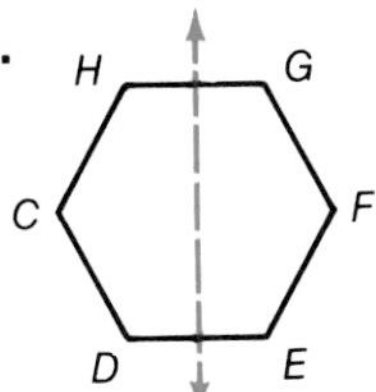

Copy the figures. Draw a mirror image to complete each figure.

★**15.**
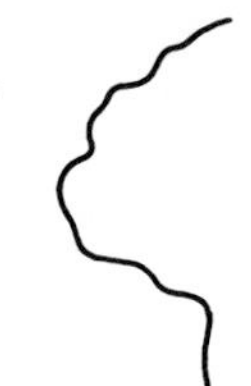

★**16.**

PROBLEM SOLVING • APPLICATIONS

17. Construct a large circle. Draw a line through the center of the circle. Is it a line of symmetry for the circle?

18. Draw other lines of symmetry for the circle. Can you draw 5 lines of symmetry? 10 lines of symmetry? Is 10 the greatest number of lines of symmetry that can be drawn for a circle?

★**19.** Construct a large equilateral triangle. Name it ABC. Construct the midpoint of each side of $\triangle ABC$. Label the midpoint of $\overline{AC}$ as D; the midpoint of $\overline{AB}$ as E; and the midpoint of $\overline{BC}$ as F.

★**20.** Draw $\overline{AF}$, $\overline{BD}$, and $\overline{CE}$. These segments are **medians** of the triangle. Is each median a line of symmetry?

Similar Polygons

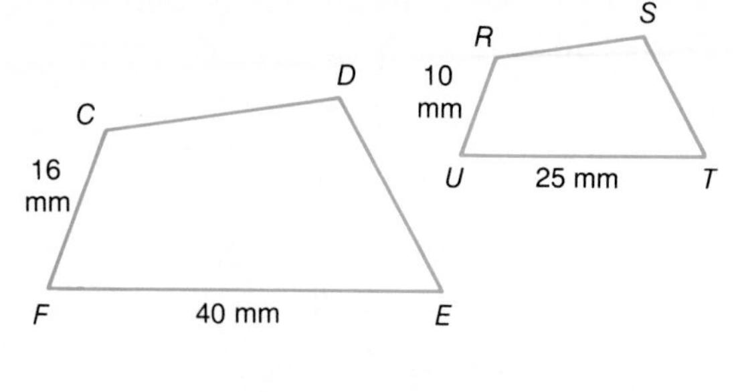

Similar polygons have the same shape.

Corresponding angles of similar polygons are congruent.

$\angle C \cong \angle R$, $\angle D \cong \angle S$, $\angle E \cong \angle T$, and $\angle F \cong \angle U$.

In similar polygons, the ratios of the lengths of corresponding sides are equal.

$$\frac{m\overline{CF}}{m\overline{RU}} = \frac{m\overline{CD}}{m\overline{RS}} = \frac{m\overline{DE}}{m\overline{ST}} = \frac{m\overline{EF}}{m\overline{TU}}$$

You can use cross products to show that the ratios are equal.

$$\begin{matrix} \text{length of } \overline{CF} \longrightarrow \\ \text{length of } \overline{RU} \longrightarrow \end{matrix} \frac{16}{10} = \frac{40}{25} \begin{matrix} \longleftarrow \text{length of } \overline{EF} \\ \longleftarrow \text{length of } \overline{TU} \end{matrix}$$

$$16 \times 25 = 10 \times 40$$
$$400 = 400$$

Triangles ABC and DEF are similar. Use cross products to find the length of $\overline{AB}$.

$$\begin{matrix} \text{length of } \overline{AB} \longrightarrow \\ \text{length of } \overline{DE} \longrightarrow \end{matrix} \frac{n}{14} = \frac{18}{12} \begin{matrix} \longleftarrow \text{length of } \overline{BC} \\ \longleftarrow \text{length of } \overline{EF} \end{matrix}$$

$$12n = 14(18)$$
$$12n = 252$$
$$n = 21$$

The length of $\overline{AB}$ is 21 millimeters.

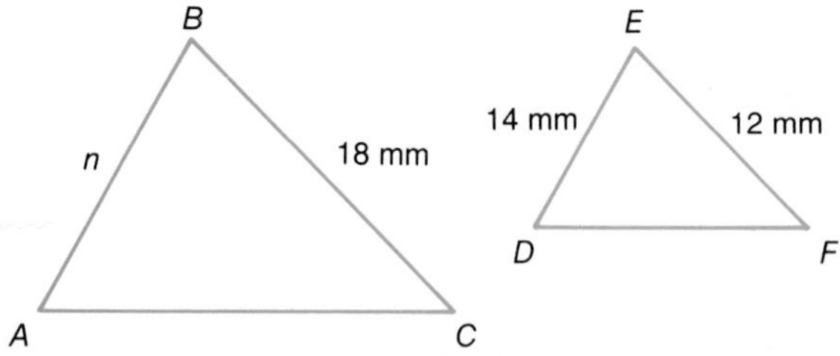

You know that congruent polygons have the same shape and size. The ratios of corresponding sides are 1:1, or $\frac{1}{1}$.

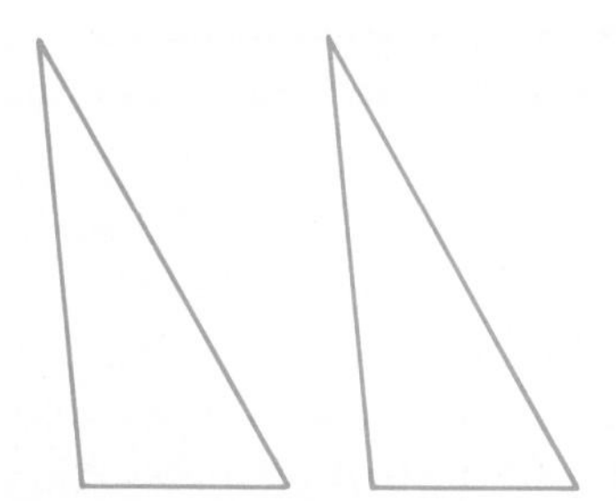

Are all congruent polygons also similar? Are all similar polygons also congruent?

Practice • The figures in each pair are similar. Find the missing length.

1. 27 cm, n; 9 cm, 21 cm

2. 10 mm, 26 mm; 15 mm, n

Mixed Practice • The corresponding angles of the figures are congruent. Compare the lengths of the corresponding sides. Are the figures similar?

3.

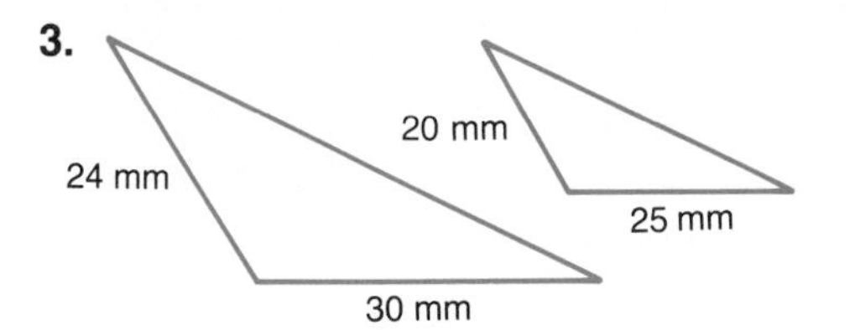

4.

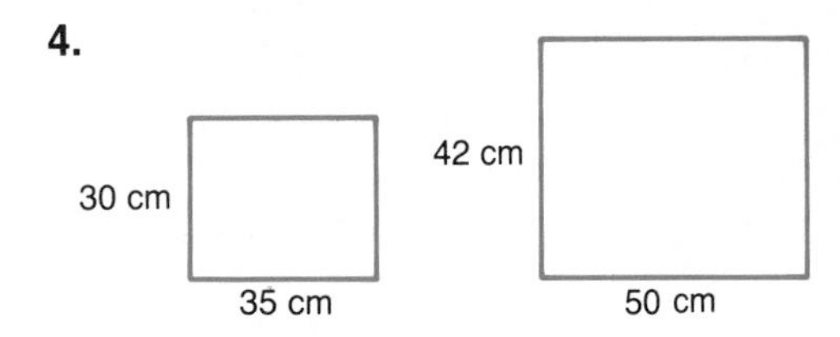

The figures in each pair are similar. Find the missing measure.

5.

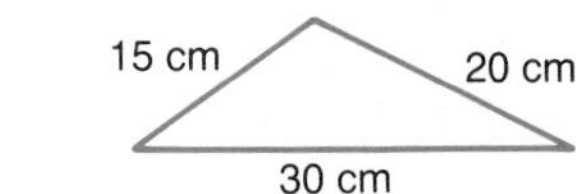

6.

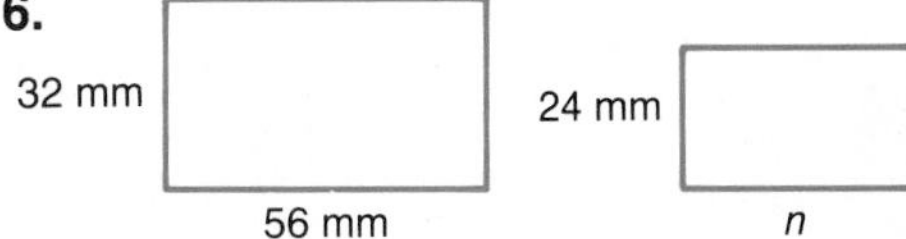

On graph paper draw

7. two similar triangles that are not congruent.

8. two similar triangles that are also congruent.

★ **9.** Draw two squares, one larger than the other. Are the squares similar? How do you know?

★ **10.** Are all squares similar to each other?

PROBLEM SOLVING • APPLICATIONS

An **enlargement** of a photograph is similar to the original photograph.

11. An original photograph is 18 centimeters high and 12 centimeters wide. If the height of the enlargement is 27 centimeters, what is its width?

12. If the width of the enlargement is 20 centimeters, what is its height?

★ **13.** Look up **shadow reckoning** in a reference library. Write a report on it.

Solid Figures

A **polyhedron** is a solid figure with flat surfaces called **faces**. Each face is a polygon.

A **prism** is a polyhedron with parallel **bases** that are congruent polygons. The shape of the base is used to name the prism. The other faces are parallelograms.

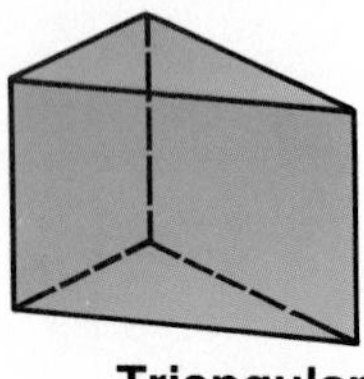
Triangular

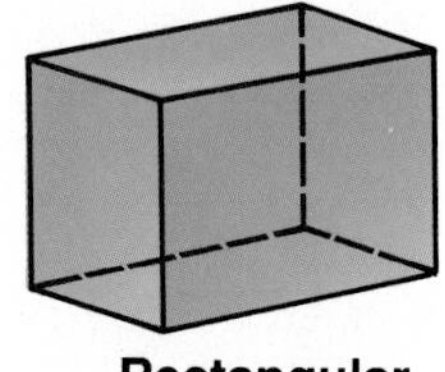
Rectangular

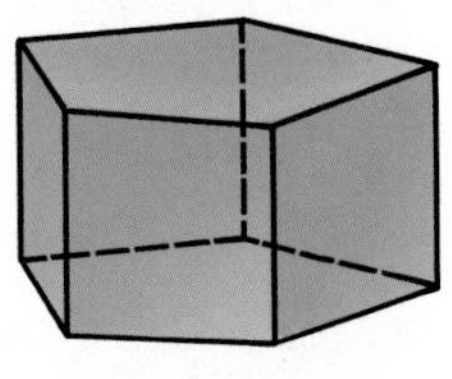
Pentagonal

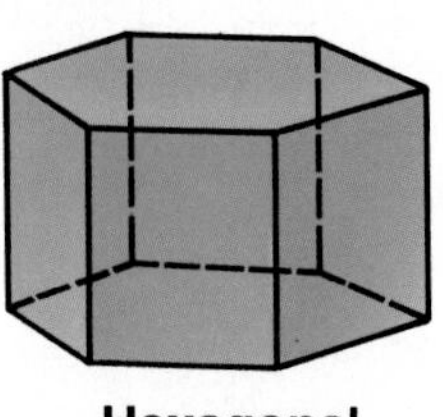
Hexagonal

A **pyramid** is a polyhedron with one base that is a polygon. The shape of the base is used to name the pyramid. The other faces are triangles.

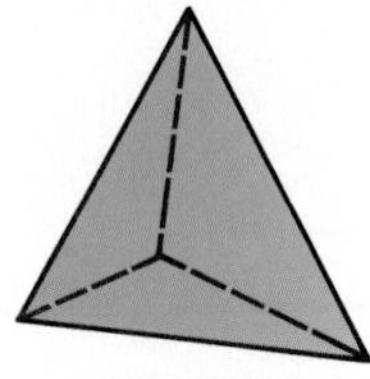
Triangular

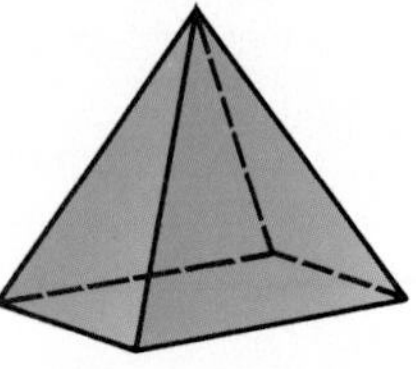
Rectangular

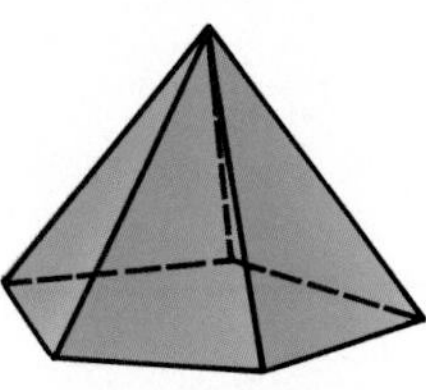
Pentagonal

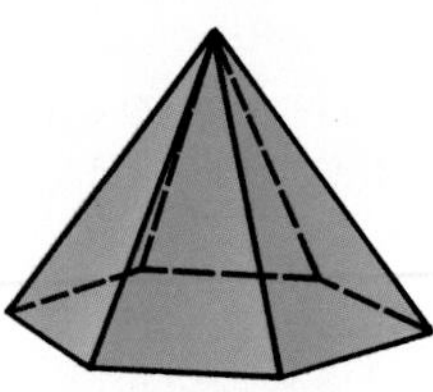
Hexagonal

Here are solid figures that are not polyhedrons. Their surfaces are not polygons.

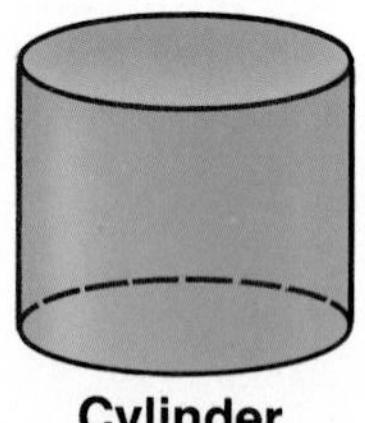
Cylinder

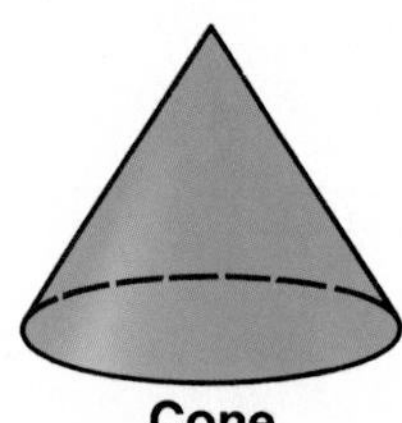
Cone

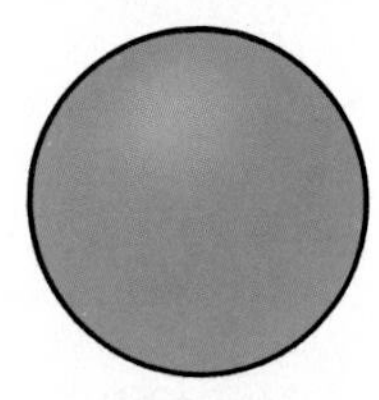
Sphere

Practice • Is it a polyhedron? Write *yes* or *no*.

1. a cone **2.** a triangular pyramid **3.** a rectangular prism

The faces or surfaces of several solid figures are shown. Name the figures. Is each a polyhedron? Write *yes* or *no*.

4. 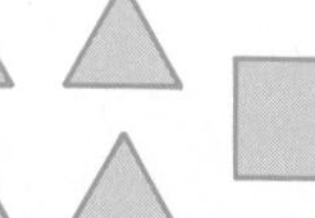

5. 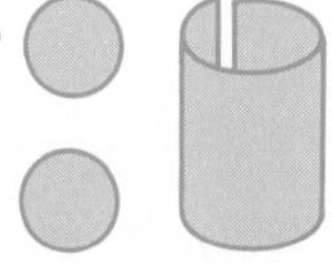

6. 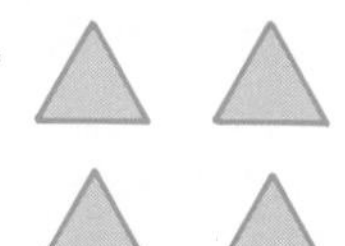

7. 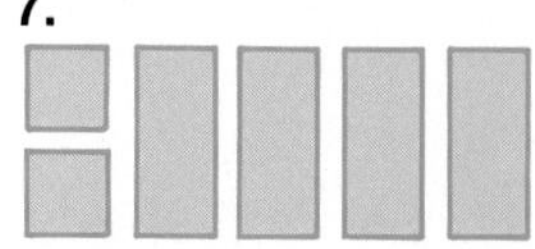

Mixed Practice • Is it a polyhedron? Write *yes* or *no*.

8. a hexagonal prism **9.** a sphere **10.** a rectangular pyramid

The faces or surfaces of several solid figures are shown. Name the figures. Is each a polyhedron? Write *yes* or *no*.

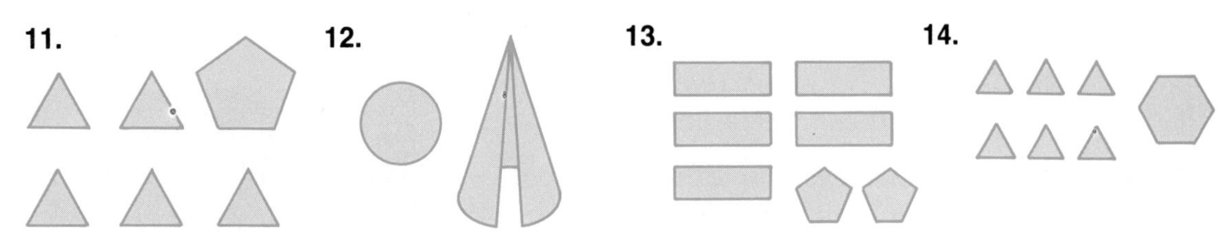

Rectangle $ABCD$ is a face of the triangular prism. Point A is a vertex. $\overline{AB}$ is an **edge**.

Copy and complete.

	Polyhedron	Number of Faces	Number of Vertices	Number of Edges
15.	Triangular Prism			
16.	Rectangular Prism			
17.	Pentagonal Prism			
18.	Hexagonal Prism			
19.	Triangular Pyramid			
20.	Rectangular Pyramid			
21.	Pentagonal Pyramid			
22.	Hexagonal Pyramid			

B E C A F D

★ **23.** Find the sum of the number of faces (F) and the number of vertices (V) for each polyhedron in exercises 15–22.

★ **24.** Write a formula to relate the sum, $F + V$, to the number of edges, E.

PROBLEM SOLVING • APPLICATIONS

★ **25.** On a piece of stiff paper, draw six congruent rectangles that are not squares. Can you make a prism from these figures?

★ **26.** Draw six congruent rectangles that are squares. Can you make a prism from these figures?

Using Logic

Logic can be used to solve many problems. In this logic puzzle, use the clues to help find the answer.

Ari, Ben, and Craig are each on different school teams. The teams are basketball, football, and soccer. Who is on each team?

Clue A Ari and the soccer player walk to school together.

Clue B The football player and the soccer player both watched Craig play in the game.

It is sometimes helpful to make a chart to show all the possibilities.

Use an X to show that a possibility cannot be true. Use a ✓ when you are certain that a possibility is true.

From Clue A, you know Ari is not the soccer player. Place an X next to Ari's name in the soccer column.

	Basketball	Football	Soccer
Ari			X
Ben			
Craig			

From Clue B, you know Craig is not the football or soccer player. Place an X next to Craig's name in the football and soccer columns. There is only one choice left for Craig. Place a ✓ in the basketball column for Craig. Then fill in the rest of the basketball column with Xs.

	Basketball	Football	Soccer
Ari	X		X
Ben	X		
Craig	✓	X	X

From what has been eliminated, you can now solve the rest of the puzzle. There is only one choice left for Ari: football. That leaves soccer for Ben. From the last chart, you have Ari on the football team, Ben on the soccer team, and Craig on the basketball team.

	Basketball	Football	Soccer
Ari	X	✓	X
Ben	X	X	✓
Craig	✓	X	X

Check the answer with the clues.

Solve. For some of the problems, you may not need to use a chart.

1. Mr. Rose, Mr. Shaw, and Mr. Turner went to Chicago by bus, by plane, and by train.

Clue A Mr. Rose and the person who went by plane live next door to each other.
Clue B Mr. Turner and the person who went by bus left at different times.
Clue C Mr. Rose did not go by bus.

How did each man get to Chicago?

2. y is a whole number.

Clue A y is not odd.
Clue B y is prime.

What number is y?

3. x is a whole number.

Clue A $x > 0$.
Clue B x is not prime.
Clue C x is not composite.

What number is x?

4. Mrs. Arthur, Mr. Bloom, and Mrs. Conway teach English, math, and science.

Clue A Mrs. Arthur and the English teacher drive to school together.
Clue B The math teacher and Mrs. Conway have lunch together.
Clue C Mrs. Conway is not the English teacher.

What does each person teach?

Check to see that you have used the facts correctly.

5. X and Y are angles.

Clue A $\angle X$ and $\angle Y$ are supplementary.
Clue B $\angle X$ is an acute angle.

What kind of angle is $\angle Y$?

$\overline{JK}$, $\overline{KL}$, and $\overline{LJ}$ form a triangle. Use $\triangle JKL$ for problems 6–10.

6. If $m\angle J = 80°$ and $m\angle K = 15°$, what kind of triangle is $\triangle JKL$?

7. If $m\angle J = 70°$ and $m\angle K = 18°$, what kind of triangle is $\triangle JKL$?

8. If $m\angle J = 30°$ and $m\angle K = 60°$, what kind of triangle is $\triangle JKL$?

9. If $m\overline{JK} = 6$ cm, $m\overline{KL} = 6$ cm, and and $m\overline{LJ} = 5.9$ cm, is $\triangle JKL$ an equilateral triangle?

★**10.** If $m\angle J = \frac{1}{3}m\angle L$ and $m\angle K = \frac{2}{3}m\angle L$, what kind of triangle is $\triangle JKL$?

★**11.** Henry, Iris, Julie, and Ken are 8 years old, 11 years old, 13 years old, and 14 years old.

Clue A Julie and the 11-year-old live next door to each other.
Clue B The 8-year-old is always following Henry and Ken.
Clue C Henry and Julie went to the 13-year-old's party.
Clue D Julie is older than Henry.

How old is each person?

CHAPTER 12

REVIEW

1. Name the point of intersection of $\overleftrightarrow{AB}$ and $\overleftrightarrow{CD}$. (pp. 304–305)

2. Name two line segments on $\overleftrightarrow{AB}$. (pp. 304–305)

3. Name two rays on $\overleftrightarrow{CD}$. (pp. 304–305)

4. Name the angle formed by $\overrightarrow{EA}$ and $\overrightarrow{ED}$. (pp. 304–305)

A D E C B

Measure the angles. Then write *right, acute,* or *obtuse.* (pp. 306–307)

5. angle AED

6. angle DEB

Use the diagram of the circle for exercises 7–14. (pp. 308–309, 314–315)

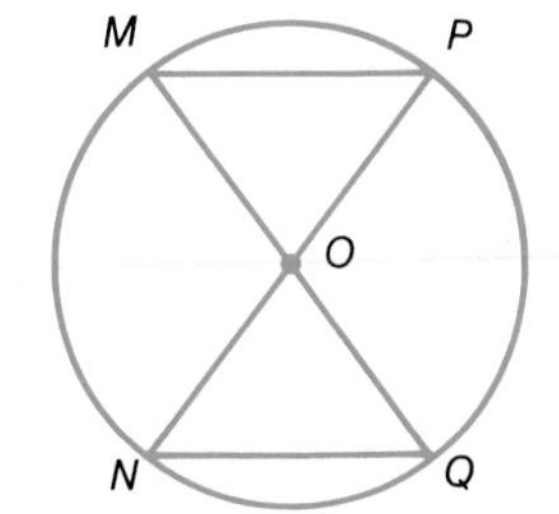

7.–12. Name the center of the circle, four radii, four chords, two diameters, four arcs, and four central angles.

13. Are angles NOQ and QOP complementary?

14. Are angles NOQ and QOP supplementary?

15. The measures of two angles of a triangle are 55° and 75°. What is the measure of the third angle? (pp. 320–321)

16. Figure $QRST$ is a parallelogram. Name the congruent sides. Name the parallel sides. (pp. 322–323)

Triangles *LMN* and *WXY* are congruent. Complete. (pp. 324–325)

L W Y X M N

17. $\overline{LN} \cong$ ___?___

18. $\overline{MN} \cong$ ___?___

19. $\angle M \cong$ ___?___

20. $\angle L \cong$ ___?___

21. The figures are similar. Find the missing length. (pp. 328–329)

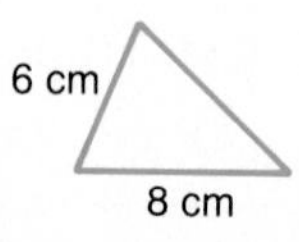

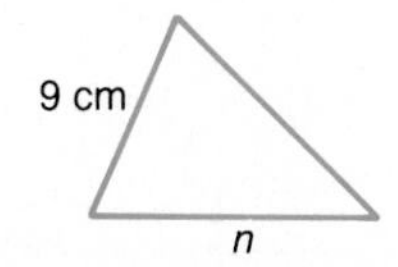

22. How many edges does a triangular prism have? (pp. 330–331)

23. X and Y are angles. $\angle X$ and $\angle Y$ are supplementary. $\angle Y$ is an obtuse angle. What kind of angle is $\angle X$? (pp. 332–333)

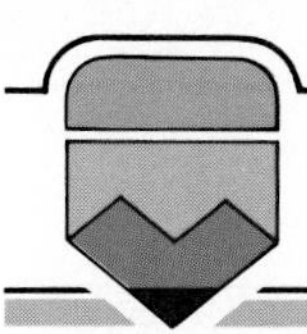

PROJECT

Exploring Constructions

Suppose you are given line n with point P on it. You want to construct a line perpendicular to n at point P.

First, place the compass point at P. Draw arcs that intersect n at A and B.

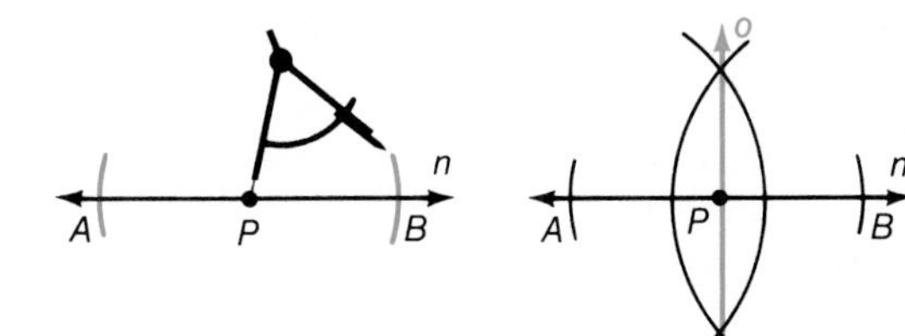

Now construct line o, the bisector of $\overline{AB}$. (See page 312 if you need help.)

Line o passes through P and is perpendicular to n. $o \perp n$.

Suppose you are given a line m and a point P not on m. You want to construct a line through P parallel to m.

Through P, draw a transversal intersecting line m, forming angle 1.

With P as vertex and the transversal as one side, construct an angle (angle 2) that is a corresponding angle for angle 1. (See page 310 if you need help.)

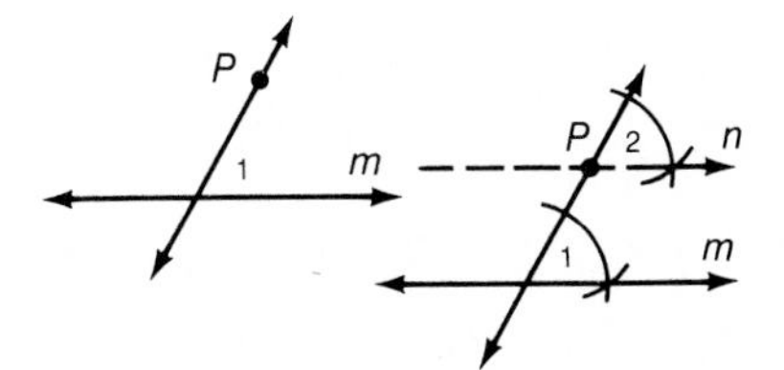

Line n passes through P and is parallel to m. $n \parallel m$.

1. Draw a large triangle. Construct the perpendicular bisector for each side of the triangle. In how many points do the bisectors intersect?

2. In a circle, draw a diameter, $\overline{AB}$. Then construct a diameter, $\overline{XY}$, perpendicular to $\overline{AB}$. Draw polygon $AXBY$. Is it a regular polygon? Name the type of polygon it is.

3. In separate circles, construct a regular triangle, quadrilateral, hexagon, and octagon. (See page 319, exercises 24-25, if you need help in constructing a regular triangle or a regular hexagon.) Draw the radii to the vertices of each figure. Then measure the central angles formed. Summarize your findings in a table or in a short paragraph.

CHAPTER 12

TEST

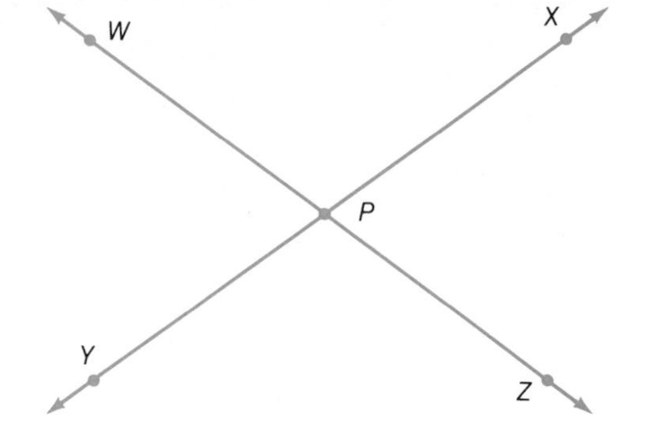

1. Name the point of intersection of $\overleftrightarrow{XY}$ and $\overleftrightarrow{WZ}$.

2. Name two segments on $\overleftrightarrow{WZ}$.

3. Name two rays on $\overleftrightarrow{XY}$.

4. Name the angle formed by $\overrightarrow{PW}$ and $\overrightarrow{PX}$.

Measure the angles.
Then write *right*, *acute*, or *obtuse*.

5. angle *WPX*
6. angle *XPZ*

Use the diagram of the circle for exercises 7–14.

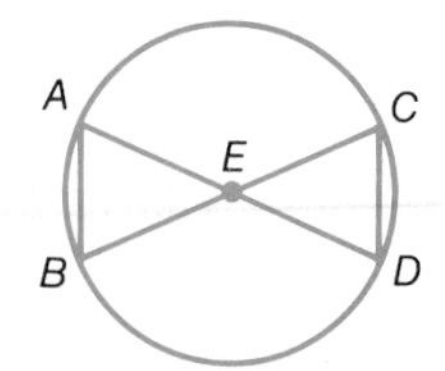

7.–12. Name the center of the circle, four radii, four chords, two diameters, four arcs, and four central angles.

13. Are angles *BED* and *DEC* complementary?

14. Are angles *BED* and *DEC* supplementary?

15. The measures of two angles of a triangle are 60° and 85°. What is the measure of the third angle?

16. Figure *ABCD* is a rhombus.
Name the congruent sides.
Name the parallel sides.

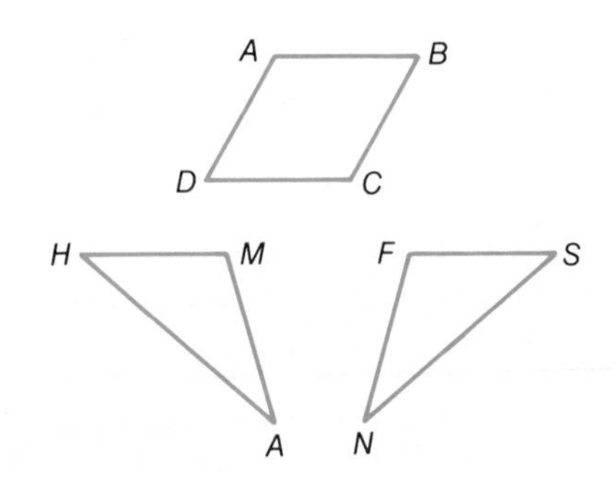

Triangles *HMA* and *SFN* are congruent.
Complete.

17. $\overline{HA} \cong$ ___?___
18. $\overline{MA} \cong$ ___?___
19. $\angle H \cong$ ___?___
20. $\angle A \cong$ ___?___

21. The figures are similar. Find the missing length.

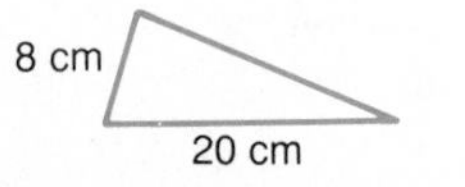

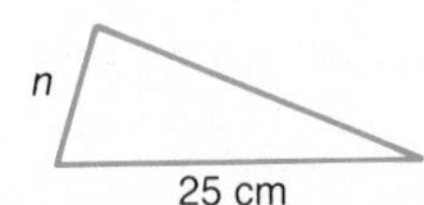

22. How many edges does a rectangular prism have?

23. *M* and *N* are angles. $\angle M$ and $\angle N$ are supplementary. $\angle N$ is a right angle. What kind of angle is $\angle M$?

ENRICHMENT

Angles and Polygons

You know that the sum of the measures of the angles of a triangle is 180°.

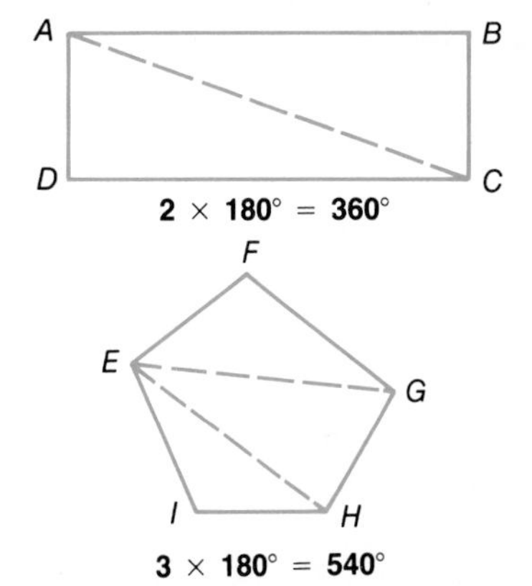

Now consider figure *ABCD*. It has 4 sides. The dotted line stands for a diagonal. It separates the figure into 2 triangles.

So the sum of the measures of the angles is 2 × 180°, or 360°.

Figure *EFGHI* has 5 sides. The dotted lines stand for diagonals drawn from one vertex. The figure is divided into 3 triangles. So the sum of the measures of the angles is 3 × 180°, or 540°.

1. Copy and complete the table below. (Draw each figure and separate it into triangles until you discover the pattern.)

Sum of the Measures of the Angles of a Polygon		
Number of Sides	**Number of Triangles**	**Sum of the Measures of the Angles**
3	1	1 × 180° = 180°
4	2	2 × 180° = 360°
5	3	3 × 180° = 540°
6	?	?
7	?	?
8	?	?

Have you discovered the pattern? If so, try the questions below. What is the sum of the measures of the angles in a polygon that has

2. 9 sides?

3. 10 sides?

4. 15 sides?

5. 20 sides?

6. 30 sides?

7. 100 sides?

8. Let n stand for the number of sides of a polygon, and let A stand for the sum of the measures of its angles. Write a rule to show how A is related to n.

COMPUTER

Operation of an Assembler

In Chapter 5 you saw that assemblers translate instructions into machine language. Now you will see how assemblers operate.

As an example, here are three instructions for a computer.

AC = *Add* the *Constants* (same as Literals) that follow.

0D = *Display* the sum on the CRT (cathode-ray tube).

0B = *Begin* the program now.

This table shows how to translate the nibbles. (Review the lesson in Chapter 3 if necessary.)

0000	0001	0010	0011	0100	0101	0110	0111	1000	1001	1010	1011	1100	1101	1110	1111
0	1	2	3	4	5	6	7	8	9	A	B	C	D	E	F

Here is a very small *program*.	These are the *bits*.
AC 4,5	10101100 0100 0101
0D	00001101
0B	00001011

Do you see how the bits correspond to the characters in the program?

The assembler would follow these steps.

1. Read the first byte: 10101100
2. Translate: *Add* the *Constants* that follow
3. Read the second byte: 0100 0101
4. Translate: The numbers to add are *4* and *5*
5. Read the third byte: 00001101
6. Translate: *Display* the sum on the CRT
7. Read the fourth byte: 01001011
8. Translate: *Begin* the program now

The computer now can follow the instructions in the program.

9. *Add* 4 and 5
10. *Display* the sum on the CRT.

Use the example on page 338. Follow these steps as the assembler and computer would.

Program: 10101100 0011 0101
00001101
00001011

Steps:

1. Read the first byte: ______
2. Translate: ______
3. Read the second byte: ______
4. Translate: ______
5. Read the third byte: ______
6. Translate: ______
7. Read the fourth byte: ______
8. Translate: ______
9. *Add* ______ and ______
10. *Display* the sum on the CRT: ______

In this example the first instruction takes two bytes. In a 16-bit computer, two bytes would fit into one *computer word*.

The second and third instructions each take one byte. In a 16-bit computer, each byte would fit into a *computer halfword*.

In a 16-bit computer, the program at the top of this page would take four computer halfwords. Four computer halfwords are the same as two computer words.

11. If the instruction were AA 32766,32767, how many bits would it take to hold the binary representation of the address 32767?
12. How many bytes would each of these two addresses require?
13. How many bytes would the AA instruction require?
14. In a 16-bit computer, how many computer halfwords would the AA instruction require?
15. In a 16-bit computer, how many computer words would the AA instruction require?

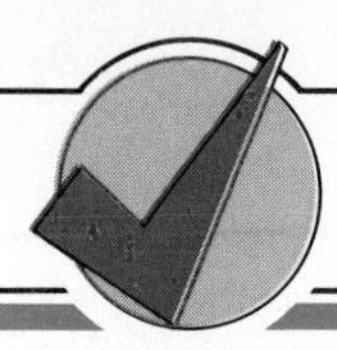

SKILLS MAINTENANCE

Chapters 1 Through 12

Choose the correct answers.

1. Round 12.865 to the nearest hundredth.

   A. 12.87
   B. 12.86
   C. 12.90
   D. not here

2. Add.

$$\begin{array}{r} 42.615 \\ 5.86 \\ +\ 0.0807 \\ \hline \end{array}$$

   A. 47.4557
   B. 48.5557
   C. 48.5577
   D. not here

3. Solve.

   $29.7 \times 3.06 = n$

   A. $n = 908.82$
   B. $n = 9.0882$
   C. $n = 90.882$
   D. not here

4. Divide. Round the quotient to the nearest hundredth.

   $6.9\overline{)4.8997}$

   A. 0.71
   B. 0.72
   C. 7.10
   D. not here

5. Find the GCF of 24 and 84.

   A. 8
   B. 6
   C. 12
   D. not here

6. Subtract.

$$\begin{array}{r} 7\frac{1}{4} \\ -4\frac{5}{8} \\ \hline \end{array}$$

   A. $2\frac{7}{8}$ B. $3\frac{5}{8}$
   C. $3\frac{3}{8}$ D. not here

7. Divide. Write the answer in lowest terms.

   $3\frac{7}{9} \div 2\frac{2}{3}$

   A. $1\frac{5}{12}$ B. $10\frac{2}{27}$
   C. $1\frac{7}{12}$ D. not here

8. 40% of what number is 34?

   A. 13.6 B. 34
   C. 85 D. not here

9. The measures of two angles of a triangle are 62° and 74°. What is the measure of the third angle?

   A. 54° B. 34°
   C. 44° D. not here

10. If $m\angle A = 30°$ and $m\angle B = 30°$, what kind of a triangle is $\triangle ABC$?

    A. acute B. obtuse
    C. right D. not here

11. If $m\,\overline{AB} = 7$ cm, $m\,\overline{BC} = 7$ cm, and $m\,\overline{AC} = 9$ cm, what kind of a triangle is $\triangle ABC$?

    A. isosceles B. equilateral
    C. scalene D. not here

Perimeter, Area, and Volume

Perimeter • Circumference • Area of Rectangles, Parallelograms, Triangles, Trapezoids, and Circles • Surface Area • Volume of Prisms and Cylinders • Problem Solving: Using a Diagram • Reviewing and Using Formulas • Problem Solving: Analyzing Conclusions • Square Roots

erimeter

The distance around a polygon is its **perimeter**. You find the perimeter by finding the sum of the lengths of its sides.

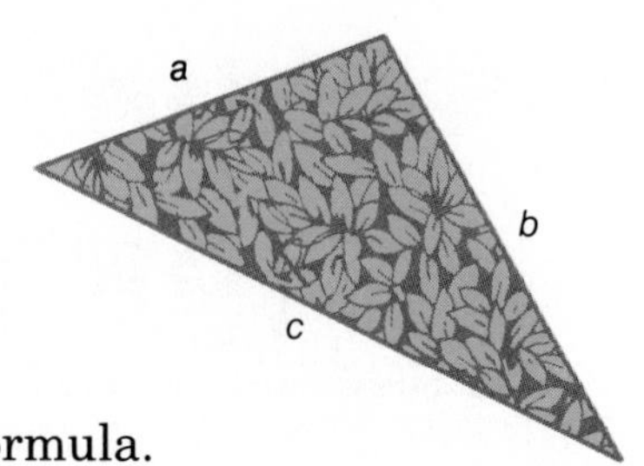

This flower garden is shaped like a triangle. Suppose a, b, and c stand for the lengths of the sides. Then the perimeter is $a + b + c$.

The perimeter (P) of the triangle is given by this formula.

$$P = a + b + c$$

Suppose a is 3.8 meters, b is 4.3 meters, and c is 6.4 meters. Then:

$$\begin{aligned} P &= 3.8 + 4.3 + 6.4 \\ &= 14.5 \end{aligned}$$

The perimeter is 14.5 meters.

In a rectangle the opposite sides are congruent. This drawing shows a rectangle with **length** l and **width** w. The perimeter (P) is given by this formula.

$$P = 2l + 2w$$

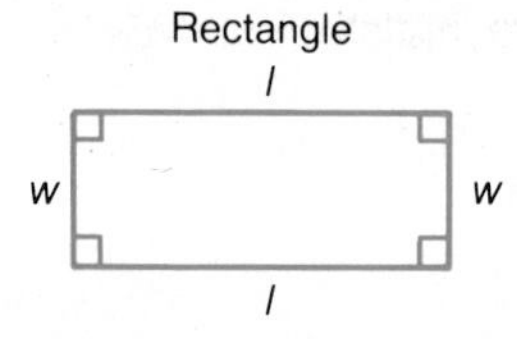

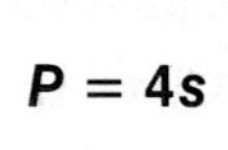

In a square all four sides are the same length. If one side of a square has length s, then the perimeter (P) is given by this formula.

$$P = 4s$$

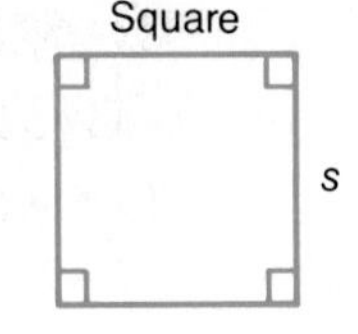

Find the perimeter of a rectangle in which l is 7.4 meters and w is 5.2 meters.

$$\begin{aligned} P &= 2l + 2w \\ &= (2 \times 7.4) + (2 \times 5.2) \\ &= 14.8 + 10.4 \\ &= 25.2 \text{ meters} \end{aligned}$$

Find the perimeter of a square in which s is 2.8 meters.

$$\begin{aligned} P &= 4s \\ &= 4 \times 2.8 \\ &= 11.2 \text{ meters} \end{aligned}$$

Practice • Find the perimeter of each polygon.

1. 10 mm, 6 mm, 9 mm

2.

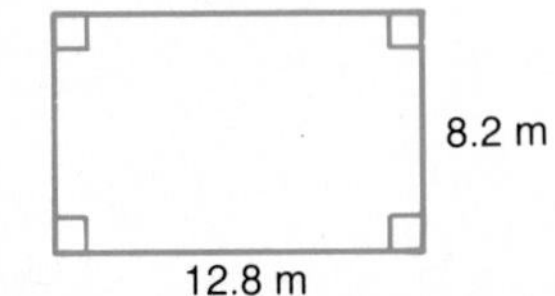

3.

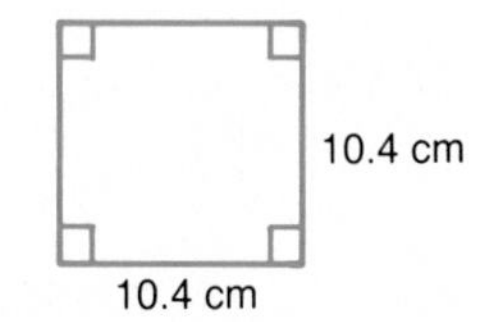

Mixed Practice • Find the perimeter of each polygon.

4.

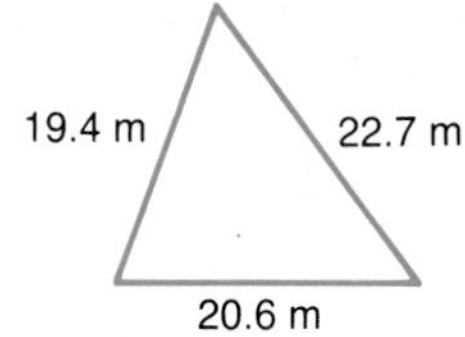

5.

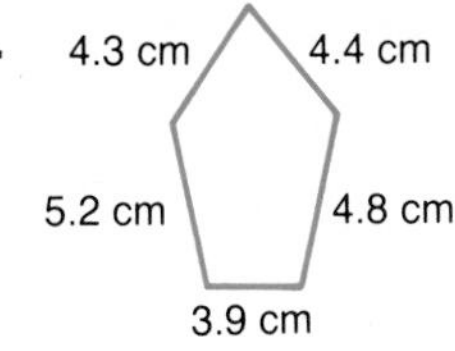

6.

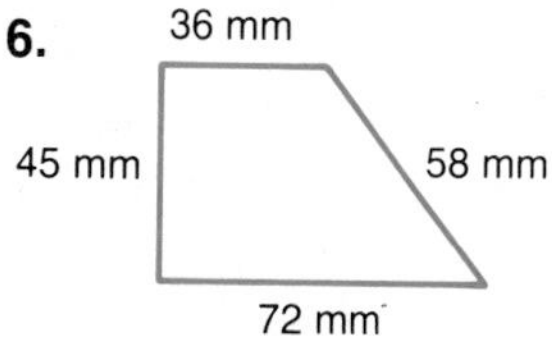

Find the perimeter of a triangle when

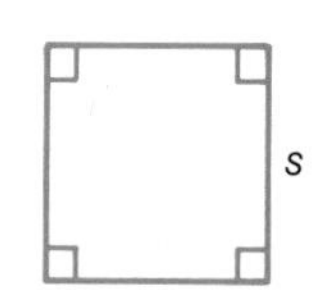

7. $a = 7.9$ cm, $b = 11.3$ cm, $c = 18.4$ cm.

8. $a = 2.75$ m, $b = 3.68$ m, $c = 4.29$ m.

Find the perimeter of a rectangle when

9. $l = 37$ cm, $w = 29$ cm.

10. $l = 4.8$ m, $w = 3.2$ m.

11. $l = 62.8$ cm, $w = 36.9$ cm.

Find the perimeter of a square when

12. $s = 184$ cm.

13. $s = 7.1$ km.

14. $s = 19.4$ m.

★ **15.** Write a formula for the perimeter of an equilateral triangle. (Use s for the length of a side.)

★ **16.** Write a formula for the perimeter of a regular hexagon.

PROBLEM SOLVING • APPLICATIONS

17. Jay wants to put a fence around his vegetable garden. The garden is shaped like a square and measures 6.5 meters on a side. How many meters of fencing are needed to go around the garden?

18. If fencing costs $2.75 a meter, how much will the fencing for Jay's garden cost?

★ **19.** Ann's vegetable garden is shaped like a square. The perimeter of the garden is 33.2 meters. How long is each side of the garden?

★ **20.** Erin's flower garden is shaped like a rectangle. The length of one side is 11.6 meters and the perimeter is 44.6 meters. How wide is the garden?

Circumference

The distance around a circle is its **circumference**.

Hisako and Tony use string to find the circumference of some circular objects. They also measure the diameters of the objects.

They use division to compare each circumference (C) to the diameter (d).

Object	C	d	$\frac{C}{d}$
can	31.8 cm	10.1 cm	3.15
jam jar	42.6 cm	13.6 cm	3.13
bowl	24.8 cm	7.9 cm	3.14

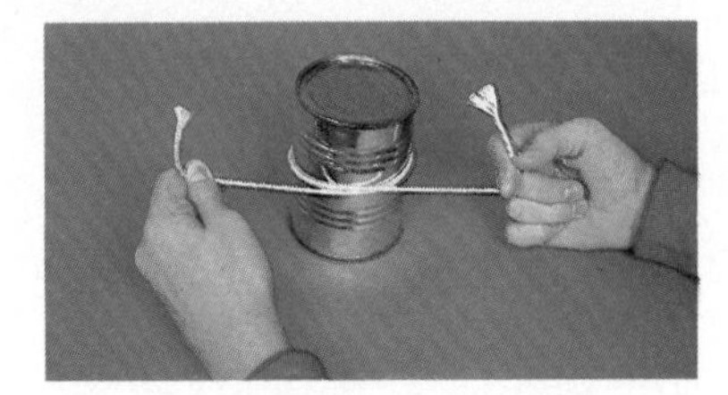

They discover that $\frac{C}{d}$ is about the same for all circular objects. For all circles, $\frac{C}{d}$ is about 3.14. C is about 3.14 times as great as d.
The number $\frac{C}{d}$ is called **pi**. The symbol for pi is the Greek letter π.
Use 3.14 or $\frac{22}{7}$ as an approximation for π.

Since $\frac{C}{d} = \pi$, you can multiply both sides by d
and obtain a formula for the circumference of a circle. ⟶ $\mathbf{C = \pi d}$

A diameter is twice as long as a radius ($d = 2r$), and so you can substitute $2r$ in place of d and obtain $C = \pi \times 2r$.
By rearranging the factors, you obtain the formula shown. ⟶ $\mathbf{C = 2\pi r}$

Here are some examples that use the formulas for circumference.

Find the circumference of a circle whose diameter is 10 centimeters.

Step 1
Choose the formula $C = \pi d$.

Step 2
Replace π with 3.14 and d with 10.

$$C \approx 3.14(10)$$
$$\approx 31.4 \text{ cm}$$
$$\approx 31 \text{ cm}$$

Find the circumference of a circle whose radius is 4 centimeters.

Step 1
Choose the formula $C = 2\pi r$.

Step 2
Replace π with 3.14 and r with 4.

$$C \approx 2(3.14)(4)$$
$$\approx 25.12 \text{ cm}$$
$$\approx 25 \text{ cm}$$

Often the relationship between C and d is described using the word *ratio*. For all circles the ratio $C{:}d$ is equal to the ratio $\pi{:}1$. The second term, 1, is sometimes omitted, and the ratio $C{:}d$ is given simply as π.

Practice • Find each circumference to the nearest whole number.

1. 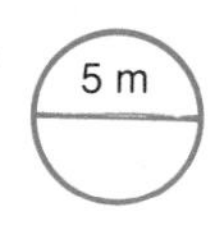

$d = 5$ m

2. 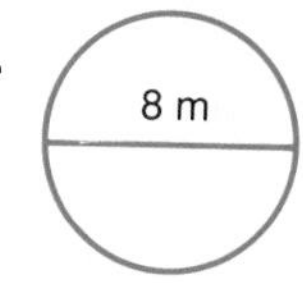

$d = 8$ cm

3. 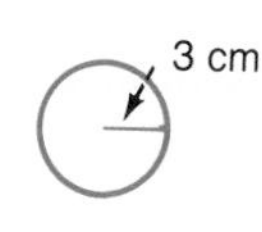

$r = 3$ cm

4. 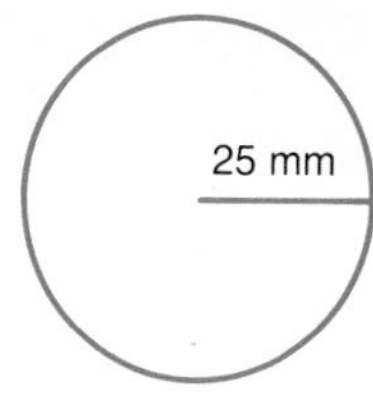

$r = 25$ mm

Mixed Practice • Find each circumference to the nearest whole number.

5. $d = 3$ cm
6. $d = 9$ m
7. $d = 24$ mm
8. $d = 7$ cm
9. $d = 20$ m
10. $d = 35$ cm
11. $d = 50$ mm
12. $d = 75$ m
13. $r = 14$ m
14. $r = 8$ mm
15. $r = 21$ cm
16. $r = 17$ m
17. $r = 28$ mm
18. $r = 41$ mm
19. $r = 70$ cm
20. $r = 11$ m

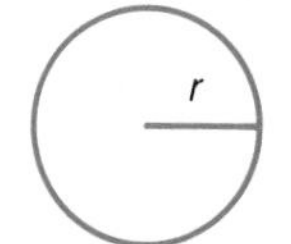

Find each circumference to the nearest tenth.

21. $d = 5.3$ m
22. $d = 8.2$ cm
23. $d = 9.3$ m
24. $d = 6.7$ cm
25. $r = 3.2$ cm
26. $r = 4.8$ m
27. $r = 7.7$ cm
28. $r = 8.6$ m

★ 29. $r = 33.7$ m

★ 30. $d = 67.4$ m

★ 31. $r = 47.2$ cm

★ 32. $d = 94.4$ cm

★ 33. Do any of the circles in exercises 29–32 have the same circumference? If so, explain why the circumferences are the same.

PROBLEM SOLVING • APPLICATIONS

Each figure is made up of rectangles and halves of circles (semicircles). Find the distance shown in blue.

34.

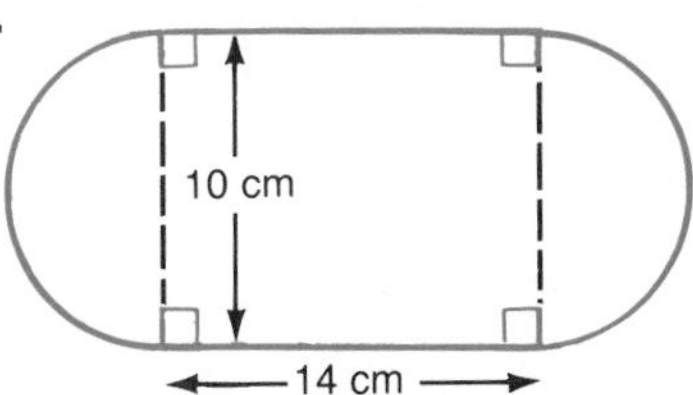

35.

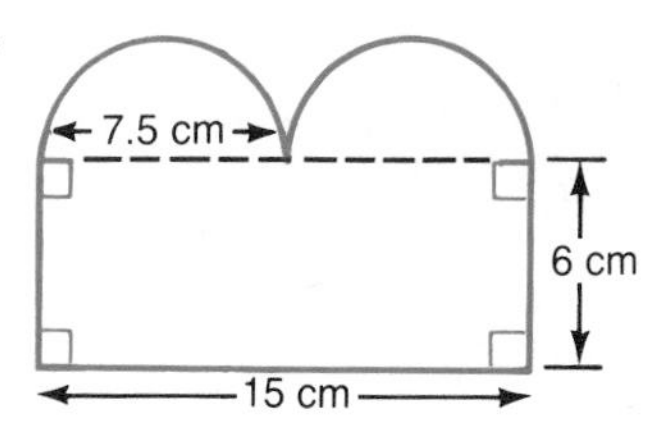

36. The diameter of Joanna's bicycle wheel is 66 centimeters. How far does the wheel travel in one revolution?

37. About how many times will the bicycle wheel turn if Joanna travels 1 kilometer?

★ 38. The diameter of a roller-skate wheel is 5 centimeters. About how many times will the wheel turn to travel 1 kilometer?

Area of Rectangles

The small square tile measures 1 centimeter along each side. It is a unit of **area** called a **square centimeter (cm^2)**.

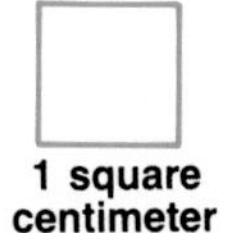

The area of the rectangle is the number of square units needed to cover it. Count to find the area.

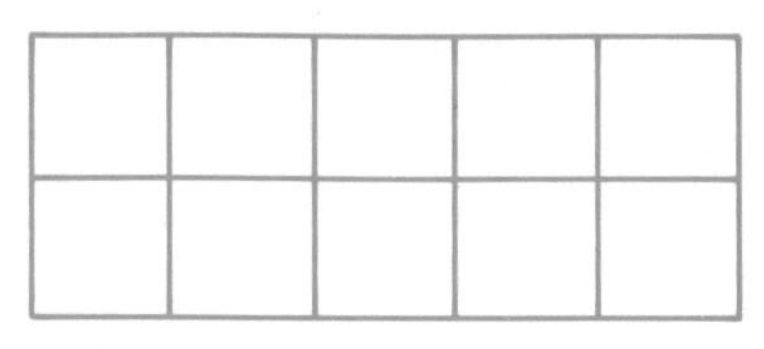

If you know the length and the width of a rectangle, you can multiply to find the area.

The length (l) tells the number of square units in a row. The width (w) tells the number of rows.

$w = 2$ cm

$l = 5$ cm

Area of a rectangle = length × width

Formula: $A = l \times w$

$A = 5 \times 2$

$= 10 \text{ cm}^2$

Since all the sides of a square are congruent, the area of a square can be found by multiplying as shown.

Area of a square = side × side

Formula: $A = s \times s$, or $A = s^2$

$A = 3 \times 3$

$= 9 \text{ cm}^2$

More Examples

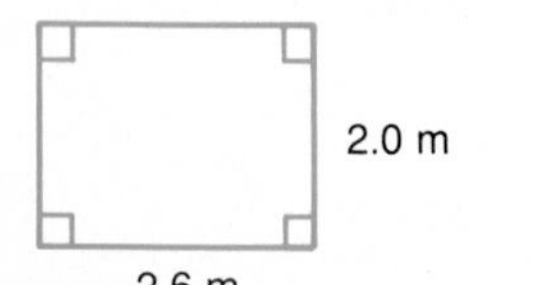

$A = lw$

$A = (2.6)(2.0)$

$= 5.2 \text{ m}^2$

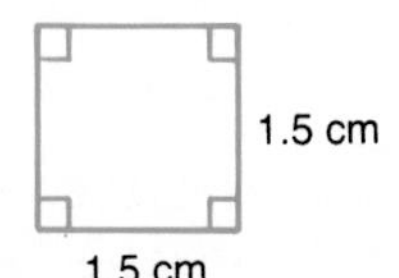

$A = s^2$

$A = (1.5)^2$

$= 2.25 \text{ cm}^2$

Practice • Find the area of each rectangle.

1. $l = 6$ m, $w = 4$ m
2. $l = 2.5$ cm, $w = 3.0$ cm
3. $l = 30$ mm, $w = 15$ mm
4. $l = 6.4$ cm, $w = 2.3$ cm

Find the area of each square.

5. $s = 7$ m
6. $s = 9$ cm
7. $s = 2.5$ cm
8. $s = 8.3$ cm

Mixed Practice • Find the area of each rectangle.

9. $l = 8$ m, $w = 6$ m
10. $l = 5.0$ cm, $w = 3.5$ cm
11. $l = 7.2$ cm, $w = 4.8$ cm
12. $l = 45$ mm, $w = 18$ mm
13. $l = 9$ cm, $w = 6$ cm
14. $l = 14$ mm, $w = 12$ mm
15. $l = 4$ km, $w = 1$ km
16. $l = 9.2$ cm, $w = 6.8$ cm
17. $l = 15$ km, $w = 13$ km
18. $l = 5.7$ m, $w = 2.3$ m
19. $l = 32.2$ cm, $w = 11.6$ cm
20. ★ $l = 184.7$ mm, $w = 184.7$ mm
21. ★ What kind of rectangle is described in exercise 20?

Find the area of each square.

22. $s = 8$ mm
23. $s = 14$ cm
24. $s = 6.5$ m
25. $s = 3.9$ km
26. $s = 35$ mm
27. $s = 70$ mm
28. $s = 4.7$ km
29. $s = 100$ cm
30. ★ How many square centimeters are in one square meter?
31. ★ How many square millimeters are in one square centimeter?

PROBLEM SOLVING • APPLICATIONS

The diagram below shows the floor plan for part of Tama's new house.

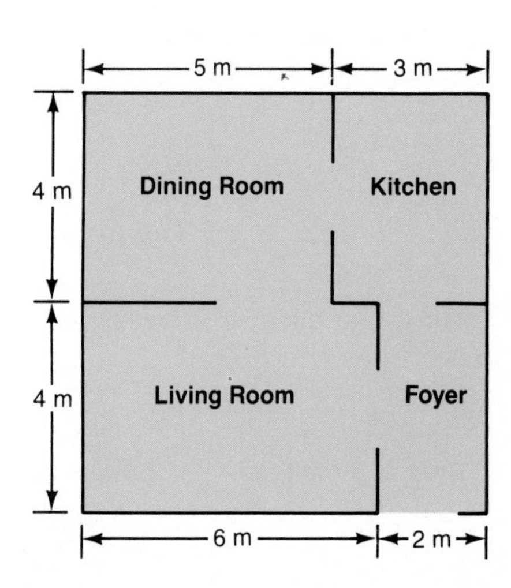

32. How many square meters of carpet will Tama need for the living room?
33. How many square meters of carpet will Tama need for the dining room?
34. If the carpeting that Tama chooses for the living and dining rooms costs $18.00 a square meter, how much will it cost to carpet both rooms?
35. ★ Square floor tiles 25 cm by 25 cm cost $1.02 each. How much would it cost Tama to cover the kitchen floor with these tiles?

Areas of Parallelograms and Triangles

The **base** of this parallelogram is 4 centimeters long. An **altitude** has been drawn from one vertex to the opposite base. The length of the altitude is the **height** of the parallelogram. In this parallelogram the height is 3 centimeters.

If you cut off one end of the parallelogram along its height, you can use the two pieces to make a rectangle.

The area of the rectangle is 4×3 or 12 cm^2. So the area of the parallelogram is also 12 cm^2.

To find the area of a parallelogram, multiply the length of the base (b) times the height (h).

Area of a parallelogram = base × height

Formula: $A = bh$

$$A = 4(3)$$
$$= 12 \text{ cm}^2$$

Below are two congruent triangles. Each triangle has a base 4 centimeters long; the height is 3 centimeters. When the triangles are put together as shown, they form a parallelogram.

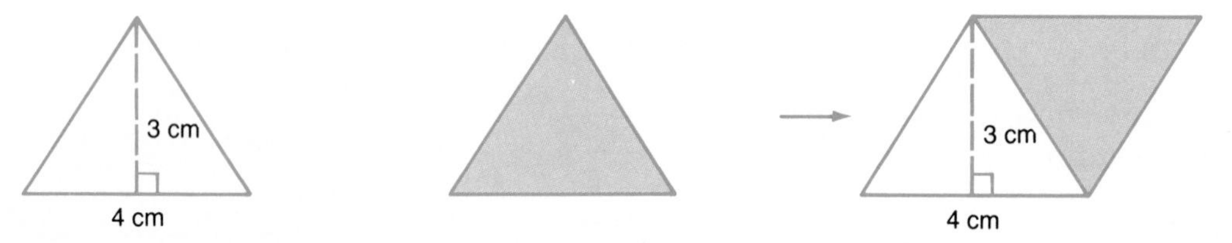

Each triangle has $\frac{1}{2}$ the area of the parallelogram.

To find the area of a triangle, multiply $\frac{1}{2}$ times the length of the base times the height.

Area of a triangle = $\frac{1}{2}$ × base × height

Formula: $A = \frac{1}{2}bh$

$$A = \frac{1}{2}(4 \times 3)$$
$$= 6 \text{ cm}^2$$

Practice • Find the area of each parallelogram.

1. $b = 14$ cm, $h = 11$ cm
2. $b = 8$ cm, $h = 6$ cm
3. $b = 23$ cm, $h = 18$ cm
4. $b = 9$ m, $h = 7$ m

Find the area of each triangle.

5. $b = 5$ cm, $h = 4$ cm
6. $b = 9$ cm, $h = 2$ cm
7. $b = 11$ cm, $h = 8$ cm
8. $b = 22$ m, $h = 16$ m

Mixed Practice • Find the area of each parallelogram.

9. $b = 6$ m, $h = 4$ m
10. $b = 13$ m, $h = 9$ m
11. $b = 3.6$ cm, $h = 2.7$ cm
12. $b = 8.4$ cm, $h = 5.2$ cm
13. $b = 9.3$ m, $h = 8.9$ m
14. $b = 9.5$ km, $h = 7.8$ km
15. $b = 6.5$ cm, $h = 5.6$ cm
★ 16. $b = 1.875$ km, $h = 150$ m

Find the area of each triangle.

17. $b = 16$ m, $h = 11$ m
18. $b = 14$ m, $h = 12$ m
19. $b = 19$ km, $h = 14$ km
20. $b = 30$ km, $h = 24$ km
21. $b = 9.3$ cm, $h = 4.2$ cm
22. $b = 7.7$ cm, $h = 6.6$ cm
23. $b = 9.4$ m, $h = 3.1$ m
★ 24. $b = 19.5$ cm, $h = 16$ mm

PROBLEM SOLVING • APPLICATIONS

Use the drawing to find the area of

25. each large blue parallelogram.
26. the white square.
27. each red triangle.
28. the entire rectangle.

★ 29. Draw two right triangles, $\triangle ABC$ and $\triangle DEF$. In $\triangle DEF$, $m\overline{EF} = 3\ m\overline{BC}$, $m\overline{FD} = 3\ m\overline{CA}$, and $m\overline{DE} = 3\ m\overline{AB}$. The area of $\triangle DEF$ is how many times as great as the area of $\triangle ABC$?

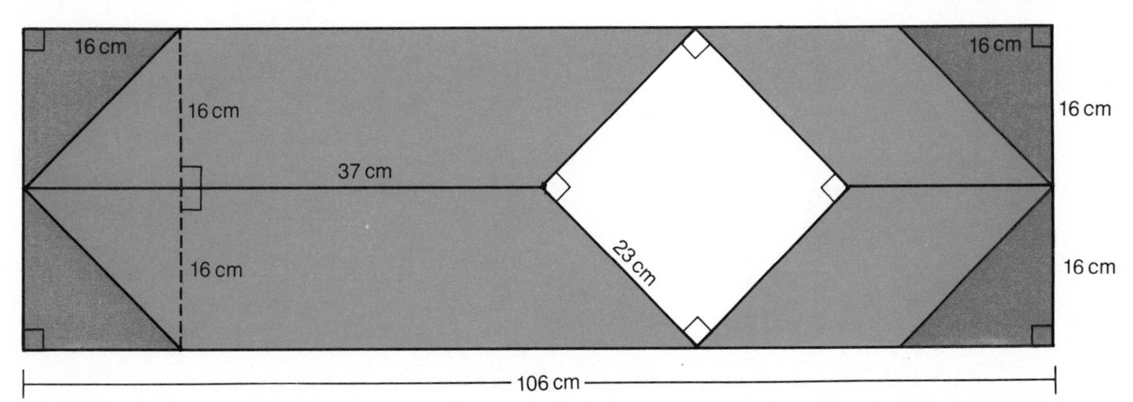

Area of Trapezoids

The parallel sides of a trapezoid are its two **bases**. Base a of this trapezoid is 2 centimeters long. Base b is 4 centimeters long. The height is 3 centimeters.

base a = 2 cm
J K
height = 3 cm
M L
base b = 4 cm

Two congruent trapezoids can be placed together to form a parallelogram. The area of each trapezoid is half the area of the parallelogram.

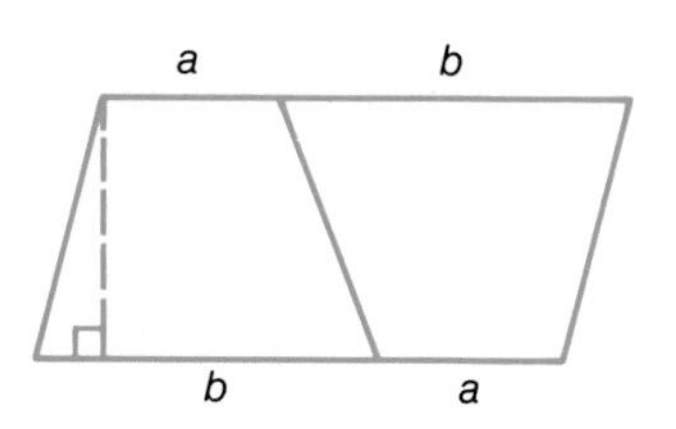

For this parallelogram:

The length of the base is $b + a$, or $a + b$.
The height is h.
The area is $h \times (a + b)$.

The area of each trapezoid is $\frac{1}{2}$ of the area of the parallelogram. So, for each trapezoid, the area is $\frac{1}{2}$ times the height times the sum of the bases.

Area of a trapezoid = $\frac{1}{2}$ × ***height*** × ***sum of the bases***

Formula: $A = \frac{1}{2}h(a + b)$

To find the area of trapezoid $JKLM$, substitute the values you know.

$$A = \frac{1}{2}(3)(2 + 4)$$
$$= 9\,\text{cm}^2$$

More Examples

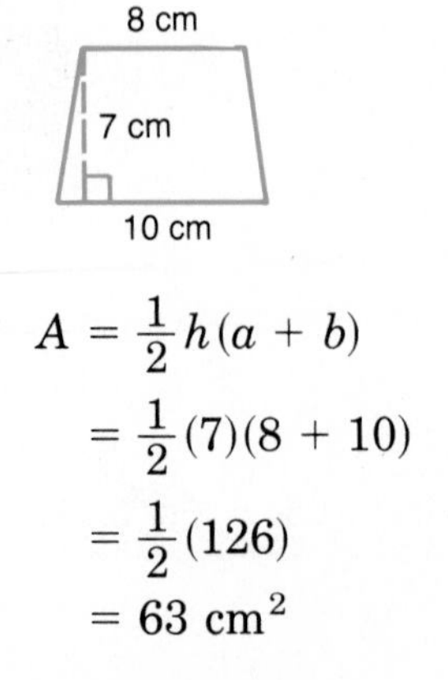

$$A = \frac{1}{2}h(a + b)$$
$$= \frac{1}{2}(7)(8 + 10)$$
$$= \frac{1}{2}(126)$$
$$= 63\text{ cm}^2$$

14.8 m
4.0 m
17.4 m

$$A = \frac{1}{2}h(a + b)$$
$$= \frac{1}{2}(4.0)(14.8 + 17.4)$$
$$= \frac{1}{2}(128.8)$$
$$= 64.4\text{ m}^2$$

Practice • Find the area of each trapezoid.

1.

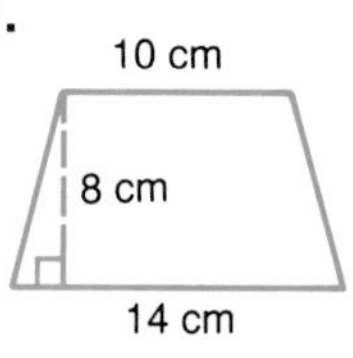

2.

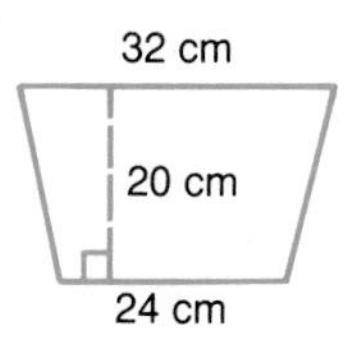

3.

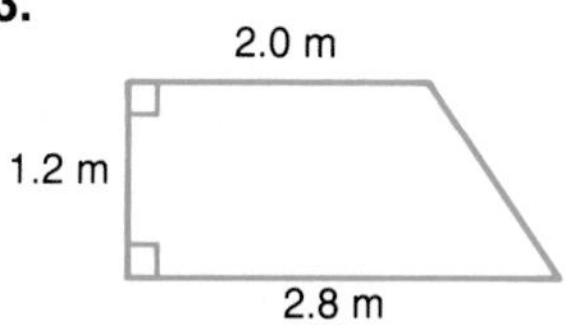

Mixed Practice • Find the area of each trapezoid.

4. $a = 4$ cm, $b = 6$ cm, $h = 5$ cm

5. $a = 7$ cm, $b = 3$ cm, $h = 9$ cm

6. $a = 3$ m, $b = 5$ m, $h = 6$ m

7. $a = 11.5$ cm, $b = 14.8$ cm, $h = 10.0$ cm

8. $a = 20$ m, $b = 21$ m, $h = 24$ m

9. $a = 9$ m, $b = 17$ m, $h = 23$ m

10. $a = 3.2$ cm, $b = 4.6$ cm, $h = 1.4$ cm

★ **11.** $a = 1.25$ m, $b = 1.36$ m, $h = 7$ cm

Find the area of each figure.

12. rectangle, $b = 2.6$ cm, $h = 3.5$ cm

13. triangle, $b = 4.8$ cm, $h = 3.4$ cm

14. parallelogram, $b = 7.6$ m, $h = 3.0$ m

15. triangle, $b = 3.6$ m, $h = 3.6$ m

PROBLEM SOLVING • APPLICATIONS

16. Richard works at a glass store. He wants to know how many square centimeters of glass he uses to replace the back window of a car. Use the drawing to find the area.

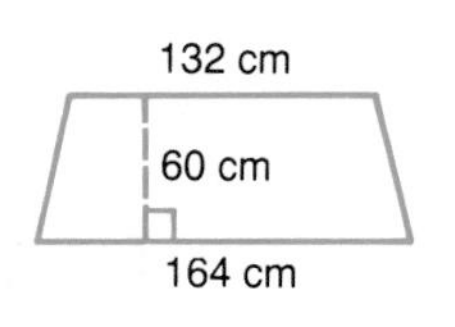

★ **17.** The area of this triangular piece of glass is 18.85 square centimeters. The base is 5.8 centimeters long. What is the height?

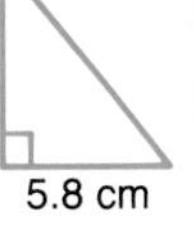

Skills Maintenance

Write as decimals. **1.** 70% **2.** 3% **3.** 8.25%

Write as fractions in lowest terms. **4.** 75% **5.** 4% **6.** $16\frac{2}{3}\%$

Write as percents. **7.** 0.87 **8.** $\frac{3}{5}$ **9.** $\frac{2}{3}$

Area of Circles

Think of the circular figure cut into many pie-shaped wedges. Fit these wedges together, and you have what looks like a parallelogram.

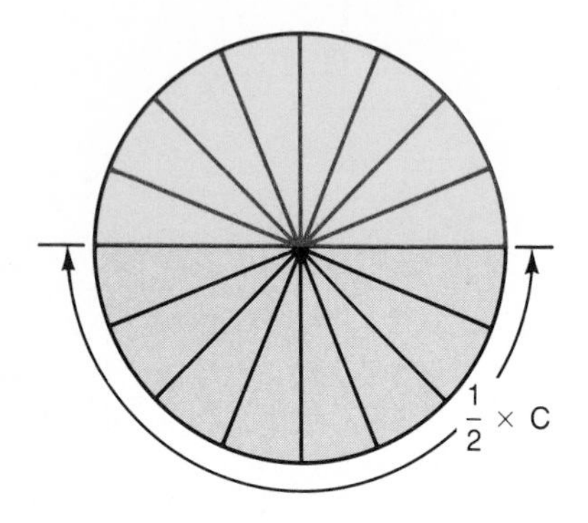

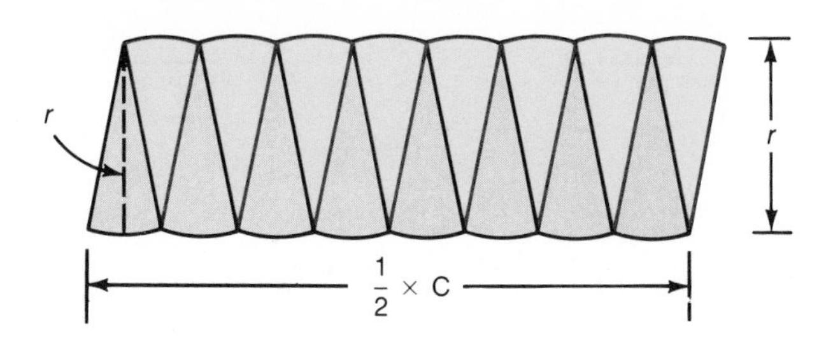

Use what you know about finding the area of a parallelogram.
The length of the base is $\frac{1}{2}$ of the circumference, or $\frac{1}{2} \times C$.
The height is the length of a radius, or r.

The area is base times height. $\longrightarrow A = \frac{1}{2} \times C \times r$

The circumference is $2 \times \pi \times r$. $\longrightarrow A = \frac{1}{2} \times 2 \times \pi \times r \times r$

You know that $\frac{1}{2} \times 2 = 1$, and $r \times r = r^2$. $\longrightarrow A = \pi \times r^2$

Area of a circle = ***pi × square of the radius***

Formula: $A = \pi r^2$

Find the area of a circular tabletop with a radius of 50 centimeters. Use 3.14 as an approximation for π.

$$A = \pi r^2$$
$$A \approx 3.14 \times 50 \times 50$$
$$\approx 7{,}850 \text{ cm}^2$$

Practice • Find the areas. Use 3.14 for π.

1.

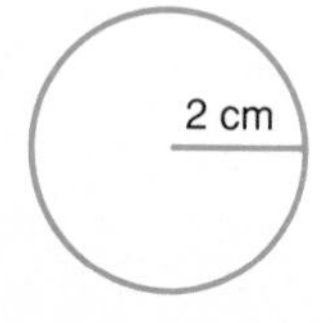

2.

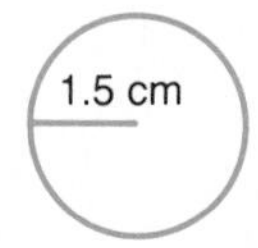

3.

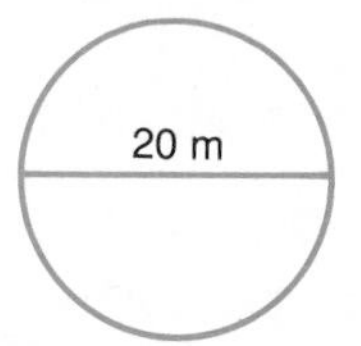

Mixed Practice • Find the area of each circle. Use 3.14 for π.

4. $r = 5$ cm
5. $r = 1$ cm
6. $r = 9$ cm
7. $r = 22$ m
8. $r = 6$ m
9. $r = 20$ m
10. $r = 7$ cm
11. $r = 16$ cm
12. $r = 100$ cm
13. $r = 30$ cm
14. $r = 18$ cm
15. $r = 8$ m
16. $r = 4.6$ cm
17. $r = 9.2$ cm
18. $r = 1.3$ m
19. $d = 2$ m
20. ★ $d = 80$ cm
21. ★ $d = 11$ m
22. ★ $d = 6.4$ cm
23. ★ $d = 1$ m

Find the area of the shaded region.

24.

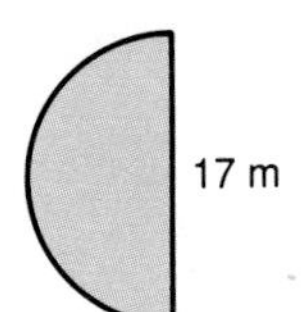

25.

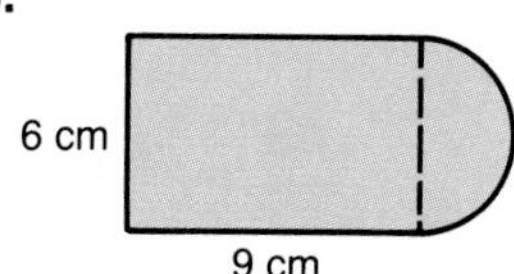

★ 26.

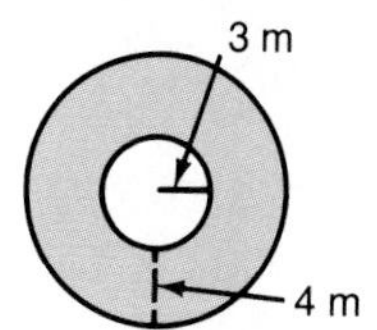

PROBLEM SOLVING • **APPLICATIONS**

27. A circular mat has a radius of 5 meters. What is the area of the mat?

★ 28. A circle has a diameter of 3.8 meters. What is its area?

★ 29. The transmitter for radio station WFAR allows the station to broadcast 48 kilometers in every direction. How many square kilometers is the area that the station reaches?

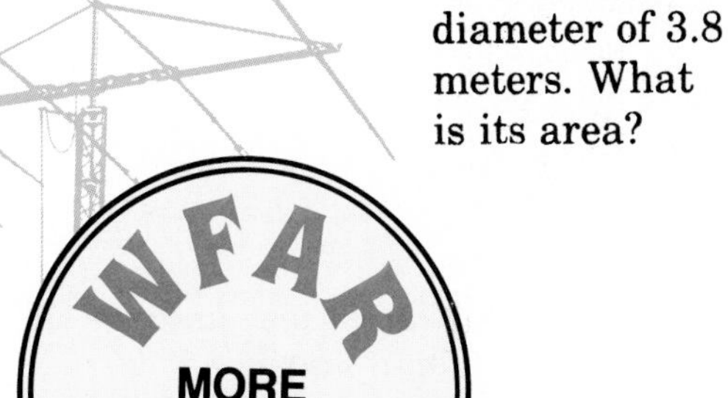

Midchapter Review

Find the perimeters and circumferences.

1. rectangle $l = 14$ cm, $w = 7$ cm
2. square $s = 2.4$ m
3. circle $d = 2$ cm
4. rectangle $l = 7.9$ cm, $w = 6.7$ cm
5. circle $r = 15$ mm

Find the areas.

6. rectangle $l = 12$ cm, $w = 8$ cm
7. parallelogram $b = 16$ m, $h = 9$ m
8. triangle $b = 2.4$ m, $h = 3.0$ m
9. trapezoid base $a = 5$ cm, base $b = 8$ cm, $h = 4$ cm
10. circle $r = 9$ m

Surface Area

The **surface area** of a solid figure is the sum of the areas of all its surfaces.

The carton is a rectangular prism. The **dimensions** of the carton are 3 centimeters by 4 centimeters by 5 centimeters. Find the total area of all its faces. This is its surface area.

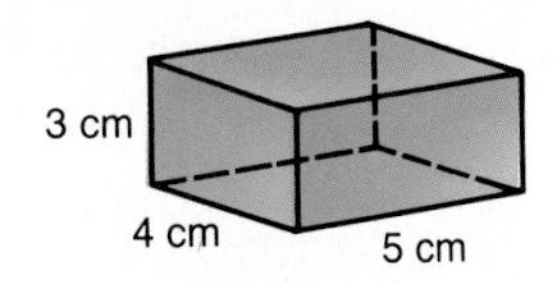

Suppose you cut it apart.

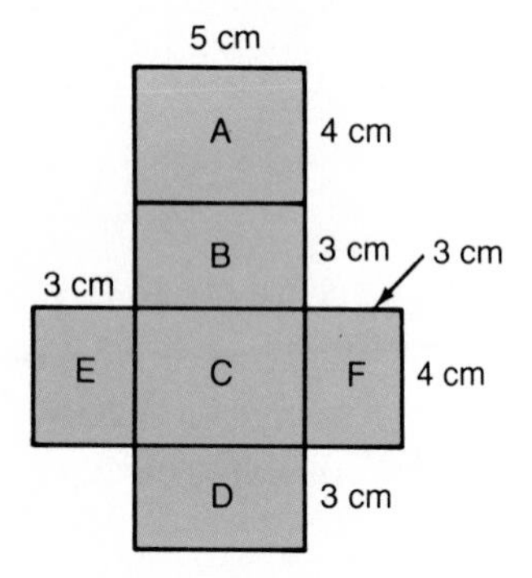

To find the surface area, find the area of each face. Then add.

Face	Area
A	$4 \times 5 = 20$
B	$3 \times 5 = 15$
C	$4 \times 5 = 20$
D	$3 \times 5 = 15$
E	$4 \times 3 = 12$
F	$4 \times 3 = 12$
Sum	Sum = 94

The surface area is 94 cm^2.

The can is a cylinder.
The radius of the bottom of the can is 3 centimeters long. The height of the can is 8 centimeters. Find the surface area of the cylinder.

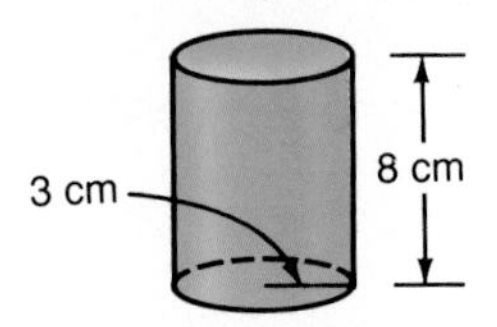

Suppose you cut it apart.

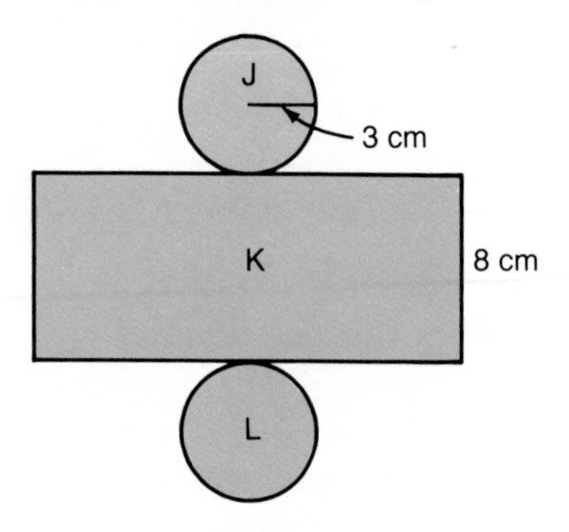

To find the surface area, find the area of each surface. Then add.

Surface	Area
J	$3.14 \times 3 \times 3 \approx 28.26$
K	(Think: circumference $\times$ height) $(2 \times 3.14 \times 3) \times 8 \approx 150.72$
L	$3.14 \times 3 \times 3 \approx 28.26$
Sum	Sum ≈ 207

The surface area is about 207 cm^2.

Practice • Find the surface areas.

1. 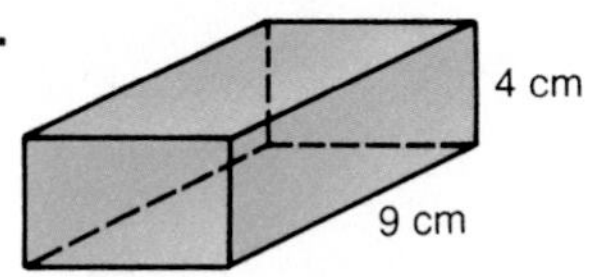

2. 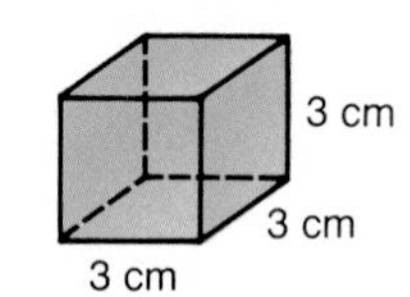

3. 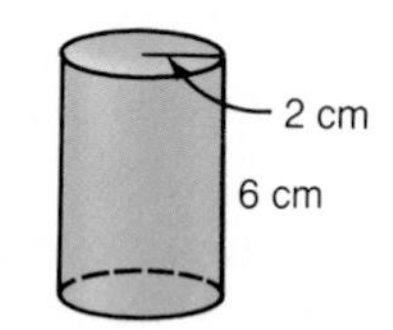

Mixed Practice • Find the surface areas.

4. 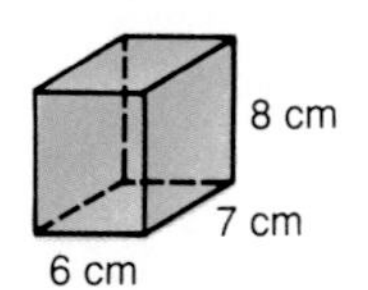

5. 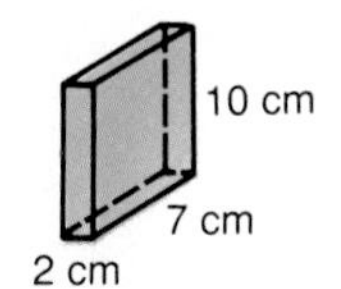

6. 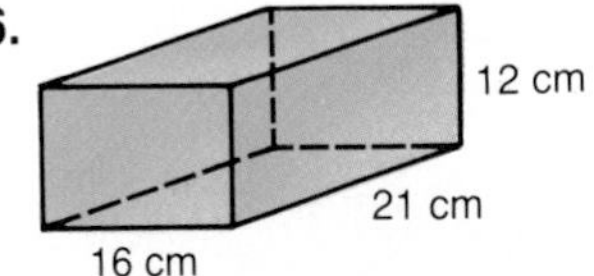

7. 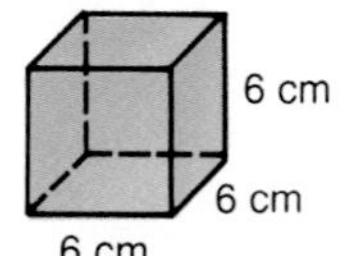

8. 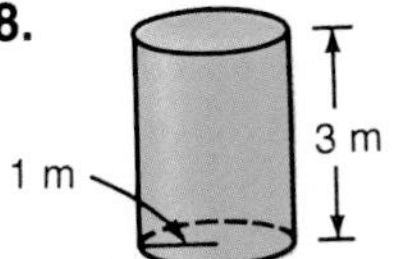

9. 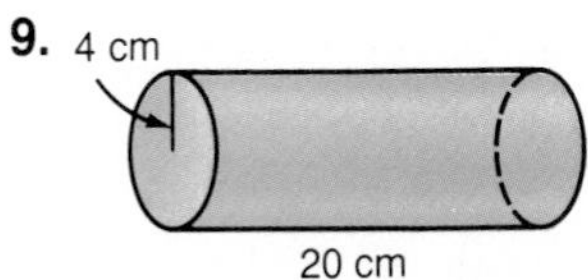

10. 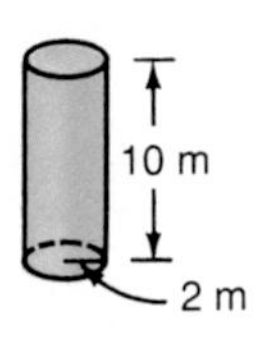

11. 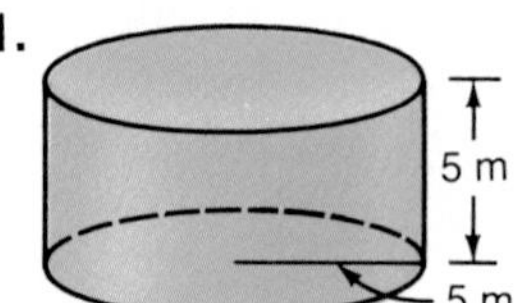

12. 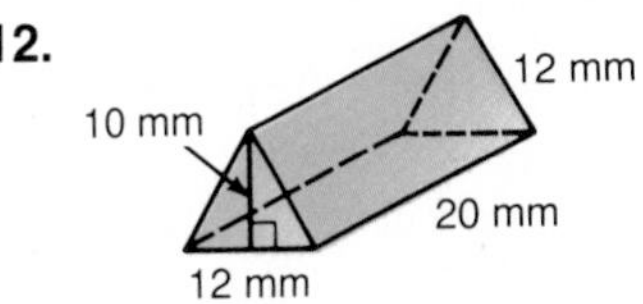

PROBLEM SOLVING • APPLICATIONS

13. Juan built a toy chest for his little brother. The dimensions of the chest are 95 centimeters by 40 centimeters by 50 centimeters. Juan wants to paint the outside (including the bottom) with enamel paint. What is the total surface area to be painted?

★ 14. If each can of enamel paint covers 2.3 square meters, how many cans will Juan have to buy?

★ 15. Write a formula for finding the surface area of a cube if the length of one edge is represented by *e*.

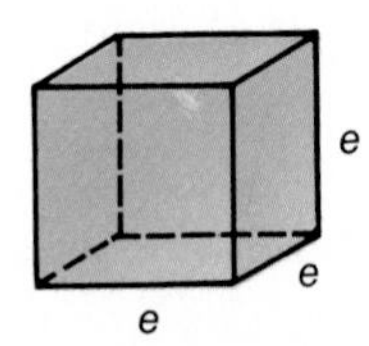

Volume of Prisms

The small cube measures 1 centimeter along each edge. It is a unit of **volume** called a **cubic centimeter (cm³).**

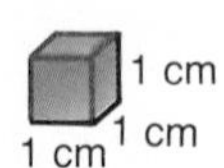

The volume of the box is the number of cubic units needed to fill it. Find the volume.

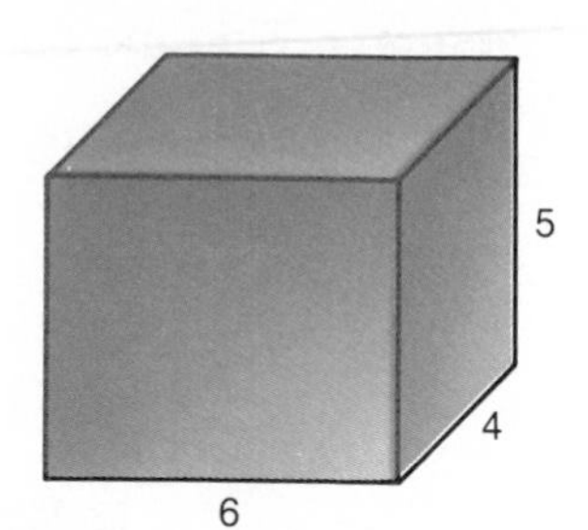

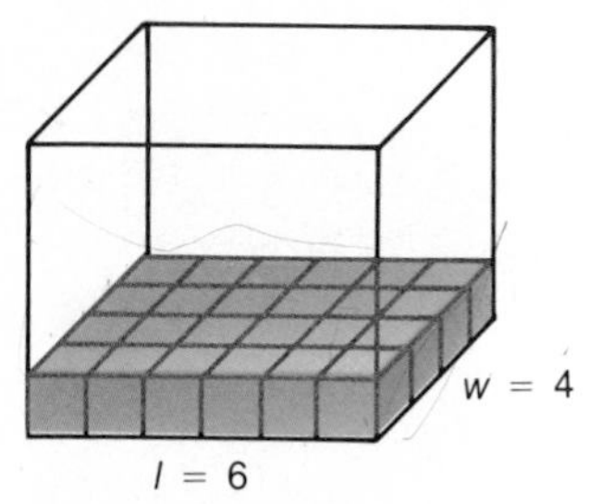

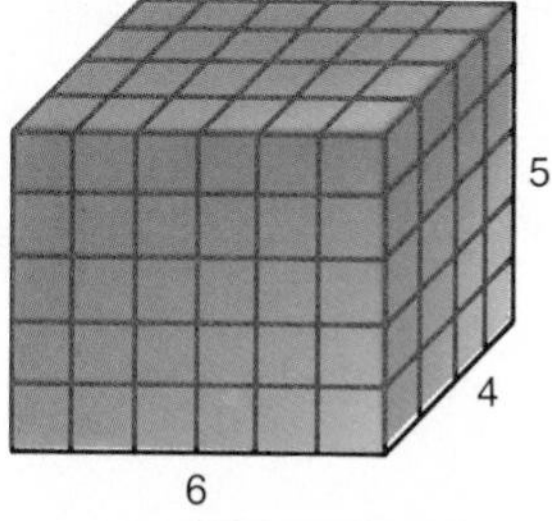

Find how many cubes will make one layer. This is the area of the base of the prism, or lw.

Count the layers. The height h tells how many layers there are. So multiply lw times h to find the total number of cubes, or volume.

To find the volume of a rectangular prism, multiply the area of the base times the height. You can compute the volume by multiplying the length times the width times the height.

Formula: $V = lwh$

$$V = 6 \times 4 \times 5$$
$$= 120 \text{ cm}^3$$

This drawing shows a cube with edge e. The area of the base is $e \times e$, and the height is e. This means that $V = e \times e \times e$, which you can express using exponents.

Suppose e is 2 centimeters. Then you can find the volume as shown.

Formula: $V = e^3$

$$V = 2^3$$
$$= 8 \text{ cm}^3$$

To find the volume of a triangular prism, multiply the area of the base (B) times the height (h).

Formula: $V = Bh$

$$V = \frac{5 \times 2}{2} \times 4$$
$$= 20 \text{ cm}^3$$

A formula for the volume of any prism is given below.

Volume of a prism = area of base × height

Formula: $V = Bh$

Practice • Find the volumes.

1. 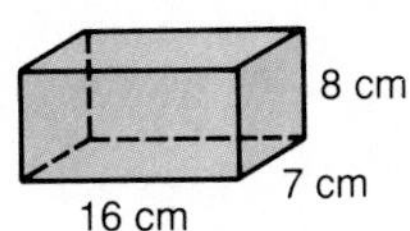

2. 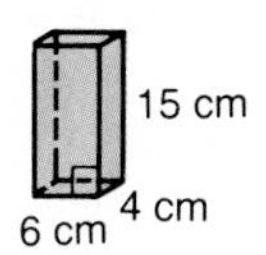

3. 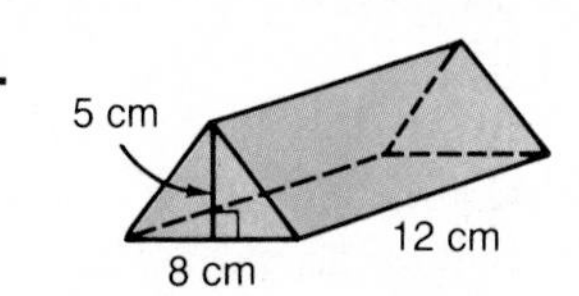

Mixed Practice • Find the volumes.

4. 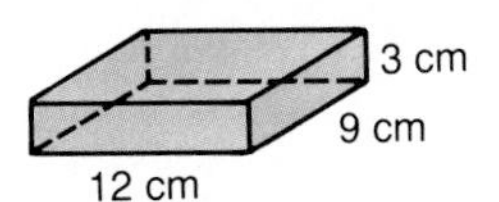

5. 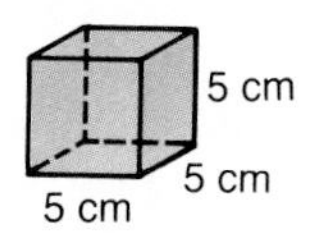

6. 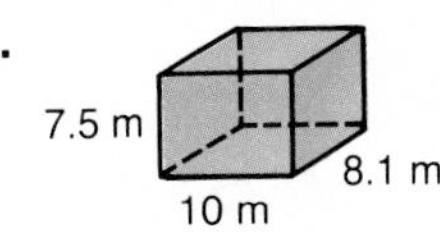

7. 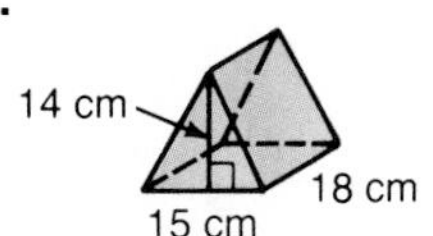

8. 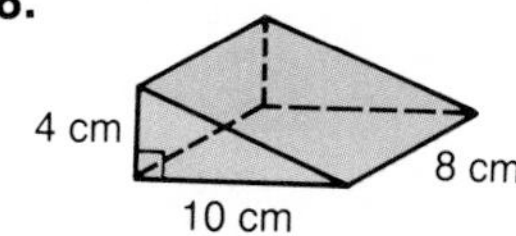

9. 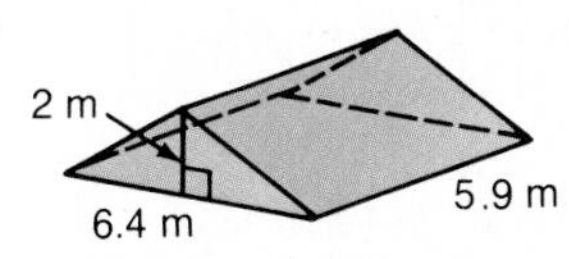

Find the volume of each rectangular prism.

	Rectangular Base		Height of Prism
	Length	Width	
10.	9 m	3 m	4 m
11.	12 cm	8 cm	5 cm
12.	2.4 cm	5.6 cm	7 cm
13.	9.3 m	7.4 m	5.5 m

Find the volume of each triangular prism.

	Triangular Face		Height of Prism
	Base	Height	
14.	6 m	4 m	8 m
15.	12 cm	7 cm	15 cm
16.	8.4 cm	6.2 cm	9.3 cm
17.	1.5 m	2.6 m	3.2 m

PROBLEM SOLVING • APPLICATIONS

18. A radio company packages 2 batteries in a box 4 centimeters long, 3 centimeters wide, and 5 centimeters high. How many batteries are in a carton 20 centimeters long, 9 centimeters wide, and 5 centimeters high?

19. Roland works in the packing department of the radio company. Each radio is packed in a box 12 centimeters long, 8 centimeters wide, and 5 centimeters high. What is the volume of each box?

20. How many radios does Roland pack in a carton that has the shape of a rectangular prism 48 centimeters long, 24 centimeters wide, and 20 centimeters high?

★ **21.** A solid cube is painted red on all sides. The cube is then cut into 27 equal smaller cubes. How many of the smaller cubes have red paint on only 2 sides?

Volume of Cylinders

To find the volume of a cylinder, you find the area of the base. Then you multiply the area times the height.

Since the area of the base is πr^2, the volume of the cylinder is $\pi r^2 \times h$, or $\pi r^2 h$.

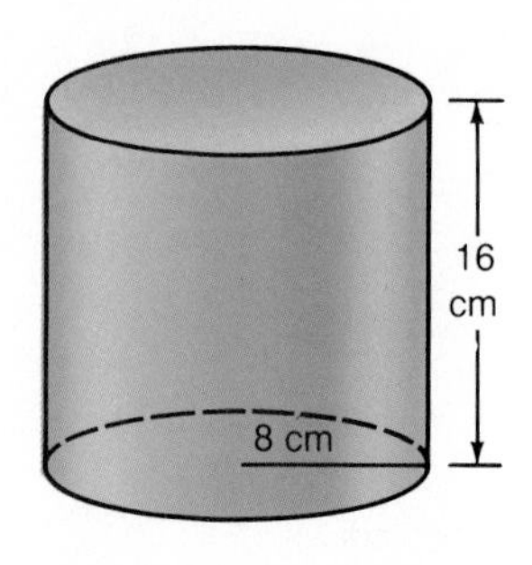

Volume of a cylinder = area of base × height

Formula: $V = \pi r^2 h$

Suppose $r = 8$ centimeters and $h = 16$ centimeters. Then:

$V = \pi r^2 h$
$V \approx (3.14 \times 8^2) \times 16$
$\approx (200.96) \times 16$
$\approx 3{,}215 \text{ cm}^3$

The volume is about 3,215 cm^3.

Practice • Find the volumes. Use 3.14 for π.

1.
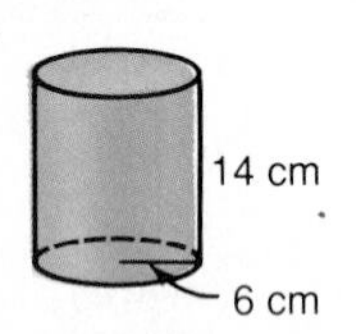

2.
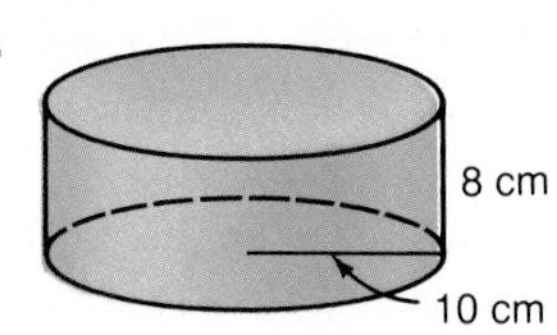

3.
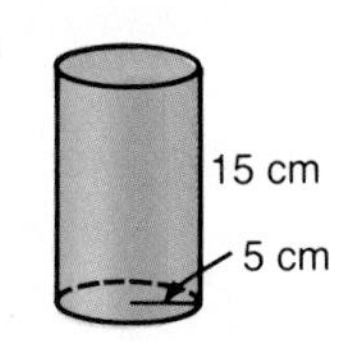

Mixed Practice • Find the volumes. Use 3.14 for π.

4.
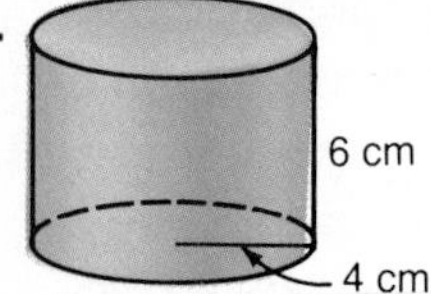

5.
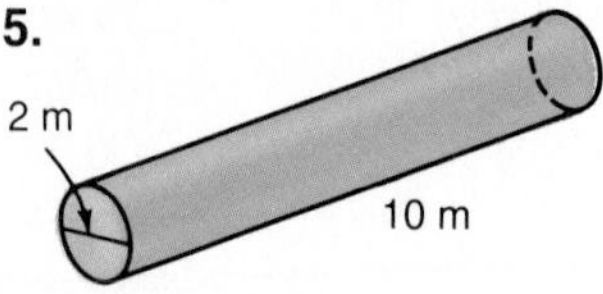

6.
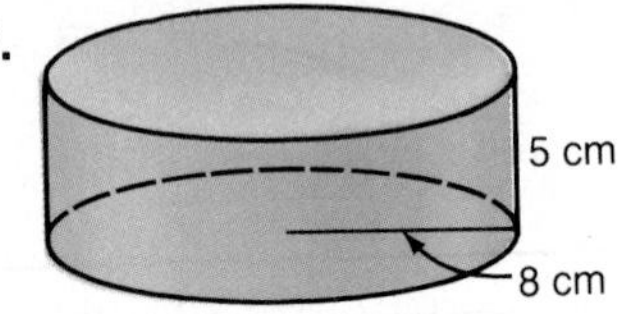

Find the volume of each cylinder. Use 3.14 for π.

7. $r = 4$ cm, $h = 9$ cm

8. $r = 10$ m, $h = 12$ m

9. $r = 7$ cm, $h = 3$ cm

10. $r = 3$ m, $h = 10$ m

11. $r = 2$ cm, $h = 8$ cm

12. $r = 9$ m, $h = 7$ m

13. $r = 5$ cm, $h = 9$ cm

14. $r = 3$ m, $h = 13$ m

15. $r = 6$ cm
$h = 15$ cm

16. $r = 2$ cm
$h = 1.4$ cm

17. $r = 3$ cm
$h = 3.9$ cm

18. $r = 2.5$ m
$h = 8.4$ m

PROBLEM SOLVING • APPLICATIONS

19. Fred Hughes has a cylindrical silo on his farm. The silo has a radius of 3 meters and a height of 20 meters. What is the volume of the silo?

20. The Hughes farm has a cylindrical water tower. The diameter is 5.0 meters and the height is 15.2 meters. What is the volume of the water tower?

★ **21.** Karen Hughes has two containers. One is a cylinder with a diameter of 10 centimeters and a height of 15 centimeters. The other is a prism with a height of 15 centimeters and a square base 10 centimeters on each side. Which container has the greater volume? How much greater is it?

★ **22.** Two cylindrical cans are equal in height. Can A has a radius twice as great as can B. Can B holds 1.2 liters of water. How many liters does can A hold?

★ **23.** Two cylindrical cans are equal in height. Can C has a radius half as great as can D. Can D holds 0.96 liter of water. What decimal part of a liter does can C hold?

Skills Maintenance

1. 10% of 90 = n

2. 50% of 64 = n

3. 75% of 12 = n

4. 20% of 300 = n

5. 60% of 750 = n

6. 1% of 2,500 = n

7. 3% of 50 = n

8. 90% of 17 = n

9. $33\frac{1}{3}\%$ of 72 = n

PROBLEM SOLVING • STRATEGIES

Using a Diagram

Drawing a diagram can often help you to solve a problem.

Problem 1

Claire is on the school track team. She jogs every morning before school. She leaves home and jogs 6 blocks north, 10 blocks east, 8 blocks south, 10 blocks west, and 2 blocks north. How many blocks does she jog each morning?

Claire's House
10
6
8
2
10

The diagram shows that Claire jogs 36 blocks before arriving home.

Claire jogs 36 blocks each morning.

Problem 2

The grocery store is 1.2 kilometers from Ella's house. She rides her bicycle to the grocery store and back home. Then she rides to Joanne's house to have lunch and returns home. The odometer shows that she rode a total distance of 3.8 kilometers. How far away does Joanne live?

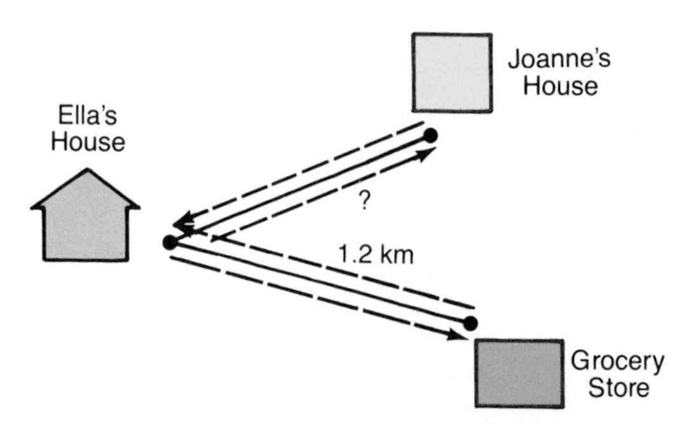

The round trip between Ella's house and the grocery store is 2.4 kilometers, and so the round trip between Ella's house and Joanne's house must be 1.4 kilometers (3.8 km − 2.4 km). Therefore Joanne must live 0.7 kilometer away.

Solve. Use a diagram if you think it will help you.

1. Bob drives a round trip of 28 kilometers between his house and office. How far is the office from his house?

2. Patricia is hanging a picture on the wall. The picture is 62 centimeters wide. The wall is 168 centimeters wide. If Patricia hangs the picture in the center of the wall, how much wall space will be on each side of the picture?

3. Sabrina needs 32 sections of fencing for the back yard. The fence will be in the shape of a rectangle. If she needs 12 sections for each length of the fence, how many sections are in each width?

Be sure the diagram shows all the facts you have.

4. Kenneth drives 65 kilometers east on Highway 64. Then he drives 135 kilometers north on Interstate 95. How many kilometers does he drive in all?

5. Anthony drives 3.6 kilometers to the bank, 2.3 kilometers to the grocery store, and 4.5 kilometers home. How many kilometers does he drive?

6. Jason is making a set of shelves for his room. He needs 5 shelves. Each one is 3.5 meters long. The boards for the shelves are in 8-meter sections. How many 8-meter sections are needed to make the shelves?

7. Laurie drives from her house to New York City. The car's odometer reads 25,153 kilometers when she leaves home. When she returns home, the odometer reads 25,269 kilometers. How far is it to New York City from her house?

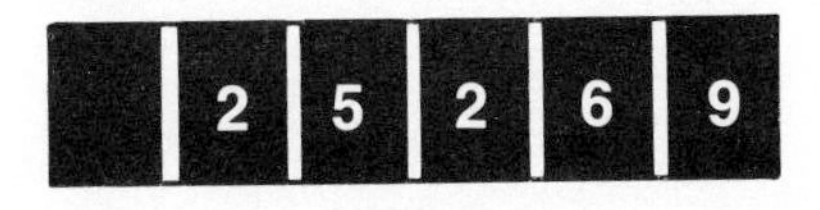

8. The living room in the Smiths' house is 5 meters × 6 meters. They buy an area rug that is 3 meters × 4 meters. If the rug is placed in the center of the room, how much of the floor will show on each side of the rug?

9. The perimeter of equilateral triangle *EFG* is either 96 centimeters or it is 97 centimeters. The length of $\overline{EF}$ is a whole number of centimeters. What is the perimeter of $\triangle EFG$?

★ 10. $\angle JKL$ and $\angle QRS$ are complementary angles. $m\angle JKL$ is not greater than $m\angle QRS$. $m\angle QRS$ is not greater than $m\angle JKL$. What is the measure of each angle?

Be sure your answer is reasonable.

★ 11. Square *MNOP* has an area of 625 cm^2. What is the length of $\overline{MN}$?

★ 12. What is the area of rectangle *UVWX* if the length of $\overline{UV}$ is 2.3 centimeters and the length of $\overline{VW}$ is twice as great as the length of $\overline{UV}$?

★ 13. The radius of circle *A* is 1.41 times as long as the radius of circle *B*. The area of circle *A* is how many times as great as the area of circle *B*?

Using Customary Units

You can find perimeter, area, circumference, and volume using customary units. Often you need to express measurements in just one unit to compute.

Find the area of the rectangle.

1 ft 3 in.

2 ft 6 in.

Step 1 Write the formula. $A = lw$

Step 2 Substitute. $A = (2 \text{ ft } 6 \text{ in.}) \times (1 \text{ ft } 3 \text{ in.})$

Step 3 Change to one unit of measurement. $A = 30 \text{ in.} \times 15 \text{ in.}$ or $A = 2\frac{1}{2} \text{ ft} \times 1\frac{1}{4} \text{ ft}$

Step 4 Solve. $A = 450 \text{ in.}^2$ $\quad A = 3\frac{1}{8} \text{ ft}^2$

The area of the rectangle is 450 in.^{2}, or $3\frac{1}{8}$ ft^2.

Find the volume of the rectangular prism.

1 yd 2 ft

2 yd 1 ft

2 ft

Step 1 Write the formula. $V = lwh$

Step 2 Substitute. $V = 2 \text{ ft} \times 2 \text{ yd } 1 \text{ ft} \times 1 \text{ yd } 2 \text{ ft}$

Step 3 Change to one unit of measurement. $V = 2 \text{ ft} \times 7 \text{ ft} \times 5 \text{ ft}$ or $V = \frac{2}{3} \text{ yd} \times 2\frac{1}{3} \text{ yd} \times 1\frac{2}{3} \text{ yd}$

Step 4 Solve. $V = 70 \text{ ft}^3$ $\quad V = 2\frac{16}{27} \text{ yd}^3$

The volume of the prism is 70 ft^3, or $2\frac{16}{27}$ yd^3.

More Examples

Find the perimeter and the circumference.

1 ft 4 in.

1 ft 4 in.

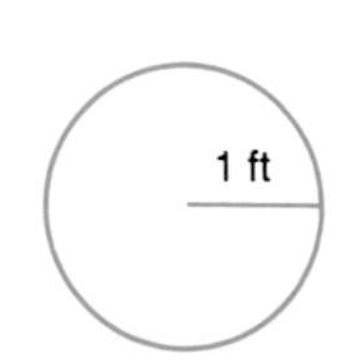

$$\begin{array}{r} 1 \text{ ft} \quad 4 \text{ in.} \\ \times \qquad 4 \\ \hline 4 \text{ ft } 16 \text{ in.} \end{array} = 5 \text{ ft } 4 \text{ in.}$$

$P = 5$ ft 4 in.

$$P = 4 \times 1\frac{1}{3} \text{ ft}$$
$$= 5\frac{1}{3} \text{ ft}$$

$$C = 2\pi r$$
$$\approx 2(3.14)(1)$$
$$\approx 6.28 \text{ ft}$$
$$\approx 6 \text{ ft}$$

Practice • Find the answers.

1. Perimeter = ?

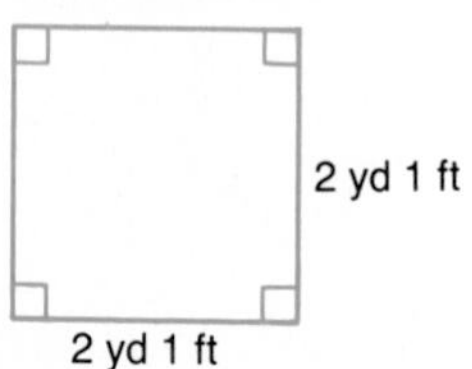

2. Area = ?

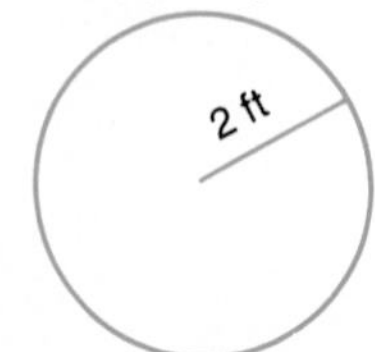

3. Volume = ?

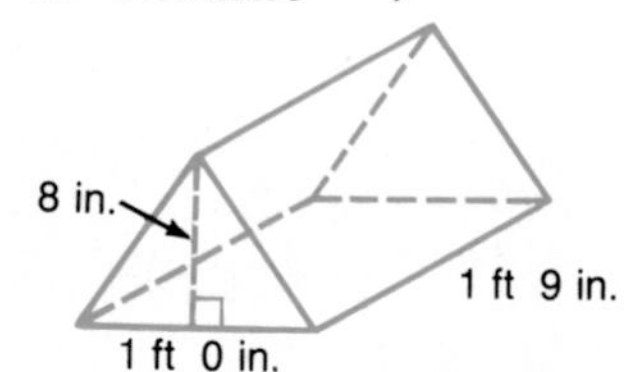

Mixed Practice • Find the answers.

4. Circumference = ?

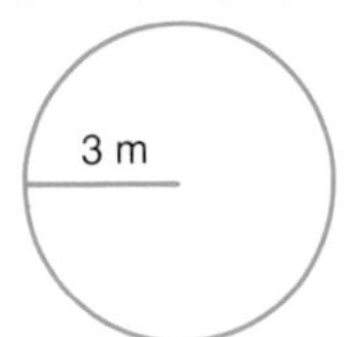

5. Area = ?

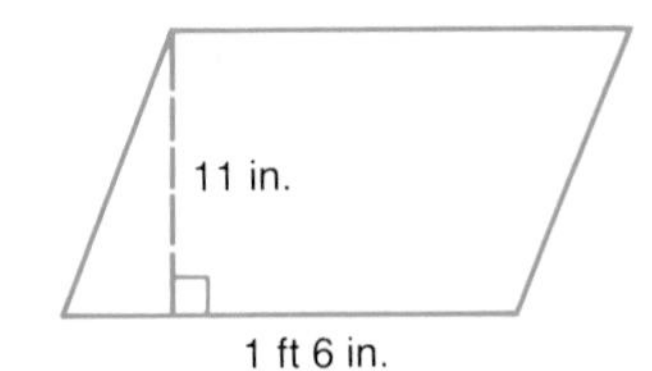

6. Area = ?

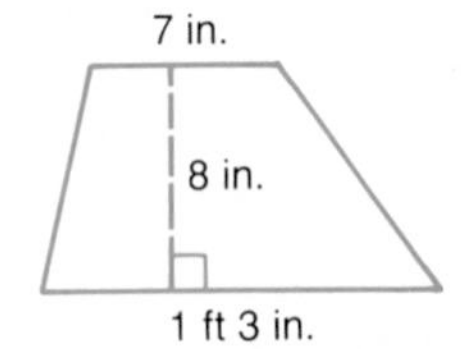

7. How many square inches are in one square foot?

8. How many square feet are in one square yard?

9. How many square inches are in one square yard?

Copy and complete.

10. $4 \text{ ft}^2 = \underline{\ ?\ } \text{ in.}^2$

11. $3 \text{ yd}^2 = \underline{\ ?\ } \text{ ft}^2$

12. $432 \text{ in.}^2 = \underline{\ ?\ } \text{ ft}^2$

Find the volumes. Use 3.14 for π.

13.

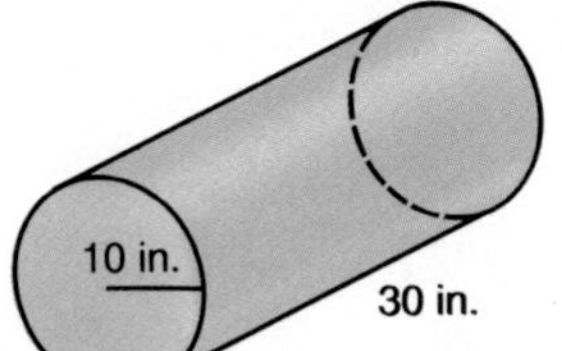

14.

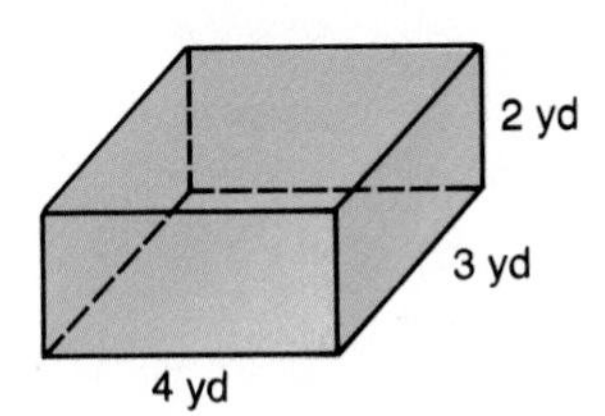

15.

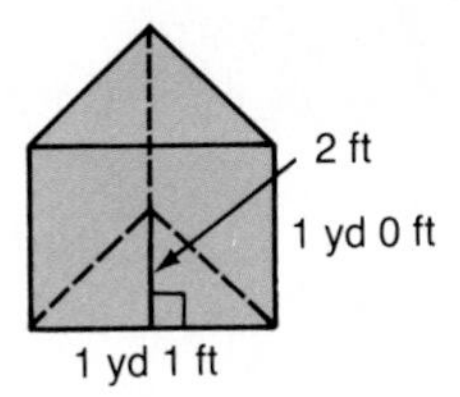

16. How many cubic inches are in one cubic foot?

17. How many cubic feet are in one cubic yard?

Copy and complete.

★ 18. $2 \text{ ft}^3 = \underline{\ ?\ } \text{ in.}^3$

★ 19. $4 \text{ yd}^3 = \underline{\ ?\ } \text{ ft}^3$

★ 20. $135 \text{ ft}^3 = \underline{\ ?\ } \text{ yd}^3$

PROBLEM SOLVING • APPLICATIONS

21. The Robinsons are building a rectangular patio. They want to make it 4 yards long and 2 yards 2 feet wide. How many square slabs, 2 feet on each side, will they need?

★ 22. Find the volume of a cylindrical whirlpool bath with a diameter of 7 feet and a water level of 3 feet 8 inches.

Reviewing and Using Formulas

The formulas in this chapter can be used to solve many different problems. When you are solving a given problem, be sure to use the correct formula.

Perimeter:	Rectangle Square	$P = 2l + 2w$ $P = 4s$
Circumference:	Circle	$C = \pi d$ $C = 2\pi r$
Area:	Rectangle Square Parallelogram Triangle Trapezoid Circle	$A = lw$ $A = s^2$ $A = bh$ $A = \frac{1}{2}bh$ $A = \frac{1}{2}h(a + b)$ $A = \pi r^2$
Volume:	Rectangular prism Triangular prism Cylinder	$V = lwh$ $V = Bh$ $V = \pi r^2 h$

A wheel has a radius of 60 centimeters. What distance does the wheel travel in making one revolution?

The distance it travels is equal to its circumference. To answer the question, you need to use the formula for the circumference of a circle. Since you know the radius of the wheel, use $C = 2\pi r$.

$$C = 2\pi r$$
$$\approx 2(3.14)(60)$$
$$\approx 377 \text{ cm}$$

Practice • In rectangle *ABCD*, l is 8.2 centimeters and w is 2.6 centimeters.

1. Find the area of rectangle *ABCD*.

2. Find the perimeter of rectangle *ABCD*.

3. The height of a cylinder is 16 centimeters. The radius of the base is 10 centimeters. What is the volume of the cylinder?

Mixed Practice • In square *EFGH*, *s* is 3.6 centimeters.

4. Find the perimeter of square *EFGH*.

5. Find the area of square *EFGH*.

6. The height of a rectangular prism is 18 centimeters. The dimensions of the base are 4 centimeters by 5 centimeters. What is the volume of the prism?

PROBLEM SOLVING • APPLICATIONS

7. A rectangular rug is 5.4 meters long and 3.6 meters wide. Find the area of the rug.

8. A rabbit pen is 4.1 meters long and 3.2 meters wide. What is its perimeter?

9. One side of a square table is 95 centimeters. Find the area of the table.

10. A cylindrical can of vegetable juice is 22 centimeters high. The radius of the can is 6 centimeters. Find the volume of the can.

11. The attic of a house is in the shape of a triangular prism. The attic floor is 14.4 meters long and 8.5 meters wide. The height of the attic is 3.6 meters. Find the volume of the attic.

12. A package in the shape of a rectangular prism is 52 centimeters long, 42 centimeters wide, and 18 centimeters high. Find the volume of the package.

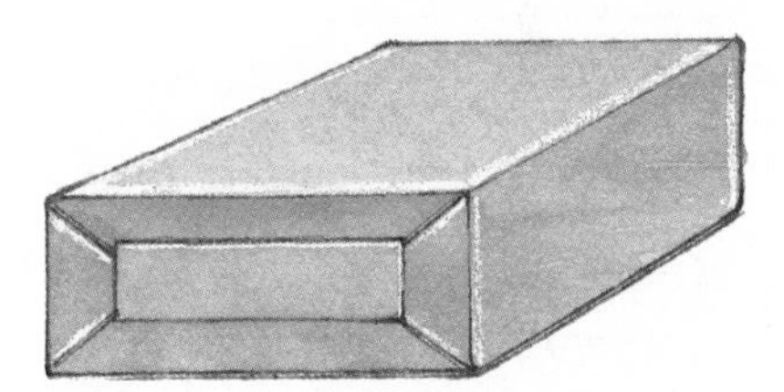

13. A wheel has a diameter of 90 centimeters. What distance does the wheel travel in making one revolution?

14. A rectangular garden is 4.6 meters long and 2.8 meters wide. You walk once around the boundary of the garden. What distance do you walk?

★ 15. A rectangular living room is 7 meters long and 4.5 meters wide. A circular rug in the middle of the floor has a diameter of 3.7 meters. Find the area of the floor not covered by the rug.

★ 16. In triangle *ABC*, $\overline{AB}$ is x centimeters long. $\overline{BC}$ is 2 centimeters longer than $\overline{AB}$. $\overline{CA}$ is 5 centimeters longer than $\overline{AB}$. The perimeter is 88 centimeters. What is the length of each side?

PROBLEM SOLVING • STRATEGIES

Analyzing Conclusions

In mathematics, patterns of logic can be used to arrive at valid conclusions.

Study these two sentences.

- If a figure is a square, then it is a rectangle.
- *ABCD* is a square.

From these two sentences, you can conclude:
- *ABCD* is a rectangle.

Now study these two sentences.

- If a figure is a square, then it is a rectangle.
- *EFGH* is not a rectangle.

From these two sentences, you can conclude:
- *EFGH* is not a square.

Use patterns of logic to answer the questions.

1. • If a figure is a rectangle, then it is a parallelogram.
   • *RSTU* is a rectangle.
   Is *RSTU* a parallelogram?

2. • If n is a multiple of 4, then it is a multiple of 2.
   • n is not a multiple of 2.
   Is n a multiple of 4?

3. • If $5y + 2 = 17$, then $5y = 15$.
   • If $5y = 15$, then $y = 3$.
   • $5y + 2 = 17$.
   What does y equal?

4. • If $3y = 12$, $y = 4$.
   • $y \neq 4$.
   Does $3y = 12$?

5. • If a figure is a parallelogram, then it is a quadrilateral.
   • *EFGH* is a parallelogram.
   Is *EFGH* a quadrilateral?

Reread the given sentences. Be sure you understand the pattern of logic.

6. • If $7n + 1 = 15$, then $7n = 14$.
   • If $7n = 14$, then $n = 2$.
   • $n \neq 2$.
   Does $7n + 1 = 15$?

7. • If Bette goes to the movies, then she spends \$2.50 for the ticket.
   • If she spends \$2.50 for the ticket, she cannot go to the concert.
   Bette goes to the movies. Can she go to the concert?

8. • If $12 - n = 12$, then $n = 0$.
   • If $n = 0$, then $n \times 100 = 0$.
   • $n \times 100 \neq 0$
   Does $12 - n = 12$?

★ 9. • If $ab = 0$, then $a = 0$ or $b = 0$.
   • $a \neq 0$ and $b \neq 0$.
   Does ab equal 0?

★ 10. • If $3n + 2 = n + 16$, then $3n = n + 14$.
   • If $3n = n + 14$, then $2n = 14$.
   • If $2n = 14$, then $n = 7$.
   • $n \neq 7$.
   Does $3n + 2 = n + 16$?

★ 11. • If $2y + 9 < 31$, then $2y < 22$.
   • If $2y < 22$, then $y < 11$.
   • $y < 11$.
   Is it true that $2y + 9 < 31$?

Does the conclusion make sense in the situation?

★ 12. • If Anne gets a part-time job, then she will earn money.
   • If she earns money, she will save money for a bicycle.
   • Anne does not save money for a bicycle.
   Did Anne get a part-time job?

★ 13. Write a problem that uses a pattern of logic. Use some situation in your own life as the topic for the problem.

CHAPTER 13

REVIEW

Find the perimeter of each polygon. (pp. 342–343)

1.

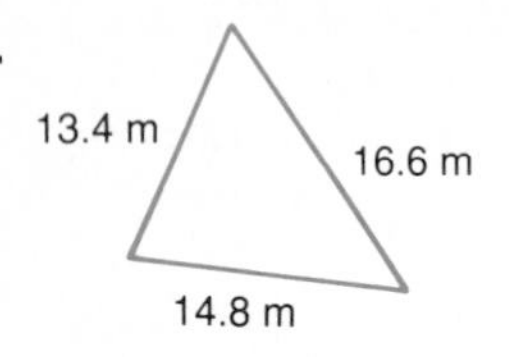

2.

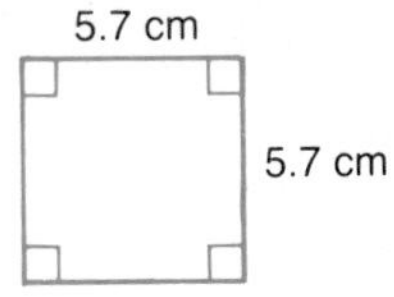

3.

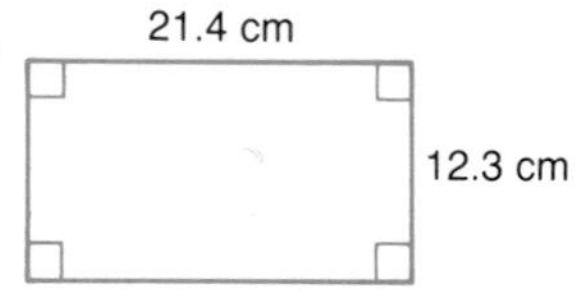

Find the circumference of each circle to the nearest whole number. (pp. 344–345)

4. $d = 4$ cm
5. $d = 34$ mm
6. $r = 16$ m
7. $r = 51$ mm

Find the area. Use 3.14 for π. (pp. 346–353)

8. Square
$s = 3.9$ m

9. Rectangle
$l = 6.4$ cm
$w = 4.7$ cm

10. Parallelogram
$b = 28$ m
$h = 18$ m

11. Triangle
$b = 4.2$ m
$h = 1.9$ m

12. Trapezoid
base $a = 16$ mm
base $b = 10$ mm
$h = 5.5$ mm

13. Circle
$d = 8$ m

Find the surface area. Use 3.14 for π. (pp. 354–355)

14.

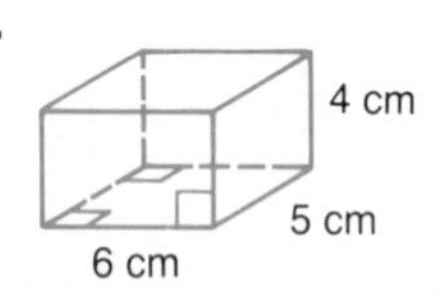

15.

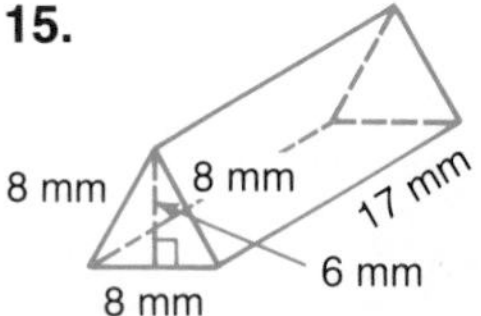

16.

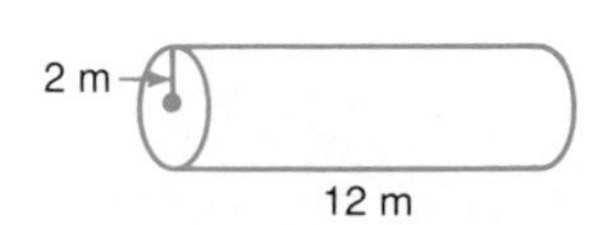

Find the volume. Use 3.14 for π. (pp. 356–359)

17.

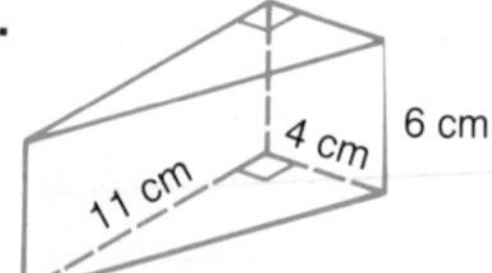

18.

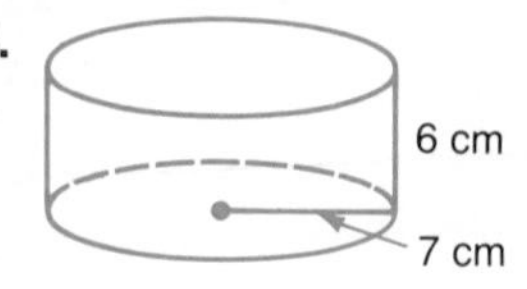

19.

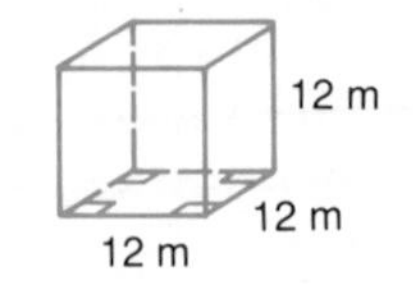

20. A cylinder-shaped reservoir has a diameter of 24 meters and a depth of 6 meters. What is the volume? (p. 364)

21. A water trough shaped like a triangular prism is 7 meters long, 8 meters wide, and 1 meter deep. What is the volume? (p. 364)

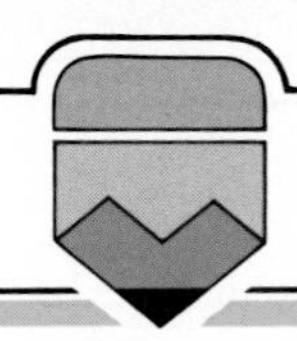

PROJECT

Direct Volume Measurement

One day Thomas A. Edison and an engineer were working in the laboratory. The engineer was trying to find the volume of a lightbulb. He was using several formulas to calculate the volume. Edison watched for a while and then walked over to the engineer. Edison drilled a hole in the top of the lightbulb and filled it with water. Then he measured the volume of water directly. The engineer smiled, a little embarrassed.

1. You can measure the volume of a cylinder directly to check that the volume formula is reasonable.

a. Collect 5 cans of different sizes. Label the cans A, B, C, D, and E. Measure the height and the radius in centimeters. Compute the volume of each can in cubic centimeters.

b. Next fill each can with sand or water. Pour the sand or water into a measuring cup marked in milliliters.
(Remember: 1 milliliter = 1 cubic centimeter.)
Find the volume of each can in milliliters.
Copy and complete this table.

Can	Formula Result	Direct Measure
A		
B		
C		
D		
E		

2. Try this experiment.

a. Use cardboard to construct a prism with a square base 10 centimeters on a side and a height of 12 centimeters. Using sand, find the prism's volume by direct measurement.

Construct a pyramid with a square base 10 centimeters on a side and a height of 12 centimeters. Find the volume by direct measurement. Is the pyramid's volume about $\frac{1}{3}$ of the volume of the prism?

b. Repeat the experiment with other pairs of prisms and pyramids. (Remember to use equal bases and equal heights.) Do you think that $V = \frac{1}{3}Bh$ is a formula for the volume of a pyramid?

3. Use cylinders and cones to find a formula for the volume of a cone.

CHAPTER 13 TEST

Find the perimeter of each polygon.

1.

4.9 m

4.9 m

2.

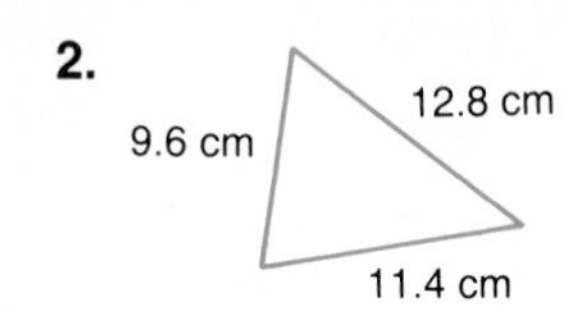

3.

18.1 mm

11.6 mm

Find the circumference of each circle to the nearest whole number.

4. $d = 6$ m

5. $d = 27$ mm

6. $r = 13$ m

7. $r = 60$ cm

Find the area. Use 3.14 for π.

8. Rectangle
$l = 8.6$ cm
$w = 6.4$ cm

9. Square
$s = 8$ m

10. Triangle
$b = 4$ m
$h = 3$ m

11. Parallelogram
$b = 21$ mm
$h = 15$ mm

12. Trapezoid
base $a = 2$ m
base $b = 6.2$ m
$h = 4$ m

13. Circle
$d = 31$ cm

Find the surface area. Use 3.14 for π.

14.

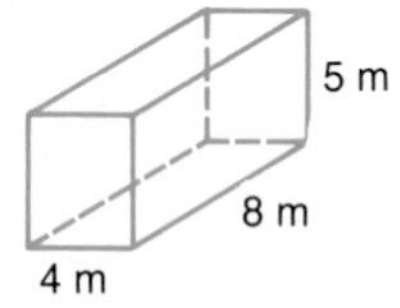

15.

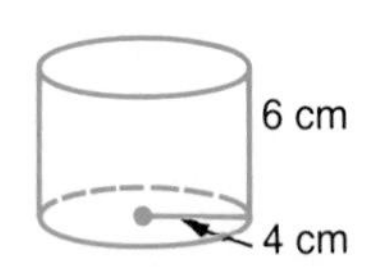

16.

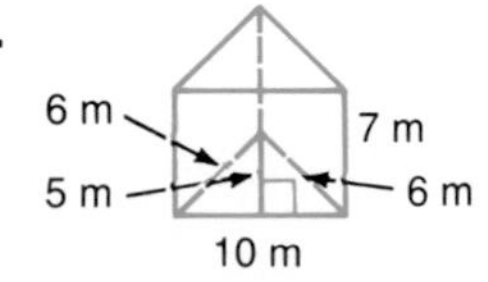

Find the volume. Use 3.14 for π.

17.

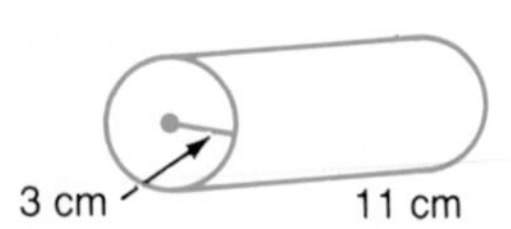

18.

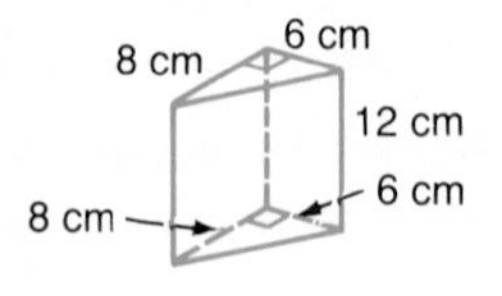

19.

20. A water tower shaped like a cylinder has a radius of 2 meters and a height of 9 meters. What is the volume?

21. A pool shaped like a rectangular prism is 30 meters long, 20 meters wide, and 3 meters deep. What is the volume?

ENRICHMENT

Square Roots

You square the length of a side to find the area of a square: $\boldsymbol{A = s^2}$.

The area of this square is 25 square centimeters. How long is each side?

The equation $25 = 5^2$ tells about the relationship of 5 and 25.

25 is the square of 5.
5 is called a **square root** of 25. Write:

square root symbol ⟶ $\sqrt{25} = 5$

Copy and complete.

1. $7^2 = 49$; so $\sqrt{49} = n$.

2. $11^2 = 121$; so $\sqrt{121} = n$.

Find each square root. Try different whole numbers that you think are reasonable until you find the correct number.

3. $\sqrt{36} = n$

4. $\sqrt{1} = n$

5. $\sqrt{144} = n$

6. $\sqrt{225} = n$

All of the square roots you have found have been whole numbers. Is there a whole number that is a square root of 30?

$\sqrt{30} = n$ $\quad 5 \times 5 = 25$ too small
$\quad 6 \times 6 = 36$ too large

There is no whole number that is a square root of 30. Nor is there any fraction in arithmetic that is a square root of 30.

Try $5\frac{4}{10}$: $\frac{54}{10} \times \frac{54}{10} = \frac{2{,}916}{100} = 29\frac{16}{100}$ too small

Try $5\frac{5}{10}$: $\frac{55}{10} \times \frac{55}{10} = \frac{3{,}025}{100} = 30\frac{25}{100}$ too large

No fraction will work!
Try others yourself.

Try to find a whole number or a fraction that is a solution for each equation. Write *No whole number or fraction* when you are sure you cannot find a solution.

7. $\sqrt{196} = n$

8. $\sqrt{200} = n$

9. $\sqrt{400} = n$

10. $\sqrt{600} = n$

COMPUTER

Computer Errors

Error conditions are important considerations in computers.

For example, the instruction AL ONE,ONE is an error for AL 1,1. The instruction to input from hard disk is an error if the computer system has no hard disk.

Computer switches can cause mistakes if a bad wire or a sudden change in electrical power changes a bit from on to off or from off to on. One bit-change is a very serious error.

Remember that a byte has eight bits. Suppose a byte is 01010101. Four bits are on. If an even number of bits are on, the byte is said to have *even parity*. A *check-bit* can be added to each byte. If the byte has *odd parity*, the check-bit is turned on. Now the byte and the check-bit have even parity. If the byte has even parity, the check-bit is left off. The combination still has even parity. If the combination ever has odd parity, the machine signals the programmer that there is a *parity error*.

A parity error is an example of a *computer error*. A control-transfer instruction that transfers control into the middle of data is usually a *programmer error*, or "*bug*."

Everyone has a favorite story about a "computer error," such as the one that produced a telephone bill of $5,000,023.75. In most cases, however, these are actually examples of programmer errors.

Choose the correct answers.

1. A byte of 01110101 has
   - **A.** a parity error.
   - **B.** even parity.
   - **C.** odd parity.
   - **D.** none of the above.

2. A check-bit
   - **A.** makes even parity odd.
   - **B.** makes odd parity even.
   - **C.** causes a parity error.
   - **D.** none of the above.

3. A computer error
   - **A.** is programmer-caused.
   - **B.** may be a parity error.
   - **C.** both A and B.
   - **D.** neither A nor B.

4. A programmer error
   - **A.** is called a "bug."
   - **B.** is a person's mistake.
   - **C.** both A and B.
   - **D.** neither A nor B.

It is the job of the computer engineer to make the computer as *reliable* as possible so that computer errors are reduced.

It is the job of the programmer to *test* the program with so many combinations of data that the program is 100% correct.

Outside influences affect computers. Here are some of them.

Dust causes data errors on floppy disks.

Increases or decreases in electricity may affect computers.

Dropping, bumping, and otherwise damaging computers and input/output devices are common problems of *carelessness*.

Magnetic disturbances from the atmosphere, telephones, stereos, or parts of the computer system may cause difficulties.

Temperature or humidity extremes affect reliability.

Improper electrical connections and delayed maintenance can cause *computer failures*.

Computer errors or outside influences are usually so dramatic that it is perfectly clear that something is wrong. The output cannot be trusted. However, if a programming error caused a telephone bill to be $75.43 rather than $65.43, this more subtle error would in the long run be far more damaging than a computer error whose effect is obvious.

Write whether these situations are *computer errors* or *programmer errors*.

5. The CRT has burned out.
6. The computer is instructed to add when it should be told to subtract.
7. The computer stops functioning in the middle of a section of data.
8. A parity error occurs.
9. A program for preparing telephone bills neglects to deduct previous payment.
10. The letter M does not work on the printer.
11. A "bug" causes an error in a telephone bill.
12. An electrical surge causes a calculator to fail.

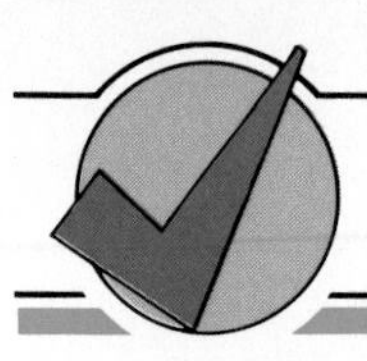

SKILLS MAINTENANCE

Chapters 1 Through 13

Choose the correct answers.

1. Write the product.

3^4

A. 27 **B.** 81
C. 12 **D.** not here

2. Multiply.

$$\begin{array}{r} 0.639 \\ \times\ 3.56 \\ \hline \end{array}$$

A. 2.27484 **B.** 227.484
C. 22.7384 **D.** not here

3. Solve.

$\frac{n}{15} = 60$

A. $n = 45$ **B.** $n = 4$
C. $n = 75$ **D.** not here

4. Add.

$4\frac{3}{5} + 2\frac{7}{8}$

A. $6\frac{1}{2}$ **B.** $7\frac{19}{40}$
C. $7\frac{1}{2}$ **D.** not here

5. Multiply.

$3\frac{2}{5} \times 2\frac{1}{2}$

A. $8\frac{1}{5}$ **B.** $6\frac{1}{5}$
C. $8\frac{1}{2}$ **D.** not here

6. Solve the proportion.

$\frac{3}{n} = \frac{7}{21}$

A. $n = 9$ **B.** $n = 7$
C. $n = 12$ **D.** not here

7. Complete.

30 mm = __?__ cm

A. 0.3 **B.** 300
C. 3 **D.** not here

8. Find the circumference of the circle to the nearest whole number. Use 3.14 for π.

$d = 28$ cm

A. 87 cm **B.** 44 cm
C. 88 cm **D.** not here

9. Find the volume.

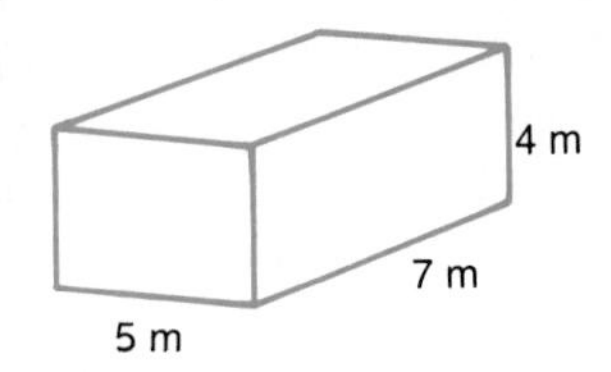

A. 16 m^3 **B.** 140 m^3
C. 63 m^3 **D.** not here

Solve. Use a diagram if you think it will help you.

10. Alex needs 6 shelves. Each one is 2.8 meters long. The boards for the shelves are in 6-meter sections. How many 6-meter sections are needed to make the shelves?

A. 6 sections **B.** 3 sections
C. 4 sections **D.** not here

11. Jamie drives 4.2 kilometers to the supermarket, 3.1 kilometers to the gas station, and 4.8 kilometers to the library. How many kilometers does she drive?

A. 11.1 km **B.** 12.0 km
C. 12.1 km **D.** not here

Probability and Statistics

Probability • Sample Spaces and Tree Diagrams • Problem Solving: Using Probability • Organizing Data • Mean, Range, Median, and Mode • Pictographs • Bar Graphs • Broken-Line Graphs • Problem Solving: Sampling • Constructing a Circle Graph

Probability

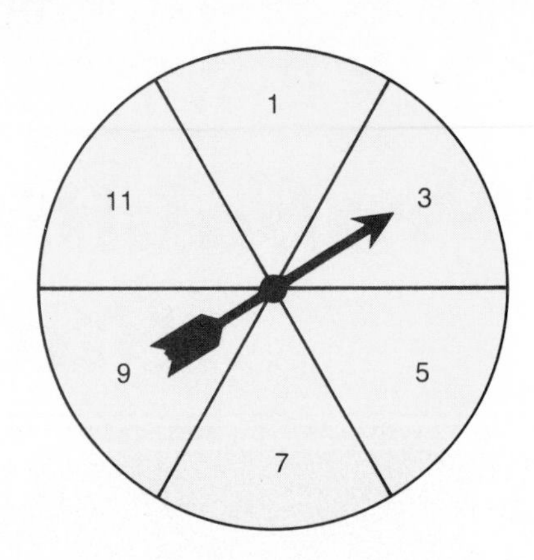

You are playing a game with this spinner. You need a 3 to win. What are the chances that you will spin a 3?

There are 6 **possible outcomes**. All of the sections on the spinner are equal in size, so the outcomes are **equally likely**.

Only 1 section has a 3 on it. Spinning a 3 is a **favorable outcome**.

The chances of spinning a 3 are 1 out of 6. The **probability (*P*)** that you will spin a 3 is $\frac{1}{6}$. $P(3) = \frac{1}{6}$.

An **event** may consist of more than one outcome.
What is the probability of this event: spinning a number that is not 3?

5 of the 6 sections do not have 3 on them, and so $P(\text{not } 3) = \frac{5}{6}$.

The probability of an event (E) is the quotient of the number of favorable outcomes (f) divided by the number of possible outcomes (n).

$$P(E) = \frac{f}{n} \quad \begin{matrix} \leftarrow \text{number of favorable outcomes} \\ \leftarrow \text{number of possible outcomes} \end{matrix}$$

↑ Probability of E

What is the probability of spinning a number greater than 12?
There are no numbers greater than 12 on the spinner.
So $P(\text{greater than } 12) = \frac{0}{6} = 0$.

What is the probability of spinning an odd number?
All 6 of the numbers are odd, so $P(\text{odd}) = \frac{6}{6} = 1$.

If an event will never occur, its probability is 0. The event is **impossible**.

If an event will always occur, its probability is 1. The event is **certain**.

Practice • Find each probability. Use the spinner shown above.

1. $P(5)$	**2.** $P(9)$	**3.** $P(\text{even})$	**4.** $P(\text{less than } 6)$
5. $P(7)$	**6.** $P(\text{not } 7)$	**7.** $P(15)$	**8.** $P(\text{not } 15)$

Mixed Practice • There are 2 white, 5 red, 1 yellow, and 4 blue marbles in a jar. You pick a marble from the jar without looking. Find each probability. (Assume that the marble is replaced before the next pick.)

9. $P(\text{blue})$
10. $P(\text{red})$
11. $P(\text{black})$
12. $P(\text{white})$
13. $P(\text{not blue})$
14. $P(\text{yellow})$
15. $P(\text{not red})$
16. $P(\text{green})$
17. $P(\text{not white})$
18. $P(\text{not green})$
19. $P(\text{not yellow})$
20. $P(\text{not black})$

One card is picked without looking. Find each probability.

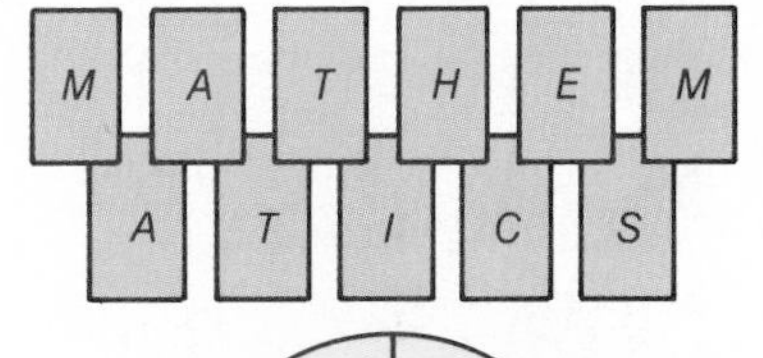

21. $P(M)$
22. $P(H)$
23. $P(\text{not } T)$
24. $P(B)$
25. $P(\text{not } S)$
★ 26. $P(\text{vowel})$

You spin this spinner once. Find each probability.

27. $P(2)$
28. $P(\text{not } 2)$
29. $P(\text{even})$
30. $P(\text{not even})$
★ 31. $P(\text{multiple of } 3)$
★ 32. $P(\text{not a multiple of } 3)$
★ 33. $P(\text{factor of } 10)$
★ 34. $P(\text{factor of } 75)$

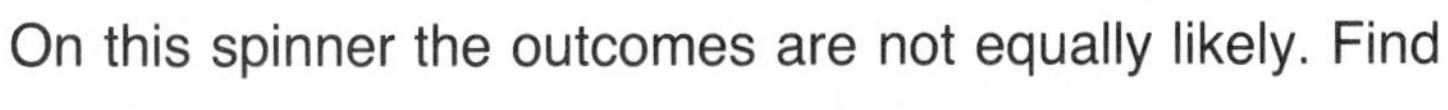

On this spinner the outcomes are not equally likely. Find

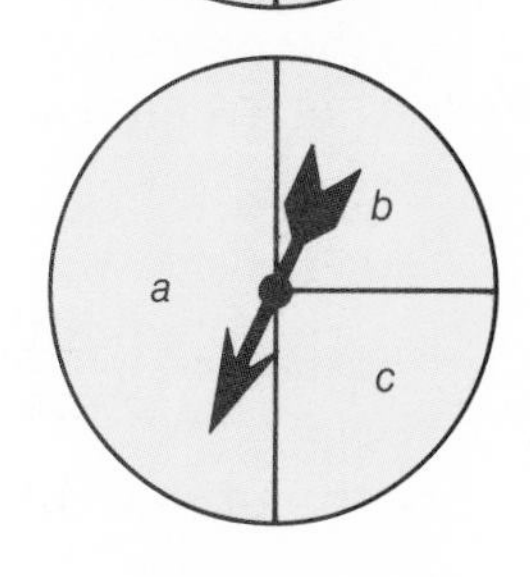

35. $P(a)$.
36. $P(b)$.
37. $P(d)$.
★ 38. $P(\text{not a vowel})$.

PROBLEM SOLVING • APPLICATIONS

39. You toss a penny. What is the probability that the outcome will be heads?

40. There are 5 red socks and 2 blue socks in a drawer. You reach into the drawer and pick a sock without looking. What is the probability that you will pick a yellow sock?

41. A newscaster says that there is a 10% probability of rain. What is the probability that it will not rain? Give your answer as a percent and as a fraction.

Using *and* and *or* in Probability

The 8 cards shown are mixed together. Ben picks one card. What is the probability that Ben will pick a red card or a card with a circle?

Think: You need to count each card that is red or has a circle on, but you must not count any card more than once.

There are 3 red cards.

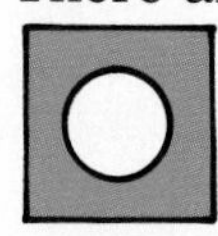

There are 3 cards that have circles on them, but 1 of these is red; so you have counted it already. Count the other 2.

In all, there are 5 favorable outcomes.

$$P(\text{red or circle}) = \frac{5}{8}$$

What is the probability that Ben will pick a card that is green and has a triangle on it?

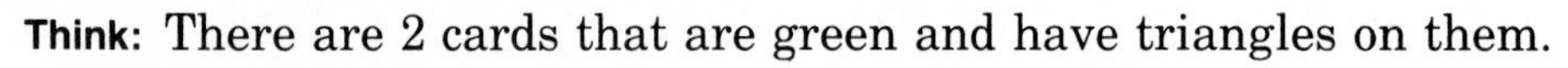

Think: There are 2 cards that are green and have triangles on them.

$$P(\text{green and triangle}) = \frac{2}{8} = \frac{1}{4}$$

What is the probability that Ben will pick a red or a green or a blue card?

Think: There are 3 red cards, 2 green cards, and 3 blue cards. So all 8 outcomes are favorable.

$$P(\text{red or green or blue}) = \frac{8}{8} = 1$$

Practice • Use the cards shown at the top of this page. One card is picked. Find each probability.

1. P(blue) **2.** P(blue or green) **3.** P(red and triangle)

4. P(blue or triangle) **5.** P(green and circle) **6.** P(circle or triangle)

Mixed Practice • A card is chosen at random, without looking. Find each probability.

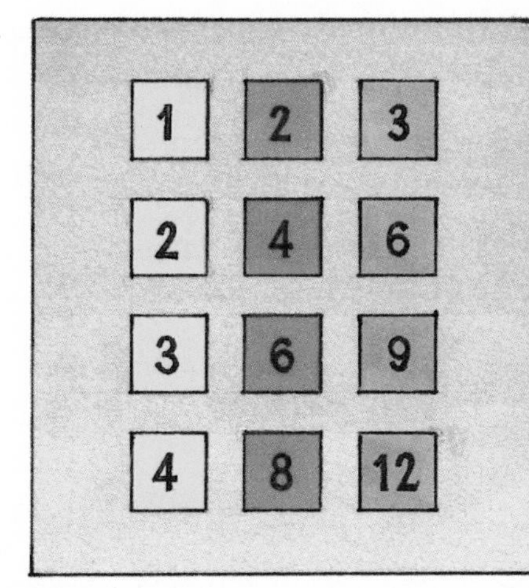

7. P(yellow)
8. P(red or green)
9. P(4 or 8)
10. P(yellow and 4)
11. P(green and even)
12. P(3 or 4)
13. P(8 or 9)
14. P(red and odd)
15. P(5 or 10)
16. P(yellow and odd)
17. P(8 or 16)
18. P(2 or 4 or 6)
19. P(green)
20. P(not green)
21. P(red)
22. P(not red)

Use your answers to exercises 19–22. Copy and complete.

★ 23. $P(\text{green}) + P(\text{not green})$

★ 24. $P(\text{red}) + P(\text{not red})$

★ 25. What is the sum of the probability of an event occurring and the probability of it not occurring?

Use the cards shown above. Find each probability.

★ 26. P(6 or less than 6)

★ 27. P(odd and a multiple of 3)

★ 28. P(8 or greater than 8)

★ 29. P(odd and a multiple of 2)

★ 30. P(12 or less than 12)

★ 31. P(green and a multiple of 3)

PROBLEM SOLVING • APPLICATIONS

32. Rochelle made a set of cards like the set shown above. She then had her sister, Femi, pick a card at random. What was the probability that Femi would pick a card that was both red and even?

★ 33. What was the probability that Femi would pick a card that was 7 or greater than 7?

Skills Maintenance

1. $n\%$ of $25 = 15$
2. $n\%$ of $140 = 98$
3. $n\%$ of $50 = 48$
4. $n\%$ of $8 = 1$
5. $n\%$ of $50 = 75$
6. $n\%$ of $3 = 2$

Sample Spaces and Tree Diagrams

A **sample space** is a systematic listing of all the possible outcomes in a given situation. Sample spaces can help you in your work with probability.

If you toss a penny once, the possible outcomes are heads or tails. You can show the sample space this way. ⟶ H T

If you toss a penny twice, what are the possible outcomes? You can use a **tree diagram** to find all the outcomes.

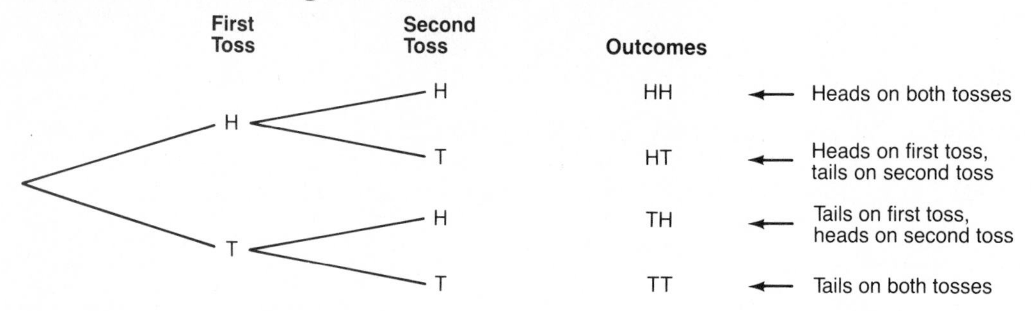

The sample space consists of 4 possible outcomes: HH, HT, TH, and TT.

How many license plates are possible using one of two letters (A or B) followed by one of five numbers (1, 2, 3, 4, or 5)? This tree diagram shows the sample space.

The tree diagram shows that there are 10 possible outcomes (10 license plates) in all.

Multiplication also shows that the number is 10.

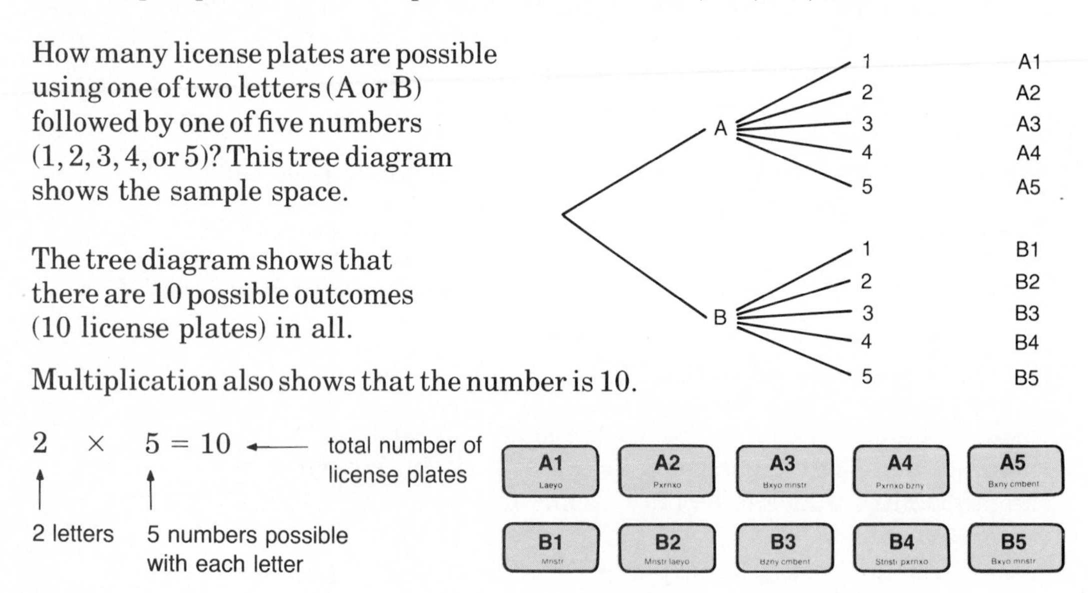

Practice • Use tree diagrams. Show the sample spaces for

1. tossing a penny three times.
2. making a license plate using one of 3 letters (A, B, or C) followed by one of 4 numbers (1, 3, 5, or 7).
3. How many different license plates are there in exercise 2?

Mixed Practice • Use tree diagrams. Show the sample spaces for

4. making a license plate using one of four letters (W, X, Y, Z) followed by one of 3 numbers (2, 4, or 6).

5. choosing a bike that is either 5-speed or 10-speed and comes in red, blue, green, or white. (Use A and B to stand for 5-speed and 10-speed; use r, b, g, and w to stand for the colors.)

A penny is tossed twice. Use the tree diagram on page 380 to help you to answer these questions.

6. How many possible outcomes are there?
7. How many of these outcomes show heads on both tosses?
8. How many of these outcomes show tails on both tosses?

9. How many of these outcomes show only one heads?
10. Which event do you think is most likely?
    heads on both tosses   tails on both tosses   only one heads

A penny is tossed three times. Use the tree diagram from exercise 1 to help you answer these questions.

11. How many possible outcomes are there?

12. How many of these outcomes show heads on all three tosses?
13. How many of these outcomes show tails on all three tosses?

★ 14. Is it more likely that the penny will land heads on two tosses than tails on two tosses?

PROBLEM SOLVING • APPLICATIONS

15. A penny is tossed four times. Is it more likely that it will land heads on three tosses than tails on one toss?

16. How many different license plates can be formed using one of 26 letters (A to Z) followed by two single-digit numbers (0 to 9 in each position)?

★ 17. There are 2,175,000 cars in a certain country. License plates in this country are formed by using one of 26 letters (A to Z) followed by five single-digit numbers (0 to 9 in each position). Which is greater—the number of cars or the number of possible license plates? How much greater?

PROBLEM SOLVING • STRATEGIES

Using Probability

Sometimes a probability can be determined from actual experience. This is called the **empirical probability** of an event.

Charles is a member of a basketball team. Out of 10 free throws he usually succeeds in making 9 baskets. The probability of a successful free throw for Charles is $\frac{9}{10}$.

If Charles tries 50 free throws, about how many baskets would you expect him to make?

$$\frac{9}{\cancel{10}_{1}} \times \cancel{50}^{5} = n$$

$$45 = n$$

Charles should make about 45 baskets out of 50 free throws.

Solve.

1. If Charles tries 180 free throws, about how many baskets would you expect him to make?

2. Gina is on the bowling team. She usually bowls more than 170 in 2 out of each 3 games. About how many times would you expect her to bowl more than 170 in 90 games?

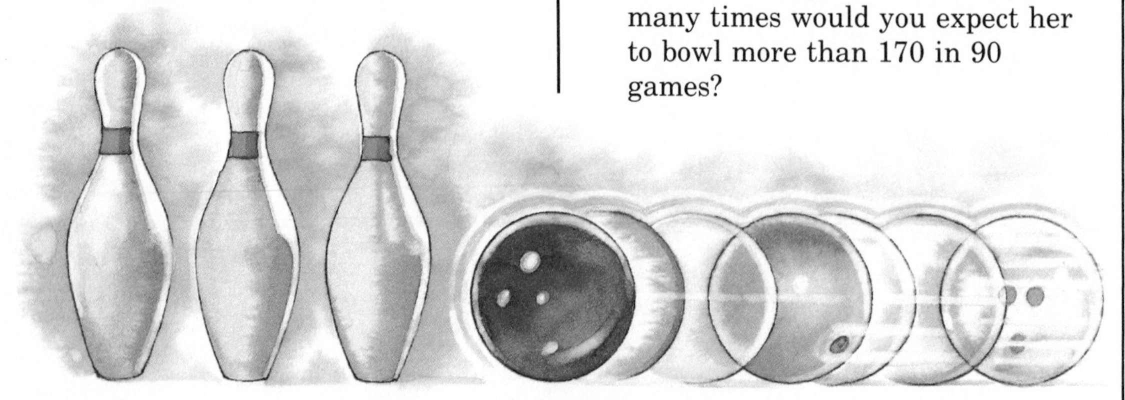

3. The Ace Appliance Company makes refrigerators. About 4 out of every 100 refrigerators turn out to be defective. About how many defective refrigerators would you expect there to be if 1,500 refrigerators are produced?

4. The Great Fun Company produces mechanical toys. After analyzing its data over a period of time, the company finds that the empirical probability of producing a defective toy is $\frac{4}{25}$. About how many of its toys would you expect to be defective in a group of 1,850 toys?

Use the wheel above for problems 5–11. How many times would you expect

5. the spinner to stop on green in 80 spins?

6. the spinner to stop on blue in 80 spins?

Use estimates to check whether your answers are reasonable.

7. the spinner to stop on red in 120 spins?

8. the spinner to stop on red or yellow in 120 spins?

9. the spinner to stop on green or orange in 184 spins?

10. the spinner to stop on purple in 1,000 spins?

11. the spinner to stop on red or blue or green in 1,000 spins?

12. You toss a penny 50 times. About how many times would you expect the penny to land heads?

Does a probability of $\frac{1}{2}$ tell you that something will always happen $\frac{1}{2}$ of the time?

★13. Toss a penny 50 times and record your results. How close to your prediction were your results?

★14. About how many times would you expect a coin to land heads in 200 tosses? Combine your results from problem 13 with the results obtained by 3 of your classmates. How close to your predictions are the combined results?

★15. You toss a coin. It lands tails. The next time you toss the coin, is the probability of tossing heads greater than $\frac{1}{2}$? Explain your answer.

★16. A number cube has 1, 2, 3, 4, 5, and 6 on its faces. About how many times would you expect to roll a number less than 5 in 150 rolls?

Probability of Independent Events

The tree diagram shows all the possible outcomes of tossing a penny and then a nickel.

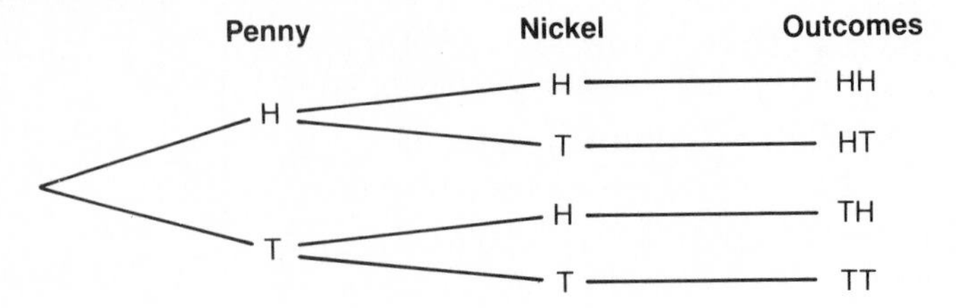

What is the probability of tossing heads on the penny and then heads on the nickel?

Think: There are 4 possible outcomes. One of the outcomes is heads on the penny and heads on the nickel.

$P(\text{heads, heads}) = \frac{1}{4}$

Tossing the penny and then the nickel are **independent events.** The outcome of tossing the penny has no effect on the outcome of tossing the nickel.

You can find the probability that two independent events will happen by multiplying the probability of the first event by the probability of the second event.

$$\begin{aligned} P(\text{heads, heads}) &= P(\text{heads}) \times P(\text{heads}) \\ &= \frac{1}{2} \times \frac{1}{2} \\ &= \frac{1}{4} \end{aligned}$$

If two events, A and B, are independent, then the probability that both will happen is P(A) × P (B).

What is the probability of tossing tails on a coin and rolling a 4 on a number cube?

$$\begin{aligned} P(\text{tails}, 4) &= P(\text{tails}) \times P(4) \\ &= \frac{1}{2} \times \frac{1}{6} \\ &= \frac{1}{12} \end{aligned}$$

Practice • A coin is tossed and a number cube is rolled. Find each probability.

1. $P(\text{heads}, 6)$ **2.** $P(\text{tails}, 1)$ **3.** $P(\text{tails}, 7)$

4. $P(\text{heads}, 2)$ **5.** $P(\text{heads, even number})$ **6.** $P(\text{tails, not } 5)$

Mixed Practice • Spin the spinner and roll the number cube. Find each probability.

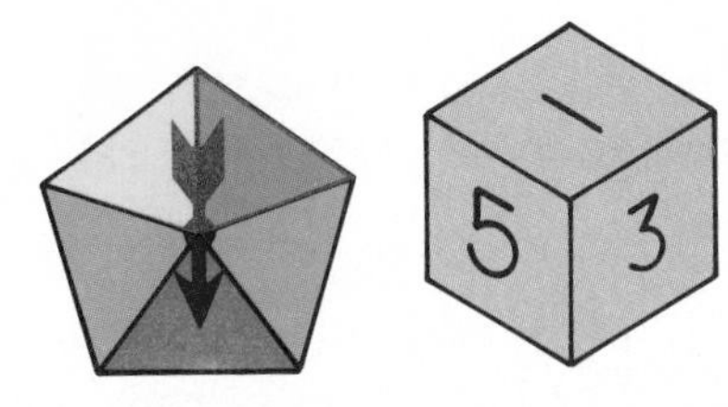

7. P(red, 2)
8. P(green, 4)
9. P(blue, 5)
10. P(yellow, 9)
11. P(red, even number)
12. P(blue, not 4)

Toss a penny, a nickel, and a dime. Find the probability of

13. exactly two tails.
14. three tails.
15. no tails.
16. three heads.
★ 17. more heads than tails.
★ 18. more tails than heads.

A crayon box contains 2 red, 3 blue, 4 black, and 1 green. Pick a crayon at random, replace it, and then pick another crayon at random. Find the probability.

19. P(red, blue)
20. P(black, green)
21. P(red, red)
22. P(blue, green)
23. P(black, black)
24. P(green, red)

PROBLEM SOLVING • APPLICATIONS

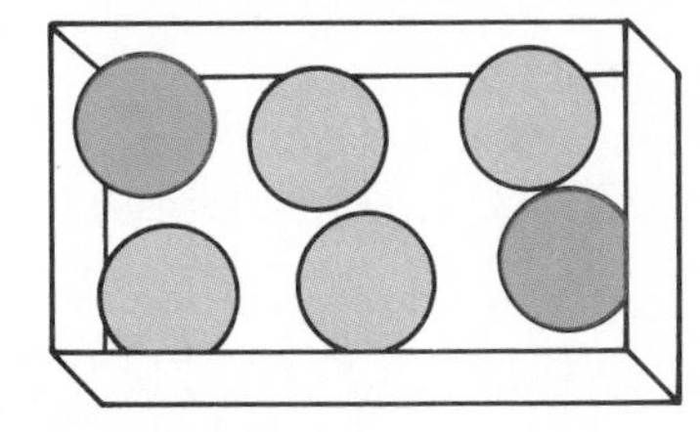

25. Suppose you pick a marble at random, replace it, and then pick another marble at random. Are the second pick and the first pick independent events?

★ 26. Suppose you pick a marble at random and you do not replace the marble in the box. Then you pick a second marble at random. Does the first pick affect the probabilities for the second pick? Are the second pick and the first pick independent events?

Midchapter Review

There are 4 red pencils and 2 blue pencils. Each pencil has either an S or a T on it. You pick a pencil at random. Find the probability.

S
T
T
S
S
T

1. P(red)
2. P(not red)
3. P(not S)
4. P(green)
5. P(red or blue)
6. P(red and S)
7. You toss a penny and a dime. What is the probability of tossing heads on the penny and tails on the dime?

Organizing Data

The students in Mrs. Hirami's science class sat and recorded their pulse rates.

The class was asked to answer these questions.

What is the highest pulse rate? How many students have a pulse rate greater than 80?

Pulse Rates				
80	81	79	82	80
78	84	82	86	83
81	80	79	83	84
85	83	82	81	82

It is easier to answer such questions if the numerical information, or **data,** is organized in a table.

Below is a **frequency table.** The **frequency** of an item is the number of times it occurs. The table shows the distribution, or **frequency distribution,** of the data.

To make a frequency table, follow these steps:

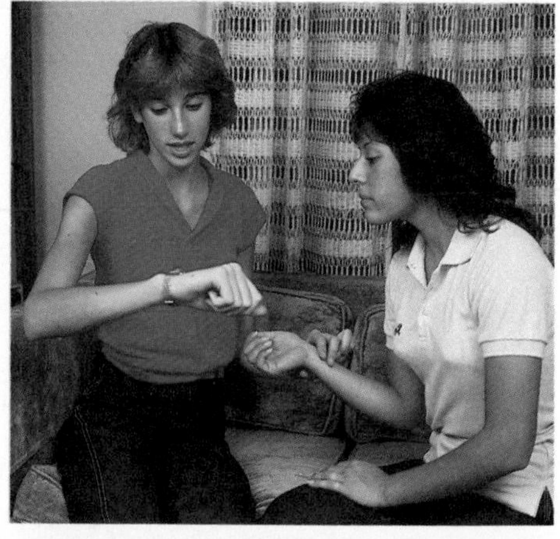

Step 1
Find the least and the greatest of the items (the pulse rate in this situation).

Step 2
List the items in order (least to greatest in this table).

Step 3
Use tally marks to record how often each item occurred.

Step 4
Count the tally marks and record the number in the frequency column.

The highest pulse rate is 86.

By adding the frequencies for pulse rates greater than 80, you can see that there are 14 students with pulse rates greater than 80.

Pulse Rate	Tally	Frequency
78	/	1
79	//	2
80	///	3
81	///	3
82	////	4
83	///	3
84	//	2
85	/	1
86	/	1

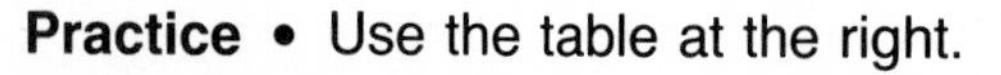

Practice • Use the table at the right.

1. What is the lowest pulse rate?

2. How many students have a pulse rate of 81?

3. How many students have a pulse rate greater than 81?

4. How many students have a pulse rate less than 81?

5. How many students are there in Mrs. Hirami's science class?

Mixed Practice • Do exercise 6. Then answer the questions.

6. Make a frequency table for these daily high temperatures (in degrees Celsius): 18, 20, 18, 21, 23, 19, 20, 22, 17, 18, 19, 22, 21, and 20.

7. What was the highest temperature?

8. How many days was the high temperature 20°?

9. How many days was the high temperature greater than 20°?

10. How many days was the high temperature less than 20°?

The students in Mrs. Lambert's gym class recorded how many sit-ups they did in 2 minutes.

Sit-Ups								
40	38	41	36	43	45	38	41	39
43	39	39	42	40	41	43	42	45
39	41	40	42	44	41	40		

11. Make a frequency table for the number of sit-ups.

12. How many students did 40 sit-ups?

13. What number of sit-ups has the greatest frequency?

14. How many students did fewer than 40 sit-ups?

15. How many students are in Mrs. Lambert's gym class?

★ 16. What percent of the students did 43 sit-ups?

★ 17. What percent of the students did more than 40 sit-ups?

PROBLEM SOLVING • APPLICATIONS

18. In your gym class, have 20 students try an exercise experiment similar to the one done by Mrs. Lambert's class. Make a frequency table to show the data.

★ 19. Write 5 questions about the data you collect for problem 18. Answer each question.

Mean and Range

Kevin took 4 tests in English during this term. To the nearest whole number, what is his average or **mean** score?

Franklin, Cara	✓	✓	✓	✓
Franklin, Kevin	84	75	80	90
Grieg, Alice	✓	~	~	~

To find the mean of his test scores, add all the scores and then divide the sum by the number of scores.

Step 1
Find the sum of the scores. $84 + 75 + 80 + 90 = 329$

Step 2
Divide the sum by the number of scores. Round to the nearest whole number.

$$4\overline{)329.0} = 82.2 \approx 82$$

Rounded to the nearest whole number, the mean of his scores is 82.

The **range** of the scores is the "spread" between the greatest and the least scores. You find the range by subtracting the least score from the greatest score.

$90 - 75 = 15$

The range of Kevin's scores is 15. Sometimes the range is stated as an interval. For example, the range of the scores can be stated as "from 75 to 90."

More Examples

Find the mean to the nearest tenth: 7.7, 8.6, 8.5.

$7.7 + 8.6 + 8.5 = 24.8$ $\qquad 3\overline{)24.80} = 8.2\overline{6} \approx 8.3$ $\qquad$ Mean: 8.3

Find the range. $8.6 - 7.7 = 0.9$ $\qquad$ Range: 0.9

Practice • Find the mean of each group.

1. 95, 75, 80, 82, 93
2. 5.4, 4.8, 6.2, 6.8

Find the range of each group.

3. 65, 65, 70, 72, 78
4. 7.8, 6.5, 7.4, 7.1

Mixed Practice • Find the mean of each group.

5. 80, 85, 90, 70, 85
6. 84, 92, 70, 75, 85, 92
7. 3.0, 2.5, 4.0, 1.7
8. 117, 119, 130, 118, 123, 125
9. $1\frac{1}{2}, 1\frac{1}{4}, 2\frac{1}{8}, 1\frac{1}{8}$
10. \$1.40, \$2.15, \$3.75, \$2.10, \$1.50

Find the range of each group.

11. 37, 24, 28, 32
12. 54, 61, 49, 58, 43
13. 5.6, 7.8, 3.4, 4.4, 8.2
14. 365, 472, 805, 766
15. 1.36, 1.85, 3.10, 2.95
16. 812 mm, 910 mm, 874 mm

Find the mean of each group. Round to the nearest whole number.

17. 36, 33, 40
18. 15, 35, 30, 27
19. 76, 85, 84, 82, 87
20. 8, 6, 5, 7, 4, 8, 7

Find the mean of each group. Round to the nearest tenth.

★ 21. 100, 85, 75, 85
★ 22. 2.5, 3.0, 2.0, 3.5
★ 23. 1.3, 1.4, 1.8, 1.7, 1.0
★ 24. 30.6, 29.8, 29.7

PROBLEM SOLVING • APPLICATIONS

25. Lily took 5 science tests. Her scores were 85, 92, 77, 85, and 94. Find the range and the mean of Lily's scores.

26. Carlos took 7 tests in math. His scores were 43, 96, 92, 93, 100, 91, and 94. Find the range and the mean of Carlos's scores.

★ 27. All but one of Carlos's scores were high. Find the mean and the range of the 6 high scores. Compare it with the mean of the 7 scores. How does one low score affect the mean?

★ 28. Yoko has bowled 2 games. Her scores were 176 and 182. She will bowl one more game today. What score must she bowl on her third game to have an average of 185?

Median and Mode

The table shows the leading scorers in the National Hockey League during a recent season.

Leading Hockey Scorers		
Player	Goals	Assists
Dionne	53	84
Gretzky	51	86
Lafleur	50	75
Perreault	40	66
Rogers	44	61
Simmer	56	44
Sittler	40	57
Stoughton	56	44
Trottier	42	62

The **median** is the middle number when the data are written in order.

To find the median for the number of goals scored, list the number of goals in order from least to greatest. Then identify the middle number.

40 40 42 44 50 51 53 56 56 Median = 50

middle number

The median is 50, the middle number.

When there is an even number of numbers, the median is the mean of the middle 2 numbers.

18 23 27 30 32 35

middle numbers

$$\text{Median} = \frac{27 + 30}{2}$$

$$= 28.5$$

The **mode** is the number that occurs most often in a set of data.

In the data for the leading hockey scorers, what is the mode for the number of assists?

Think: 44 occurs twice.
No other number occurs as often in the assists column. → 44 is the mode.

What is the mode for the number of goals?

Think: 56 occurs twice in the goals column; so does 40.
No other number occurs more than once. → 56 and 40 are the modes.

Note that there can be more than one mode for a set of data.

Practice • Find the median.

1. 33, 58, 39, 49, 52
2. 92, 81, 85, 82, 86, 90

Find the mode or modes.

3. 65, 70, 72, 65, 68, 65
4. 23, 33, 19, 23, 27, 24, 19

Mixed Practice • Find the median and the mode or modes.

5. 103, 111, 100, 111, 108
6. 88, 74, 83, 78, 74, 83
7. 43, 36, 41, 38, 36, 40
8. 0.55, 0.61, 0.58, 0.61, 0.60, 0.61
9. 2.5, 2.1, 3.3, 2.4, 3.7
10. 7.6, 7.3, 7.6, 7.1, 6.8, 7.3

Find the mean, the median, and the mode.

11. 4, 5, 12, 6, 4, 4, 7
12. 2, 19, 8, 9, 8, 10, 3, 5

PROBLEM SOLVING • APPLICATIONS

13. In a 50-meter race, 5 female runners had these times: 6.35 seconds, 6.50 seconds, 7.10 seconds, 7.85 seconds, and 7.10 seconds. What was the mean time?
14. What was the mode for the running times?
15. What was the median for the running times?

How many of the runners had running times that were

16. less than the mode?
17. greater than the mode?
18. less than the mean?
19. greater than the mean?

★ 20. Construct a set of 5 numbers in which the mode, the mean, and the median are equal.

Skills Maintenance

1. 10% of $x = 8$
2. 25% of $y = 70$
3. 60% of $x = 150$
4. 12% of $y = 60$
5. 130% of $x = 52$
6. 2.5% of $y = 24$

Pictographs

Six schools in District 7 take part in a recycling project. This **pictograph** shows the number of glass bottles collected during the project.

Glass Bottles Collected	Each stands for 500 bottles.
Allen School	
Brooks School	
Finley School	
Sampson School	
Bradley School	
Madison School	

If each stands for 500 bottles, what does stand for?

The graph shows that 1,750 glass bottles were collected by the students at Allen School. $3\frac{1}{2} \times 500 = 1{,}750$

To make a pictograph:

Step 1
Choose a symbol that can be used to show the data conveniently.

Step 2
Find how many symbols (and parts of symbols) are needed to represent each item.

Step 3
Draw the symbols and label the graph. Be sure to include the title and a sentence telling what the symbol represents.

Practice • Answer the questions.

1. Which school collected the greatest number of bottles?
2. Which school collected the least number of bottles?

About how many glass bottles were collected by the students at

3. Brooks School?
4. Sampson School?
5. Madison School?
6. Bradley School?

Mixed Practice • Answer the questions.

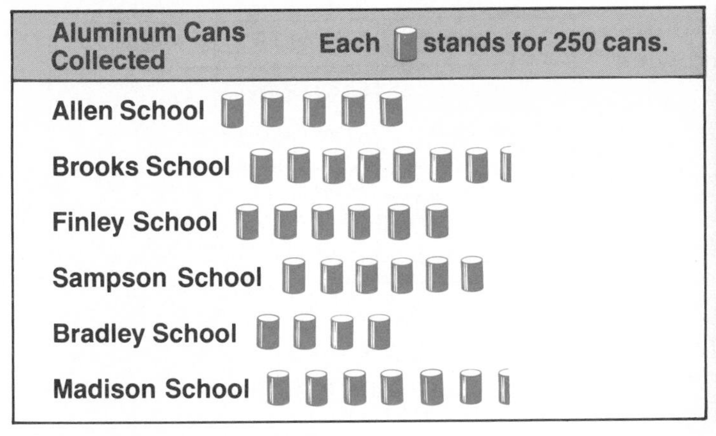

7. Which school collected the greatest number of aluminum cans?

8. Which school collected the least number of aluminum cans?

About how many cans were collected by the students at

9. Allen School?

10. Brooks School?

11. Bradley School?

12. Madison School?

13. List the names of the schools in order from least to greatest according to the number of cans collected.

14. About how many more cans were collected by the students at Brooks School than by the students at Madison School?

PROBLEM SOLVING • APPLICATIONS

Often you need to round data before you can make a pictograph.

15. Use this table to make a pictograph showing the number of glass bottles collected by each student. Round each number to the nearest ten. Then use to stand for 10 bottles.

Name	Glass Bottles Collected
John	48
Jennifer	62
Larry	37
Sue	73

★ 16. This table shows data about the population of five states. Round each number to the nearest 500,000. Then make a pictograph for these populations.

Name	Population (1980 Census)
Alabama	3,890,061
Colorado	2,888,834
Tennessee	4,590,750
Utah	1,461,037
Virginia	5,346,279

Bar Graphs

Anne and Julio collected data in the school cafeteria. They recorded what each of 115 students chose for dessert. They organized the data in a frequency table.

Dessert	Tally	Frequency
Fruit	卌 卌 卌 卌 卌	25
Yogurt	卌 卌 卌 卌 |	21
Ice Cream	卌 卌 卌 卌 卌 卌 卌 |||	38
No Dessert	卌 卌 卌 |||	18
Granola Bars	卌 卌 |||	13

Anne and Julio used the table to make a **bar graph** that can help them compare the data.

Since the bars in the graph are vertical, this is called a **vertical bar graph**. A **horizontal bar graph** can also be drawn for the same data.

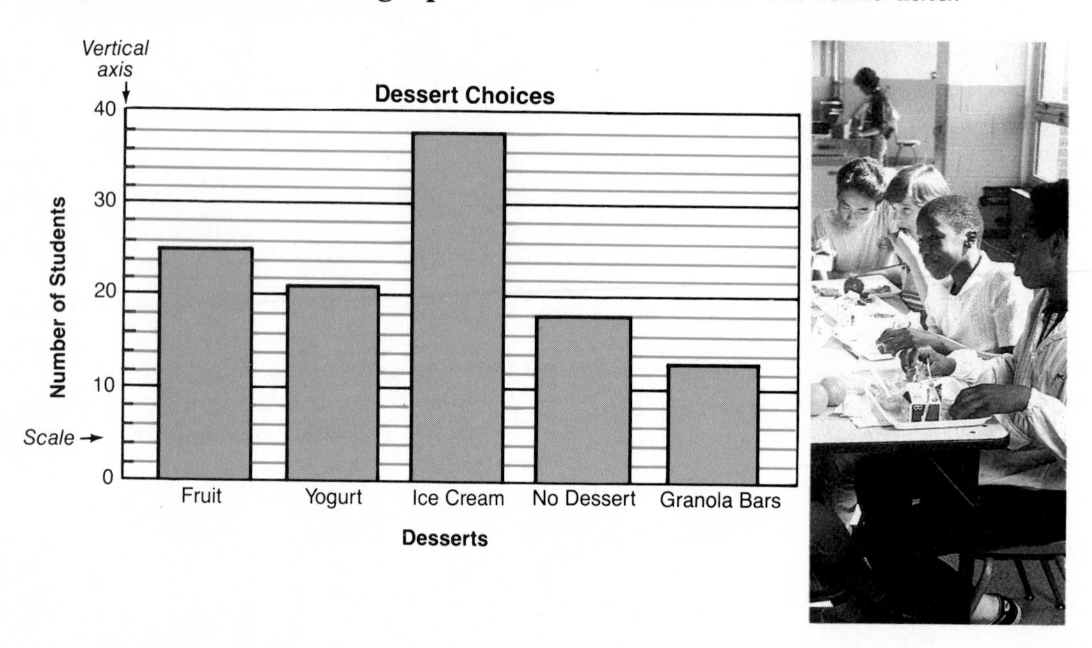

To make a bar graph:

Step 1
Choose a scale that can show the data conveniently.

Step 2
Mark and label the scale at equal intervals on the vertical axis.

Step 3
Draw a bar for each item in the table. The height or the length of the bar shows the frequency. Label each bar and that axis.

Step 4
Be sure to include a title for the graph.

Practice • Answer the questions.

1. Which dessert was the most popular? the least popular?
2. Which dessert was more popular—yogurt or fruit?
3. How many more students chose yogurt than granola bars?

Mixed Practice • Answer the questions.

4. How many students chose no dessert?
5. Which desserts were chosen by more than 20 students?
6. This table shows the sandwich choices of 100 students.

Sandwich Choice	Tuna	Ham	Cheese	Bologna
Number of Students	37	28	14	21

Make a bar graph to show the sandwich choices.

7. Which sandwich was most popular? Do you need a graph to answer this question?

A **double-bar graph** can be used to show data for more than one group. A different color is used to show the data for each group.

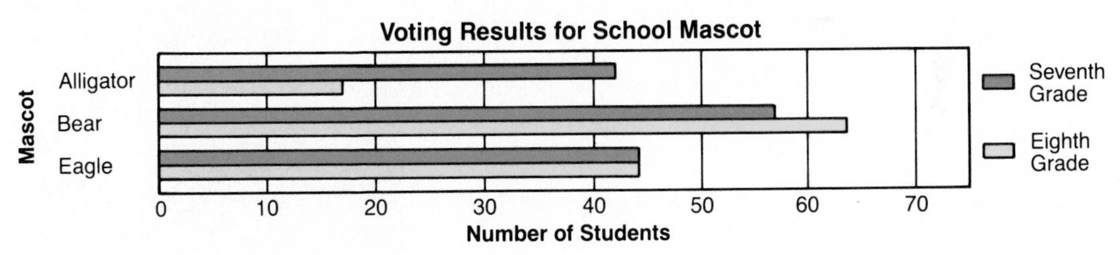

8. Which mascot was chosen by more seventh-graders than eighth-graders?
9. Which mascot was chosen by the same number of students from each grade?
10. Which mascot was chosen by the greatest number of seventh-graders?

PROBLEM SOLVING • APPLICATIONS

★ 11. Make a bar graph that shows the recycling data in the graph on page 392.

★ 12. Take a survey in your class. Find out how each of your classmates travels to school. Organize your data in a frequency table. Then make a bar graph to show the results of your survey.

Broken-Line Graphs

A **broken-line graph** can be used to show change over a period of time. Sharp increases or decreases can be seen easily on a broken-line graph. The steeper the line, the sharper is the increase or the decrease.

The numbers shown on this graph have been rounded to the nearest thousand.

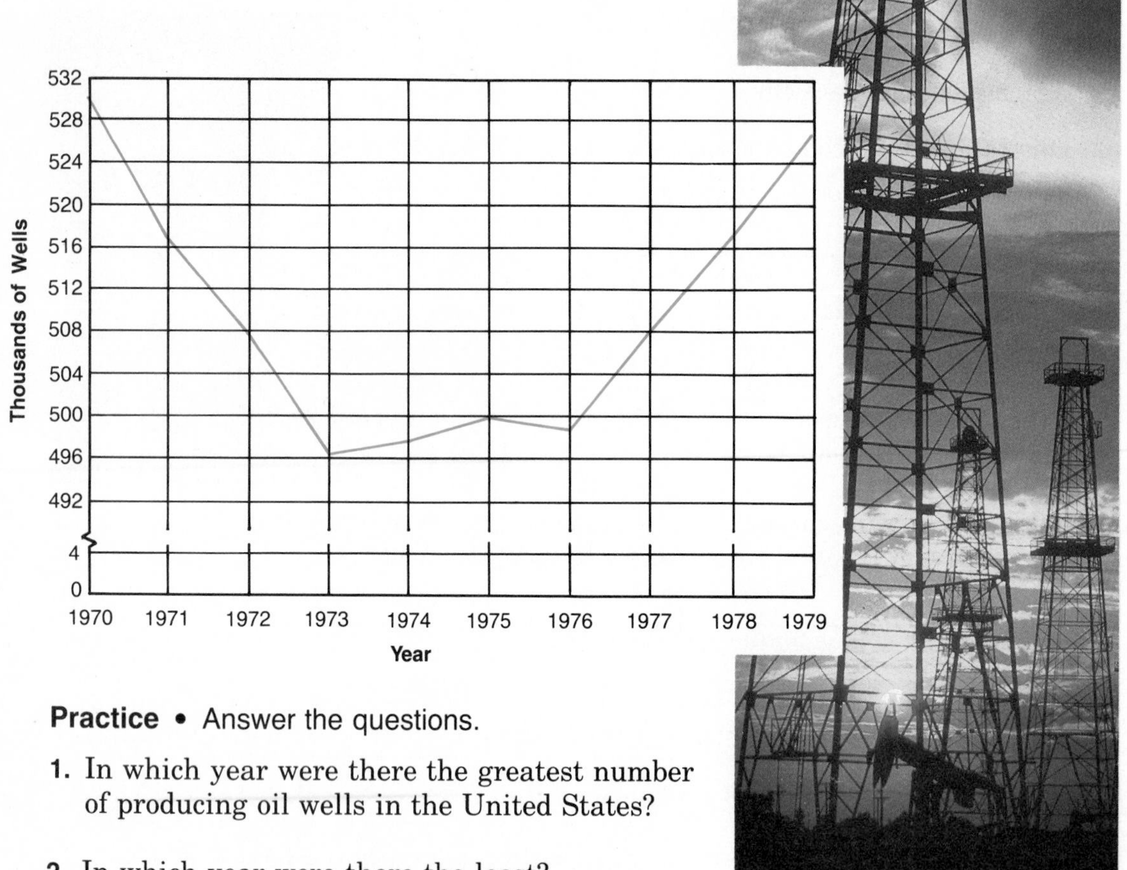

Practice • Answer the questions.

1. In which year were there the greatest number of producing oil wells in the United States?

2. In which year were there the least?

3. During which three-year period was there the greatest decrease in the number of producing oil wells?

Mixed Practice • Answer the questions.

4. During which years were there fewer than 500,000 producing oil wells in the United States?

5. During which three-year period was there the greatest increase in the number of producing oil wells?

6. Use the table to make a broken-line graph.

Year	1970	1971	1972	1973	1974	1975	1976	1977	1978	1979
Oil Production in U.S. (Billions of Barrels)	3.5	3.5	3.5	3.4	3.2	3.1	3.0	3.0	3.2	3.1

A **double broken-line graph** can be used to compare different data.

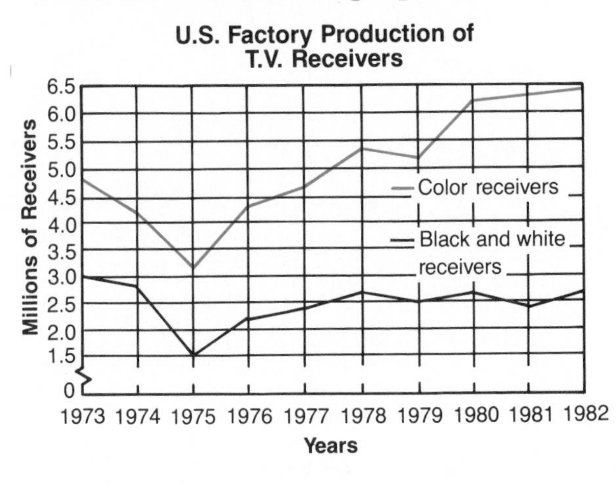

7. Was production of black-and-white receivers greater than production of color receivers in any of the years?

8. In which year was the least number of color receivers and black-and-white receivers produced?

9. Was production of black-and-white receivers greater in 1982 than in 1973?

10. Was production of color receivers greater in 1982 than in 1973?

11. In which years did the production of color receivers exceed the production of black-and-white receivers by 3 million or more?

PROBLEM SOLVING • APPLICATIONS

12. Keep a record of how much time you spend doing homework each day for two weeks. Then make a broken-line graph to show the data.

13. Keep a record of how much money you spend each day for two weeks. Then make a double broken-line graph to compare the first week with the second week.

PROBLEM SOLVING • STRATEGIES

Sampling

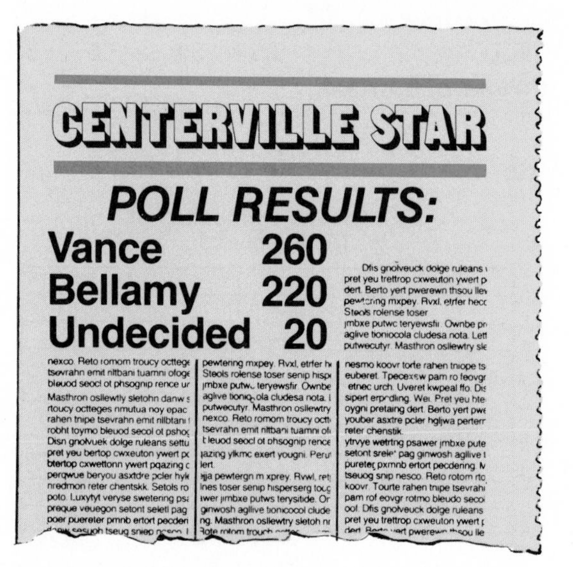

CENTERVILLE STAR

POLL RESULTS:

Vance	260
Bellamy	220
Undecided	20

Sometimes you can use a sample of a group of people or things to make predictions or solve problems that involve the entire group.

The *Centerville Star* wants to find out which of two candidates will win the election for mayor.

About 35,000 votes are usually cast in mayoral elections in Centerville. It would be impractical to ask 35,000 people how they plan to vote. So the *Centerville Star* uses a **sample** of 500 voters in its poll.

In the poll the *Centerville Star* finds that 260 of the 500 voters plan to vote for Vance. Since $\frac{260}{500} = \frac{13}{25} = 52\%$, the poll indicates that Vance currently is the choice of about 52% of the voters.

If 35,000 people voted and 52% voted for Vance, how many votes would she receive?

52% of $35{,}000 = n$
$0.52 \times 35{,}000 = n$
$18{,}200 = n$ She would receive about 18,200 votes.

Remember, a sample is useful only if it is unbiased and representative of the entire group. In statistics the entire group is called the **population** (even when the group does not consist of people).

Suppose the *Centerville Star* poll had been taken at a rally for Vance. Would the sample have been unbiased and representative of the population?

Solve.

1. In the *Centerville Star* poll, what percent of the sample indicated Bellamy as its choice?
2. If 35,000 votes are cast, how many votes for Bellamy can be expected?

Sample results must be interpreted carefully.

3. You want to find out the average distance that students travel to come to school. You poll the first 50 students you see bicycling to school. Is this likely to be a good sample of the population? Explain your answer.

4. Often a very small sample cannot be used to make judgments about a large population. Suppose your school has 2,000 students and you ask 5 students which type of music they like best—jazz, pop, or classical. All 5 say they like pop best. Does this mean that all of the 2,000 students like pop best?

This table shows the results of three polls about the candidates for mayor in Centerville. Use the table for problems 5–9.

Choices	Dates of Polls 10/15	10/22	10/29*
Vance	260	240	220
Bellamy	220	225	270
Undecided	20	35	10

*Final poll before election

5. What percent of the voters choose Vance in the 10/22 poll?

6. What percent of the voters choose Bellamy in the 10/22 poll?

7. The election will be held on 11/2. Which candidate is likely to win? Explain your answer.

8. If 35,000 votes are cast, about how many votes for Vance can be expected (according to the final poll)?

9. If 35,000 votes are cast, about how many votes for Bellamy can be expected (according to the final poll)?

To choose the best of three possible names for a new toothpaste, a company uses a sample of 1,000 consumers. Their choices are shown in this set of data.

Cleano	280
Quicko	180
All-Bright	540

Use the data for problems 10–13.

10. Which of the three names was chosen by the greatest number of people in the sample?

11. What percent chose Cleano?

12. What percent chose All-Bright?

★ 13. From the poll, can you tell how many people will buy the toothpaste if it is named All-Bright? Explain.

★ 14. Find a way to use a sample to see which letter of the alphabet is used most often in a science textbook. Write an explanation of your method and why you think it is reasonable.

CHAPTER 14

REVIEW

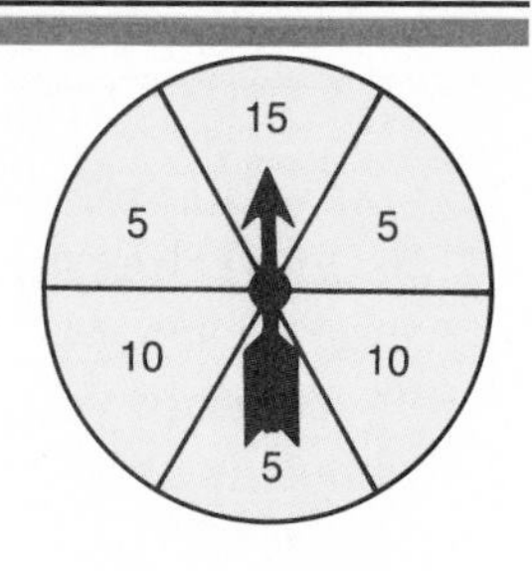

You spin this spinner once. Find each probability. (pp. 376–379)

1. $P(15)$ 2. $P(5)$ 3. $P(4)$

4. $P(5 \text{ or } 10)$ 5. $P(\text{odd and less than } 12)$

6. Use a tree diagram to show the sample space for making a license plate using one of 2 letters (A or B) followed by one of 4 numbers (1, 2, 3, or 4). (pp. 380–381)

You spin this spinner and toss a number cube that has 1, 2, 3, 4, 5, and 6 on it. Find each probability. (pp. 384–385)

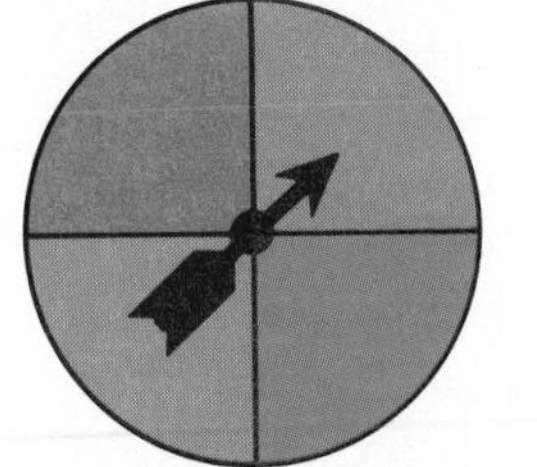

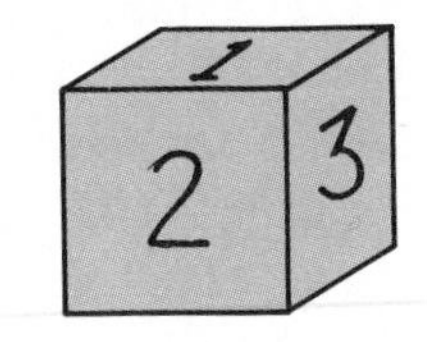

7. $P(\text{orange}, 1)$
8. $P(\text{green}, 5)$
9. $P(\text{red, odd number})$
10. $P(\text{green, not } 3)$
11. Make a frequency table for these daily high temperatures: 21°C, 19°C, 23°C, 20°C, 23°C, 22°C, 18°C, 19°C, 21°C, 24°C. (pp. 386–387)
12. What was the highest temperature? (pp. 386–387)
13. How many days was the high temperature greater than 21°C? (pp. 386–387)

Find the mean. (pp. 388–389)

14. 35, 33, 29, 31, 27

Find the range. (pp. 388–389)

15. 256, 315, 248, 508, 491

Find the median and the mode. (pp. 390–391)

16. 6, 7, 14, 8, 6, 6, 9

17. 4, 16, 7, 6, 9, 7, 12, 8

18. This table shows the number of people who bought water purifiers in the ABC Store during a five-day sale. Use the table to make a broken-line graph. (pp. 396–397)

Day	Monday	Tuesday	Wednesday	Thursday	Friday
Number of People	50	60	40	70	90

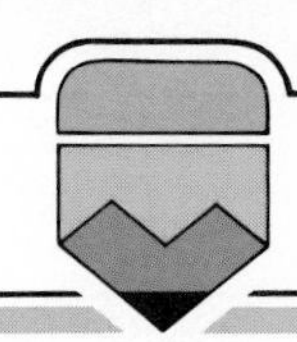

PROJECT

Constructing a Circle Graph

Miriam is treasurer of the student council. She wants to make a circle graph to show how the council budgets its money for the year.

There are 360 degrees in a circle. To find the angle measure for each item, Miriam multiplies the percent times 360 degrees.

Student Council Budget

Item	*Percent*	*Angle Measure*
School Activities	40%	$0.40 \times 360 = 144$
Transportation	25%	$0.25 \times 360 = 90$
Supplies	20%	$0.20 \times 360 = 72$
Other	15%	$0.15 \times 360 = 54$
	100%	360°

Miriam then constructs a circle and uses a protractor to draw the angles. Finally she labels the graph.

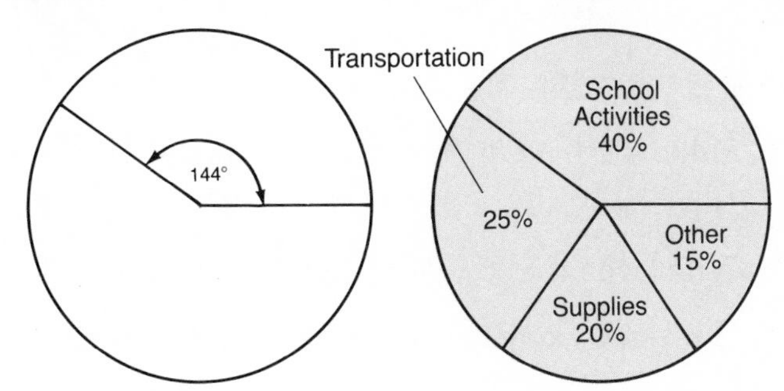

1. Copy and complete the chart below. Then make the circle graph.

School Library Budget

Item	*Percent*	*Angle Measure*
Books and Periodicals	55%	$0.55 \times 360 =$?
Supplies	20%	?
Furniture	15%	?
Other	10%	?

2. Use percents to show the monthly budget you expect to use when you reach the age of thirty. (You can also indicate the total monthly income you hope to have!) Then make a circle graph to show your budget.

CHAPTER 14

TEST

You spin this spinner once. Find each probability.

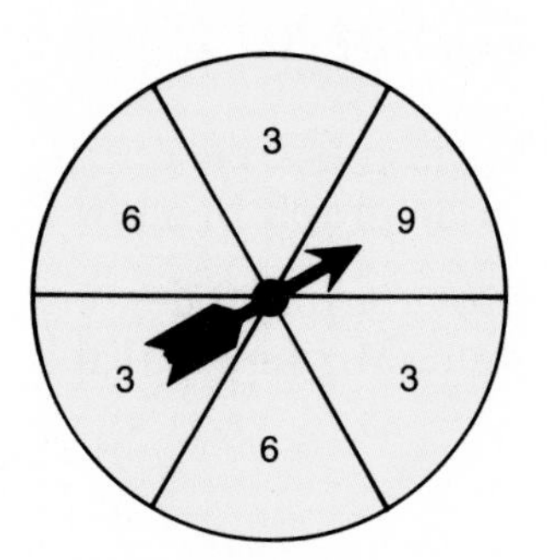

1. $P(9)$
2. $P(6)$
3. $P(\text{less than } 15)$
4. $P(3 \text{ or } 6)$
5. $P(\text{odd and less than } 8)$
6. Use a tree diagram to show the sample space for making a license plate using one of 3 letters (X, Y, or Z) followed by one of 3 numbers (2, 4, or 6).

You spin this spinner and toss a number cube that has 1, 2, 3, 4, 5, and 6 on it. Find each probability.

7. $P(\text{yellow}, 4)$
8. $P(\text{green}, 3)$
9. $P(\text{blue, even number})$
10. $P(\text{yellow, not } 5)$
11. Make a frequency table for these daily low temperatures: 13°C, 10°C, 12°C, 13°C, 14°C, 9°C, 11°C, 10°C, 13°C, 9°C.
12. What was the lowest temperature?
13. How many days was the low temperature less than 11°C?

Find the mean.

14. 27, 31, 34, 17, 13

Find the range.

15. 98, 115, 129, 164, 157

Find the median and the mode.

16. 8, 9, 16, 10, 8, 7, 11
17. 17, 5, 8, 15, 16, 17, 14, 9
18. This table shows the number of people who attended a workshop on five different days. Use the table to make a broken-line graph.

Day	Monday	Tuesday	Wednesday	Thursday	Friday
Number of People	70	90	100	80	110

ENRICHMENT

Finding the Mean from a Frequency Table

Mr. Lee made a frequency table to show the test scores of his students.

Then he used these steps to find the mean from the frequency table.

Step 1
Multiply each test score by its frequency. (Score × Frequency column)

Step 2
Add all the products in the Score × Frequency column to get the total number of points.

Step 3
Add all the frequencies in the Frequency column to get the total number of students.

Step 4
Mean = total number of points ÷ total number of students
= 2,370 ÷ 30
Mean = 79

Test Score	Tally	Frequency	Score × Frequency
55	/	1	55
60	///	3	180
65	/	1	65
70	///	3	210
75	////	4	300
80	HHT //	7	560
85	///	3	255
90	HHT	5	450
95	/	1	95
100	//	2	200
	Totals	30	2,370

Find the mean for this frequency table.

1.

Score	Tally	Frequency
48	//	2
50	/	1
52	/	1
54	///	3
56	HHT	5
58	HHT	5
60	//	2
62	/	1

2. The students in Mr. Imperato's class recorded how many seconds it took them to run 100 meters. Make a frequency table for the data and then find the mean.

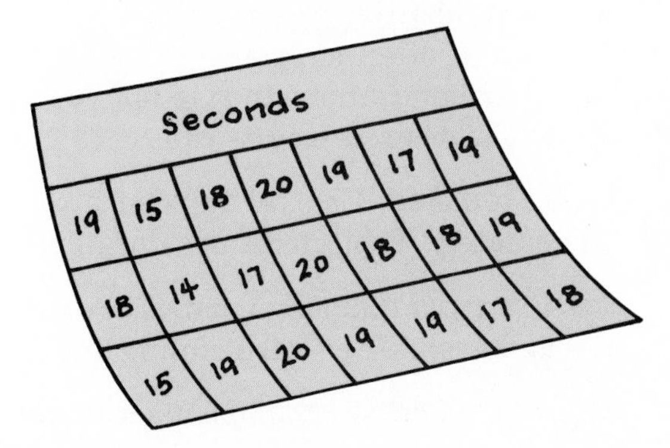

COMPUTER

Careers: Systems Analyst

Systems analysts decide what information and equipment are needed for a job. Essentially, systems analysts work through systems flowcharts.

A *systems flowchart* shows all the following elements.
Computer: kind and size
Input: kinds, types, quantities, and timing required
Output: kinds, types, quantities, and timing required
Connections among computer, input, and output

Systems analysts need state-of-the-art knowledge of different kinds.

State-of-the-art knowledge means knowledge about what is currently available and what will be available in both the near and more distant future. For a small project, knowledge of new products during the next few months may be sufficient. For a project lasting many years, planning is needed for new equipment through those many years.

The following two kinds of knowledge are needed to analyze *any* job.

Hardware knowledge means knowledge about the capacities, capabilities, and prices for current and near-future computers, input devices, and output devices.

Software knowledge means knowledge about the capabilities and limitations of current and near-future programming languages and whether it will be advisable to design a completely new programming language.

Then there are the particular kinds of knowledge needed to analyze an individual job.

Results desired: Usually it is best to "start at the end" by specifying the results desired before looking at available input. When exact results are specified, it often happens that much available input simply is not needed. On the other hand, input that is not currently available may have to be generated before the desired results can be calculated.

Timing required: Control data for a rocket booster in flight are needed immediately. Projected sales data for 1990 are not subject to such critical timing.

Possible input quantity means knowing what input frequency is required. This is clearly connected with timing considerations.

Possible output quantity means knowing what output frequency is required.

Analysts also must determine:

The number and type of *input devices needed* based on timing considerations and possible input quantity. Keyboard input is slow but can be highly interactive. *Interactive* means that results needed for the next steps in the job itself can be provided quickly (usually by the programmer). Hard disks input quantities of data quickly, but a programmer cannot interact quickly with each piece of data.

The number and type of *output devices needed* based on timing considerations and possible output quantity.

You can begin to act as a systems analyst right now. The first requirement for a systems analysis is *information.*

1. Search through magazines and newspapers for display advertisements and make a list of those that apply to hardware and those that apply to software. Then look at the classified advertisements for job opportunities and classify those as hardware (engineering) and software (programming). As you do this, make a list of the technical terms that you know and those that you do not know. Bring the words you do not know to class and see if you can find the meanings of them. You may have to search for more information to answer your questions.
2. If you need more information, you can ask your teacher, a school librarian, or a public librarian about books and magazines you might borrow and read.
3. You might wish to visit a nearby computer shop for a demonstration of a computer or for computer literature. You can write to computer hardware and software manufacturers to ask them to send you information about their products.

The problem is not in finding information about computers. It is in sorting through all the possible sources and finding the two or three that are most likely to have the information you seek. The whole science of *information retrieval* is devoted to the study of *how* to get to the information you want.

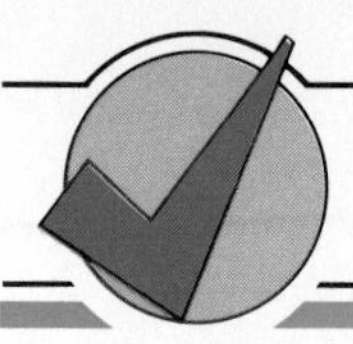

SKILLS MAINTENANCE

Chapters 1 Through 14

Choose the correct answers.

1. Subtract.

$$\begin{array}{r} 70.06 \\ -25.763 \\ \hline \end{array}$$

A. 44.397
B. 44.297
C. 44.303
D. not here

2. Divide. Round the quotient to the nearest hundredth.

$0.46\overline{)0.7539}$

A. 1.64
B. 1.63
C. 1.74
D. not here

3. Solve this equation.

$7n = 126$

A. $n = 18$
B. $n = 17$
C. $n = 19$
D. not here

4. Find all the factors of 45. List them in order.

A. 1, 3, 5, 7, 15, 45
B. 1, 3, 8, 15, 45
C. 1, 5, 8, 15, 45
D. not here

5. Divide. Write the answer in lowest terms.

$3\frac{2}{3} \div 1\frac{1}{6}$

A. $4\frac{5}{18}$
B. $3\frac{1}{7}$
C. $3\frac{1}{3}$
D. not here

6. Compute.

$$\begin{array}{r} 4 \text{ gal } 3 \text{ qt} \\ +3 \text{ gal } 2 \text{ qt} \\ \hline \end{array}$$

A. 1 gal 1 qt
B. 7 gal 1 qt
C. 8 gal 1 qt
D. not here

7. The figures are similar. Find the missing length.

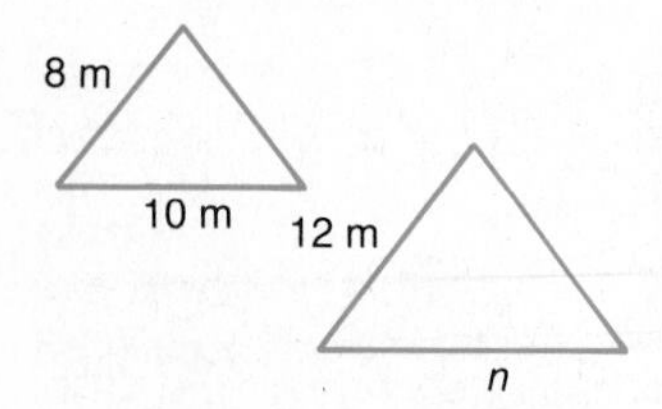

A. $n = 15$ m
B. $n = 14$ m
C. $n = 10$ m
D. not here

8. Find the mean. Round to the nearest whole number.

13, 24, 33, 18, 12, 29

A. 21
B. 22
C. 23
D. not here

9. The Acme Company makes heaters. About 6 out of every 100 heaters turn out to be defective. About how many defective heaters would you expect if 1,200 are produced?

A. 180
B. 72
C. 120
D. not here

Integers

CHAPTER 15

Integers and Temperature • Adding and Subtracting Integers • Multiplying and Dividing Integers • Rational Numbers • Points in a Coordinate Plane • Graphing Equations • Problem Solving: Using Tables and Graphs • Translations and Rotations • Extending Exponents and Scientific Notation

Integers

In a football game, a gain of 4 yards may be represented by $^{+}4$, or 4. A loss of 4 yards may be represented by $^{-}4$.

$^{+}4$	$^{-}4$
Read: positive four	Read: negative four

$^{+}4$ and $^{-}4$ are **opposites** of each other. Similarly, $^{+}10$ and $^{-}10$ are opposites of each other.

Numbers such as $^{+}4$, $^{-}4$, $^{+}10$, and $^{-}10$ are **integers.**
The set of integers can be shown as

$\ldots, ^{-}3, ^{-}2, ^{-}1, 0, ^{+}1, ^{+}2, ^{+}3, \ldots$ or **$\ldots, ^{-}3, ^{-}2, ^{-}1, 0, 1, 2, 3, \ldots$**

The integers include the whole numbers and their opposites.

The integers from $^{-}4$ to $^{+}4$ are shown on the number line below.
Integers to the right of 0 are **positive integers.**
Integers to the left of 0 are **negative integers.**
0 is an integer, but it is neither positive nor negative.

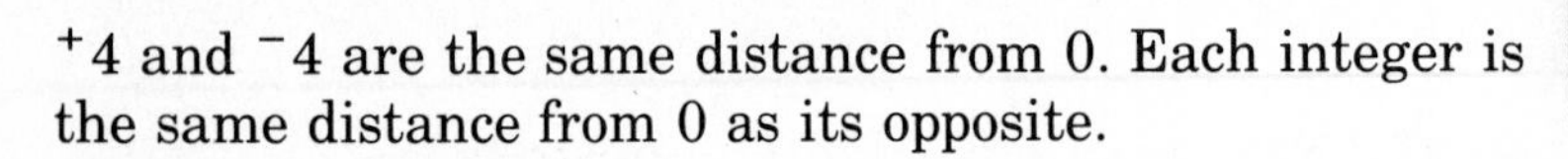

$^{+}4$ and $^{-}4$ are the same distance from 0. Each integer is the same distance from 0 as its opposite.

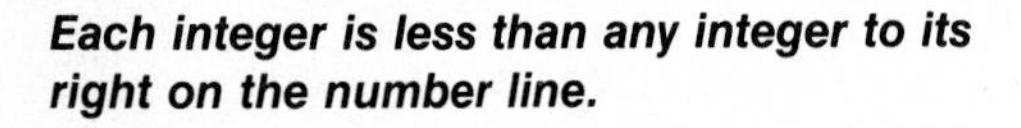

Each integer is less than any integer to its right on the number line.

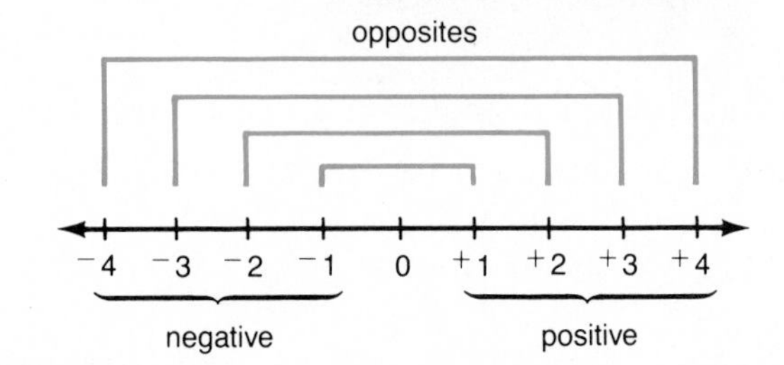

$^{-}4$ is less than $^{+}4$. $\quad ^{-}4 < ^{+}4$
$^{-}2$ is less than $^{+}1$. $\quad ^{-}2 < ^{+}1$
$^{-}2$ is less than $^{-}1$. $\quad ^{-}2 < ^{-}1$

You can also use > to write these inequalities.

$^{+}4 > ^{-}4 \qquad ^{+}1 > ^{-}2 \qquad ^{-}1 > ^{-}2$

Practice • What is the opposite?

1. Saving 5 dollars. **2.** Losing 4 kilograms **3.** 2 meters above sea level

Write the opposite integers.

4. $^{+}9$ **5.** $^{-}8$ **6.** $^{-}12$ **7.** $^{+}14$ **8.** $^{+}27$ **9.** $^{-}50$

Write < or >.

10. $^{+}8$ ● $^{+}10$ **11.** $^{+}1$ ● $^{-}3$ **12.** $^{-}2$ ● $^{-}4$ **13.** $^{-}3$ ● $^{+}3$

Mixed Practice • Write the opposite integers.

14. $^-1$	**15.** $^+12$	**16.** $^+6$	**17.** $^-8$	**18.** $^-7$	**19.** $^-15$
20. $^-20$	**21.** $^+31$	**22.** $^+9$	**23.** $^+16$	**24.** $^-40$	**25.** $^-49$
26. $^+115$	**27.** $^+87$	**28.** $^+103$	**29.** $^-99$	**30.** $^+100$	★**31.** 0

32. On graph paper draw a number line that shows the integers from $^-15$ to $^+15$.

Write < or >.

33. $^+7$ ● $^+4$	**34.** $^-4$ ● $^-8$	**35.** $^+3$ ● $^+4$	**36.** $^-8$ ● $^+4$
37. $^-6$ ● $^-4$	**38.** $^-11$ ● $^+13$	**39.** $^+10$ ● $^-12$	**40.** $^-6$ ● $^-2$
41. $^-12$ ● $^-6$	**42.** $^-2$ ● $^+2$	**43.** 0 ● $^-8$	**44.** $^+6$ ● 0
45. $^-1$ ● 0	★**46.** $^-75$ ● $^+1$	★**47.** $^+25$ ● $^-50$	★**48.** $^-20$ ● $^-80$

Write in order from least to greatest.

49. $^+1$, $^+3$, $^-1$

50. $^+6$, $^+2$, $^-2$, 0

★**51.** $^+37$, $^+34$, $^-27$, $^-18$, $^+10$

★**52.** $^-91$, $^+78$, $^-72$, $^-100$, $^+83$, $^+52$

The **absolute value** of a number is the distance the number is from 0.

$^-3$ is 3 units from 0.
The absolute value of $^-3$ is 3.
Write: $|^-3| = 3$.

$^+3$ is 3 units from 0.
The absolute value of $^+3$ is 3.
Write: $|^+3| = 3$.

The short vertical bars indicate absolute value.

3 units 3 units

$^-3$ $^-2$ $^-1$ 0 $^+1$ $^+2$ $^+3$

The absolute value of 0 is 0.

Find the absolute values.

53. $|^+2| = n$ **54.** $|^-2| = n$ **55.** $|^-1| = n$ **56.** $|^-30| = n$ **57.** $|^+75| = n$

PROBLEM SOLVING • APPLICATIONS

Write an integer to represent the total gain or loss.

58. A 5-yard gain followed by a 27-yard gain

★**59.** An 8-yard gain followed by a 9-yard loss

Integers and Temperature

A thermometer is like a vertical number line. Positive integers represent temperatures above 0 degrees Celsius (0°C). Negative integers represent temperatures below 0°C. 0°C is the temperature at which water freezes.

$^{+}20°C$ is 20 degrees above 0.
$^{-}10°C$ is 10 degrees below 0.

The warmer the temperature, the higher the liquid in the tube rises.

$^{+}10°C$ is warmer than $^{+}5°C$.
$^{+}10°C > {}^{+}5°C$
$^{-}5°C$ is warmer than $^{-}10°C$.
$^{-}5°C > {}^{-}10°C$

The liquid in the tube goes up and down as the temperature changes.

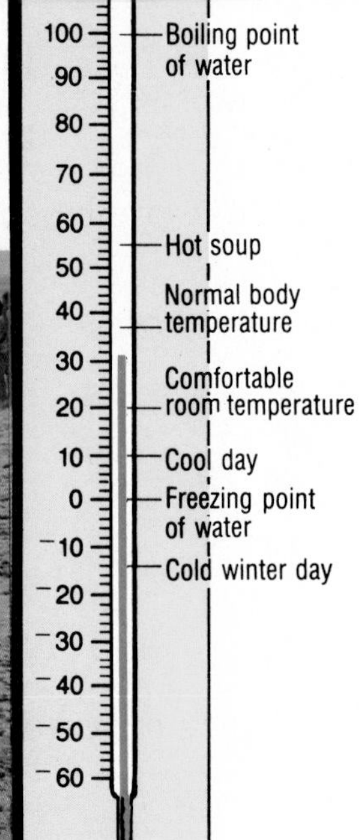

Suppose the temperature is $^{+}20°C$. Then it falls 6 degrees. What is the temperature now?

Step 1 Start at $^{+}20°C$.

Step 2 Move down 6°.

Step 3 The temperature is $^{+}14°C$.

Suppose the temperature is $^{-}8°C$. Then it rises 12 degrees. What is the temperature now?

Step 1 Start at $^{-}8°C$.

Step 2 Move up 12°.

Step 3 The temperature is $^{+}4°C$.

Practice • Which is warmer?

1. $^{+}30°C$, $^{+}20°C$
2. $^{+}30°C$, $^{-}20°C$
3. $^{-}30°C$, $^{+}20°C$
4. $^{-}30°C$, $^{-}20°C$

Which is cooler?

5. $^{+}10°C$, $^{+}5°C$
6. $^{+}10°C$, $^{-}5°C$
7. $^{-}10°C$, $^{+}5°C$
8. $^{-}10°C$, $^{-}5°C$

Write < or >.

9. $^{-}20°C$ ● $^{-}10°C$
10. $^{+}10°C$ ● $^{+}30°C$
11. 0°C ● $^{-}10°C$
12. $^{+}10°C$ ● $^{-}10°C$

13. What is normal body temperature? (Find it on the thermometer above.)

14. The temperature is $^{+}4°C$. It falls 6 degrees. What is the temperature now?

Mixed Practice • Which is warmer?

15. $^{+}50^\circ\text{C}$, $^{+}60^\circ\text{C}$ **16.** $^{+}50^\circ\text{C}$, $^{-}60^\circ\text{C}$ **17.** $^{-}50^\circ\text{C}$, $^{+}60^\circ\text{C}$ **18.** $^{-}50^\circ\text{C}$, $^{-}60^\circ\text{C}$

Which is cooler?

19. $^{+}16^\circ\text{C}$, $^{+}10^\circ\text{C}$ **20.** $^{+}16^\circ\text{C}$, $^{-}10^\circ\text{C}$ **21.** $^{-}16^\circ\text{C}$, $^{+}10^\circ\text{C}$ **22.** $^{-}16^\circ\text{C}$, $^{-}10^\circ\text{C}$

Write $<$ or $>$.

23. $^{+}10^\circ\text{C}$ ● $^{+}40^\circ\text{C}$ **24.** $^{-}10^\circ\text{C}$ ● $^{-}40^\circ\text{C}$ **25.** $^{+}8^\circ\text{C}$ ● 0°C

26. 0°C ● $^{-}8^\circ\text{C}$ **27.** $^{+}14^\circ\text{C}$ ● $^{-}20^\circ\text{C}$ **28.** $^{-}14^\circ\text{C}$ ● $^{+}20^\circ\text{C}$

29. $^{-}20^\circ\text{C}$ ● $^{+}20^\circ\text{C}$ **30.** $^{-}20^\circ\text{C}$ ● $^{-}26^\circ\text{C}$ **31.** $^{+}16^\circ\text{C}$ ● $^{+}18^\circ\text{C}$

32. $^{-}16^\circ\text{C}$ ● $^{-}18^\circ\text{C}$ **33.** $^{-}18^\circ\text{C}$ ● $^{-}16^\circ\text{C}$ **34.** $^{-}18^\circ\text{C}$ ● $^{+}16^\circ\text{C}$

★ **35.** $^{-}3^\circ\text{C}$ ● $^{-}1^\circ\text{C}$ ★ **36.** 0°C ● $^{-}1^\circ\text{C}$ ★ **37.** $^{-}39^\circ\text{C}$ ● $^{-}37^\circ\text{C}$

Write the temperature that is 0.5 degree

★ **38.** higher than $^{-}2^\circ\text{C}$. ★ **39.** lower than $^{-}4^\circ\text{C}$.

Write the temperatures in order from least to greatest.

★ **40.** $^{+}12^\circ\text{C}$, $^{-}6^\circ\text{C}$, $^{-}2^\circ\text{C}$, $^{+}4^\circ\text{C}$ ★ **41.** $^{-}8^\circ\text{C}$, $^{-}18^\circ\text{C}$, $^{+}18^\circ\text{C}$, $^{+}8^\circ\text{C}$, 0°C

Use the thermometer on page 410. Write the temperature of

42. the boiling point of water. **43.** the freezing point of water.

44. comfortable room temperature. **45.** a cool day.

Choose the most reasonable temperature estimate.

46. ice cubes

$^{+}10^\circ\text{C}$ $^{-}10^\circ\text{C}$ $^{+}32^\circ\text{C}$

★ **47.** a good day for swimming

$^{+}80^\circ\text{C}$ $^{+}14^\circ\text{C}$ $^{+}34^\circ\text{C}$

PROBLEM SOLVING • APPLICATIONS

What is the temperature now?

48. The temperature starts at $^{+}6^\circ\text{C}$. It rises 8 degrees.

49. The temperature starts at $^{+}6^\circ\text{C}$. It falls 8 degrees.

50. The temperature starts at $^{-}4^\circ\text{C}$. It falls 4 degrees.

★ **51.** The temperature starts at $^{-}2^\circ\text{C}$. It rises 1 degree. Then it falls 2 degrees.

Adding Integers with Like Signs

Sarita earns 4 dollars baby-sitting. She earns 3 dollars doing yard work. How much does she earn in all?

You know the answer is 7 dollars. Each of these equations shows the addition.

$4 + 3 = 7$ $\quad$ $^{+}4 + {}^{+}3 = {}^{+}7$

> ***You can add two positive integers just as you add whole numbers.***

You can use a number line to help you add integers. In adding, a positive sign means a move to the right. A negative sign means a move to the left.

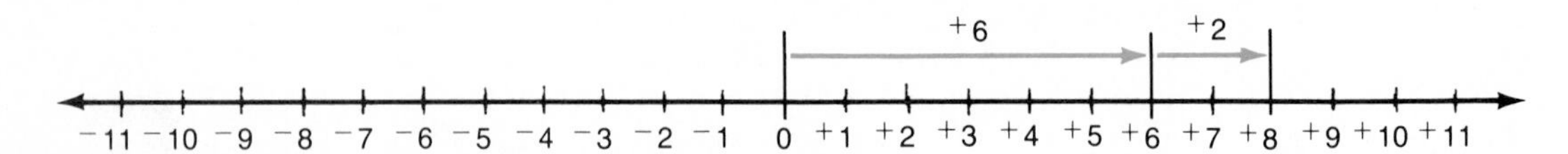

Solve: $^{+}6 + {}^{+}2 = n$.

Start at 0.
Move 6 spaces to the right. Move 2 more spaces to the right.
You stop at $^{+}8$.

$^{+}6 + {}^{+}2 = {}^{+}8$

> ***The sum of two positive integers is positive.***

What does $^{+}7 + {}^{+}3$ equal?

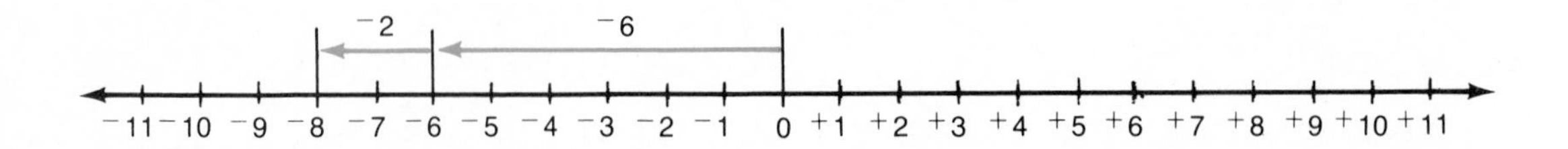

Solve: $^{-}6 + {}^{-}2 = n$.

Start at 0.
Move 6 spaces to the left. Move 2 more spaces to the left.
You stop at $^{-}8$.

$^{-}6 + {}^{-}2 = {}^{-}8$

> ***The sum of two negative integers is negative.***

What does $^{-}7 + {}^{-}3$ equal?

Practice • Add.

1. $^{+}3 + ^{+}2$
2. $^{-}6 + ^{-}1$
3. $^{+}7 + ^{+}6$
4. $^{-}5 + ^{-}2$
5. $^{-}4 + ^{-}4$
6. $^{+}8 + ^{+}4$
7. $^{-}9 + ^{-}2$
8. $^{-}10 + ^{-}8$

Mixed Practice • Add.

9. $^{+}2 + ^{+}4$
10. $^{-}3 + ^{-}5$
11. $^{-}7 + ^{-}3$
12. $^{+}8 + ^{+}3$
13. $^{+}9 + ^{+}6$
14. $^{-}8 + ^{-}8$
15. $^{+}7 + ^{+}6$
16. $^{-}9 + ^{-}3$
17. $^{+}7 + ^{+}11$
18. $^{-}12 + ^{-}3$
19. $^{+}19 + ^{+}23$
20. $^{-}6 + ^{-}24$
21. $^{-}13 + ^{-}49$
22. $0 + ^{+}32$
23. $0 + ^{-}18$
24. $^{-}17 + ^{-}25$

★25. $^{+}4 + ^{+}5 + ^{+}6$

★26. $^{-}14 + ^{-}16 + ^{-}18$

Write = or ≠.

27. $^{+}6 + ^{+}4$ ● $^{+}4 + ^{+}6$
28. $^{-}6 + ^{-}4$ ● $^{-}4 + ^{-}6$
29. $^{+}6 + ^{+}4$ ● $^{-}6 + ^{-}4$
30. $0 + ^{+}35$ ● $^{+}35 + 0$

★31. $(^{-}3 + ^{-}2) + ^{-}7$ ● $^{-}3 + (^{-}2 + ^{-}7)$

★32. $(^{-}1 + ^{-}2) + ^{-}3$ ● $(^{+}1 + ^{+}2) + ^{+}3$

Solve the equations.

33. $^{-}15 + ^{-}12 = n$
34. $^{+}75 + ^{+}25 = n$

★35. $^{+}15 + ^{+}11 + n = ^{+}40$

PROBLEM SOLVING • APPLICATIONS

36. Sarita deposits 38 dollars in the bank. Then she deposits 33 dollars more. How much does she deposit in all?

★37. Sarita uses positive and negative integers to keep a monthly record of her gains and losses in weight. Use an integer to represent her total gain or loss for the four months.

January	$^{-}3$ kg
February	$^{-}1$ kg
March	$^{-}2$ kg
April	$^{+}2$ kg

38. If n is a negative integer, is $n + ^{-}1$ greater than n?

Skills Maintenance

Write as terminating or repeating decimals.

1. $\frac{7}{10}$
2. $\frac{3}{100}$
3. $\frac{1}{4}$
4. $\frac{2}{3}$
5. $\frac{9}{40}$
6. $\frac{1}{8}$
7. $\frac{1}{6}$
8. $\frac{4}{3}$
9. $2\frac{1}{5}$
10. $3\frac{5}{6}$

Adding with Unlike Signs

The Northridge football team gains 6 yards. Then the team loses 8 yards. What is the total gain or loss of yards?

Think: Gain of 6 yards → $^{+}6$
Loss of 8 yards → $^{-}8$
$^{+}6 + {}^{-}8 = n$

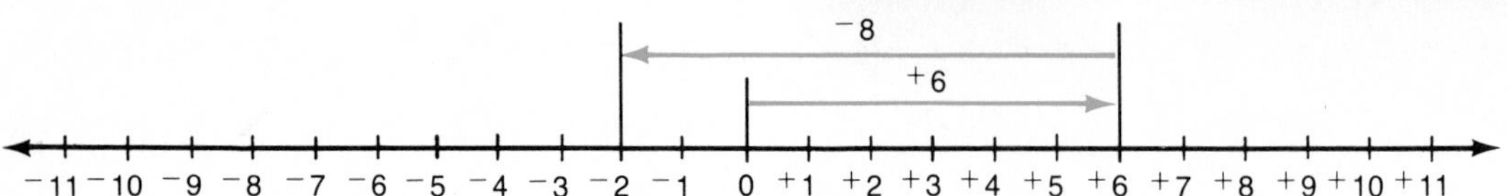

You can use a number line to help you find the sum.

Start at 0. Move 6 spaces to the right. Move 8 spaces to the left. You stop at $^{-}2$. $^{+}6 + {}^{-}8 = {}^{-}2$ The Northridge team loses 2 yards.

Add: $^{+}7 + {}^{-}6$.

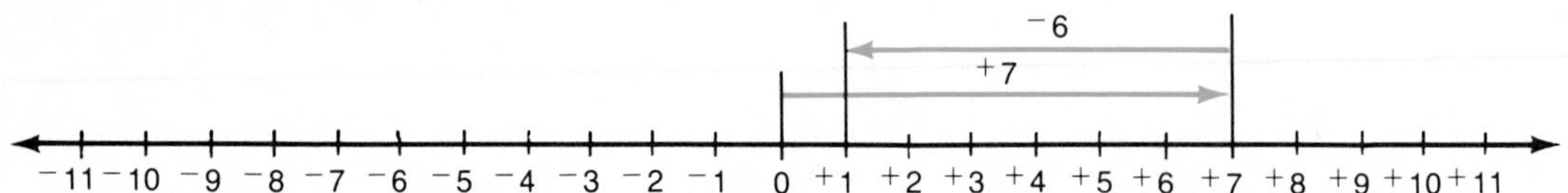

Start at 0. Move 7 spaces to the right. Move 6 spaces to the left. You stop at $^{+}1$. $^{+}7 + {}^{-}6 = {}^{+}1$

Are these equations true? Use a number line to check.

$^{+}4 + {}^{-}3 = {}^{+}1$
$^{+}4 + {}^{-}4 = 0$
$^{+}4 + {}^{-}5 = {}^{-}1$

$^{-}3 + {}^{+}5 = {}^{+}2$
$^{-}3 + {}^{+}3 = 0$
$^{-}3 + {}^{+}1 = {}^{-}2$

The sum of a positive integer and a negative integer is
- ***positive if the positive integer is farther from 0;***
- ***negative if the negative integer is farther from 0;***
- ***0 if the integers are opposites.***

Opposites are sometimes called **additive inverses** because their sum is 0.

Practice • Add.

1. $^{+}8 + {}^{-}4$
2. $^{+}2 + {}^{-}6$
3. $^{-}7 + {}^{+}4$
4. $^{+}5 + {}^{-}5$
5. $^{-}3 + {}^{+}5$
6. $^{-}8 + {}^{+}8$
7. $^{-}12 + {}^{+}10$
8. $^{+}13 + {}^{-}10$

Mixed Practice • Add.

9. ${}^{+}7 + {}^{-}5$	**10.** ${}^{+}3 + {}^{-}8$	**11.** ${}^{-}9 + {}^{+}2$	**12.** ${}^{+}7 + {}^{-}7$
13. ${}^{-}1 + {}^{+}5$	**14.** ${}^{-}2 + {}^{+}2$	**15.** ${}^{-}8 + {}^{+}9$	**16.** ${}^{-}5 + {}^{+}2$
17. ${}^{+}6 + {}^{-}10$	**18.** ${}^{-}9 + {}^{+}7$	**19.** ${}^{+}8 + {}^{-}5$	**20.** ${}^{+}6 + {}^{-}9$
21. ${}^{+}12 + {}^{+}3$	**22.** ${}^{-}12 + {}^{-}3$	**23.** ${}^{-}12 + {}^{+}3$	**24.** ${}^{+}12 + {}^{-}3$

Without adding, tell whether each sum is *positive* or *negative*.

25. ${}^{+}18 + {}^{-}14$ **26.** ${}^{-}19 + {}^{+}13$ ★ **27.** ${}^{-}20 + {}^{+}112$ ★ **28.** ${}^{+}21 + {}^{-}115$

Give the sum for

29. exercise 25. **30.** exercise 26. ★ **31.** exercise 27. ★ **32.** exercise 28.

Here is a way to find the sum of two integers with unlike signs.

Consider the distance each integer is from 0.

Find the difference between the distances.

The sum has the sign of the integer that is farther from 0.

${}^{-}27 + {}^{+}18 = n$

${}^{-}27$ is 27 units from 0.

${}^{+}18$ is 18 units from 0.

$27 - 18 = 9$

${}^{-}27 + {}^{+}18 = {}^{-}9$ ← Use sign of ${}^{-}27$.

Solve the equations.

33. ${}^{-}54 + {}^{+}31 = n$ **34.** ${}^{+}48 + {}^{-}22 = n$ **35.** ${}^{-}39 + {}^{+}50 = n$

36. ${}^{-}96 + {}^{+}78 = n$ **37.** ${}^{-}46 + {}^{+}135 = n$ ★ **38.** $n + {}^{+}15 = {}^{-}2$

PROBLEM SOLVING • APPLICATIONS

39. A quarterback loses 7 yards on a play. Then he completes a pass for a 26-yard gain. What is the total gain or loss in yards?

Use several different integers for *a*, *b*, and *c* to test the properties listed in the table.

Commutative Property $a + b = b + a$
Associative Property $(a + b) + c = a + (b + c)$
Property of Zero $a + 0 = a$

★ **40.** Does addition of integers seem to be commutative? associative?

★ **41.** Does $a + 0 = a$ for all integers?

Subtracting Integers

If two integers are positive and the first is greater than the second, then they are subtracted like whole numbers.

$8 - 3 = 5$ $\qquad$ $^+8 - {}^+5 = {}^+3$

Patterns can help you learn about subtracting integers. Study the pattern in the subtraction and addition equations below.

Subtraction Equations		**Addition Equations**
	← opposites →	
$^+8 - {}^+3 = {}^+5$		$^+8 + {}^-3 = {}^+5$
$^+8 - {}^+2 = {}^+6$		$^+8 + {}^-2 = {}^+6$
$^+8 - {}^+1 = {}^+7$		$^+8 + {}^-1 = {}^+7$
$^+8 - 0 = {}^+8$		$^+8 + 0 = {}^+8$
$^+8 - {}^-1 = ?$		$^+8 + {}^+1 = ?$
$^+8 - {}^-2 = ?$		$^+8 + {}^+2 = ?$
⋮		⋮

The differences are increasing by 1, just as the sums are.

If you continue the pattern, you obtain:

← opposites →

$^+8 - {}^-1 = {}^+9$ just as $^+8 + {}^+1 = {}^+9$

$^+8 - {}^-2 = {}^+10$ just as $^+8 + {}^+2 = {}^+10$

Subtraction can be changed to addition by adding the opposite of the second number.

> ***To subtract an integer, add its opposite.***

← opposites →

$^+4 - {}^+6 = {}^+4 + {}^-6 = {}^-2$

$^-1 - {}^+8 = {}^-1 + {}^-8 = {}^-9$

$^-3 - {}^-5 = {}^-3 + {}^+5 = {}^+2$

Practice • Copy and write the missing number.

1. $^+7 - {}^+2 = {}^+7 + ?$

2. $^+6 - {}^+9 = {}^+6 + ?$

3. $^-1 - {}^-5 = {}^-1 + ?$

4. $^-8 - {}^-2 = {}^-8 + ?$

Subtract.

5. $^+9 - {}^+2$

6. $^+8 - {}^+10$

7. $^-3 - {}^-4$

8. $^-6 - {}^-1$

9. $0 - {}^-3$

10. $^-2 - {}^-10$

11. $0 - {}^+5$

12. $^-7 - {}^+2$

Mixed Practice • Copy and write the missing number.

13. $^+10 - ^+3 = ^+10 + ?$

14. $^+5 - ^+8 = ^+5 + ?$

15. $^-6 - ^-10 = ^-6 + ?$

16. $^+7 - ^-4 = ^+7 + ?$

Subtract.

17. $^+9 - ^+6$ **18.** $^-12 - ^-3$ **19.** $^-11 - ^+4$ **20.** $^-12 - ^-12$

21. $^+15 - ^-9$ **22.** $^+7 - ^+2$ **23.** $^-7 - ^-11$ **24.** $^-9 - ^+9$

25. $^-2 - ^+1$ **26.** $^-7 - 0$ **27.** $^+9 - ^+11$ **28.** $^+11 - ^-12$

29. $^+4 - ^+12$ **30.** $^+13 - ^-12$ **31.** $^-13 - ^-10$ **32.** $^+6 - ^+10$

33. $0 - ^-4$ **34.** $^-10 - ^+6$ **35.** $0 - ^+4$ **36.** $^-21 - ^+7$

37. $^+3 - ^-7$ **38.** $^-4 - ^-10$ **39.** $^-24 - ^+12$ ★ **40.** $^-500 - ^-101$

Write = or ≠.

41. $^+6 - ^+2$ ● $^+2 - ^+6$

42. $^-8 - ^-3$ ● $^-3 - ^-8$

43. $(^+9 - ^+4) - ^+2$ ● $^+9 - (^+4 - ^+2)$

★ **44.** $(^-9 - ^-2) - ^+3$ ● $^-9 - (^-2 - ^+3)$

★ **45.** Is subtraction of integers commutative? associative?

Solve the equations.

★ **46.** $n - ^-5 = ^-2$

★ **47.** $n + ^-8 = ^-2$

★ **48.** $n - (^+6 + ^-2) = ^-8$

PROBLEM SOLVING • APPLICATIONS

49. The temperature at midnight was $^+3$°C. At 4:00 A.M. the temperature was $^-1$°C. By how many degrees had it risen or fallen?

50. In June the average temperature in Nesta is $^+15$°C. In December the average temperature is 18 degrees less. What is the average temperature in December?

Midchapter Review

Write the opposite integer.

1. $^+24$ **2.** $^-59$

Write > or <.

3. $^-12$ ● $^-5$ **4.** 0 ● $^-7$ **5.** $^-10$°C ● $^+2$°C

Add.

6. $^-13 + ^-8$ **7.** $^+18 + ^-6$

Subtract.

8. $^+7 - ^-3$ **9.** $^-8 - ^-3$ **10.** $^-18 - ^+7$

Multiplying Integers

$+5 = 5$
$+3 = 3$

Since positive integers are like whole numbers, you need not write the small + signs. The equations below tell about multiplying positive integers.

$5 \times 3 = 15$ $6 \times 4 = 24$

The product of two positive integers is positive.

Patterns can help you learn about multiplying positive and negative integers. Study the pattern in these equations.

$5 \times 3 = 15$
$5 \times 2 = 10$
$5 \times 1 = 5$
$5 \times 0 = 0$
$5 \times {}^{-}1 = ?$
$5 \times {}^{-}2 = ?$
$5 \times {}^{-}3 = ?$

The products are decreasing by 5. So the next product will be ⁻5, then ⁻10, and so on.

$5 \times {}^{-}1 = {}^{-}5$
$5 \times {}^{-}2 = {}^{-}10$
$5 \times {}^{-}3 = {}^{-}15$

The product of a positive integer and a negative integer is negative.

Now study the pattern in these equations.

$3 \times {}^{-}2 = {}^{-}6$
$2 \times {}^{-}2 = {}^{-}4$
$1 \times {}^{-}2 = {}^{-}2$
$0 \times {}^{-}2 = 0$
${}^{-}1 \times {}^{-}2 = ?$
${}^{-}2 \times {}^{-}2 = ?$
${}^{-}3 \times {}^{-}2 = ?$

The products are increasing by 2. So the next product will be 2, then 4, and so on.

${}^{-}1 \times {}^{-}2 = 2$
${}^{-}2 \times {}^{-}2 = 4$
${}^{-}3 \times {}^{-}2 = 6$

The product of two negative integers is positive.

As you can see, when the signs of two integers are alike, the product is positive.

Like signs
${}^{-}6 \times {}^{-}4 = 24$
$6 \times 4 = 24$

When the signs of two integers are unlike, the product is negative.

Unlike signs
${}^{-}6 \times 4 = {}^{-}24$
$4 \times {}^{-}6 = {}^{-}24$

What is the product of 0 and any number?

Practice • Multiply.

1. 2×9
2. $2 \times {}^-9$
3. ${}^-2 \times 9$
4. ${}^-2 \times {}^-9$
5. $4 \times {}^-3$
6. ${}^-4 \times {}^-3$
7. ${}^-4 \times 3$
8. ${}^-3 \times 4$
9. ${}^-8 \times 5$
10. ${}^-5 \times 8$
11. ${}^-8 \times {}^-5$
12. ${}^-5 \times {}^-8$

Mixed Practice • Multiply.

13. ${}^-3 \times 9$
14. ${}^-3 \times {}^-9$
15. 9×3
16. $9 \times {}^-3$
17. $7 \times {}^-4$
18. ${}^-7 \times 4$
19. ${}^-7 \times {}^-4$
20. ${}^-4 \times {}^-7$
21. ${}^-2 \times {}^-6$
22. 2×6
23. ${}^-2 \times 6$
24. ${}^-6 \times 2$
25. $8 \times {}^-1$
26. ${}^-8 \times 1$
27. ${}^-1 \times {}^-8$
28. ${}^-8 \times {}^-1$
29. $5 \times {}^-15$
30. ${}^-8 \times {}^-12$

★ 31. $(2 \times 7) \times {}^-3$

★ 32. $(4 \times {}^-5) \times {}^-4$

Solve the equations.

33. $5 \times {}^-8 = n$
34. ${}^-9 \times {}^-4 = n$
35. $7 \times {}^-7 = n$
36. ${}^-8 \times {}^-9 = n$
37. ${}^-6 \times 7 = n$
38. $0 \times {}^-8 = n$

★ 39. $n \times {}^-2 = {}^-12$

★ 40. ${}^-4 \times n = 16$

★ 41. $9 \times n = {}^-81$

★ 42. $n \times {}^-8 = 88$

★ 43. $5 \times n = {}^-75$

★ 44. ${}^-12 \times n = {}^-24$

PROBLEM SOLVING • APPLICATIONS

45. The XYZ stock loses 2 points on each of 3 days. Write its total gain or loss as an integer.

★ 46. The QRS stock loses 3 points on each of 4 days. Then it gains 2 points on the next day. Write its total gain or loss as an integer.

Use several different integers for *a*, *b*, and *c* to test the properties listed in the table.

★ 47. Does multiplication of integers seem to be commutative? associative?

★ 48. Does $a \times 1 = a$ for all integers?

★ 49. Does multiplication of integers seem to be distributive over addition?

Property
Commutative Property $a \times b = b \times a$
Associative Property $(a \times b) \times c = a \times (b \times c)$
Property of One $a \times 1 = a$
Distributive Property $a \times (b + c) = (a \times b) + (a \times c)$

Dividing Integers

These equations show that multiplication and division are inverse operations.

$$a \times b = c \Leftrightarrow c \div b = a$$

$3 \times 5 = 15 \longleftrightarrow 15 \div 5 = 3$

To divide integers, you can think of the related multiplication equation. Begin with division in which the integers have like signs.

Solve: $24 \div 3 = n$.

Think: $n \times 3 = 24$.

The product is positive.
One factor is positive.
The missing factor is positive.
n is 8.

$24 \div 3 = 8$

Solve: $^-24 \div {}^-3 = n$.

Think: $n \times {}^-3 = {}^-24$.

The product is negative.
The factors must have unlike signs.
So the missing factor is positive.
n is 8.

$^-24 \div {}^-3 = 8$

We can think of these division examples as shown below.

positive ÷ positive = positive
negative ÷ negative = positive

If two integers have like signs, their quotient is positive.

Now consider division in which two integers have unlike signs.

Solve: $^-24 \div 3 = n$.

Think: $n \times 3 = {}^-24$.

The product is negative.
One factor is positive.
So the missing factor is negative.
n is $^-8$.

$^-24 \div 3 = {}^-8$

Solve: $24 \div {}^-3 = n$.

Think: $n \times {}^-3 = 24$.

The product is positive.
One factor is negative.
So the missing factor is negative.
n is $^-8$.

$24 \div {}^-3 = {}^-8$

Think of these division examples as shown below.

negative ÷ positive = negative
positive ÷ negative = negative

If two integers have unlike signs, their quotient is negative.

Remember, 0 divided by any nonzero integer is 0.

$0 \div 6 = 0 \quad \frac{0}{5} = 0 \quad 0 \div {}^-3 = 0 \quad \frac{0}{^-8} = 0$

Practice • Divide.

1. $10 \div 2$	**2.** $^-10 \div {}^-2$	**3.** $10 \div {}^-2$	**4.** $^-10 \div 2$
5. $^-18 \div {}^-6$	**6.** $^-18 \div 6$	**7.** $18 \div {}^-6$	**8.** $18 \div 6$
9. $27 \div {}^-3$	**10.** $^-20 \div 5$	**11.** $^-35 \div {}^-7$	**12.** $42 \div {}^-7$

Mixed Practice • Divide.

13. $^-5 \div {}^-1$	**14.** $^-36 \div {}^-6$	**15.** $18 \div {}^-2$	**16.** $^-9 \div 9$
17. $0 \div {}^-5$	**18.** $81 \div 9$	**19.** $16 \div {}^-8$	**20.** $^-15 \div 5$
21. $63 \div 9$	**22.** $^-36 \div {}^-9$	**23.** $^-32 \div 4$	**24.** $^-12 \div 2$
25. $^-21 \div 7$	**26.** $^-35 \div {}^-7$	**27.** $30 \div 6$	**28.** $^-27 \div {}^-3$
29. $^-8 \div {}^-8$	**30.** $56 \div 7$	**31.** $24 \div {}^-3$	**32.** $20 \div {}^-4$
33. $72 \div {}^-9$	**34.** $^-42 \div 6$	**35.** $^-50 \div 5$	**36.** $^-16 \div {}^-4$
37. $^-18 \div {}^-9$	**38.** $^-5 \div {}^-5$	★ **39.** $156 \div {}^-12$	★ **40.** $^-240 \div {}^-15$

Add, subtract, multiply, or divide.

41. $6 + {}^-11$	**42.** $^-8 + 2$	★ **43.** $13 + {}^-42$	★ **44.** $60 + {}^-24$
45. $5 - 9$	**46.** $^-7 - {}^-4$	★ **47.** $18 - {}^-18$	★ **48.** $^-33 - 47$
49. $^-4 \times {}^-9$	**50.** $^-6 \times 8$	★ **51.** $13 \times {}^-27$	★ **52.** $^-40 \times {}^-97$
53. $72 \div {}^-8$	**54.** $^-49 \div {}^-7$	★ **55.** $^-312 \div 8$	★ **56.** $1{,}260 \div {}^-12$

Solve the equations.

57. $(8 + {}^-6) - 2 = n$

58. $(7 - 10) + {}^-6 = n$

★ **59.** $({}^-160 \div {}^-20) \div {}^-4 = n$

★ **60.** $^-160 \div ({}^-20 \div {}^-4) = n$

PROBLEM SOLVING • APPLICATIONS

61. A stock loses 12 points during a period of 4 weeks. Write the integer that represents its average loss per week.

62. The temperature drops 10 degrees from 8:00 P.M. to 6:00 A.M. Write the integer that represents its average loss per hour.

63. n is a positive integer. What does $n \div n$ equal?

★ **64.** n is a negative integer. What does $n \div n$ equal?

Solving Equations with Integers

You have solved equations with whole numbers by using these rules:

- Add the same number to both sides.
- Subtract the same number from both sides.
- Multiply both sides by the same number (not zero).
- Divide both sides by the same number (not zero).

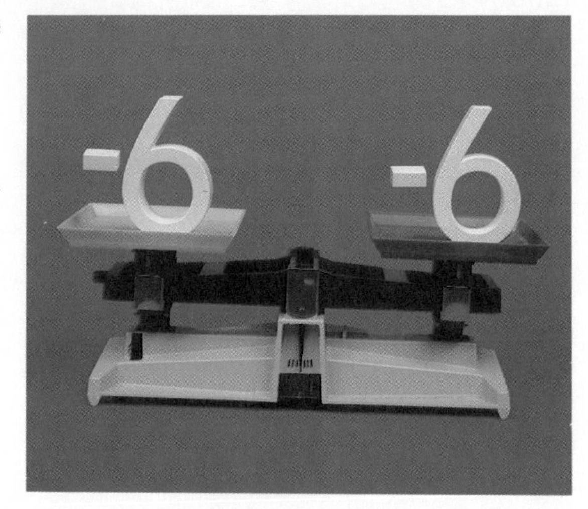

You can use the same rules with equations that involve positive and negative integers. Study the equations below.

Think: Since $^-6$ is subtracted from n, add $^-6$ to both sides.

$$n - {}^-6 = 2$$
$$n - {}^-6 + {}^-6 = 2 + {}^-6$$
$$n = {}^-4$$

Think: Since 8 is added to x, subtract 8 from both sides.

$$x + 8 = 3$$
$$x + 8 - 8 = 3 - 8$$
$$x = {}^-5$$

The equation $x + 8 = 3$ can also be solved using addition. Instead of subtracting 8 from both sides, you can add $^-8$ (the additive inverse of 8).

$$x + 8 = 3$$
$$x + 8 + {}^-8 = 3 + {}^-8$$
$$x = {}^-5$$

Now consider equations such as $\frac{n}{^-4} = {}^-2$ and $^-3y = 6$.

Think: Since n is divided by $^-4$, multiply by $^-4$.

$$\frac{n}{^-4} = {}^-2$$
$${}^-4\left(\frac{n}{^-4}\right) = {}^-4({}^-2)$$

$^-4(^-2)$ equals positive 8.

$$n = 8$$

Think: Since y is multiplied by $^-3$, divide both sides by $^-3$.

$${}^-3y = 6$$
$$\frac{^-3y}{^-3} = \frac{6}{^-3}$$

Positive 6 divided by $^-3$ equals $^-2$.

$$y = {}^-2$$

Practice • Solve the equations.

1. $n - {}^{-}2 = 5$ **2.** $x - 3 = {}^{-}1$ **3.** $y + 6 = 2$ **4.** $n + {}^{-}2 = 8$

5. $\frac{x}{3} = {}^{-}4$ **6.** $\frac{n}{{}^{-}2} = 8$ **7.** $2y = {}^{-}14$ **8.** ${}^{-}5x = {}^{-}15$

Mixed Practice • Solve the equations.

9. $n - {}^{-}3 = 7$ **10.** $y - 8 = {}^{-}2$ **11.** $n - {}^{-}1 = 10$ **12.** $x - 5 = {}^{-}3$

13. $x + 5 = 3$ **14.** $n + {}^{-}6 = 8$ **15.** $y + {}^{-}2 = {}^{-}1$ **16.** $n + 12 = 0$

17. $\frac{n}{2} = 8$ **18.** $\frac{x}{{}^{-}2} = 5$ **19.** $\frac{y}{{}^{-}6} = {}^{-}3$ **20.** $\frac{x}{7} = {}^{-}4$

21. $3y = 27$ **22.** ${}^{-}4n = 24$ **23.** ${}^{-}7n = {}^{-}14$ **24.** $5x = {}^{-}40$

25. $n - 3 = {}^{-}2$ **26.** $x + 3 = {}^{-}4$ **27.** $8y = {}^{-}48$ **28.** $\frac{n}{4} = {}^{-}10$

★ **29.** $32 = {}^{-}4y$ ★ **30.** ${}^{-}2 = n - 9$ ★ **31.** $3y + 8 = 2$ ★ **32.** $2n - 16 = 4$

The solutions for inequalities such as $n + 4 > 6$ or $n + 4 < 6$ can be found by using the related equation, $n + 4 = 6$.

$n + 4 = 6$ $n = 2$	Solution: 2	$n + 4 > 6$ $n > 2$	Solutions: All integers greater than 2: 3, 4, 5, . . .	$n + 4 < 6$ $n < 2$	Solutions: All integers less than 2: 1, 0, ${}^{-}1$, ${}^{-}2$, ${}^{-}3$, . . .

The solutions of these sentences can be graphed on number lines.

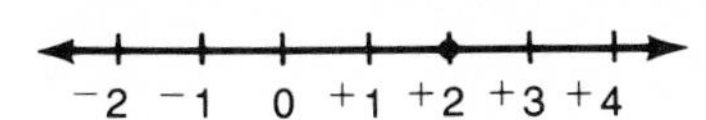

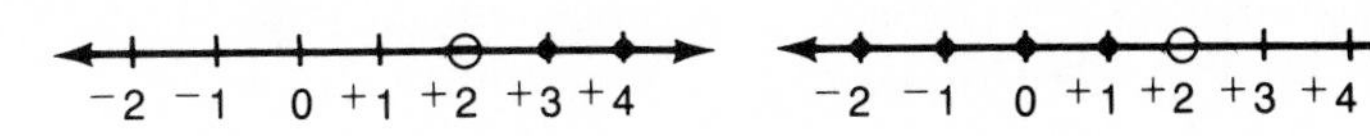

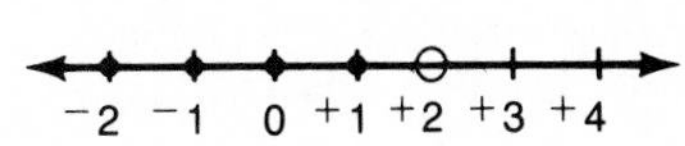

Write the solutions and graph them on number lines.

33. $n + 3 = 7$ **34.** $n + 3 > 7$ **35.** $n + 3 < 7$

36. $2y = {}^{-}2$ ★ **37.** $2y > {}^{-}2$ ★ **38.** $2y < {}^{-}2$

PROBLEM SOLVING • APPLICATIONS

39. n is an integer.
$n < 4$ and $n > {}^{-}4$
What numbers can n be?

★ **40.** x is an integer.
$2x < 14$ and $2x > {}^{-}6$
What numbers can x be?

Rational Numbers

Integers, fractions, and their opposites are called **rational numbers.**

A rational number can be expressed as $\frac{a}{b}$ where a and b are integers and b does not equal 0. Rational numbers can be shown on a number line.

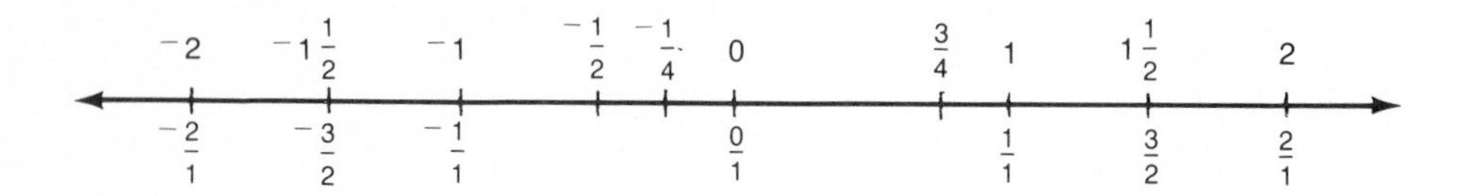

You know that $0.5 = \frac{1}{2}$ and $0.\overline{3} = \frac{1}{3}$. Every terminating or repeating decimal is a rational number.

Each rational number is less than any rational number to its right on the number line.

$^{-}1\frac{1}{2} < \frac{3}{4}$ $\qquad$ $^{-}2 < {}^{-}1\frac{1}{2}$

$^{-}1.5 < 0.5$ $\qquad$ $^{-}1.5 < {}^{-}0.5$

You can also use > to write these inequalities.

$\frac{3}{4} > {}^{-}1\frac{1}{2}$ $\qquad$ $^{-}1\frac{1}{2} > {}^{-}2$

$0.5 > {}^{-}1.5$ $\qquad$ $^{-}0.5 > {}^{-}1.5$

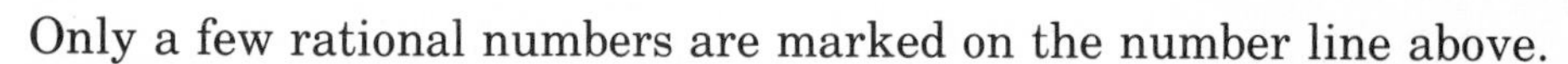

Only a few rational numbers are marked on the number line above.

Between any two rational numbers such as 0.84 and 0.85, you can find as many rational numbers as you wish.

0.84 = 0.840000 $\qquad$ 0.85 = 0.850000

So 0.840001, 0.840002, 0.840003, . . ., 0.849999 are all between 0.84 and 0.85.

It is said that the rational numbers are dense.
The set of rational numbers has the property of density.

In computing with rational numbers, use what you know about fractions, decimals, and integers.

$\frac{3}{4} + \frac{^{-}1}{4} = \frac{2}{4} = \frac{1}{2}$ $\qquad$ $\frac{5}{6} - \frac{^{-}1}{6} = \frac{5}{6} + \frac{1}{6} = \frac{6}{6} = 1$

$^{-}2(^{-}2.5) = 5.0$ $\qquad$ $4.5 \div {}^{-}1.5 = {}^{-}3$

Practice • Write <, =, or >.

1. $^-3 \bullet \frac{^-1}{2}$
2. $\frac{^-1}{2} \bullet \frac{1}{2}$
3. $1 \bullet {}^-2$
4. $\frac{1}{2} \bullet {}^-2$
5. $^-2.5 \bullet {}^-1.5$
6. $0 \bullet {}^-1.5$
7. $^-4.5 \bullet {}^-4\frac{1}{2}$
8. $1.3 \bullet {}^-2.3$

Mixed Practice • Write <, =, or >.

9. $2 \bullet \frac{5}{4}$
10. $^-2 \bullet \frac{^-2}{3}$
11. $2 \bullet {}^-3$
12. $\frac{1}{10} \bullet 0.1$
13. $^-1.4 \bullet {}^-3.4$
14. $\frac{7}{10} \bullet \frac{3}{10}$
15. $\frac{^-9}{10} \bullet \frac{3}{10}$
16. $0.6 \bullet 0.2$
17. $0 \bullet {}^-0.3$
18. $^-0.3 \bullet 0.3$
19. $\frac{1}{4} \bullet \frac{1}{5}$
20. $^-2.7 \bullet {}^-2.70$
21. $\frac{3}{4} \bullet \frac{4}{5}$
22. ★ $\frac{^-3}{4} \bullet \frac{^-4}{5}$
23. ★ $\frac{2}{3} \bullet 0.\overline{6}$
24. ★ $\frac{5}{3} \bullet 1.6$

Solve the equations.

25. $1\frac{3}{8} + 1\frac{5}{8} = n$
26. $0.4 + 1.3 = n$
27. $8.6 + {}^-2.4 = n$
28. $3\frac{1}{2} - 1\frac{2}{3} = n$
29. $5.6 - 2.5 = n$
30. $^-3.8 - 1.3 = n$
31. $\left(\frac{3}{5}\right)\left(\frac{2}{3}\right) = n$
32. $(3)({}^-1.2) = n$
33. $({}^-0.5)({}^-0.5) = n$
34. $\frac{4}{9} \div \frac{5}{6} = n$
35. $0.8 \div 0.2 = n$
36. $^-3.6 \div 0.4 = n$
37. ★ $\left(\frac{^-1}{2}\right)^2 = n$
38. ★ $\left(\frac{^-1}{2}\right)^3 = n$
39. ★ $({}^-0.8)^4 = n$
40. ★ $({}^-0.8)^5 = n$

PROBLEM SOLVING • APPLICATIONS

41. The Acme Toy Company stock lost $1\frac{1}{4}$ points on each of three days. Write a rational number that represents its total gain or loss.

42. The Star Toy Company stock gained $1\frac{1}{8}$ points one day and lost $1\frac{5}{8}$ points the next day. Write a rational number that represents its total gain or loss.

43. The Electronic Toy Company stock gained $1\frac{1}{2}$ points one day and lost $2\frac{1}{8}$ points the next day. Write a rational number that represents its total gain or loss.

44. ★ The Zoom Toy Company stock lost $4\frac{1}{2}$ points over a total period of 4 days. Write a rational number that represents its average loss per day.

Points in a Coordinate Plane

This drawing shows a **coordinate plane**.

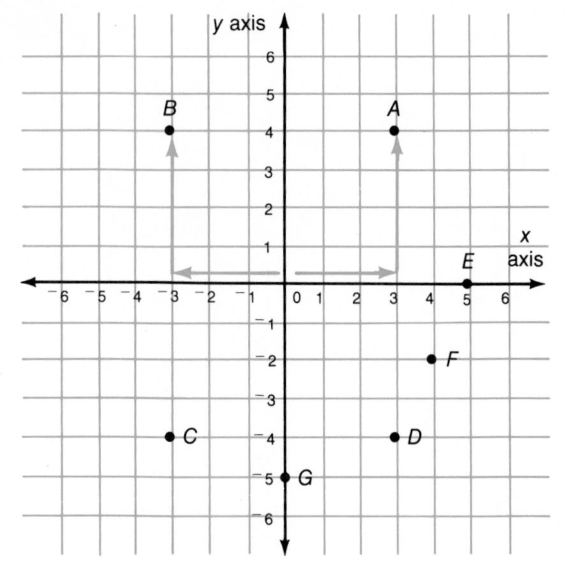

A coordinate plane has a horizontal number line (the x axis) and a vertical number line (the y axis).

These axes intersect at a point called the **origin**.

You can use an **ordered pair** of numbers to locate a point in the plane.

The first number tells the direction and the number of spaces to move horizontally.
The second number tells the direction and the number of spaces to move vertically.
Always start at the origin.

The ordered pair (3, 4) means start at the origin,
move 3 spaces to the right,
move 4 spaces up.
The ordered pair (3, 4) locates point A.

The ordered pair ($^-3$, 4) locates point B.
Point B is 3 spaces to the left and 4 spaces up.

The ordered pair ($^-3$, $^-4$) locates point C.
Point C is 3 spaces to the left and 4 spaces down.

The ordered pair (3, $^-4$) locates point D.
Point D is 3 spaces to the right and 4 spaces down.

Some points are located on an axis.
The ordered pair (5, 0) locates point E.

You can write ordered pairs for given points.

The ordered pair for point F is (4, $^-2$).
The ordered pair for point G is (0, $^-5$).
The ordered pair for the origin is (0, 0).

The numbers in an ordered pair are called the **coordinates** of the point.

Practice • What is the letter at the point?

1. $(3, 2)$ **2.** $(^-5, 2)$

3. $(6, ^-3)$ **4.** $(^-1, ^-6)$

Write the ordered pair for the point.

5. K **6.** L

7. M **8.** N

Mixed Practice • What is the letter at the point?

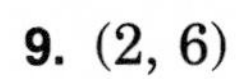

9. $(2, 6)$ **10.** $(^-4, ^-4)$

11. $(^-2, 0)$ **12.** $(2, ^-5)$

13. $(^-6, 3)$ ★ **14.** $\left(5\frac{1}{2}, 1\right)$

Write the ordered pair for the point.

15. P **16.** Q

17. R **18.** S

19. T **20.** U

21. V **22.** W ★ **23.** Y ★ **24.** Z

For each exercise draw a coordinate plane on graph paper. Then mark dots for the points. You do not have to name the points.

25. $(5, 7)$ $(5, 5)$ $(5, 3)$ $(5, 0)$ $(5, ^-2)$ $(5, ^-5)$

26. $(^-2, 6)$ $(^-2, 4)$ $(^-2, 2)$ $(^-2, 0)$ $(^-2, ^-3)$ $(^-2, ^-4)$

27. $(6, 4)$ $(5, 3)$ $(4, 2)$ $(3, 1)$ $(2, 0)$ $(1, ^-1)$

28. $(^-3, ^-3)$ $(^-2, ^-2)$ $(^-1, ^-1)$ $(0, 0)$ $(1, 1)$ $(2, 2)$

PROBLEM SOLVING • APPLICATIONS

In each problem look for a pattern in the ordered pairs. Write the next three ordered pairs in the pattern. Then mark the six points in a coordinate plane.

29. $(^-4, ^-1)$, $(^-3, 0)$, $(^-2, 1)$, ?, ?, ? ★ **30.** $(1, 2)$, $(0, 0)$, $(^-1, ^-2)$, ?, ?, ?

Graphing Equations

The equation $y = x + 4$ has two variables.
The solutions of the equation are pairs of numbers.

If x is 2, then $y = 2 + 4$, or 6.
If x is 0, then $y = 0 + 4$, or 4.
If x is $^-1$, then $y = {}^-1 + 4$, or 3.

You can make a table of values to list the solutions. The solutions can be shown as ordered pairs (x, y).

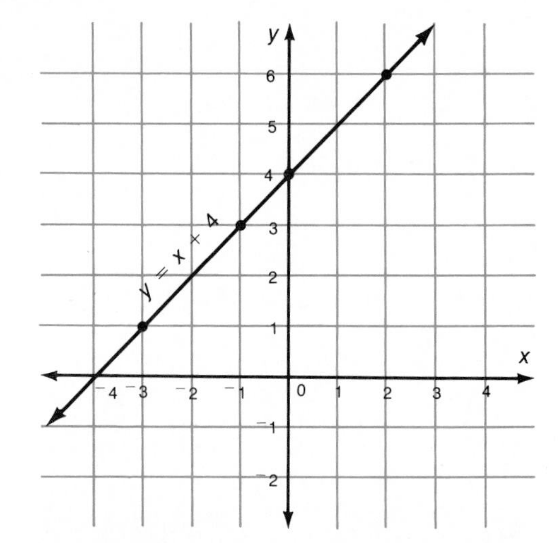

x	y
2	6
0	4
$^-1$	3
$^-3$	1

Solutions:

(2, 6)
(0, 4)
($^-1$, 3)
($^-3$, 1)

There are an unlimited number of solutions for the equation. A graph can indicate the solutions.

Step 1
Graph the ordered pairs you listed as solutions.

Step 2
Draw a line through the points.

The graph of $y = x + 4$ is a line.
For each point on the line, there is an ordered pair that is a solution of $y = x + 4$.
Some of the solutions are not integers.
For example, $\left(1\frac{1}{2}, 5\frac{1}{2}\right)$ is a solution.

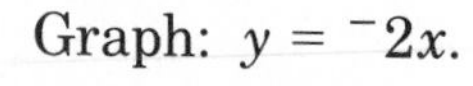

Graph: $y = {}^-2x$.

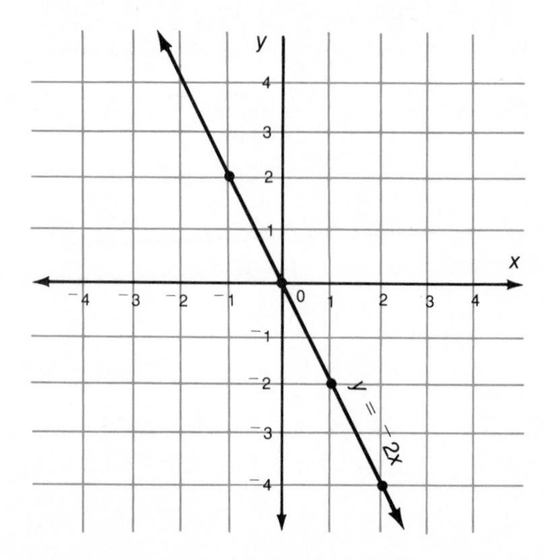

x	y
2	$^-4$
1	$^-2$
0	0
$^-1$	2

Practice • Copy and complete each table. Graph each equation.

1. $y = x - 1$

x	y
3	2
2	1
0	
$^{-}1$	

2. $y = 2x$

x	y
2	4
0	
$^{-}2$	$^{-}4$
$^{-}4$	

3. $y = x + 3$

x	y
2	5
0	
$^{-}2$	
$^{-}4$	$^{-}1$

4. $y = x - 2$

x	y
3	1
1	
$^{-}1$	
$^{-}3$	

Mixed Practice • Copy and complete each table. Graph each equation.

5. $y = x - 3$

x	y
3	0
2	
0	
$^{-}2$	

6. $y = x + 2$

x	y
2	4
0	
$^{-}2$	
$^{-}4$	

7. $y = x$

x	y
3	3
1	
$^{-}1$	
$^{-}3$	

8. $y = \frac{x}{2}$

x	y
4	2
2	
0	
$^{-}2$	

Graph each equation.

9. $y = 4 - x$ **10.** $y = 1 + x$ **11.** $x + y = 3$ **12.** $x + y = 0$

13. $y = 2x - 3$ **14.** $y = \frac{x}{4}$ **15.** $y = 2x + 6$ **16.** $y = {}^{-}3x$

★ **17.** $y = 0(x) + 2$ ★ **18.** $y = 0(x) + 3$ ★ **19.** $y = 0(x) - 5$ ★ **20.** $y = 0(x) - 2$

PROBLEM SOLVING • APPLICATIONS

Write an equation for each table of values.

21.

x	y
8	1
6	$^{-}1$
4	$^{-}3$
2	$^{-}5$

22.

x	y
1	3
2	5
3	7
4	9

★ **23.** The temperature at Avon Beach is usually 5 Celsius degrees cooler than the temperature at Mapleview. Draw a graph to show this relationship.

Skills Maintenance

1. $10^2 = n$ **2.** $10^4 = n$ **3.** $10^5 = n$ **4.** $10^7 = n$

5. $10^3 \times 3.1 = n$ **6.** $10^5 \times 4.7 = n$ **7.** $14{,}265 \div 10^4 = n$ **8.** $458{,}679 \div 10^5 = n$

PROBLEM SOLVING • STRATEGIES

Using Tables and Graphs

You can use tables and graphs to solve some problems.

Pilar starts walking the nature trail in Hocking Park at 9:00 A.M. She walks at a rate of 3 kilometers per hour. Matthew starts walking the trail at 10:00 A.M. at a rate of 4 kilometers per hour.

Pilar	
Time	Distance in Kilometers
9:00	0
10:00	3
11:00	6
12:00	9
1:00	12

Matthew	
Time	Distance in Kilometers
10:00	0
11:00	4
12:00	8
1:00	12
2:00	16

At what time will Matthew overtake Pilar on the trail? How far will they have walked?

Step 1
Make a table for each hiker. Show the time and distance traveled.

Step 2
Graph the ordered pairs for Pilar and draw the line. In the same plane, graph the ordered pairs for Matthew and draw the line.

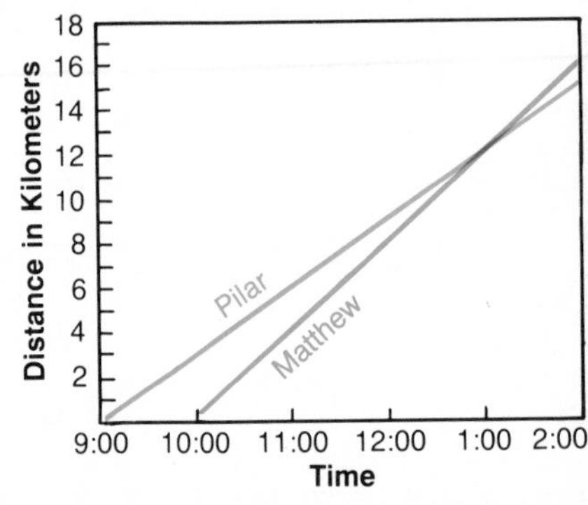

The two graphs intersect at the point (1:00, 12 km). Matthew will overtake Pilar at 1:00 P.M. on the trail. They will have walked 12 kilometers.

Solve the problems. Use tables and graphs if you think they will be helpful.

1. Jeremy rides his bicycle in a marathon to raise money for charity. He leaves the starting line at 12 noon, riding at a rate of 8 km/h. Salim starts the marathon an hour later, riding at a rate of 12 km/h. At what time will Salim overtake Jeremy?

Jeremy	
Time	Distance in Kilometers
12:00	0
1:00	8
2:00	16
3:00	?

Salim	
Time	Distance in Kilometers
1:00	0
2:00	12
3:00	?
4:00	?

2. A jet plane leaves Dulles Airport at 1:00 P.M., flying at a rate of 850 km/h. A supersonic jet leaves Dulles Airport at 3:00 P.M., flying the same route as the jet plane at a higher altitude. The supersonic jet is flying at a rate of 1,700 km/h. How far from Dulles Airport will the supersonic jet pass over the jet plane?

3. Tisa is driving to Toronto. She leaves her house at 8:00 A.M., driving at a rate of 60 km/h. Tisa's father leaves the house at 9:00 A.M., driving the same route to Toronto at 80 km/h. At what time will Tisa's father pass her on the highway?

4. Death Valley is 85 meters below sea level, and so its elevation is $^{-}85$ meters. Mt. McKinley's elevation is $^{+}6{,}194$ meters. What is the difference between their elevations?

5. Katie draws the graph of $y = 2x$ on a coordinate plane. Les draws the graph of $y = x + 5$ on the same coordinate plane. Do their graphs intersect? If so, at what point?

Make sure the line goes through the points when you draw a graph.

6. Miyuki draws the graph of $y = x + 2$ on a coordinate plane. Nancy draws the graph of $y = 3x$ on the same coordinate plane. Do their graphs intersect? If so, at what point?

7. Paula says, "My dog's age, x, plus my cat's age, y, is 12. The difference between x and y is 8." What are the ages of the two animals?

★8. Steve says, "My dog is 4 times as old as my cat. The sum of their ages is 15." What are the ages of the two animals?

★9. Tina says, "My cousin is 5 times as old as my brother. The sum of their ages is 36." How old is Tina's cousin? How old is Tina's brother?

★10. Carrie has 0.5 times as many dollars as Doris. Together, they have 18 dollars. How many dollars does each girl have?

★11. Ann has 1.5 times as much money as her sister, Beth. The difference between Ann's money and Beth's money is 10 cents. How much money does each girl have?

★12. Evita draws the graph of $x + 3 = y$ on a coordinate plane. Deven draws the graph of $x + 5 = y$ on the same coordinate plane. Do their two graphs intersect? If so, at what point? If not, why not?

CHAPTER 15

REVIEW

Write the opposite integers. (pp. 408–409)

1. $^{+}7$ **2.** $^{-}11$

3. $^{+}24$ **4.** $^{-}40$

Write $<$ or $>$. (pp. 408–411)

5. $^{-}6$ ● $^{-}15$ **6.** $^{-}13$ ● $^{+}9$

7. $^{+}15°C$ ● $^{+}21°C$ **8.** $^{+}12°C$ ● $0°C$

Add, subtract, multiply, or divide. (pp. 412–421)

9. $^{+}6 + {}^{+}3$ **10.** $^{-}5 + {}^{-}10$ **11.** $^{+}14 + {}^{-}11$ **12.** $^{-}18 + {}^{+}14$

13. $^{-}10 - {}^{-}3$ **14.** $^{-}15 - {}^{+}6$ **15.** $0 - {}^{-}8$ **16.** $^{-}13 - {}^{+}19$

17. $^{-}5 \times {}^{-}9$ **18.** $^{+}3 \times {}^{+}8$ **19.** $^{+}7 \times {}^{-}7$ **20.** $^{-}3 \times {}^{+}4$

21. $^{+}24 \div {}^{+}6$ **22.** $^{+}32 \div {}^{-}4$ **23.** $^{-}18 \div {}^{+}2$ **24.** $^{-}54 \div {}^{-}9$

Solve. (pp. 422–423)

25. $x + 7 = 5$ **26.** $\frac{n}{2} = {}^{-}4$

Write $<$, $=$, or $>$. (pp. 424–425)

27. $\frac{^{-}3}{4}$ ● $\frac{^{-}1}{8}$ **28.** 1.75 ● 1.7500

What is the letter at the point? (pp. 426–427)

29. $(^{-}3, 2)$ **30.** $(5, {}^{-}2)$ **31.** $(^{-}1, {}^{-}4)$ **32.** $(0, 4)$

Write the ordered pair for the point. (pp. 426–427)

33. B **34.** I **35.** A **36.** C

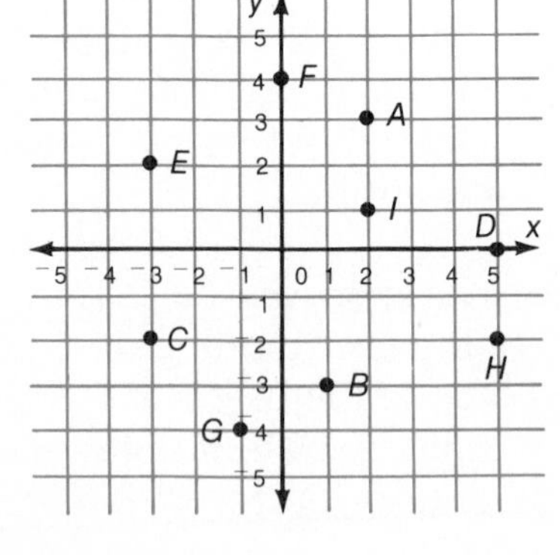

37. Copy and complete the table. Graph the equation. (pp. 428–429)

$y = x + 2$

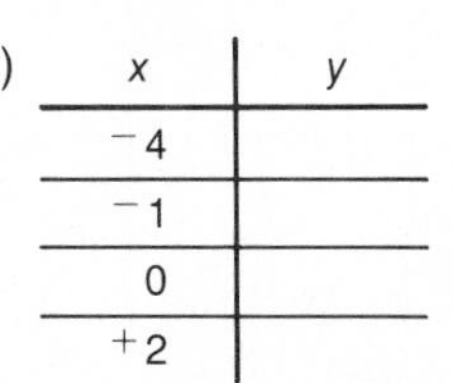

x	y
$^{-}4$	
$^{-}1$	
0	
$^{+}2$	

38. The QRS stock loses 2 points on each of 4 days. Write the integer that represents its total gain or loss. (pp. 418–419)

39. Gail is driving to Boston. She leaves her house at 7:00 A.M., driving at a rate of 60 km/h. Her mother leaves the house at 8:00 A.M., driving 90 km/h on the same route to Boston. At what time will Gail's mother pass her on the highway? (pp. 430–431)

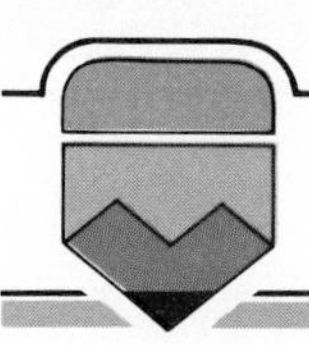

PROJECT

Translations and Rotations

You can change the position of a geometric figure. In Chapter 12 you obtained the **reflection image** of a figure by flipping it along its line of symmetry.

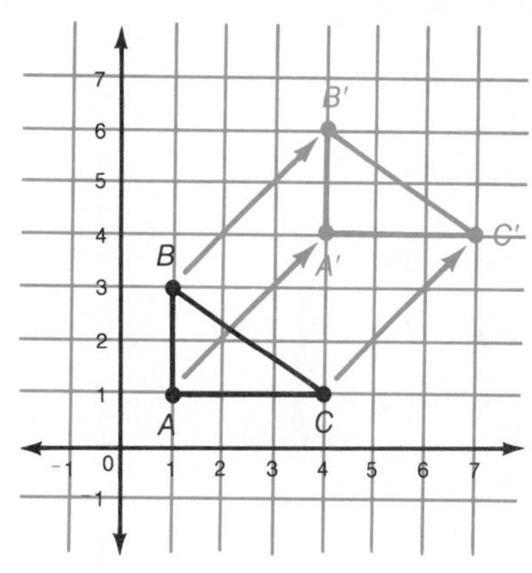

If you **slide** a geometric figure to a new position, you obtain a **translation image**. The drawing at the right shows $\triangle A'B'C'$, the translation image of $\triangle ABC$. $\triangle A'B'C'$ is the result of a slide 3 units to the right and 3 units up. Point A has moved 3 units to the right and 3 units up to become A'. (Read A' as "A prime.") Point B has moved 3 units to the right and 3 units up to become B'. Point C has moved 3 units to the right and 3 units up to become C'.

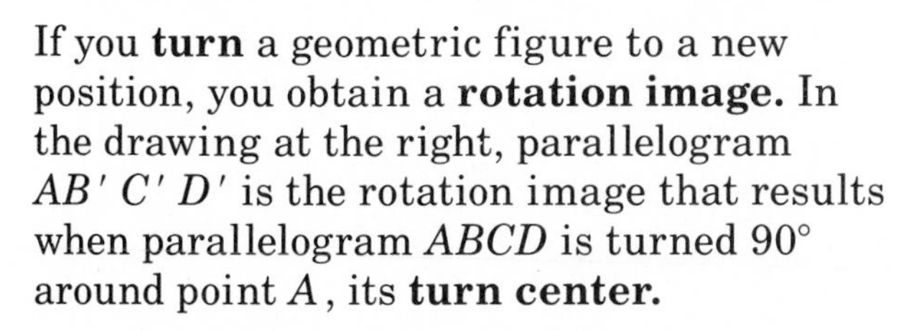

If you **turn** a geometric figure to a new position, you obtain a **rotation image.** In the drawing at the right, parallelogram $AB'C'D'$ is the rotation image that results when parallelogram $ABCD$ is turned 90° around point A, its **turn center.**

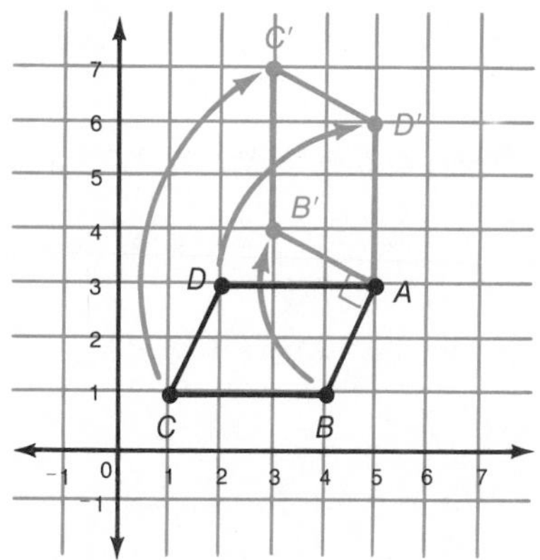

Are the two triangles in the first drawing congruent? Are the two parallelograms in the second drawing congruent? How can you tell?

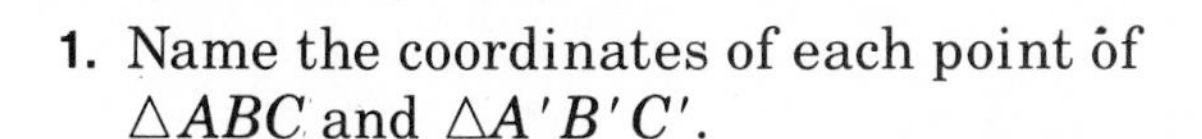

1. Name the coordinates of each point of $\triangle ABC$ and $\triangle A'B'C'$.

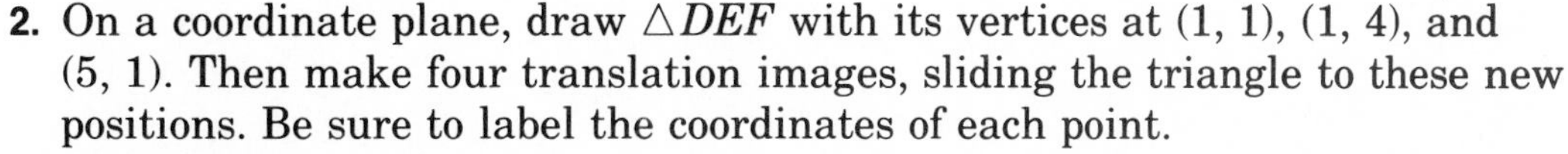

2. On a coordinate plane, draw $\triangle DEF$ with its vertices at (1, 1), (1, 4), and (5, 1). Then make four translation images, sliding the triangle to these new positions. Be sure to label the coordinates of each point.
   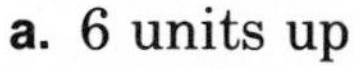
   a. 6 units up
   b. 7 units to the left
   c. 5 units to the right and 4 units up
   d. 4 units to the left and 5 units down

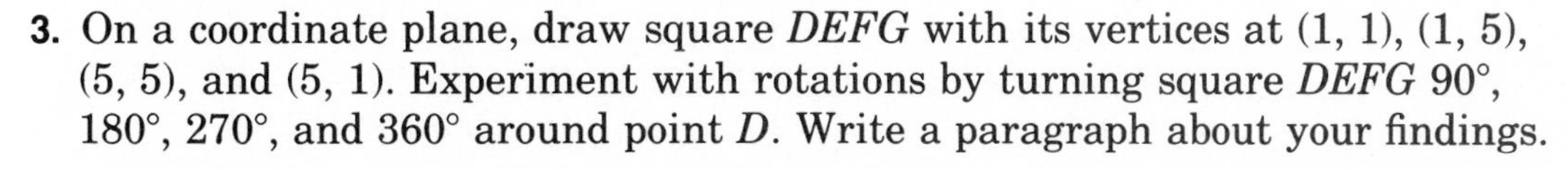

3. On a coordinate plane, draw square $DEFG$ with its vertices at (1, 1), (1, 5), (5, 5), and (5, 1). Experiment with rotations by turning square $DEFG$ 90°, 180°, 270°, and 360° around point D. Write a paragraph about your findings.

CHAPTER 15

TEST

Write the opposite integer.

1. $^{+}8$
2. $^{-}16$
3. $^{-}30$
4. $^{+}25$

Write < or >.

5. $^{+}2$ ● $^{+}1$
6. $^{-}8$ ● $^{-}1$
7. $^{-}16°C$ ● $^{-}19°C$
8. $0°C$ ● $^{+}9°C$

Add, subtract, multiply, or divide.

9. $^{+}3 + {}^{+}8$
10. $^{-}12 + {}^{-}3$
11. $^{+}5 + {}^{-}3$
12. $^{-}16 + {}^{+}12$
13. $^{-}8 - {}^{-}9$
14. $^{-}5 - {}^{-}7$
15. $^{-}11 - {}^{+}6$
16. $^{+}16 - {}^{-}4$
17. $^{-}7 \times {}^{-}6$
18. $^{+}8 \times {}^{+}9$
19. $^{+}6 \times {}^{-}8$
20. $^{-}4 \times {}^{+}8$
21. $^{+}48 \div {}^{+}6$
22. $^{-}42 \div {}^{-}7$
23. $^{-}36 \div {}^{+}6$
24. $^{+}56 \div {}^{-}8$

Solve.

25. $n - {}^{-}3 = 10$
26. $5x = {}^{-}15$

Write <, =, or >.

27. $\frac{1}{4}$ ● $\frac{5}{8}$
28. 0.7 ● $^{-}0.7$

What is the letter at the point?

29. $(^{-}4, 3)$
30. $(1, {}^{-}2)$
31. $(^{-}2, 0)$
32. $(1, 4)$

Write the ordered pair for the point.

33. C
34. E
35. G
36. D

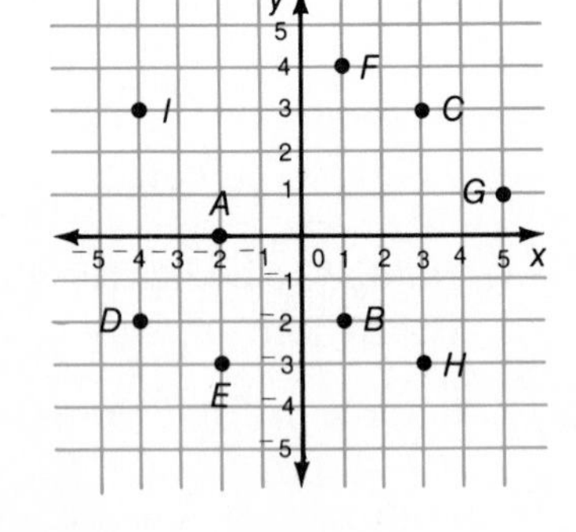

37. Copy and complete the table. Graph the equation.

$y = x - 4$

x	y
+3	
+2	
0	
−1	

38. The LMN stock lost 3 points on each of 4 days. Write the integer that represents its total gain or loss.

39. A jet plane leaves Kennedy Airport at 3:00 P.M., flying at a rate of 700 km/h. A supersonic jet leaves Kennedy Airport at 6:00 P.M., flying the same route but at a higher altitude. The supersonic jet is flying at a rate of 1,750 km/h. How far from Kennedy Airport will the supersonic jet pass over the jet plane?

ENRICHMENT

Extending Exponents and Scientific Notation

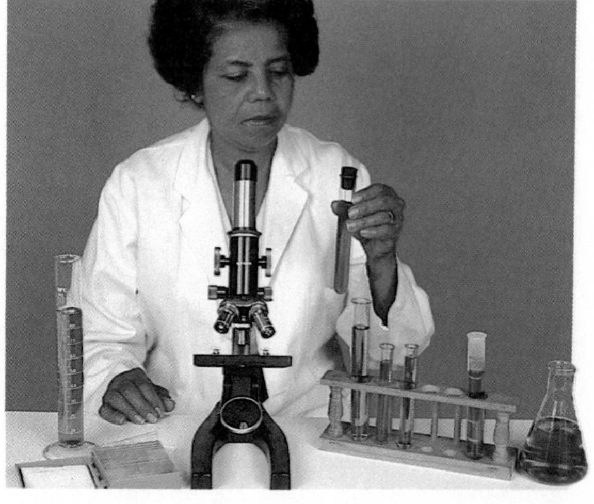

These equations show multiplication of powers of the same base. Look for a pattern.

$$\underbrace{10^3}_{(10)(10)(10)} \times \underbrace{10^2}_{(10)(10)} = \underbrace{10^5}_{100{,}000}$$

$$\underbrace{10^4}_{(10)(10)(10)(10)} \times \underbrace{10^3}_{(10)(10)(10)} = \underbrace{10^7}_{10{,}000{,}000}$$

When you multiply powers of the same base, can you add the exponents?

$$10^a \times 10^b = 10^{a+b} \qquad n^a \times n^b = n^{a+b}$$

Now think about division with powers of the same base.

$$\frac{10^5}{10^2} = \frac{(10)(10)(10)(10)(10)}{(10)(10)} = 10^3 \qquad \frac{10^7}{10^3} = \frac{(10)(10)(10)(10)(10)(10)(10)}{(10)(10)(10)} = 10^4$$

To divide with powers of the same base, can you subtract the exponents?

$$10^a \div 10^b = 10^{a-b} \qquad n^a \div n^b = n^{a-b}$$

Study the equations at the right. Note that when the numerator has an exponent less than the denominator, we have used a negative exponent for the answer.

Now study the column labeled Value of Answer. Is each number $\frac{1}{10}$ of the number above it?

Then does $10^{-1} = \frac{1}{10^1}$?

Does $10^{-2} = \frac{1}{10^2}$?

What fraction can you write for 10^{-3}?

	Answer		Value of Answer
$\frac{10^5}{10^3} = 10^{5-3}$	$= 10^2$	⟶	100
$\frac{10^5}{10^4} = 10^{5-4}$	$= 10^1$	⟶	10
$\frac{10^5}{10^5} = 10^{5-5}$	$= 10^0$	⟶	1
$\frac{10^5}{10^6} = 10^{5-6}$	$= 10^{-1}$	⟶	?
$\frac{10^5}{10^7} = 10^{5-7}$	$= 10^{-2}$	⟶	?
$\frac{10^5}{10^8} = 10^{5-8}$	$= 10^{-3}$	⟶	?

Enrichment, *continued*

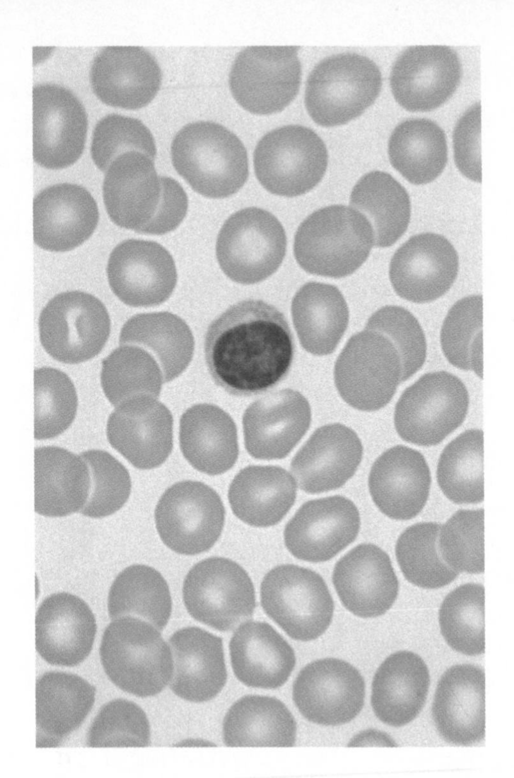

Study the equation below.
Pick 5 different integers for a and show the resulting equations.

$$10^{-a} = \frac{1}{10^{a}}$$

Negative exponents can be used in writing scientific notation for numbers less than 1. (Look back at page 128 if you do not remember scientific notation.)

For example, the diameter of a white blood cell is given in scientific notation as 1.5×10^{-3} centimeters. Thus, the diameter is 1.5×0.001 centimeter, or 0.0015 centimeter.

If you understand exponents and scientific notation, then try these exercises.

Copy and write the missing exponent.

1. $10^{4} \times 10^{2} = 10^{?}$
2. $10^{-4} \times 10^{-2} = 10^{?}$
3. $10^{5} \times 10^{3} = 10^{?}$
4. $10^{-5} \times 10^{-3} = 10^{?}$
5. $10^{-2} \times 10^{-2} = 10^{?}$
6. $10^{6} \times 10^{1} = 10^{?}$
7. $10^{6} \div 10^{5} = 10^{?}$
8. $10^{6} \div 10^{6} = 10^{?}$
9. $10^{6} \div 10^{9} = 10^{?}$
10. $10^{2} \div 10^{3} = 10^{?}$
11. $10^{3} \div 10^{5} = 10^{?}$
12. $10^{4} \div 10^{8} = 10^{?}$

Write each expression as a decimal (without exponents).

13. 4.6×10^{-1}
14. 3.9×10^{-2}
15. 2.5×10^{-3}

16. Study the equation below. Note how the factors have been rearranged at the right of the equal sign. Express the product, n, in scientific notation.

$$(1.5 \times 10^{6}) \times (1.7 \times 10^{2}) = (1.5 \times 1.7) \times (10^{6} \times 10^{2}) = n$$

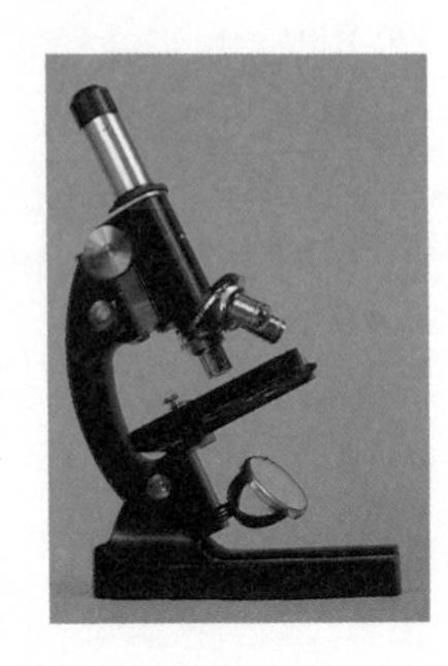

17. Express the product, n, in scientific notation.

$$(2.6 \times 10^{-3}) \times (3.2 \times 10^{-2}) = (2.6 \times 3.2) \times (10^{-3} \times 10^{-2}) = n$$

COMPUTER

Computer Control

In Chapter 12 you saw how computer instructions might require one, two, or three computer words.

In computer control *instruction timing* is important. For example, the instruction AL 17,23 provides the addends for addition. The instruction AA 1000,1001, however, requires a computer to retrieve data from address 1000, retrieve data from address 1001, and then to add those addends. The AA instruction takes much longer.

A computer needs to keep track of these instruction facts: the word length of the instruction, the timing of the instruction, and the error conditions from the instruction.

Index registers are often basic to computer control. You learned before that the highest address of a 32K computer filled 15 bits. Computers can expand to thousands of K of storage.

Index registers can be thought of as keeping track of the "millions period" for addresses that have a limit of 999,999. If an index register contains 5 and an address is 444,444, the effective address is 5,444,444. Increasing the address by 1 gives the next sequential address: 5,444,445. But increasing the index register by 1 gives a far-distant address: 6,444,444.

Subroutines are also basic to computer control. If computer programmers had to write the hundreds of instructions to get a CRT to display the pixels forming "6" each time they wanted a 6 to appear on the screen, programming would be impossible. But a subroutine can be written once and *called* from a program. For example, a subroutine call instruction with an op-code SC might call a "6-writing-subroutine" 6W in this way: SC 6W.

Macro-instructions, also called *macros*, control computers. These are "super instructions" that combine many instructions into one. For example, a "6-writing-macro" instruction with an op-code 6M could be used as a simple instruction: 6M.

At this point you know enough about computers to make one of your own on paper. Construct a computer, on paper, that acts as a calculator. The idea of this exercise is to pretend to be a computer engineer coming up with a new gift for your friend's next birthday. This is not a "problem"; have fun with it. You must consider all of the following items.

1. Input, storage, processing, programs, output. One way of keeping track of these designs is to use a systems flowchart.
2. Input: Keyboard, floppy disk, or hard disk?
3. Storage: How many bytes, bytes per word, and index registers?
4. Processing: What are the instructions and op-codes?
5. Programs: A program flowchart can keep track of input, processing, and output. Will you use subroutines or macros for adding, subtracting, multiplying, and dividing? Will you program the functions of the C and the CE buttons? Will you allow repeated operations? What indication will you give when the numbers get too large to handle?
6. Output: Printer, CRT, floppy disk, or hard disk?

There are no right or wrong answers to this exercise. Put yourself into the position of the computer's CPU (central processing unit): Exactly what do you have to know to process the data correctly? Try to be as detailed as you can. Sets of instruction op-codes like RF = Read floppy disk
CO = Check operation
AD = Add decimals
WH = Write hard disk
are more detailed than an instruction like GA (Get answer).

When you are finished, exchange designs with the person next to you. He or she will try to use your computer design, and you will try to use his or her computer design. You may want to ask these questions: Can you handle decimal points? Can you handle fractions? How do you know when to divide?

SKILLS MAINTENANCE

Chapters 1 Through 15

Choose the correct answers.

1. Add.

$$\begin{array}{r} 72.578 \\ 0.7321 \\ +49.36 \\ \hline \end{array}$$

A. 112.6701
B. 122.6701
C. 1,226.701
D. not here

2. Multiply.

$$\begin{array}{r} 0.576 \\ \times\ 0.07 \\ \hline \end{array}$$

A. 0.04032
B. 0.40320
C. 0.00432
D. not here

3. Solve.

$\frac{3}{8} + \frac{5}{6} = n$

A. $n = \frac{1}{6}$
B. $n = 1\frac{5}{24}$
C. $n = \frac{4}{7}$
D. not here

4. Subtract.

$8 - 6\frac{7}{10}$

A. $1\frac{7}{10}$ **B.** $2\frac{7}{10}$
C. $1\frac{3}{10}$ **D.** not here

5. Find the repeating decimal for $\frac{1}{3}$.

A. $0.\overline{3}$ **B.** $0.\overline{13}$
C. $0.\overline{6}$ **D.** not here

6. Solve.

$6\% \text{ of } 75 = n$

A. $n = 45$ **B.** $n = 4.5$
C. $n = 0.45$ **D.** not here

7. How many sides does an octagon have?

A. 6 **B.** 8
C. 10 **D.** not here

8. Find the perimeter of this polygon.

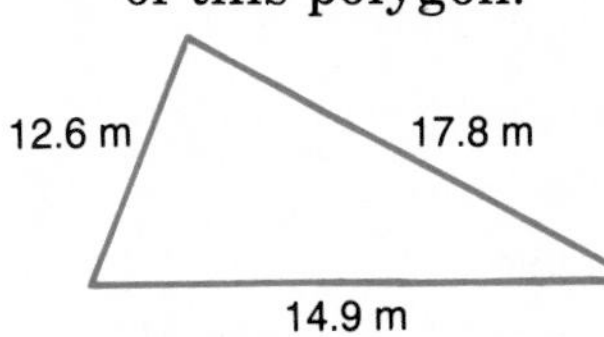

A. 453 m **B.** 25.7 m
C. 45.3 m **D.** not here

9. You toss a number cube that has 1, 2, 3, 4, 5, and 6 on it. Find this probability.

P(less than 5)

A. $\frac{1}{6}$ **B.** $\frac{1}{3}$
C. $\frac{2}{3}$ **D.** not here

10. Write <, =, or >.

$^{-}12 \bullet {}^{+}2$

A. >
B. <
C. =
D. not here

11. Subtract.

$^{-}15 - {}^{-}8$

A. $^{-}7$
B. $^{-}23$
C. $^{+}7$
D. not here

12. Divide.

$^{+}42 \div {}^{-}6$

A. $^{-}8$
B. $^{+}7$
C. $^{-}7$
D. not here

Choose the correct answers.

13. Judy buys a sweater for $25, a hat for $12.98, and a scarf for $6.50. Kim buys a jacket for $79. How much money does Judy spend?

A. $44.48 **B.** $79
C. $123.48 **D.** not here

14. Nashota buys 4 packages of paper plates with the same number of plates in each package. There are 288 plates in all. How many plates are there in each package?

A. 1,152 **B.** 284
C. 72 **D.** not here

15. Jessica buys 3 records for $7.98 each and 4 tapes for $9.25 each. How much money does Jessica spend?

A. $60.94 **B.** $17.23
C. $33.19 **D.** not here

16. Mr. Wayne earns a 7% commission on the sales he makes. His sales amounted to $21,800 in April. What was the amount of his commission?

A. $150 **B.** $1,526
C. $15.26 **D.** not here

17. Last year tickets for the Winter Carnival were $3.00 each. This year the price was $.75 more. The increase ($.75) is what percent of the old price ($3.00)?

A. 4% **B.** 75%
C. 25% **D.** not here

18. Erik is taking a 225-kilometer trip. He drives 75 kilometers north on Route 202. Then he drives 132 kilometers east on Interstate 82. How many more kilometers does he have to drive?

A. 18 km **B.** 81 km
C. 28 km **D.** not here

19. A dog's age, x, plus a cat's age, y, is 14. The difference between x and y is 10. What are the ages of the two animals?

A. dog—2; cat—12
B. dog—12; cat—2
C. dog—14; cat—4
D. not here

20. The Ace Tool Company produces chain saws. About 7 out of every 100 saws turn out to be defective. About how many defective saws would you expect there to be if 1,500 saws are produced?

A. 70 **B.** 700
C. 105 **D.** not here

Extra Practice

Set 1 (pages 2–9)

Write in expanded form. **1.** 63,172 **2.** 5,048 **3.** 291,435 **4.** 7,068,193

Write $<$ or $>$. **5.** 917 ● 719 **6.** 1,065 ● 1,605

7. 61,493 ● 60,493 **8.** 305,746 ● 350,476 **9.** 2,591,195 ● 2,195,591

Write in order from least to greatest. **10.** 627; 672; 276 **11.** 1,098; 890; 918; 1,089

Write in exponent form.

12. $2 \times 2 \times 2 \times 2$ **13.** $5 \times 5 \times 5$

Write the products.

14. 2^7 **15.** 10^3 **16.** 5^5

Write in expanded form using powers of 10 and exponents.

17. 5,463 **18.** 19,802 **19.** 725,871 **20.** 2,469,031

Set 2 (pages 12–17)

Estimate each sum or difference. Then find the actual answer.

1. $735 + 481$ **2.** $3,805 + 1,394$ **3.** $70,452 + 16,178$ **4.** $259,018 + 443,592$ **5.** $\$426.19 + 557.92$

6. $720 - 374$ **7.** $8,812 - 6,078$ **8.** $94,531 - 17,600$ **9.** $65,281 - 41,093$ **10.** $\$353.04 - 97.85$

Solve.

11. $2,157 + 884 = n$ **12.** $5,710 - 1,975 = n$ **13.** $n + 3,058 = 6,871$

14. $n - 4,286 = 4,035$ **15.** $n + 697 + 3,809 = 8,112$ **16.** $(5,139 - 740) - 2,253 = n$

Problem Solving for Chapter 1 (pages 10–11, 18–19)

Use the table on page 10. Solve and check.

1. In 1960, the population of Houston was how much less than 1,000,000?
2. How many cities showed an increase in population both from 1960 to 1970 and from 1970 to 1980?

Set 3 (pages 28–37)

Multiply or divide.

1. $6 \times 9 = n$ **2.** $8 \times 4 = n$ **3.** $56 \div 8 = n$ **4.** $18 \div 2 = n$ **5.** $40 \div 5 = n$

Multiply.

6. $\begin{array}{r} 37{,}594 \\ \times\ 8{,}000 \\ \hline \end{array}$ **7.** $\begin{array}{r} \$7{,}802.38 \\ \times\ \quad 67 \\ \hline \end{array}$ **8.** $\begin{array}{r} 4{,}785 \\ \times\ 246 \\ \hline \end{array}$ **9.** $\begin{array}{r} \$768.49 \\ \times\ \quad 853 \\ \hline \end{array}$

Solve.

10. $4 \times 9{,}327 = n$ **11.** $2 \times 8{,}763 \times 6 = n$

12. $4^7 = n$ **13.** $90 \times 237 = n$ **14.** $700 \times 1{,}854 = n$

15. $13{,}000 \times 24{,}762 = n$ **16.** $85 \times 1{,}793 = n$ **17.** $46 \times 20{,}875 = n$

18. $73 \times 356{,}148 = n$ **19.** $215 \times 809 = n$ **20.** $374 \times 2{,}761 = n$

21. $657 \times 11{,}898 = n$ **22.** $300^4 = n$ **23.** $512^3 = n$

Set 4 (pages 40–47, 50–51)

Divide.

1. $5\overline{)372}$ **2.** $7\overline{)\$1{,}180.34}$ **3.** $70\overline{)5{,}794}$ **4.** $62\overline{)10{,}354}$ **5.** $84\overline{)42{,}945}$

6. $44\overline{)51{,}107}$ **7.** $157\overline{)1{,}178}$ **8.** $768\overline{)9{,}000}$ **9.** $449\overline{)68{,}213}$ **10.** $5{,}150\overline{)44{,}000}$

Solve.

11. $2{,}952 \div 9 = n$ **12.** $58{,}233 \div 7 = n$ **13.** $1{,}000{,}656 \div 8 = n$

14. $n \times 6 = 44{,}244$ **15.** $5{,}170 \div 94 = n$ **16.** $7{,}661 \div 47 = n$

17. $83{,}068 \div 38 = n$ **18.** $1{,}344 \div 192 = n$ **19.** $10{,}790 \div 415 = n$

20. $72{,}001 \div 809 = n$ **21.** $88{,}605 \div 537 = n$ **22.** $703{,}836 \div 342 = n$

Compute.

23. $8 - (5 - 3)$ **24.** $3 \times 7 + 2$ **25.** $3 \times (7 + 2)$

26. $2 \times 6 \div 4$ **27.** $(12 \div 6) \div 2$ **28.** $12 \div (6 - 2)$ **29.** $(4 - 2) \times (5 - 3)$

Problem Solving for Chapter 2 (pages 38–39, 48–49)

Write the operation needed. Solve the problem.

1. Consuelo earns \$455 per week. How much does she earn in one year?

Solve if you have enough information. If not, tell what is needed.

2. Terry buys 8 pens. Each pen costs \$1.29. How much change will she receive?

Set 5 (pages 60–67)

Evaluate the expressions shown for the given values.

$37 - n$: **1.** $n = 12$ **2.** $n = 5$ **3.** $n = 27$ **4.** $n = 18$

$6y$: **5.** $y = 9$ **6.** $y = 13$ **7.** $y = 37$ **8.** $y = 140$

$a = 48$: **9.** $a + 27$ **10.** $3a$ **11.** $\frac{a}{8}$ **12.** $\frac{2(a - 8)}{5}$

Solve. **13.** $w - 17 = 25$ **14.** $k + 81 = 100$ **15.** $183 - z = 84$

16. $x + 17 = 17$ **17.** $41 + n = 213$ **18.** $6x = 72$ **19.** $\frac{w}{7} = 21$

20. $99 = 11x$ **21.** $11 = \frac{n}{11}$ **22.** $3n + 7 = 25$ **23.** $5y - 30 = 10$

Set 6 (pages 70–73, 76–77)

Write *true* or *false*. **1.** $(24 \div 12) \div 2 = 24 \div (12 \div 2)$ **2.** $(6 \times 4) \times 7 = 6 \times (4 \times 7)$

3. $(35 - 15) - 5 = 35 - (15 - 5)$ **4.** $14 \div 7 = 7 \div 14$ **5.** $8 + 3 = 3 + 8$

6. $(8 + 6) - 2 = 8 + (6 - 2)$ **7.** $(8 - 6) + 2 = 8 - (6 + 2)$

Use the distance formula. Solve.

8. $r = 48$ km/h
$t = 7$ hours
Find d.

9. $d = 451$ km
$r = 11$ km/h
Find t.

10. $d = 225$ km
$t = 15$ hours
Find r.

11. $r = 60$ km/h
$t = 1$ hour
Find d.

Solve and graph. **12.** $x + 5 > 12$ **13.** $x + 5 < 12$ **14.** $\frac{a}{3} = 4$

15. $\frac{a}{3} > 4$ **16.** $\frac{a}{3} < 4$ **17.** $7x > 35$ **18.** $7x < 35$

Problem Solving for Chapter 3 (pages 68–69, 74–75)

Write an equation. Then solve the problem.

1. June bought 13 crayons for 91 cents. How much does each crayon cost?
2. Dina needs art supplies that cost \$27. She saved \$8 and her mother gave her \$10. How much money does Dina need?
3. Arnie bought 48 liters of cider. The price for one liter is \$2. After paying for the cider, he still had \$4 left. How much money did Arnie have originally?

Set 7 (pages 86–91)

Write <, =, or >.

1. 0.099 ● 0.90
2. 3.765 ● 3.0765
3. 8.663 ● 8.66300
4. 0.507 ● 0.57
5. 193.20 ● 19.320
6. 66.050 ● 66.05
7. 142.0 ● 0.142
8. 1.100 ● 1.100001

Write in order from least to greatest.

9. 1.3; 1.03; 1.33
10. 30.630; 30.603; 30.6003
11. 27.81; 2.781; 2,781; 278.1

Set 8 (pages 92–95, 98–99)

Round to the nearest

Whole number:	1. 12.2	2. 6.51	3. 149.499	4. 149.601
Tenth:	5. 16.38	6. 8.24	7. 0.361	8. 15.829
Hundredth:	9. 0.752	10. 15.333	11. 27.206	12. 5.699
Thousandth:	13. 0.9652	14. 13.8022	15. 7.0404	16. 1.2195

Add or subtract.

17. $\begin{array}{r} 17.5 \\ +18.7 \\ \hline \end{array}$

18. $\begin{array}{r} 259.4 \\ +\ 67.8 \\ \hline \end{array}$

19. $\begin{array}{r} 0.19 \\ +2.98 \\ \hline \end{array}$

20. $\begin{array}{r} 568.37 \\ +\ 11.69 \\ \hline \end{array}$

21. $\begin{array}{r} 55.38 \\ +26.759 \\ \hline \end{array}$

22. $\begin{array}{l} 836.7732 \\ +\quad 3.0 \\ \hline \end{array}$

23. $\begin{array}{r} 17.269 \\ 956.8 \\ +\ \ 4.05 \\ \hline \end{array}$

24. $\begin{array}{r} 3.3798 \\ 0.65 \\ +14.7 \\ \hline \end{array}$

25. $\begin{array}{r} 2.6 \\ -1.5 \\ \hline \end{array}$

26. $\begin{array}{r} 32.7 \\ -15.8 \\ \hline \end{array}$

27. $\begin{array}{r} 0.76 \\ -0.27 \\ \hline \end{array}$

28. $\begin{array}{r} 57.23 \\ -28.17 \\ \hline \end{array}$

29. $\begin{array}{r} 17.228 \\ -10.158 \\ \hline \end{array}$

30. $\begin{array}{r} 11.611 \\ -\ \ 3.908 \\ \hline \end{array}$

31. $\begin{array}{r} 565.0563 \\ -\ \ 19.3985 \\ \hline \end{array}$

32. $\begin{array}{r} 7 \\ -4.35 \\ \hline \end{array}$

Problem Solving for Chapter 4 (pages 96–97, 100–101)

Use the map on page 96 to answer the question.

1. Which highways would you take to drive from Plainville to Wakeeny?

Do you have enough money? Estimate using the menu on page 100.

2. You have $3.00. You want arroz con pollo, mixed green salad, egg drop soup, and milk.

Set 9 (pages 110–117)

Multiply.

1. $\begin{array}{r} 1.38 \\ \times\ 9.5 \\ \hline \end{array}$
2. $\begin{array}{r} 4.64 \\ \times 0.18 \\ \hline \end{array}$
3. $\begin{array}{r} 5.333 \\ \times\ 1.02 \\ \hline \end{array}$
4. $\begin{array}{r} 0.532 \\ \times\ 0.05 \\ \hline \end{array}$

5. 0.1×9.2
6. 0.01×9.2
7. 0.001×9.2
8. 0.1×0.038
9. 0.001×8.725
10. $1{,}000 \times 56.4$
11. 0.00001×1.7
12. $10{,}000 \times 49.65$

Solve.

13. $4.1 \times 6.12 = n$
14. $0.57 \times 19.25 = n$
15. $12.7 \times 2.269 = n$
16. $0.03 \times 13.4 = n$
17. $0.19 \times 0.37 = n$
18. $0.03 \times 0.04 \times 0.007 = n$
19. $(0.1)^6 = n$
20. $(10)^6 = n$
21. $(0.1)^{12} = n$

Set 10 (pages 120–129)

Divide.

1. $6\overline{)35.4}$
2. $8\overline{)0.56}$
3. $37\overline{)8.288}$
4. $0.6\overline{)5.58}$
5. $0.15\overline{)1.035}$
6. $4.7\overline{)16.262}$
7. $3.8\overline{)0.8968}$
8. $0.051\overline{)0.3264}$
9. $0.06\overline{)1.8}$
10. $0.138\overline{)3.45}$

Solve.

11. $0.153 \div 3 = n$
12. $2.872 \div 8 = n$
13. $3.22 \div 0.7 = n$
14. $0.0294 \div 0.021 = n$
15. $2.7 \div 0.06 = n$
16. $39.9 \div 10 = n$
17. $39.9 \div 1{,}000 = n$

Divide. Round each quotient to the nearest hundredth.

18. $7\overline{)16.5}$
19. $3.8\overline{)9.6}$
20. $16\overline{)18.725}$
21. $0.67\overline{)3.2}$

Write the correct exponents.

22. $8{,}650 = 8.65 \times 10^{\blacksquare}$
23. $380{,}000 = 3.8 \times 10^{\blacksquare}$
24. $96{,}490{,}000 = 9.649 \times 10^{\blacksquare}$
25. $2{,}580{,}000 = 2.58 \times 10^{\blacksquare}$

Use scientific notation to name the numbers.

26. 9,500
27. 6,730
28. 74,400
29. 136,900,000

Write the numbers.

30. 4.7×10^9
31. 2.93×10^5
32. 9.10×10^4
33. 6.77×10^6

Problem Solving for Chapter 5 (pages 118–119, 130–131)

1. Romy can run 22 kilometers in 4 hours. What is his average speed per hour?
2. Amelia earns \$500 a week. She spends \$250 each week and saves the rest. How much money does Amelia save in 7 weeks?

Set 11 (pages 140–145)

Divisible by 2?	**1.** 27	**2.** 58	**3.** 810	**4.** 4,861
Divisible by 3?	**5.** 45	**6.** 133	**7.** 111	**8.** 12,303
Divisible by 4?	**9.** 144	**10.** 2,748	**11.** 17,822	**12.** 198,000
Divisible by 5?	**13.** 49	**14.** 810	**15.** 50,542	**16.** 737,895
Divisible by 6?	**17.** 84	**18.** 739	**19.** 7,656	**20.** 11,966
Divisible by 9?	**21.** 72	**22.** 207	**23.** 854	**24.** 14,999

Find all the factors. List them in order. **25.** 33 **26.** 95

27. 130 **28.** 144 **29.** 98 **30.** 115

Write *prime* or *composite*. **31.** 87 **32.** 53 **33.** 91 **34.** 139 **35.** 163

Set 12 (pages 146–151)

Find the prime factorization. Use a factor tree. Write your answers using exponents.

1. 81 **2.** 22 **3.** 90 **4.** 56 **5.** 162 **6.** 216

Write the number. **7.** $2^2 \times 3^3$ **8.** $2^3 \times 3^2 \times 7$ **9.** $2 \times 3 \times 5^2$

List all factors. Then find the GCF. **10.** 12, 27 **11.** 14, 42 **12.** 18, 81 **13.** 25, 100

Use the prime factorizations of each pair of numbers to find their GCF.

14. 15, 18 **15.** 20, 60 **16.** 18, 32 **17.** 80, 68

18. 36, 54 **19.** 25, 65 **20.** 12, 36, 60 **21.** 8, 32, 44

Find the LCM. **22.** 4, 28 **23.** 14, 35 **24.** 10, 25 **25.** 9, 22 **26.** 15, 35

Use the prime factorization to find the LCM.

27. 20, 30 **28.** 30, 100 **29.** 56, 64 **30.** 51, 63

Problem Solving for Chapter 6 (pages 152–153)

1. Alycia has 7 coins. They are nickels and dimes. She has more nickels than dimes. What is the greatest and the least amounts of money she could have?

2. Henry has 6 coins. All are nickels, dimes, and pennies. Can he have $.47?

Set 13 (pages 162–171)

Solve.

1. $\frac{5}{8} = \frac{n}{40}$
2. $\frac{6}{9} = \frac{2}{n}$
3. $\frac{10}{25} = \frac{n}{5}$
4. $\frac{3}{7} = \frac{n}{42}$

Write equivalent fractions for each pair. Use the least common denominator.

5. $\frac{3}{7}, \frac{1}{3}$
6. $\frac{7}{9}, \frac{4}{5}$
7. $\frac{3}{4}, \frac{9}{16}$
8. $\frac{3}{10}, \frac{5}{8}$
9. $\frac{3}{5}, \frac{2}{3}$

Write <, =, or >.

10. $\frac{7}{8}$ ● $\frac{8}{9}$
11. $\frac{6}{9}$ ● $\frac{18}{27}$
12. $3\frac{2}{3}$ ● $3\frac{1}{6}$
13. $\frac{18}{5}$ ● $\frac{16}{4}$

Set 14 (pages 172–175, 178–183)

Add or subtract. Write the answers in lowest terms.

1. $\frac{4}{9} + \frac{1}{3}$
2. $\frac{7}{10} + \frac{1}{2}$
3. $5\frac{3}{10} + 2\frac{3}{5}$
4. $3\frac{7}{8} + 2\frac{1}{4}$
5. $7\frac{6}{7} + 2\frac{1}{3}$
6. $\frac{2}{3} + \frac{3}{5} + \frac{1}{6}$
7. $1\frac{5}{6} + 2\frac{3}{4} + 1\frac{2}{5}$
8. $\frac{3}{7} - \frac{1}{3}$
9. $\frac{2}{9} - \frac{1}{8}$
10. $7 - 4\frac{5}{11}$
11. $4\frac{3}{50} - 2\frac{29}{50}$
12. $3\frac{7}{8} - 1\frac{5}{6}$
13. $2\frac{1}{9} - 1\frac{2}{3}$
14. $5\frac{2}{5} - 3\frac{2}{7}$
15. $3\frac{5}{10} - \frac{1}{3}$

Solve.

16. $\frac{7}{18} + \frac{5}{18} = n$
17. $\frac{3}{10} + \frac{2}{3} = n$
18. $6\frac{7}{9} + 2\frac{1}{3} = n$
19. $n + 1\frac{2}{7} + 3\frac{9}{14} + 2\frac{1}{14} = 10$
20. $9 - 8\frac{2}{7} = n$
21. $7\frac{2}{9} - 3\frac{5}{9} = n$
22. $5\frac{3}{5} - 1\frac{2}{3} = n$
23. $8\frac{8}{12} - 6\frac{3}{4} = n$

Problem Solving for Chapter 7 (pages 176–177, 184–185)

1. Ariel has \$11.50. How many liters of gas can he buy if a liter costs \$.40?
2. Mr. and Mrs. Badillo take their daughter, Marta, to the movies. They pay \$5.00 for each adult's ticket and \$3.00 for Marta's ticket. Mr. Badillo buys popcorn for \$1.35 and a drink for \$.60. If he left the house with \$20.00, how much money does he have left?

Set 15 (pages 194–199, 202–203)

Multiply. Write the answers in lowest terms.

1. $\frac{1}{4} \times \frac{4}{7}$ **2.** $\frac{5}{6} \times \frac{2}{5}$ **3.** $\frac{2}{5} \times \frac{5}{8}$ **4.** $\frac{3}{4} \times \frac{5}{6}$ **5.** $8 \times \frac{3}{4}$

6. $3 \times 3\frac{2}{3}$ **7.** $1\frac{4}{5} \times 3\frac{1}{3}$ **8.** $\frac{1}{6} \times \frac{3}{5} \times 15$ **9.** $\frac{18}{25} \times \frac{15}{72}$ **10.** $1\frac{1}{3} \times 1\frac{1}{4} \times 1\frac{1}{5}$

Solve. **11.** $\frac{3}{8} \times \frac{4}{5} \times \frac{10}{11} = n$ **12.** $4\frac{2}{3} \times \frac{3}{14} = n$ **13.** $\frac{5}{6} \times \frac{6}{5} \times \frac{5}{6} = n$

Find the reciprocal. **14.** $\frac{3}{4}$ **15.** $\frac{1}{9}$ **16.** 5 **17.** $2\frac{2}{9}$ **18.** $4\frac{99}{100}$

Set 16 (pages 204–213)

Divide. Write answers in lowest terms. **1.** $\frac{4}{5} \div \frac{3}{10}$ **2.** $\frac{8}{9} \div \frac{1}{6}$ **3.** $\frac{9}{8} \div \frac{1}{2}$

4. $1\frac{2}{5} \div \frac{7}{9}$ **5.** $2\frac{1}{10} \div 7$ **6.** $5 \div 1\frac{2}{3}$ **7.** $2\frac{2}{5} \div 1\frac{1}{3}$ **8.** $\frac{3}{100} \div \frac{3}{1,000}$

Solve. **9.** $\frac{2}{3} \div \frac{1}{4} = n$ **10.** $\left(\frac{1}{3} + \frac{1}{6}\right) \div 3 = n$

11. $40 \div 100 = n$ **12.** $22\frac{2}{9} \div 10 = n$ **13.** $\left(\frac{1}{2} \div \frac{2}{3}\right) \div \frac{4}{3} = n$

14. $\frac{2}{5} \times \frac{2}{3} \times n = 4$ **15.** $111\frac{1}{9} \div 100 = n$ **16.** $125 \div 100 = n$

Write as fractions, whole numbers, or mixed numbers in lowest terms.

17. 0.7 **18.** 0.62 **19.** 3.125 **20.** 2.009

Write the fractions as decimals. Round to the nearest hundredth.

21. $\frac{4}{9}$ **22.** $\frac{4}{125}$ **23.** $\frac{13}{15}$ **24.** $\frac{14}{3}$ **25.** $1\frac{13}{18}$

Write the fractions as terminating decimals or as repeating decimals.

26. $\frac{1}{22}$ **27.** $\frac{4}{33}$ **28.** $\frac{32}{15}$ **29.** $\frac{7}{25}$ **30.** $\frac{17}{18}$

Problem Solving for Chapter 8 (pages 200–201, 214–215)

Use the graph on page 200 to solve problem 1.

1. Which category of expenses uses the least fractional part of Carol's money?
2. Stuart can type 5 pages in one hour. How much can he type in one minute?

Set 17 (pages 224–229)

Write equal ratios in lowest terms. 1. $\frac{15}{25}$ 2. $\frac{56}{64}$ 3. $\frac{17}{51}$ 4. $\frac{320}{100}$

Write = or ≠. 5. $\frac{2}{3}$ ● $\frac{4}{5}$ 6. $\frac{2}{8}$ ● $\frac{7}{28}$ 7. $\frac{2}{12}$ ● $\frac{8}{7}$ 8. $\frac{16}{18}$ ● $\frac{24}{27}$

Solve the proportions. 9. $\frac{5}{7} = \frac{30}{n}$ 10. $\frac{6}{n} = \frac{15}{5}$ 11. $\frac{9}{3.5} = \frac{n}{21}$

12. $\frac{2.7}{3} = \frac{n}{10}$ 13. $\frac{6}{5} = \frac{15}{n}$ 14. $\frac{14}{15} = \frac{n}{3.75}$ 15. $\frac{4}{7.5} = \frac{10}{n}$ 16. $\frac{0.625}{3.75} = \frac{n}{30.0}$

Set 18 (pages 230–233)

What do they cost?

1. 4 for 80¢ You buy 6.
2. 6 for 78¢ You buy 13.
3. 3 for 59¢ You buy 12.
4. 6 for 69¢ You buy 10.
5. 5 for 72¢ You buy 15.
6. 6 for $3.84 You buy 15.
7. 9 for $8.35 You buy 7.
8. 7 for $2.38 You buy 2.

How many do you buy?

9. 3 for 72¢ You spend 96¢.
10. 2 for 21¢ You spend $1.47.
11. 7 for $3.64. You spend $2.08.
12. 6 for $2.58 You spend 86¢.
13. 3 for $1.23 You spend $4.10.

Find the times.

14. 430 km in 5 hours To travel 344 km?
15. 212 km in 5 hours To travel 360.4 km?

Find the distances.

16. 360 km in 12 hours How far in 15 hours?
17. 279 km in 3 hours How far in 7.8 hours?

Use the scale drawing on page 232. Find the actual dimensions.

18. Length and width of the house.
19. Width of the living room.
20. The closet between bathroom 1 and bedroom 1.
21. The dimensions of an attic to be added to this house are 7.5 m × 4.5 m. Find the dimensions of the scale drawing of this attic, if the same scale is used.

Use the drawing on page 233. Find the actual dimensions of the rooms.

22. Art room
23. Gym
24. Dressing room
25. The 4 classrooms

Problem Solving for Chapter 9 (pages 234–235)

1. 3 liters of fruit juice cost $2.85. To the nearest cent, what is the unit cost?
2. Which is the better buy: 16 ounces for $.60 or 24 ounces for $1.39?

Set 19 (pages 244–251)

Write as percents.

1. $16:100$
2. $\frac{4}{25}$
3. $\frac{17}{5}$
4. 0.38
5. 0.06
6. 1.29
7. $1\frac{3}{100}$
8. $1\frac{3}{8}$
9. 0.026

Solve.

10. $\frac{n}{60} = \frac{30}{100}$
11. $\frac{n}{125} = \frac{8}{100}$
12. $\frac{n}{45} = \frac{20}{100}$
13. $\frac{n}{88} = \frac{25}{100}$
14. $\frac{n}{460} = \frac{40}{100}$
15. $\frac{n}{1{,}000{,}000} = \frac{7}{100}$
16. $\frac{n}{1{,}000{,}000} = \frac{13}{100}$

Set 20 (pages 252–257, 260–264)

Solve.

1. 12% of $250 = n$
2. 45% of $86 = n$
3. 5% of $120 = n$
4. 23% of $300 = n$
5. 60% of $495 = n$
6. 60% of $n = 30$
7. 165% of $80 = n$
8. 27 is what percent of 60?
9. 55 is 62.5% of what number?
10. What percent of 200 is 450?
11. 160% of what number is 40?

What percent is the first number of the second?

12. 15, 45
13. 20, 50
14. 1, 9
15. 14, 4

Find the sale price.

16. Original price: \$7.00
Discount rate: 35%
17. Original price: \$2.73
Discount rate: $66\frac{2}{3}\%$

Find the tax and total cost.

18. Price: \$145.00
Sales tax rate: 3%
19. Price: \$4.00
Sales tax rate: 8%

Find the interest.

20. $p = \$300$
$r = 17\%$
$t = 1$ year
21. $p = \$550$
$r = 8\%$
$t = 2$ years
22. $p = \$700$
$r = 17.5\%$
$t = 6$ months

Use the circle graph on page 264. Suppose Ann's yearly income is \$24,000. How much does she budget for

23. food?
24. taxes?
25. transportation?

Problem Solving for Chapter 10 (pages 258–259, 266–267)

1. Use the equation $101\% \times b = p$. Replace b with 90. Is p greater than b?
2. Bus fare was originally 75¢. Due to inflation, the bus fare became \$1.00. The increase (25¢) is what percent of the old fare?
3. Amelia saved \$350. This was 12.5% of what she earned. How much did Amelia earn?

Set 21 (pages 276–283)

To the nearest cm, which of these lengths would be expressed as 21 cm?

1. 20.4 cm **2.** 21.4 cm **3.** 20.499 cm **4.** 20.51 cm

Copy and complete. **5.** 5 km = ? m **6.** 8 cm = ? mm **7.** 7.3 m = ? cm

8. 396 mm = ? m **9.** 5 L = ? mL **10.** 8,000 L = ? kL **11.** 350 mL = ? L

12. 8.5 kL = ? L **13.** 8.6 g = ? mg **14.** 235 g = ? kg **15.** 30 mg = ? g

Compute.

16. $\begin{array}{r} 7.9 \text{ mL} \\ +5.6 \text{ mL} \\ \hline \end{array}$

17. $3\overline{)2.82 \text{ m}}$

18. $\begin{array}{r} 2.51 \text{ mg} \\ \times \quad 5 \\ \hline \end{array}$

19. $\begin{array}{r} 27.0 \text{ kg} \\ -\ 2.39 \text{ kg} \\ \hline \end{array}$

Set 22 (pages 286–293)

Copy and complete. **1.** 2 yd 1 ft = ? ft **2.** 3 ft 10 in. = ? in. **3.** 3 gal = ? qt

4. 7 qt = ? c **5.** 29 qt = ? gal ? qt **6.** 12 tbsp = ? fl. oz

7. 2 lb 15 oz = ? oz **8.** 15,750 lb = ? T ? lb **9.** 3 min = ? s

10. 687 s = ? min ? s **11.** 7 yr 3 mo = ? mo **12.** $6\frac{1}{8}$ lb = ? oz

Compute.

13. $\begin{array}{r} 2 \text{ yd } 1 \text{ ft } 9 \text{ in.} \\ +5 \text{ yd } 1 \text{ ft } 8 \text{ in.} \\ \hline \end{array}$

14. $\begin{array}{r} 3 \text{ qt } 1 \text{ pt} \\ \times \quad 5 \\ \hline \end{array}$

15. $\begin{array}{r} 1 \text{ c } 5 \text{ fl. oz} \\ +1 \text{ c } 6 \text{ fl. oz} \\ \hline \end{array}$

16. $\begin{array}{r} 7 \text{ gal} \\ -2 \text{ gal } 3 \text{ qt} \\ \hline \end{array}$

17. $\begin{array}{r} 6 \text{ min } 18 \text{ s} \\ -3 \text{ min } 43 \text{ s} \\ \hline \end{array}$

18. 3×8 wk 6 d

19. 7 h 39 min $\div$ 3

Write answers as fractions. **20.** 1,500 lb = ? T **21.** 9 in. = ? ft **22.** 3 h = ? d

Problem Solving for Chapter 11 (pages 284–285, 294–295)

Make up one question that can be answered from the information given. Answer it.

1. The space shuttle carries 800,000 kg of propellant. It can travel 8 days and 8 hours at a speed of 8,000 km per hour.

Use the table on page 294 to solve the problems.

2. Find the cost of a 3-minute call at 1:30 A.M. on Monday from Central City to Pleasant Grove.

3. Cheryl made a 3-minute call from Central City to Liberty at 7:30 A.M. instead of 8:15 A.M. Saturday. How much did she save by calling earlier?

Set 23 (pages 304–317)

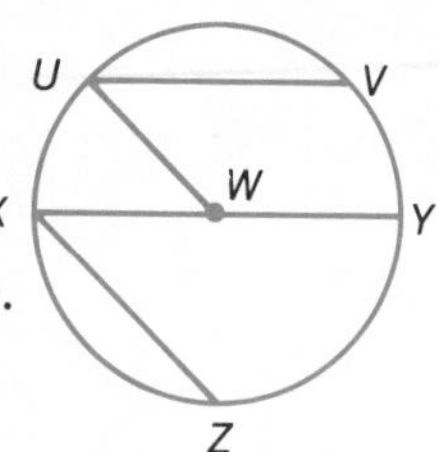

Use this drawing for exercises 1–6. Name

1. the circle. **2.** a central angle. **3.** three radii.

4. three chords. **5.** a diameter. **6.** five arcs.

The angles are complementary. Find the missing measures.

7. $60°, n$ **8.** $28°, n$ **9.** $83°, n$ **10.** $56.5°, n$

The angles are supplementary. Find the missing measures.

11. $20°, n$ **12.** $168°, n$ **13.** $91°, n$ **14.** $137.5°, n$

Set 24 (pages 318–331)

Two angles of a triangle are given. Find the measure of the other angle.

1. $30°, 80°, n$ **2.** $70°, 60°, n$ **3.** $45°, 90°, n$ **4.** $39.5°, 109.5°, n$

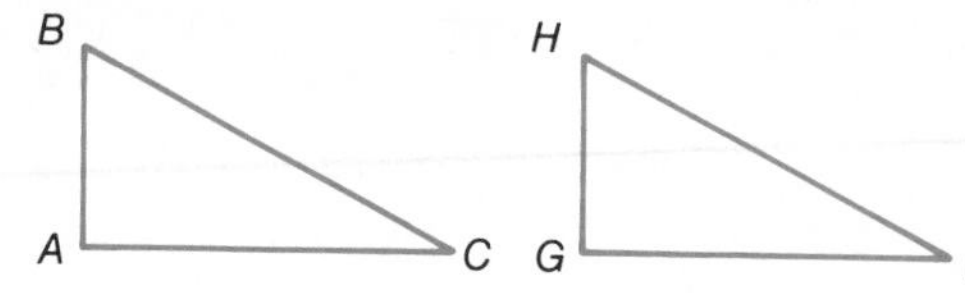

$\triangle ABC \cong \triangle GHI$. Complete.

5. $\overline{AC} \cong$ _?_ **6.** $\overline{BC} \cong$ _?_ **7.** $\angle B \cong$ _?_ **8.** $\angle C \cong$ _?_

9. $m\angle B = 60°$. What is $m\angle H$? **10.** $m\overline{AB} = 3$ cm. What is $m\overline{GH}$?

The figures in each pair are similar. Find the missing length.

11.

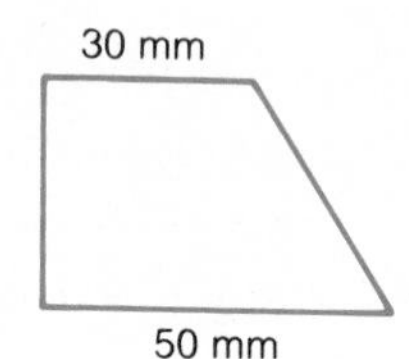

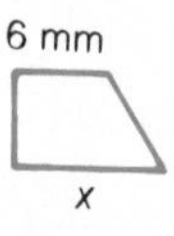

12.

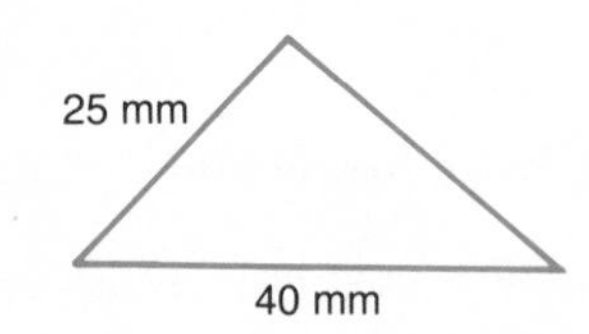

Problem Solving for Chapter 12 (pages 332–333)

1. x is a whole number. x is less than 10. x is not odd. x can be divided by 3 with no remainder. What number is x?

2. Roberta, Louise, and Milton are a psychiatrist, a pediatrician, and a cardiologist. Milton is married to the cardiologist. The psychiatrist is marrying an architect, and Roberta is the matron of honor for the upcoming wedding. What is each doctor's specialty?

Set 25 (pages 342–353)

Find each circumference. **1.** $d = 5.8$ m **2.** $d = 12.7$ cm **3.** $r = 21.1$ m

Find the area of each figure.

Square: **4.** $s = 7$ cm **5.** $s = 15$ mm **6.** $s = 2.6$ m

Parallelogram: **7.** $b = 15$ m, $h = 12$ m **8.** $b = 6.3$ cm, $h = 4.5$ cm **9.** $b = 8.8$ mm, $h = 2.1$ mm

Triangle: **10.** $b = 12$ mm, $h = 8$ mm **11.** $b = 15.3$ m, $h = 2.6$ m **12.** $b = 6.7$ cm, $h = 3.9$ cm

Trapezoid: **13.** $a = 17$ m, $b = 28$ m, $h = 12$ m **14.** $a = 11.3$ m, $b = 8.6$ m, $h = 2.4$ m

Circle (use 3.14 for π): **15.** $r = 25$ mm **16.** $r = 1.7$ cm **17.** $d = 18$ mm

Set 26 (pages 354–359, 362–365)

1.–6. Find the surface areas and the volumes.

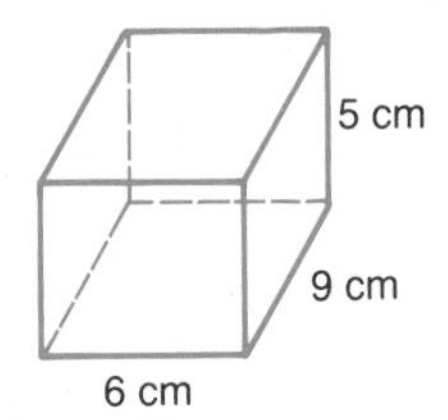

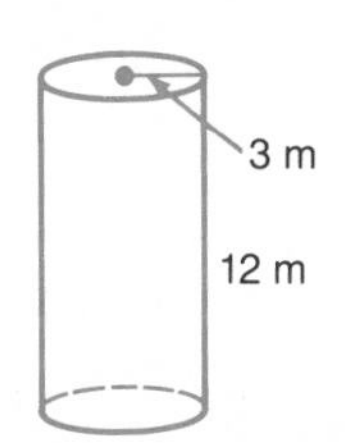

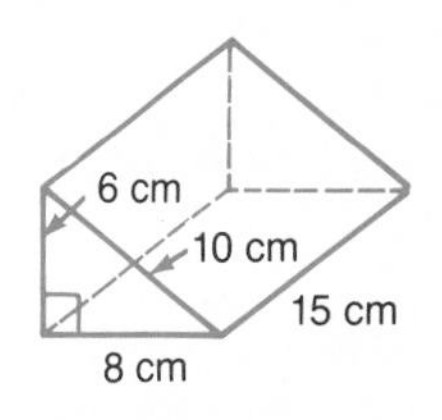

Find the volume of each prism.

	Rectangular Base		Height of Prism
	Length	Width	
7.	7 m	5 m	3 m
8.	12 cm	8 cm	6 cm
9.	3.8 mm	2.6 mm	4.9 mm

	Triangular Face		Height of Prism
	Base	Height	
10.	6 cm	3 cm	9 cm
11.	11 mm	6 mm	10 mm
12.	1.8 cm	7.1 cm	8.2 cm

Problem Solving for Chapter 13 (pages 360–361, 366–367)

1. The plane trip from California to Manila requires refueling at two stops. Most planes stop in Hawaii and then in Guam. The round trip between California and Manila is 13,400 miles. The distance between Hawaii and Guam is 3,000 miles, and the distance between Guam and Manila is 1,500 miles. What is the distance between California and Hawaii?

2. • If Gisela and Rafael buy their uncle a watch, they will spend $26.45.
   • If they spend $26.45, they cannot buy themselves Explorers Club jackets.
   • Gisela and Rafael can buy the jackets. Did they buy the watch?

Set 27 (pages 376–381, 384–387)

There are 5 green, 3 black, 8 blue, and 4 red pens. Pick a pen. Find each probability.

1. P(black) **2.** P(blue) **3.** P(yellow) **4.** P(red) **5.** P(not green)

Toss a penny and a nickel and roll a number cube. Find each probability.

6. P (heads, heads, 6) **7.** P (heads, tails, 2) **8.** P (tails, tails, not 4)

9. P (tails, tails, odd) **10.** P (heads, heads, 8) **11.** P (tails, heads, factor of 4)

The students in Mr. Forte's classes recorded the birthdate of those born during the first two weeks of each month. The dates were 12, 6, 2, 7, 11, 12, 7, 3, 5, 7, 6, 4, 6, 9, 7, 8, 1, 9, 8, 2, 5, 1, 3, 8. **12.** Make a frequency table.

13. How many were born on the sixth? during the first week? before the tenth?

14. What date occurred with the greatest frequency?

Set 28 (pages 388–393)

Find the range. **1.** 108, 213, 97, 275, 400 **2.** 3.7, 6.9, 4.3, 6.8, 5.6

3. 2.63, 7.08, 3.29, 9.72, 7.81 **4.** 456, 501, 493, 444, 452

Find the mean, median, and mode. **5.** 17, 20, 15, 23, 17, 10

6. 60, 50, 45, 75, 80, 95 **7.** 2.7, 5.8, 2.6, 2.0, 5.8, 2.7

8. 2, 3, 4, 2, 3, 4, 5, 6 **9.** 3.4, 9.1, 5.9, 2.1, 7.8, 5.3

10. Which company produces the most? the least?

11. How much more does Reed produce in one week than Johnson?

12. If Johnson and Smith merge, would they be producing the most?

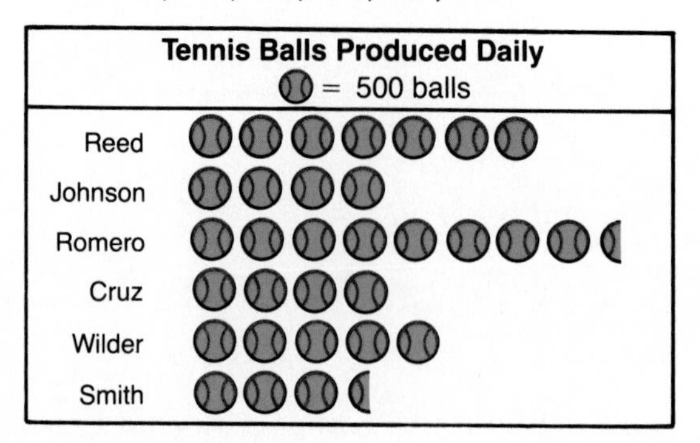

Problem Solving for Chapter 14 (pages 382–383, 398–399)

1. Carlos usually gets a perfect score on 3 out of every 5 mathematics exams. About how many perfect scores would Carlos get if he took 35 exams?

2. At 9 o'clock one night, 750 Americans were called. When asked if their television was on, 625 said "yes." If there were 80 million televisions in the country and the sample is representative, how many televisions were on (to the nearest million)?

Set 29 (pages 408–417)

Write < or >. **1.** $^-6 \bullet {}^-8$ **2.** $^-12 \bullet {}^+7$ **3.** $^-14°C \bullet {}^-2°C$ **4.** $^-45°C \bullet {}^-49°C$

Add. **5.** $^-4 + {}^-5$ **6.** $0 + {}^-18$ **7.** $^-15 + {}^-12$

8. $^+32 + {}^+2$ **9.** $^+7 + {}^-13$ **10.** $^-16 + {}^+12$ **11.** $^+17 + {}^-6$

12. $^-8 + {}^+8$ **13.** $^-6 + {}^+15$ **14.** $^-7 + {}^-12 + {}^-15$ **15.** $^+8 + {}^+9 + {}^+14$

Solve. **16.** $^-31 + {}^-39 = n$ **17.** $^-29 + n = {}^-68$ **18.** $n + {}^-18 = {}^-2$

Subtract. **19.** $^+8 - {}^+13$ **20.** $^-6 - {}^-8$ **21.** $^-15 - {}^-2$

22. $^+3 - {}^-2$ **23.** $^-17 - {}^+3$ **24.** $^+11 - {}^-5$ **25.** $^-400 - {}^-188$

Set 30 (pages 418–429)

Multiply. **1.** $5 \times {}^-3$ **2.** $^-5 \times {}^-3$ **3.** 12×8 **4.** $^-12 \times 8$

Divide. **5.** $^-35 \div 5$ **6.** $^-35 \div {}^-5$ **7.** $^-90 \div {}^-15$ **8.** $90 \div {}^-15$

9. $^-75 \div {}^-3$ **10.** $^-28 \div 7$ **11.** $56 \div {}^-8$ **12.** $^-323 \div {}^-17$ **13.** $444 \div {}^-12$

Solve. **14.** $^-14 \times {}^-3 = n$ **15.** $x - {}^-3 = {}^-7$

16. $\frac{x}{6} = {}^-9$ **17.** $\frac{y}{^-14} = 7$ **18.** $^-3y = {}^-57$

19. $^-8 \times y = 56$ **20.** $4n + {}^-8 = 40$ **21.** $({}^-300 \div 15) \div {}^-2 = n$

22. $\left(\frac{3}{7}\right)\left(\frac{14}{9}\right) = n$ **23.** $0.9 \div 0.3 = n$ **24.** $\left(\frac{^-1}{3}\right)^3 = n$

Solve and graph the solutions. **25.** $x + 8 = {}^-3$ **26.** $3y > {}^-9$

Graph each equation. **27.** $y = 2x + 1$ **28.** $y = 3x$ **29.** $y = \frac{x}{3} - 1$ **30.** $y = 0(x) + 5$

Problem Solving for Chapter 15 (pages 430–431)

Amie bicycles to school every weekday. She leaves at 8:00 A.M. and rides at the rate of 240 m/min. Wilfredo, Amie's brother, also rides along the same route. He leaves at 8:30 A.M. and rides at the rate of 600 m/min.

1. What time do they meet?
2. If they meet at school, how far is the school from their house?
3. If the school were 7,300m from their house, who would arrive at school first?

TABLE OF MEASURES

Metric		United States Customary	
Length			
1 millimeter (mm)	= 0.001 m	1 foot (ft)	= 12 inches (in.)
1 centimeter (cm)	= 0.01 m	1 yard (yd)	= 3 feet; 36 in.
1 decimeter (dm)	= 0.1 m	1 mile (mi)	= 1,760 yd; 5,280 ft
1 meter (m)	= 1 m		
1 dekameter (dam)	= 10 m		
1 hectometer (hm)	= 100 m		
1 kilometer (km)	= 1,000 m		
Area			
1 square centimeter (cm^2)	= 100 square millimeters (mm^2)	1 square foot (ft^2)	= 144 square inches ($in.^2$)
1 square meter (m^2)	= 10,000 cm^2	1 square yard (yd^2)	= 9 ft^2
Volume			
1 cubic centimeter (cm^3)	= 1,000 cubic millimeters (mm^3)	1 cubic foot (ft^3)	= 1,728 cubic inches ($in.^3$)
1 cubic meter (m^3)	= 1,000,000 cm^3	1 cubic yard (yd^3)	= 27 ft^3
Capacity			
1 milliliter (mL)	= 0.001 L	1 fluid ounce (fl. oz)	= 2 tablespoons (tbsp)
1 centiliter (cL)	= 0.01 L	1 cup (c)	= 8 fl. oz
1 deciliter (dL)	= 0.1 L	1 pint (pt)	= 2 c
1 liter (L)	= 1 L	1 quart (qt)	= 2 pt
1 dekaliter (daL)	= 10 L	1 gallon (gal)	= 4 qt
1 hectoliter (hL)	= 100 L		
1 kiloliter (kL)	= 1,000 L		
1 metric cup (c)	= 250 mL		
Mass/Weight			
1 milligram (mg)	= 0.001 g	1 pound (lb)	= 16 ounces (oz)
1 centigram (cg)	= 0.01 g	1 ton (T)	= 2,000 lb
1 decigram (dg)	= 0.1 g		
1 gram (g)	= 1 g		
1 dekagram (dag)	= 10 g		
1 hectogram (hg)	= 100 g		
1 kilogram (kg)	= 1,000 g		
1 metric ton (t)	= 1,000 kg		

Time

1 minute (min)	= 60 seconds (s)
1 hour (h)	= 60 min
1 day (d)	= 24 h
1 week (wk)	= 7 d
1 month (mo)	= 28–31 d
1 year (yr)	= 12 mo
1 century (cen)	= 100 yr

TABLE OF SYMBOLS

$+$ plus

$-$ minus

$\times$ times

$\div$ divided by

$=$ equals or is equal to

$\neq$ is not equal to

$>$ is greater than

$<$ is less than

$\geq$ is greater than or equal to

$\leq$ is less than or equal to

$\approx$ is approximately equal to

$\sim$ is similar to

$\cong$ is congruent to

$\ldots$ pattern continues without end (and so on)

8.5 decimal point: eight and five-tenths

$0.\overline{24}$ repeating decimal; 0.242424. . .

35% percent; thirty-five percent

3:2 ratio; three to two

6^2 six to the second power or six squared

$\sqrt{36}$ square root; square root of thirty-six

$^{+}2$ positive two

$^{-}2$ negative two

$(^{-}1, 2)$ ordered pair; $(x = {}^{-}1, y = 2)$

$|{}^{-}4|$ absolute value; absolute value of negative four

∟ right angle

$\angle ABC$ angle ABC

$^\circ$ degree (angle or temperature)

$.A$ point A

$\overline{AB}$ line segment with endpoints A and B

$\overrightarrow{AB}$ ray AB with endpoint A

$\overleftrightarrow{AB}$ line through points A and B

$\parallel$ is parallel to

$\perp$ is perpendicular to

$\triangle ABC$ triangle ABC

π pi (approximately 3.14 or $\frac{22}{7}$)

$P(E)$ probability of event E

GLOSSARY

Absolute value The distance from a point on the number line to 0. (p. 409)
Example: $|^-2| = 2$ means the absolute value of $^-2$ is 2.

Acute angle An angle whose measure is greater than 0° and less than 90°. (p. 306)

Acute triangle A triangle with three acute angles. (p. 320)

Addition (+) An operation on two numbers, called addends, that results in a sum. (p. 12)

Adjacent angles Two angles with a common vertex, a common ray, and no common interior points. (p. 314)
Example: $\angle ABC$ and $\angle CBD$ are adjacent angles.

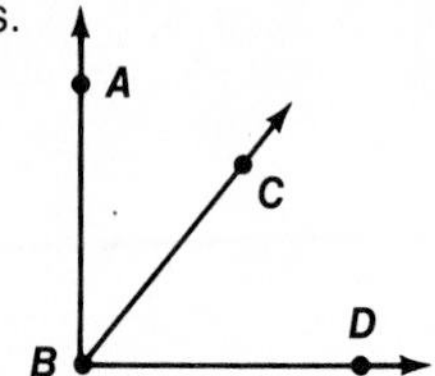

Angle Two rays with the same endpoint. The endpoint is called the vertex of the angle. (p. 304)

Arc Part of the circumference of a circle. (p. 308)

Area The number of square units needed to cover a surface. (p. 346)
Examples: Some formulas to find area are:

rectangle	$A = lw$
parallelogram	$A = bh$
square	$A = s^2$
triangle	$A = \frac{1}{2}bh$
trapezoid	$A = \frac{1}{2}h(a + b)$
circle	$A = \pi r^2$

Associative property of addition The sum is always the same when the addends are grouped differently. (p. 12)
Examples: For any numbers *a*, *b*, and *c*:
$(a + b) + c = a + (b + c)$;
$(3 + 2) + 7 = 3 + (2 + 7)$.

Associative property of multiplication The product is always the same when the factors are grouped differently. (p. 28)
Examples: For any numbers *a*, *b*, and *c*:
$(a \times b) \times c = a \times (b \times c)$;
$(5 \times 2) \times 3 = 5 \times (2 \times 3)$.

Bar graph A graph with bars (rectangles) of different heights to show and compare data. (p. 394)

Between A number is between two numbers *a* and *b* if it is greater than *a* and less than *b*. (p. 219)

Binary system A numeration system whose base is two. (p. 23)
Example: $11010_{two} = 26$

Bisect To divide into two congruent parts. (p. 312)

Broken-line graph A graph used to show how data changes over a period of time. A double broken-line graph is used for comparisons. (p. 396)

Capacity The amount a container will hold when filled. (p. 280)

Celsius (C) A metric scale for measuring temperature, according to which the freezing point of water is 0°C and the boiling point of water is 100°C. (p. 410)

Central angle An angle whose vertex is at the center of a circle. (p. 308)

Chord A line segment with endpoints on a circle. (p. 308)

Circle A closed curve with all points an equal distance from a point inside the circle, called the center. (p. 308)

Circle graph A graph in the shape of a circle that shows percents or parts of a whole. (p. 264)

Circumference The distance around a circle; $C = \pi d$ or $C = 2\pi r$. (p. 344)

Commutative property of addition Two numbers can be added in either order. The sums are the same. (p. 12)
Examples: For any numbers a and b:
$a + b = b + a$; $3 + 4 = 4 + 3$.

Commutative property of multiplication Two numbers can be multiplied in either order. The products are the same. (p. 28)
Examples: For any numbers a and b:
$a \times b = b \times a$; $3 \times 4 = 4 \times 3$.

Complementary angles Two angles whose sum is 90°. (p. 314)

Complex fraction A fraction such as $\frac{\frac{1}{2}}{\frac{3}{4}}$ is called a complex fraction. (p. 209)

Composite number A whole number greater than 1 that has more than two factors. (p. 144)
Example: 9 is a composite number since its factors are 1, 3, 9.

Cone A solid with a circular base and one vertex. (p. 330)

Congruent angles Two angles that have the same measure. (p. 310)

Congruent line segments Two line segments that have the same length. (p. 310)

Congruent polygons Two figures are congruent if their corresponding angles and sides are congruent. (p. 324)

Coordinate system A graph with a horizontal number line (x axis) and a vertical number line (y axis) that are perpendicular to each other. The point of intersection is called the origin and labeled 0 on the graph. An ordered pair, (x, y), is used to name a point on a coordinate system. (p. 426)

Cube A rectangular solid with six congruent square faces. (p. 356)

Customary measurement system A measurement system that uses inches, feet, yards, and miles as units of length; cups, pints, quarts, and gallons as units of liquid capacity; ounces, pounds, and tons as units of weight; and degrees Fahrenheit as units of temperature. (p. 286)

Cylinder A solid with two bases that are congruent circles. (p. 330)

Decimal A number that uses place value and a decimal point to show tenths, hundredths, thousandths, and so on. (p. 86)
Example: 2.457 is read as two and four hundred fifty-seven thousandths.

Degree (°) A standard unit for measuring angles. (p. 306)

Density property Between any two rational numbers, there is at least one other rational number. (p. 220)

Diagonal A line segment that joins the vertices of a polygon but is not a side. (p. 319)

Diameter A line segment through the center of a circle with endpoints on the circle. (p. 308)

Distributive property of multiplication over addition The product of a number and the sum of two numbers equals the sum of the two products. (p. 28)
Examples: For any numbers a, b, and c:
$a \times (b + c) = (a \times b) + (a \times c)$;
$2 \times (3 + 4) = (2 \times 3) + (2 \times 4)$.

Divisible When one number is divided by another and the remainder is 0, the first number is divisible by the second number. (p. 140)

Division ($\overline{)}$ or ÷) An operation on two numbers that results in a quotient and a remainder. (p. 40)

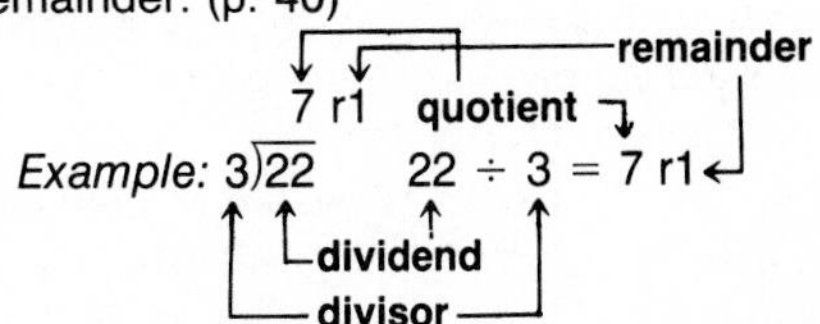

Endpoint A point at the end of a line segment or a ray. (p. 304)

Equation A number sentence with an equal sign (=). (p. 8)
Examples: $3 + 4 = 7$, $n + 5 = 12$

Equilateral triangle A triangle with three congruent sides. Each angle measures 60°. (p. 320)

Equivalent fractions Fractions that name the same number. (p. 164)

Evaluate To evaluate an expression, substitute a number for the variable. (p. 60)
Example: When $a = 3$ and $b = 2$, then $a^2b = (3)^2(2) = 18$.

Even number A whole number that is a multiple of 2. (p. 140)

Expanded form A representation of a number as a sum of powers of 10. (p. 2)

Exponent A number that tells how many times the base is to be used as a factor. (p. 8)
Example: $2^3 = 2 \times 2 \times 2$ or 8 (3 = **exponent**, 2 = **base**)

Expression A mathematical phrase. (p. 60)
Example: $y - 6$, 6 less than a number

Face A flat surface of a solid. (p. 330)

Factor A factor of a number is a whole number that divides it exactly, leaving a remainder of zero. (p. 144)
Example: 1, 2, 5, and 10 are factors of 10.

Fahrenheit (F) A customary scale for measuring temperature, according to which the freezing point of water is 32°F and the boiling point of water is 212°F.

Flow chart A diagram that shows the steps used from start to end. (p. 189)

Fraction The quotient of two whole numbers; $a \div b = \frac{a}{b}$. In the fraction $\frac{a}{b}$, a is called the numerator and b is called the denominator. (p. 162)

Frequency The number of times a score appears in a list of data. (p. 386)

Function A rule that assigns one number for y when a number for x is chosen. (p. 79)

Graph of an equation All the points whose coordinates are ordered pairs satisfying the equation. (p. 428)

Greatest common factor (GCF) The largest factor by which you can divide two or more numbers. (p.148)
Example: The GCF of 8 and 12 is 4.

Heptagon A polygon with seven sides. (p. 318)

Hexagon A polygon with six sides. (p. 318)

Independent events If two events A and B are independent, then the probability that both will happen is $P(A) \times P(B)$. (p. 384)

Inequality A number sentence that uses a symbol such as $<$, $>$ or $\neq$. (p. 76)
Examples: $n + 7 > 9$, $11 < 2n - 3$, $n \neq 2$.

Integers The whole numbers and their opposites.
$\ldots, {}^-3, {}^-2, {}^-1, 0, {}^+1, {}^+2, {}^+3, \ldots$
${}^-3$ is a negative integer. ${}^+3$ or 3 is a positive integer. (p. 408)

Interest (I) The money paid on the principal (p) at a fixed rate of interest (r) for a period of time (t). The formula to compute simple interest is $I = p \times r \times t$. (p. 262)

Inverse operations Operations that undo each other. Addition and subtraction as well as multiplication and division are inverse operations. (p. 12)
Examples: $38 - 15 = 23$ and $23 + 15 = 38$
$24 \div 3 = 8$ and $8 \times 3 = 24$

Isosceles triangle A triangle with at least two congruent sides. (p. 320)

Latitude Latitude lines measure the number of degrees north or south of the equator. (p. 297)

Least common denominator (LCD) The least common multiple of the denominators of two or more fractions. (p. 168)

Least common multiple (LCM) The smallest nonzero multiple that two or more numbers have in common. (p. 150)
Example: The LCM of 4 and 6 is 12.

Line A straight path extending in both directions with no endpoints. (p. 304)

Line segment Part of a line with two endpoints. (p. 304)

Longitude Longitude lines measure the number of degrees east or west of the prime meridian (the longitude line passing through Greenwich, England). (p. 297)

Mean (average) The mean of a group of numbers is found by dividing the sum of the numbers by the number of addends. (p. 388)
Example: The mean of 3, 5, 6, 8, and 13 is 7 since $3 + 5 + 6 + 8 + 13 = 35$ and $35 \div 5 = 7$.

Median The middle number of a group of numbers, or the average of the two middle numbers, when they are arranged in order. (p. 390)
Examples: 4 is the median of 1, 3, 4, 6, 7.
5.5 is the median of 2, 3, 5, 6, 8, 9.

Metric system A measurement system that uses centimeters, meters, and kilometers as units of length; milliliters and liters as units of liquid capacity; grams and kilograms as units of mass; and degrees Celsius as units of temperature. (p. 276)

Midpoint A point that divides a line segment into two congruent parts. (p. 312)

Multiplication ($\times$) An operation on two numbers, called factors, that results in a product. (p. 28)

Negative integer A number less than zero. (p. 408)

Number line A line with equally spaced points named by numbers. (p. 76)

Obtuse angle An angle whose measure is greater than 90° and less than 180°. (p. 306)

Obtuse triangle A triangle with one obtuse angle. (p. 320)

Octagon A polygon with eight sides. (p. 318)

Odd number A whole number that is not a multiple of two. (p. 140)

Opposite numbers Two numbers whose points on the number line are the same distance from 0, but in opposite directions. (p. 408)
Examples: 2 and $^{-}2$ are opposites.
$^{-}\frac{2}{3}$ and $\frac{2}{3}$ are opposites.

Ordered pair A pair of numbers, (x, y), arranged in order so that x is first and y is second. (p. 426)

Order of operations When there is more than one operation and parentheses are used, first do what is inside the parentheses. Next, multiply or divide from left to right. Then add or subtract from left to right. (p. 50)

Origin The origin of the number line is zero. (p. 426)

Outcome Each possible result in a probability experiment. (p. 376)

Parallel lines Lines in the same plane that do not intersect. Parallel lines have no points in common. (p. 316)

Parallelogram A quadrilateral with opposite sides parallel and congruent. (p. 322)

Pentagon A polygon with five sides. (p. 318)

Percent (%) Percent means per hundred. $p\% = \frac{p}{100}$. (p. 244)

Perimeter The sum of the lengths of the sides of a polygon. (p. 342)
Examples: Some ways to find perimeter are:

triangle	$P = a + b + c$
quadrilateral	$P = a + b + c + d$
square	$P = 4s$
rectangle	$P = 2l + 2w$

Perpendicular lines Two lines that intersect to form right angles. (p. 316)

Pi (π) The number that is the ratio of the circumference of any circle to the length of a diameter of that circle. Approximations for π are 3.14 and $\frac{22}{7}$. (p. 344)

Pictograph A visual representation used to make comparisons. A key always appears on a pictograph or picture graph showing how many each object represents. (p. 392)

Plane A flat surface that extends indefinitely in all directions. (p. 304)

Polygon A closed plane figure formed by three or more line segments joined at the endpoints. (p. 318)

Polyhedron A solid whose faces are polygons. (p. 330)

Positive integer A number greater than zero. Zero is neither positive nor negative. (p. 408)

Power of a number A number found by multiplying the number by itself one or more times. (p. 8)
Example: 27 is a power of 3 because $27 = 3 \times 3 \times 3$.

Prime factorization Any composite number can be factored as a product of primes. This product is called the prime factorization of that number. (p. 146)

Prime number A whole number greater than 1 that has only two factors, 1 and itself. (p. 144)
Examples: 2, 3, 5, 7, 11, 13, 17, 19 are all prime numbers.

Probability A number from 0 to 1 that tells how likely it is that an event will take place. (p. 376)

Property of one The product of any number and 1 is that number. (p. 28)
Examples: $a \times 1 = a$; $5 \times 1 = 5$

Proportion An equality of two ratios. The terms in a proportion are called the means and extremes. If $\frac{a}{b} = \frac{c}{d}$ then $a \times d = b \times c$. (p. 226)
Example: $\frac{5}{8} = \frac{15}{24}$ since $5 \times 24 = 8 \times 15$.

Pyramid A solid whose base is a polygon and three or more triangular faces that share a common vertex. (p. 330)

Quadrilateral A polygon with four sides. (p. 318)

Quotient The result of a division problem. (p. 40)

Radius (*pl.* radii) A line segment with one endpoint at the center of a circle and the other endpoint on the circle. All radii of a circle are equal. (p. 308)

Ratio A comparison of two numbers. (p. 224)
Example: The ratio three to two can be written as 3 to 2, 3:2, or $\frac{3}{2}$.

Rational number Any number that can be expressed as a fraction, $\frac{a}{b}$, where a and b are integers and $b \neq 0$. (p. 424)

Ray A part of a line that has one endpoint and extends on and on in only one direction. (p. 304)

Reciprocals Two numbers whose product is 1. (p. 202)
Examples: $\frac{2}{5}$ and $\frac{5}{2}$ are reciprocals.
4 and $\frac{1}{4}$ are reciprocals.

Rectangle A parallelogram with four right angles. (p. 322)

Reflection (flip) A motion in which a geometric figure is flipped about a line. (p. 326)

Regular polygon A polygon with all sides congruent and all angles congruent. (p. 318)

Remainder The number left over in a division problem. (p. 40)
Example: $17 \div 3$ has a quotient of 5 and a remainder of 2.

Repeating decimal A decimal in which a digit or group of digits repeats indefinitely. A bar over the digit or digits shows repetition. (p. 212)
Examples: $\frac{1}{3} = 0.333\ldots$, or $0.\overline{3}$
$\frac{4}{11} = 0.3636\ldots$, or $0.\overline{36}$

Rhombus A parallelogram with four congruent sides. (p. 322)

Right angle An angle that measures 90°. (p. 306)

Right triangle A triangle with one right angle. (p. 320)

Rotation (turn) A motion in which a geometric figure is turned about a fixed point. (p. 433)

Rounding To round a number, look at the first digit to the right of the place to which you are rounding. If the digit is less than 5, round down. If the digit is 5 or greater, round up. (p. 6)

Sample space A systematic listing of all the possible outcomes in a given situation. (p. 380)

Scale drawing A drawing that is the same shape as an actual object, but not the same size. The scale gives the ratio of the size in the drawing to the size of the actual object. (p. 232)

Scalene triangle A triangle with three unequal sides. (p. 320)

Scientific notation Writing a number as the product of two factors. The first factor is between 1 and 10. The second factor is a power of 10. (p. 128)
Examples: $524{,}000 = 5.24 \times 10^5$
$0.0007 = 7.0 \times 10^{-4}$

Similar polygons Polygons that have the same shape. Corresponding sides of similar polygons are in proportion. Corresponding angles are congruent. (p. 328)

Solution of an equation The value (or values) of a variable that make an equation a true statement. (p. 62)
Example:
$$3x + 2 = 14$$
$$3x + 2 - 2 = 14 - 2$$
$$3x = 12$$
$$\frac{3x}{3} = \frac{12}{3}$$
$$x = 4 \quad \textit{Solution: } x = 4$$

Solution of an inequality All values of the variable that make an inequality a true statement. (p. 76)
Example:
$$2x - 5 > 7$$
$$2x - 5 + 5 > 7 + 5$$
$$2x > 12$$
$$\frac{2x}{2} > \frac{12}{2}$$
$$x > 6 \quad \textit{Solution: } x > 6$$

Sphere A solid with all points an equal distance from the center. (p. 330)

Square A rectangle with 4 congruent sides. (p. 322)

Square root One of the two equal factors of a number. (p. 371)
Example: $\sqrt{25} = 5$ because $5^2 = 25$.

Straight angle An angle that measures 180°. (p. 314)

Subtraction (−) An operation on two numbers that results in a difference. (p. 12)
Example:
$$\begin{array}{r l} 35 & \longleftarrow \text{minuend} \\ \underline{-17} & \longleftarrow \text{subtrahend} \\ 18 & \longleftarrow \text{difference} \end{array}$$

Supplementary angles Two angles whose sum is 180°. (p. 314)

Surface area The sum of the areas of all the surfaces of a solid. (p. 354)

Symmetry (line) A figure has line symmetry if it can be folded about a line so that the two halves of the figure are congruent. The fold line is called the line of symmetry. (p. 326)

Table of values A table of values is used to graph an equation. Each (x, y) ordered pair is plotted and the points are connected with a straightedge. (p. 428)

Example: $y = 3x - 1$

Table of Values

x	$3x - 1$	y
$^-1$	$3(^-1) - 1$	$^-4$
1	$3(1) - 1$	2
3	$3(3) - 1$	8

Terminating decimal A decimal in which the division operation results in a remainder of zero. (p. 210)

Examples: $\frac{1}{4} = 0.25$; $\frac{7}{16} = 0.4375$

Translation (slide) A motion in which each point of a geometric figure is moved in the same direction and by the same distance. (p.433)

Transversal A line that intersects two or more parallel lines at a different point on each line. (p. 316)

Example: $\angle 1 \cong \angle 3$, $\angle 2 \cong \angle 4$, $\angle 5 \cong \angle 7$, and $\angle 6 \cong \angle 8$ (vertical angles)

$\angle 3 \cong \angle 5$, $\angle 4 \cong \angle 6$ (alternate interior angles)

$\angle 1 \cong \angle 5$, $\angle 4 \cong \angle 8$, $2 \cong \angle 6$, and $\angle 3 \cong \angle 7$ (corresponding angles)

transversal

Trapezoid A quadrilateral with one pair of parallel sides. These sides are called the upper and lower bases. (p. 322)

Tree diagram A diagram used to find the total number of outcomes in a probability experiment. (p. 380)

Triangle A polygon with three sides. (p. 318)

Unit price The ratio of the total cost to the number of units. (p. 234)

Variable A symbol, usually a letter, that stands for an unknown quantity. (p. 60)

Venn diagram A useful diagram showing relationships. (p. 155)

Example: Some numbers divisible by 3 are odd numbers.

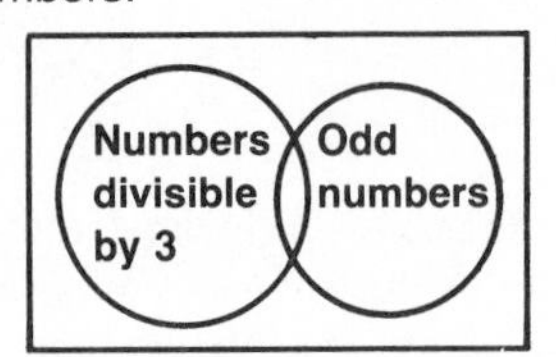

Vertex (*pl.* vertices) The point at which two rays of an angle, two sides of a polygon, or three or more edges of a solid meet. (p. 304)

Vertical angles Angles that are formed by two intersecting lines. (p. 314)

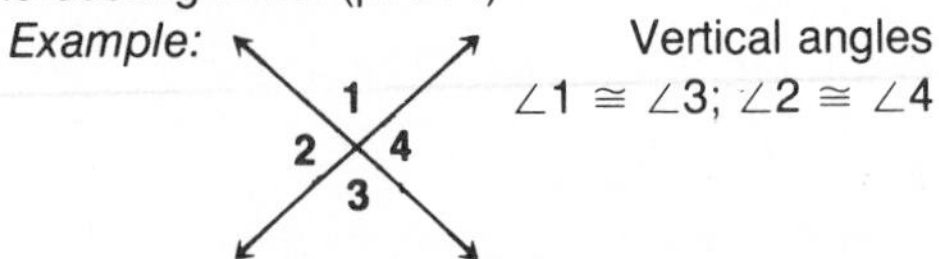

Volume The number of cubic units needed to fill a solid. (p. 356)

Examples: Some formulas to find volume are:

rectangular prism	$V = lwh$
cube	$V = e^3$
cylinder	$V = \pi r^2 h$
cone	$V = \frac{1}{3} Bh$
rectangular pyramid	$V = \frac{1}{3} lwh$

Whole number Any one of the numbers 0, 1, 2, 3, 4, ... There is no largest whole number. The smallest whole number is zero. (p. 4)

Zero property for addition and subtraction For any number n, $n + 0 = n$ and $n - 0 = n$. Zero is the additive identity for addition. (p. 12)

Zero property for multiplication For any number n, $n \times 0 = 0$. When one of the factors in a multiplication problem is zero, then the product is always zero. (p. 28)

INDEX

Absolute value, 409, 458
Acute angles, 306–307, 458
Acute triangles, 320–321, 458
Addends, 12
Addition, 458
  column, 12
  of decimals, 94–95
  of dollars and cents, 15
  estimation in, 14–15, 94–95, 118–119
  of fractions, 172–173
  of integers, 412–415
  of measurements, 281, 283, 286–287, 289, 291, 293
  of mixed numbers, 174–175
  properties, 12–13
  with regrouping, 14–15, 94–95
  and subtraction, 12–13
  of three or more addends, 14–15
  using, to solve equations, 13, 15, 62–63, 95, 111, 127, 149
  zero in, 12, 70
Additive inverses, 414–415
Adjacent angles, 314–315, 458
Altitude, 348
Ancient systems of numeration, 21
AND rule of logic, 159, 240–241, 300
Angles, 304–311, 314–317, 458
Arcs of a circle, 308–309, 458
Area, 458
  of circles, 352–353
  customary units of, 362–363
  metric units of, 346
  of parallelograms, 348–349, 364
  of rectangles, 346–347
  of squares, 346–347
  of trapezoids, 350–351
  of triangles, 348–349, 364
Associative properties, 458
  of addition, 12–13, 70–71, 219
  of multiplication, 28–29, 70–71, 219
Averages, 388–389. *See also* Mean

Bar graphs, 200–201, 394–395, 458
Base
  of parallelograms, 348
  of a power, 8
  of prisms, 330
  of pyramids, 330
  of trapezoids, 350–351
  of triangles, 348
BASIC, 137
Between, 219–220
Binary System, 23, 82, 240, 458
Bisect, 312–313, 458
Bits, 82, 159, 240–241, 300, 338–339, 372
Broken-line graphs, 396–397, 458
Budgets, 200–201, 264–265, 401
Bytes, 82–83, 221, 338–339, 372

Calculators
  addition with, 24–25, 190
  basics, 24–25
  buttons on, 24–25, 272
  decimals with, 106
  discount, 272–273
  dividing with, 24–25, 56–57, 190
  estimating with, 56–57
  multiplying with, 24–25
  order of operations, 106
  percent with, 272–273
  sales tax, 272–273
  subtraction with, 24–25, 190
Capacity, 458
  customary units of, 288–289
  estimating, 281, 289
  metric units of, 280–281
Celsius degrees, 285, 410–411, 458
Centigrams, 282
Centiliters, 280
Centimeters, 276
Central angles, 308–309, 458
Checking accounts, 103, 133
Choices, 55
Chords of a circle, 308–309, 458
Circle graphs, 264–265, 401, 459
Circles, 308–309, 458
  arcs of, 308–309
  area of, 352–353
  chords of, 308–309
  circumference of, 344–345
  diameters of, 308–309
  radii of, 308–309
  semicircles, 345
Circumference of a circle, 344–345, 459
Clock arithmetic, 157–158
COBOL, 137
Common factors, 148
Common multiples, 150
Commutative properties, 459
  of addition, 12–13, 70–71, 219
  of multiplication, 28–29, 70–71, 219
Comparing. *See* Ordering
Compass, 308–313, 319, 335
Complementary angles, 314–315, 459
Complex fractions, 209, 459
Composite numbers, 144–145, 459
Computers
  address, 221, 339, 437–438
  assembler, 136, 338–339
  basics, 82–83
  binary numbers, 82, 240
  bits, 82, 159, 240–241, 300, 338–339, 372
  bytes, 82–83, 221, 338–339, 372
  cathode-ray tube (CRT), 82–83, 338–339
  central processing unit (CPU), 438
  compiler, 136
  computer word, 339, 437
  control, 221, 300, 372, 437–438
  cycle time, 159
  data, 82, 137, 221, 437–438
  disks, 82, 372–373, 438
  errors, 372–373
  hardware, 82, 404–405
  input, 82, 300, 404–405, 438
  instructions, 82, 136, 221, 300, 338, 437–438
  interpreter, 136
  keyboard, 82
  machine language, 221
  operation codes, 221, 438
  output, 82, 300, 404–405, 438
  parity, 372
  printer, 82
  programmer, 82
  programming languages, 136–137
  programs, 82, 136, 338–339, 438
  punched cards, 82
  rules of logic, 159, 240–241, 300
  software, 82, 136, 338, 404–405
  storage, 83, 159, 437–438
  switches, 240–241
  systems analyst, 404–405
  systems flowchart, 404, 438
  subroutines, 437
  tapes, 82
  timing, 159, 404, 437–438
Cones, 330–331, 459
Congruence, 310–311, 324–325, 459
Constructions, 309–313, 335

Consumer mathematics
  budgets, 200–201, 264–265, 401
  checking accounts, 103, 133
  compound interest, 269
  discount and sales tax, 260–261, 272–273
  rate tables, 294–295
  recipes, 217
  simple interest, 262–263
  stock market, 187
  unit pricing, 234–235
Coordinate plane, 426–427, 459
Corresponding angles, 316–317
Cross products, 226–231
Cubes, 356, 459
Cubic units
  customary, 362–363
  metric, 280, 356
Cups, 280, 288
Customary units of measurement, 286–291, 459
Cylinders, 330–331, 354–355, 459

Data, organizing, 386–387
Decigrams, 282
Deciliters, 280
Decimals, 459
  addition of, 94–95
  division of, 120–127
  equivalent, 90–91
  estimation in, 94–95, 98–99
  and fractions, 210–211
  in the metric system, 276–283
  multiplication of, 110–117
  ordering, 90–91
  for percents, 248–249
  place value, 88–89
  reading, 86–89
  repeating, 212–213
  rounding, 92–95, 98–99, 126–127
  in scientific notation, 128–129, 436
  subtraction of, 98–99
  terminating, 210–211
  writing, 86–89
Decimeters, 276
Degrees
  Celsius, 410–411, 458
  Fahrenheit, 460
  for measuring angles, 306–307
Dekagrams, 282
Dekaliters, 280
Dekameters, 276
Denominators, 162, 168
Density, property of, 220, 424, 459
Diagonals of a polygon, 319, 459
Diameters of a circle, 308–309, 459
Differences, 12, 16–17
Digits, 2
Discount, 260–261, 272–273
Disks, 82, 372–373, 438

Distributive property, 28–30, 70–71, 219, 459
Dividends, 40
Divisibility rules, 140–143
Division, 459
  of decimals, 120–127
  of decimals by whole numbers, 120–121
  of dollars and cents, 40–41
  estimation in, 42–43, 56
  to find averages, 388–389
  of fractions, 204–209
  of integers, 420–421
  interpreting remainders, 176–177
  of measurements, 281, 283, 290
  and multiplication, 28–29
  by one-digit divisors, 40–41, 115, 169
  by tens, hundreds, thousands, 125
  by three-digit divisors, 46–47, 115, 169
  by two-digit divisors, 44–45, 115, 169
  using, to solve equations, 29, 43, 45, 47, 66–67, 121, 123, 127, 149
  of whole numbers by fractions, 204–205
Divisors, 40
Dollars and cents. *See* Money
Drawing
  making a, 360–361
  scale, 232–233
  See *also* Constructions

Edges, 280, 356
Endpoints, 304–305, 460
Enrichment, 23, 55, 81, 105, 135, 157–158, 189, 219, 239, 271, 299, 337, 371, 403, 435–436
Equal ratios, 224–225
Equations, 8, 460
  graphing, 428–429
  with integers, 422–423
  and problem solving, 63, 67, 74–75
  proportions, 226, 231
  solving, by addition or subtraction, 62–63, 81, 111, 127, 149
  solving, by multiplication or division, 66–67, 127, 149
  solving, by substitution, 81
  writing, 63
Equilateral triangles, 320–321, 460
Equivalent decimals, 90–91
Equivalent fractions, 164–165, 460
Estimating
  differences, 16–17, 98–101
  measurements, 277, 281, 283, 287, 289, 290–291
  products, 34–35, 214–215
  quotients, 42–43, 214–215
  sums, 14–15, 94–95, 100–101
Evaluating expressions, 60–61, 64–65, 147, 460
Even numbers, 140, 460
Events, 376–377, 384–385
Expanded form, 2–3, 95, 460
Exponents, 8–9, 117, 435–436, 460
Expressions, 460
  addition and subtraction, 60–61
  multiplication and division, 64–65

Faces, 330–331, 354–355, 460
Factors, 8, 144–145, 460
  greatest common (GCF), 148–149
  prime, 144–145
Factor trees, 146–147
Fahrenheit degrees, 460
Feet, 286
Flips, 326, 433
Flowcharts, 189, 404, 438, 460
Fluid ounces, 288
Formulas
  areas of circles, 352–353, 364
  area of parallelograms, 348–349, 364
  area of rectangles, 346–347, 364
  area of squares, 346–347, 364, 371
  area of trapezoids, 350–351, 364
  area of triangles, 348–349, 364
  circumference of circles, 344–345, 364
  distance, 72–73
  interest, compound, 269
  interest, simple, 262–263
  list of, 364
  perimeter of rectangles, 342–343, 364
  perimeter of squares, 342–343, 364
  surface area, 354–355
  volume of cylinders, 358–359, 364
  volume of prisms, 356–357, 364
FORTRAN, 137
Fractions, 460
  addition of, 172–175
  comparing, 168–169
  complex, 209
  cross products, 165
  and decimals, 165, 210–211
  denominators, 162
  division of, 204–209
  equal to one, 164
  equal to whole numbers, 170–171
  equivalent, 164–165
  least common denominator (LCD), 168–169
  lowest terms, 166–167
  and mixed numbers, 170–171, 174–175

Fractions, *continued*
multiplication of, 194–199
numerators, 162
ordering, 168–169
and percents, 244–245, 250–251
proper, 162–163
ratios as, 224–225
reciprocals, 202–203
as repeating or terminating decimals, 210–213
subtraction of, 178–183
Frequency distribution, 386–387, 460
Frequency table, 386–387, 403
Functions, 79, 239, 460

Gallons, 288
Geometry
angles, 304–307, 314–315, 320–321
arcs of circles, 308–309
chords of circles, 308–309
circles, 308–309, 344–345, 352–353
cones, 330–331
congruence, 310, 324–325, 433
cylinders, 330–331, 354–355
diagonals of polygons, 319
heptagons, 318–319
hexagons, 318–319
lines, 304–305
line segments, 304–305
octagons, 318–319
parallel lines, 316–317
parallelograms, 322–323, 348–349
pentagons, 318–319
perimeter, 342–343
perpendicular lines, 316–317
planes, 304–305
points, 304–305, 433
polygons, 318–319
prisms, 330–331, 356–357
pyramids, 330–331
quadrilaterals, 318–319, 322–323
rays, 304–305
rectangles, 322–323, 346–347
rectangular pyramids, 330–331
reflections, 326–327
regular polygons, 318–319
rhombuses, 322–323
rotations, 433
semicircles, 345
similar polygons, 328–329
solid figures, 330–331
spheres, 330–331
squares, 322–323, 346–347
symmetry, 326–327
translations, 433
transversals, 316–317
trapezoids, 322–323
triangles, 318–321, 348–349
Grams, 282
Graphs
bar, 200–201, 394–395
broken-line, 396–397
circle, 264–265, 401
coordinate, 426–427
of equations, 76–77, 428–429, 460
of inequalities, 76–77
of ordered pairs, 426–427
pictographs, 392–393
and tables of values, 428–429
Greatest common factor (GCF), 148–149, 460

Hardware, 82, 404–405
Hectograms, 282
Hectoliters, 280
Hectometers, 276
Heights of figures, 348–351, 354–359
Heptagons, 318, 460
Hexagons, 318–319, 460

Improper fractions, 170–171
Inches, 286
Independent events, 384–385, 460
Inequalities, 76–77, 460
Input, 82, 300, 404–405, 438
Integers, 408–427, 460
absolute values of, 409
adding, with like signs, 412–413
adding, with unlike signs, 414–415
on a coordinate plane, 426–427
dividing, 420–421
in equations, 413, 415, 417, 419, 421–423, 425
multiplying, 418–419
negative, 408–409
on a number line, 408–409, 412, 414
opposites, 408–409
ordering, 408–409
positive, 408–409
subtracting, 416–417
Interest, 460
compound, 269
simple, 262–263
Intersecting lines, 316–317
Inverse operations, 460
addition and subtracation, 12, 18–19, 62
multiplication and division, 28–29
Isosceles triangles, 320–321, 461

Kilograms, 282
Kiloliters, 280
Kilometers, 276

Latitude, 297, 461
Least common denominators (LCD), 168–169, 461
Least common multiples (LCM), 150–151, 461
Length
customary units of, 286–287
estimating, 277, 287
measuring, 287
metric units of, 276–277
ratios of, 237
Lines, 304–305, 461
intersecting, 316–317
parallel, 316–317
perpendicular, 316–317
of symmetry, 326–327, 433
Line segments, 304–305, 461
congruent, 310–311
Liquid measurement
customary units of, 288–289
metric units of, 280–281
Liters, 280
Logic, using, 53, 155, 159, 240–241, 300, 332–333, 366–367
Longitude, 297, 461
Lowest terms, 166–167

Maps, 96–97
Mass, 282–283
estimating, 283
Mean, 388–389, 461
Measurement
angle, 306–307
area, 346–353, 363–364
capacity, 280–281, 288–289, 291
computing with, 281, 283, 286–291
estimating, 277, 281, 283, 287, 289, 291
finding equal, 278–283, 286–293
length, 276–277, 286–287
mass, 282–283
perimeter, 342–343
precision in, 299
surface area, 354–355
temperature, 410–411
time, 292–293
volume, 356–359, 369
weight, 282, 290–291
Median, 390–391, 461
Meters, 276
Metric units of measurement, 276–283, 461
Midchapter Review, 9, 37, 67, 93, 117, 145, 171, 203, 229, 251, 283, 315, 353, 385, 417
Midpoints, 312–313, 461
Miles, 286
Milligrams, 282
Milliliters, 280
Millimeters, 276

Mixed numbers
  addition of, 174–175
  division of, 208–209
  and fractions, 170–171
  lowest terms, 170–171
  multiplication of, 198–199
  subtraction of, 180–183
Mode, 390–391
Money
  addition of, 15
  and decimals, 95, 99
  division of, 41, 44–45, 234–235
  multiplication of, 30–31, 34–37
  rounding, 73, 100–101
  subtraction of, 17, 19
Multiples, 150–151
Multiplication, 461
  of decimals, 110–117
  and division, 28–29
  of dollars and cents, 30, 34–35
  estimation in, 34–35, 110–111, 118–119
  of fractions, 194–199
  of integers, 418–419
  of measurements, 281, 283, 289
  of mixed numbers, 198–199
  by one, 28
  by one-digit numbers, 30–31
  properties, 28–29
  by tens, hundreds, thousands, 32–33, 116–117
  by three-digit numbers, 36–37
  by two-digit numbers, 34–35
  using, to solve equations, 29, 31, 33, 35, 37, 66–67, 113, 115, 127, 149
  by zero, 28
  zeros in the product, 114–115

Negative integers, 408, 461
NOT rule of logic, 159, 240–241, 300
Number lines, 76–77, 412–415, 461
Numbers
  composite, 144–145
  even, 140
  expanded form, 2–3, 95
  exponential form, 8–9
  integers, 408–427
  mixed, 170–171, 174–175
  negative, 408–409
  odd, 140
  ordering, 4–5, 90–91, 168–169, 408–409
  place value, 2–3
  positive, 408–409
  prime, 144–145
  rational, 424–425
  reading, 2–3
  rounding, 6–7, 14–17
  sequences of, 105
  whole, 2–19
  writing, 2–3
Number theory, 140–151
Numeration, 2–19
  ancient systems of, 21
  binary, 23, 82, 240
Numerators, 162

Obtuse angles, 306–307, 461
Obtuse triangles, 320–321, 461
Octagons, 318–319, 461
Odd numbers, 140, 461
One
  fractions equal to, 164
  in multiplication, 28
  probability of, 376
  property of, 28–29, 70–71, 219
Opposite numbers, 408–409, 461
Ordered pairs, 426–427, 461
Ordering
  decimals, 90–91
  fractions, 168–169
  integers, 408–409
  whole numbers, 4–5
Order of operations, 50–51, 461
Origin, 426, 461
OR rule of logic, 159, 240–241, 300
Ounces, 290
Outcomes, 376–377, 461
Output, 82, 300, 404–405, 438

Parallel lines, 316–317, 461
  cut by transversal, 316–317
Parallelograms, 322–323, 462
  area of, 348–349
  base and height of, 348–349
Parentheses, 8, 17, 33, 50–51
PASCAL, 137
Patterns, 53
  in multiplication, 116–117
  in division, 125
Pentagons, 318–319, 462
Percent, 462
  and circle graphs, 264–265
  commission, 267
  for decimals, 248–249
  discount, 260–261, 272–273
  finding the number, 256–257
  finding the percent of increase or decrease, 271
  finding the percent of a number, 246–247, 252–253
  finding what percent one number is of another, 254–255
  for fractions, 244–245, 250–251
  interest, 262–263, 269
  and proportion, 246–247
  and ratio, 244–245
  sales tax, 260–261
Perimeter, 462
  of rectangles, 342–343
  of squares, 342–343
  of triangles, 342–343
Perpendicular lines, 316–317, 462
Phrases, 60, 64
Pi (π), 344–345, 462
Pictographs, 392–393, 462
Pints, 288
Place value
  for decimals, 88–89
  for whole numbers, 2–3
Planes
  coordinate, 426–427
  in geometry, 304, 462
Points, 304–305, 426–427
Polygons, 462
  congruent, 324–325
  diagonals of, 319
  lines of symmetry of, 326–327
  regular, 318–319
  similar, 328–329
  sum of angles, 337
Polyhedrons, 330–331, 462
Positive integers, 408–409, 462
Pounds, 290
Powers of numbers, 8–9, 462
Precision in measurement, 299
Prime factorization, 146–149, 462
Prime numbers, 144–145, 462
Prisms, 330–331, 354–357
Probability, 376–385, 462
  and and *or* in, 378–379
  certain events, 376
  empirical, 382–383
  impossible events, 376
  independent events, 384–385
  sample spaces, 380–381
  tree diagrams, 380–381
  of two events, 378–379, 384–385
Problem solving applications
  decimals: addition and subtraction, 87, 89, 91, 93, 95, 99
  decimals: multiplication and division, 111, 113, 115, 117, 121, 123, 125, 127, 129
  equations, 61, 63, 65, 67, 71, 73, 77
  fractions: addition and subtraction, 163, 165, 167, 169, 171, 173, 175, 179, 181, 183
  fractions: multiplication and division, 195, 197, 199, 203, 205, 207, 209, 211, 213
  geometry, 305, 307, 309, 311, 313, 315, 317, 319, 321, 323, 325, 327, 329, 331
  integers, 409, 411, 413, 415, 417, 419, 421, 423, 425, 427, 429
  measurement, 277, 279, 281, 283, 287, 289, 291, 293
  number theory, 141, 143, 145, 149, 151
  percent, 245, 247, 249, 251, 253, 255, 257, 261, 263, 265
  perimeter, area, and volume, 343, 345, 347, 349, 351, 353, 355, 357, 359, 363, 365

Problem solving applications, *continued*
probability and statistics, 377, 379, 381, 385, 387, 389, 391, 393, 395, 397
ratio and proportion, 225, 227, 229, 231, 233
whole numbers: addition and subtraction, 3, 5, 7, 13, 15, 17
whole numbers: multiplication and division, 29, 31, 33, 35, 37, 41, 43, 45, 47, 51
Problem solving strategies
analyzing conclusions, 366–367
choosing equations, 68–69
choosing a method, 266–267
choosing the operation, 38–39
making an organized list, 152–153
multistep problems, 130–131, 184–185
reading a map, 96–97
reasonable answers, 118–119
sampling, 398–399
sensible answers, 176–177
too much or not enough information, 48–49
unit prices: choosing a method, 234–235
using a diagram, 360–361
using equations, 74–75
using estimates, 100–101, 214–215
using graphs, 200–201
using inverse operations, 18–19
using logic, 332–333
using a percent formula, 258–259
using probability, 382–383
using a table, 10–11, 294–295
using tables and graphs, 430–431
write your own question, 284–285
Products, 28, 110–111, 165
Programming languages, 136–137
Project, 21, 53, 79, 103, 133, 155, 187, 217, 237, 269, 297, 335, 369, 401, 433
Proper fractions, 162–163
Properties
of addition, 12–13, 70–71, 219, 415
of multiplication, 28–29, 70–71, 219, 419
Proportions, 462
cross products, 226–229
for percents, 246–247
in scale drawings, 232–233
in similar figures, 328–329
solving, 228–229
writing, 228–229
Protractor, 306–307, 309–313, 315, 317, 321
Pyramids, 330, 331, 462

Quadrilaterals, 318–319, 462
classification of, 322-323
sum of angle measurements, 337
Quarts, 288
Quotients, 28–29, 462

Radius (radii) of a circle, 308–309, 462
Range, 388–389
Rates
of discount, 260–261
of interest, 262–263, 269
sales tax, 260–261
Rational numbers, 424–425, 462
Ratios, 224–225, 462
equal, 224–225
and functions, 239
of lengths, 232–233, 237
and measurement, 237
and percents, 244–245
probability, 376–379
rates, 230–231
scale drawings, 232–233
lowest terms, 224–225
writing, 224–225
Rays, 304–305, 462
Recipes, 217
Reciprocals, 202–203, 462
Rectangles, 322–323, 346–347, 463
area of, 346–347
perimeter of, 342–343
Rectangular prisms, 330–331, 354–355
Rectangular pyramids, 330–331
Reflections, 326–327, 433, 463
Regular polygons, 318–319, 463
Remainders, 40–41, 176–177, 463
Repeating decimals, 212–213, 463
Review, 20, 52, 78, 102, 132, 154, 186, 216, 236, 268, 296, 334, 368, 400, 432
Rhombuses, 322–323, 463
Right angles, 306–307, 463
Right triangles, 320–321, 463
Roman numerals, 21
Rotations, 433, 463
Rounding, 463
decimals, 92–93, 110–111, 126–127
dollars and cents, 73, 100–101
whole numbers, 6–7

Sample spaces, 380–381, 463
Sampling, 398–399
Scale drawings, 232–233, 463
Scalene triangles, 320–321, 463
Scientific notation, 128–129, 435–436, 463
Sequences, 105
Similar polygons, 328–329, 463
Skills Maintenance (cumulative), 26, 58, 84, 107–108, 138, 160, 191–192, 222, 242, 274, 301–302, 340, 374, 406, 439–440
Skills Maintenance (periodic), 5, 17, 43, 47, 63, 73, 91, 99, 115, 129, 147, 149, 169, 183, 199, 211, 227, 231, 247, 257, 281, 291, 309, 325, 351, 359, 379, 391, 413, 429
Slides, 433
Software, 82, 136, 338, 404–405
Solid figures, 330–331
faces of, 330–331
surface area of, 354–355
vertices of, 331
volume of, 356–359, 362–363, 369
Solutions
of equations, 62–63, 463
of inequalities, 76–77, 463
Spheres, 330–331, 463
Square root, 371, 463
Squares, 322–323, 463
area of, 346–347
perimeter of, 342–343
Square units
customary, 362–363
metric, 346
Stock market, 187
Straight angles, 314–315, 463
Subtraction, 463
and addition, 12–13
of decimals, 98–99
of dollars and cents, 16–17, 19
estimation in, 16–17, 98–99, 118–119
of fractions, 178–183
of integers, 416–417
of measurements, 281, 283, 287, 289, 291
of mixed numbers, 180–183
using, to solve equations, 13, 15, 17, 62–63, 99, 111, 127, 149
of whole numbers, 16–17
Sums, 12, 14–15
Supplementary angles, 314–315, 463
Surface area, 464
of cylinders, 354–355
of prisms, 354–355
Symmetry, 326–327, 433, 464

Table, using a, 430–431
Table of values, 428, 464
Tax, sales, 260–261, 272–273
Temperatures
above or below zero, 410–411
in degrees Celsius, 410–411, 458
in degrees Fahrenheit, 460
Terminating decimals, 210, 464
Test, 22, 54, 80, 104, 134, 156, 188, 218, 238, 270, 298, 336, 370, 402, 434
Time, 292–293
Tons, metric, 282
Translations, 433, 464

Transversals, 316–317, 464
Trapezoids, 322–323, 464
  area of, 350–351
Tree diagrams, 380–381, 464
Triangles, 318–319, 464
  acute, 320–321
  area of, 348–349
  base and height of, 348–349
  classification of, 320–321
  congruent, 324–325
  equilateral, 320–321
  isosceles, 320–321
  obtuse, 320–321
  perimeter of, 342–343
  right, 320–321
  scalene, 320–321
  similar, 328–329
  sum of angle measurements, 320–321
Triangular prisms, 330–331
Triangular pyramids, 330–331

Unit pricing, 234–235, 464

Variables, 60, 464
Venn diagrams, 155, 464
Vertex (vertices), 304, 464
Vertical angles, 314–315, 464
Volume, 464
  customery units of, 362–363
  of cylinders, 358–359
  direct measurement, 369
  metric units of, 356–357
  of prisms, 356–357

Weight, 282, 290, 291
  estimating, 290–291
Whole numbers, 2–26, 28–58, 464
Writing checks, 103

Yards, 286

Zero(s), 464
  in addition, 12–13, 70–71
  as an exponent, 8–9
  as an integer, 408–409
  in multiplication, 28–29
  probability of, 376–377
  in products, 114–115
  property of, 12, 28, 70–71, 219

1
I 2
J 3